EXTINCTION GOVERNANCE, FINANCE AND ACCOUNTING

The planet is currently experiencing a mass extinction event, with human and business activity being the root cause of species loss and habitat destruction. Industries, companies, banks, investors, accountants and auditors have all played their role. This book explores how they can also provide a solution.

The book presents plans, metrics, frameworks, mechanisms and financial innovations that can be, and are being, implemented through the financial markets in order to save and protect species, enhance biodiversity and, at the same time, preserve the financial markets and the business world.

This biodiversity handbook addresses the intersection between species extinction and the global capitalist system. With contributions from leading non-governmental organisations such as the Capitals Coalition, Business for Nature, the Ecojustice Foundation, ShareAction and the Endangered Wildlife Trust, plus senior researchers in the field, as well as industry experts from Moody's, EOS at Hermes Federated Investment Management, BlueBay Asset Management, ODDO BHF Asset Management and OSSIAM (to mention just a few), this book is at the forefront of addressing the crucially important topics of extinction accounting, finance and governance.

Drawing on leading research, the book is written in an accessible style and is relevant to researchers and students in the fields of sustainability, governance, accounting, finance, corporate social responsibility and corporate governance. It is essential reading for investors, responsible investors, bankers, business leaders and policy makers in the field of sustainable financial markets. Given the interdisciplinary nature of this book, it is useful to conservationists, ecologists and others involved in species and biodiversity protection.

Jill Atkins holds a Chair in Financial Management at Sheffield University Management School, UK, and is a visiting professor of Accounting at the University of the Witwatersrand, South Africa.

Martina Macpherson is Head of ESG Strategy and GMC Member at ODDO BHF Asset Management, President of NSFM NextGen and Visiting Fellow at Henley Business School, UK.

EXTINCTION GOVERNANCE, FINANCE AND ACCOUNTING

Implementing a Species Protection Action Plan for the Financial Markets

Edited by Jill Atkins and Martina Macpherson

Routledge
Taylor & Francis Group

LONDON AND NEW YORK

Cover image: © Jill Atkins

First published 2022
by Routledge
4 Park Square, Milton Park, Abingdon, Oxon OX14 4RN

and by Routledge
605 Third Avenue, New York, NY 10158

Routledge is an imprint of the Taylor & Francis Group, an informa business

British Library Cataloguing-in-Publication Data
A catalogue record for this book is available from the British Library

Library of Congress Cataloging-in-Publication Data
Names: Atkins, Jill (Research director) editor. | Macpherson, Martina, editor.
Title: Extinction governance, finance, and accounting: implementing
a species protection action plan for the financial markets / edited by
Jill Atkins and Martina Macpherson.
Description: New York, NY: Routledge, 2022. |
Includes bibliographical references and index.
Subjects: LCSH: Biodiversity conservation—Economic aspects. |
Habitat conservation—Economic aspects. | Extinction (Biology) |
Capitalism—Environmental aspects. | Social responsibility of business.
Classification: LCC QH75 .E97 2022 (print) | LCC QH75 (ebook) |
DDC 333.95/16—dc23/eng/20220119
LC record available at https://lccn.loc.gov/2021051958
LC ebook record available at https://lccn.loc.gov/2021051959

ISBN: 978-0-367-49297-7 (hbk)
ISBN: 978-0-367-49298-4 (pbk)
ISBN: 978-1-003-04555-7 (ebk)

DOI: 10.4324/9781003045557

Typeset in Bembo
by codeMantra

To our children and their future:
Aedan, Euan
&
Zoe

CONTENTS

CONTRIBUTORS

Maizatulakma Abdullah is an assistant professor at the Faculty of Economics and Management, Universiti Kebangsaan Malaysia (The National University of Malaysia). She is a member of the Editorial Board of *Jurnal Pengurusan (UKM Journal of Management)*. Her research areas include risk management reporting and environmental, social and governance reporting.

Tariq Almontaser joined the School of Economics, Finance and Accounting at Coventry University in January 2022 as a lecturer in accounting after a year of working as an associate lecturer. Tariq has around 15 years of teaching and research experience in academic accounting programmes at higher/further education institutions in the UK and internationally. He has previously held lectureship posts in accounting and finance at The College of Applied Administrative and Financial Sciences (CAAF) in Libya, the University of Reading, De Montfort University and University of Sheffield. Tariq has developed, reviewed, coordinated, lectured, tutored, contributed to, assessed and/or examined a wide range of courses in Accounting. Tariq was awarded his PhD from the University of Reading in December 2019. Also, he possesses an MSc in Accounting (Libyan Academy of Postgraduate Studies-Tripoli/Libya, July 2001), and a BSc in Accounting (Faculty of Accounting - Libya, July 1992). Most recently, Tariq has been awarded his Fellowship in the Higher Education Academy (FHEA) in September 2020. Tariq is a Member of the British Accounting and Finance Association (BAFA) and CorpTax Alliance (based in the Netherlands). He is continuing research interests in social and environmental accounting, corporate sustainability and SDG reporting and disclosure. He has published his research in ABS, ABDC and Scopus listed accounting and finance journals.

Natalie Ambrosio Preudhomme is a Director at Four Twenty Seven, part of Moody's ESG Solutions. She leads publications, thought leadership and outreach related to climate risk. Her recent publications include *Community Resilience and Adaptive Capacity: A Meaningful Investment Across Assets*, published by the Federal Reserve Bank of San Francisco, and the chapter "Asset Level Physical Climate Risk Disclosure" in the book *Values at Work: Sustainable Investing and ESG Reporting*.

Sonia Artuso, CEFA, CIIA, CESGA, is lead ESG Expert of AIAF Sustainability and ESG Observatory. She is a member of EFFAS Commission on Environment, Social and Governance (EFFAS CESG) and a member of EFFAS CESGA® Expert Team and EFFAS ESG Review Panel.

Christoph Biehl works as Senior Active Ownership Analyst for Credit Suisse Asset Management and guest lectures at the University of Birmingham. In his previous role he was Lecturer in Responsible Business at the University of Birmingham and part of the Lloyds Banking Group Centre for Responsible Business. He holds a PhD from Henley Business School in Accounting, an MLitt in Management from the University of St Andrews and a BA from the University of Bayreuth in Philosophy and Economics. As an academic he is passionate about understanding the past and researching the present to provide solutions for the future. This research forms the basis for his academic teaching and as a Fellow of the Higher Education Academy he uses innovative teaching methods in order to make academic research accessible and provide his MBA students with the best possible learning experience. Before joining the University of Birmingham Dr. Biehl has taught and researched at a variety of universities, including Henley Business School, Beijing Institute of Technology and the University of St Andrews. Dr. Biehl's field of research is accountability with a focus on stewardship in the UK and Japan, which can be seen in his research on the Japanese Principles for Responsible Institutional Investors. As one of the directors of the Network for Sustainable Financial Markets (#NSFMNextGen) Dr. Biehl regularly co-organises and speaks at workshops to bridge the gap between industry and academia, and to provide steppingstones for the next generation of responsible investment professionals.

Danielle Carreira is an environment and sustainable finance specialist and brings nearly fifteen years' experience developing and implementing multi-stakeholder initiatives that helps the global finance sector to understand and integrate environmental risks and opportunities into investment and lending processes. As Head of Finance Sector Engagement at the Tropical Forest Alliance, an initiative hosted by the WEF, she is responsible for the strategic development, implementation and coordination of a platform that brings together public policy makers, financial institutions, global companies and commodity producers from key countries, towards an inclusive and collective action agenda to reduce deforestation and accelerate the transition towards more sustainable land use practices. Danielle is a member of the Expert Review Committee of the World Benchmarking Alliance's Food and Agriculture Benchmark and supports the development of the Food and Agriculture Benchmark. Danielle has previously worked at the Principle for Responsible Investment (PRI), the Natural Capital Finance Alliance, Trucost, FTSE Russell, Reuters and Bloomberg. She has co-authored the report "Natural Capital Risk Exposure of the Finance Sector in Brazil in 2015". Her most recent publication, "The State of Finance for Nature," was published in May 2021. Danielle holds an MA in International Finance and a BSc in Economic Sciences.

A. Cherrington is a Chartered Director (SA) and is the former Chief Executive Officer (CEO) of the Institute of Directors in Southern Africa (IoDSA). She originally joined the IoDSA in 2004 to formalise and grow the organisation's director education focus. She has previously held the position of Chief Operating Officer having been promoted to the role in 2008, was appointed as an executive director in 2009 and then as CEO in 2014. She has been involved in the field of director education for 16 years, has been in an executive leadership role within the professional body landscape for 11 of those years and was recognised with the Executive Director of the Year 2018 award at the Association of Association Executives World Congress in Belgium. Angela is a trustee of the Endangered Wildlife Trust (EWT), she is a non-executive director of South African Institute of Tax Professionals (SAIT) and the Independent Chair of the Nominations Committee for the Water Research Institute South Africa. She is a shareholder and director of Professional Service Hub (Pty) Limited – YourHub, an organisation established to offer leadership and management support services in the association community and helped form and is currently the Chair of the Independent Professional Body Forum (IPBF).

Carmine de Franco joined Ossiam in May 2012 as a quantitative analyst after working for four years at the Faculty of Mathematics of the University of Paris VII (Université Denis Diderot). Carmine de Franco is a graduate of the University of Paris VII, Denis Diderot. He holds a PhD in financial mathematics and a Master's degree in random financial modelling.

Federica Doni, PhD, is Associate Professor in Business Administration and Accounting at the Department of Business and Law, University of Milano-Bicocca, Milan, Italy. Her main publications are on intangibles, sustainability and integrated reporting, and ESG and SDG issues. She is the Principal Investigator of the Jean Monnet Module Application No. 611698-EPP-1–2019-1-IT-EPPJMO-MODULE "Sustainability Disclosure in Corporate Reporting. Improvement and harmonization of best practices in European Union" that has been selected for EU support (2019–2022).

Ali Elfadli is a lecturer in accounting at Sheffield University, south and city college and performance through people training centre. His research interests are corporate governance and social and environmental accounting, more specifically their impact on biodiversity.

Andrea Gasperini is an AIAF member (Italian Association for Financial Analysis) and Head of Sustainability and ESG Observatory. Andrea is a member of the EFFAS Commission of ESG issues (CESG), part of the expert team of the EFFAS Certified ESG Analyst (CESGA) and a member of the ESG Review Panel. He is a former member European Lab@EFRAG Project Task Force on Climate-related Reporting. He is author and co-author of many books and more than one hundred essays, published in several management and economics journals about sustainable finance and intangible assets, and is a keynote speaker at university master's courses and conferences planned in these fields by national and international organisations.

Mark Gough is the CEO of the Capitals Coalition, a global collaboration transforming the way decisions are made by including the value provided by nature and people. Mark has worked extensively in the private sector and sits on various boards including TEEB, UN CEO Water Mandate and Digital with Purpose.

Abeer Hassan is Reader in Accounting, School of Business and Creative industries at the University of West of Scotland, UK. She is a leading scholar in the field of Corporate social responsibility and environmental management, Private equity and venture capital as sources of finance for SMEs, Female entrepreneurship, Higher Education, Gender in Accounting Integrated Reporting, Biodiversity and Extinction Accounting. Her innovative, evidence-based research has appeared in highly regarded outlets. Abeer has published more than 75 articles in peer-reviewed journals and conferences. Before joining academia, Abeer worked as an auditor for 10 years at the National Authority of Auditing and Performance Evaluation in Egypt. More details on Abeer Hassan publications are available on https://research-portal.uws.ac.uk/en/persons/abeer-hassan. In terms of Teaching & Learning and Students' Success. As a reflective practitioner, Abeer has more than 17years teaching experience in UK HE sector, leading modules and programmes. She believes that having passion for teaching and learning activities to embody the enthusiasm for the subjects and bring research expertise into classroom is one of her qualities. She supports delivering teaching that is based on contemporary approaches to learning and is constantly scanning for improvements, based on students' feedback as partners in the learning process. This is to ensure students are capable of transferring knowledge into practice. She is keen advocate of embedding employability and graduate skills into courses and provide supportive learning environment that ensures maximum student engagement and promote the interactive approach in staff-student contact time to develop independent learners.

C. Hoogstad, has more than 20 years' experience in the conservation industry, ranging from field work to Executive Management. He has also been fortunate enough to be exposed to working with industry extensively over his career including working with Eskom in South Africa since 2010. This has allowed him to study, understand and be able to find mutually beneficial solutions for both business and the environment. Further to that he has been actively involved in the National Business and Biodiversity Network for the last seven years who focussed on assisting business with biodiversity compliance, disclosure and biodiversity accounting. He joined the company as a junior field officer for the Wildlife and Energy Programme, a partnership between the Endangered Wildlife Trust and Eskom, which aims to mitigate and prevent interactions between wildlife and energy infrastructure. In his current role as Senior Manager: Industry Partnerships/Operations and member of the EWT's Exco, he is responsible for building new partnerships with industry leaders throughout Africa. He has been involved in international networking, having been elected as the Chair of the United Nations Convention of Migratory Species Energy Task Force, which encompasses 265 countries, and Chairing the Energy Task Force for the International Crane Foundation.

J. Houdet is an internationally recognised expert on business and biodiversity, as well as on natural capital measurement, valuation, accounting and reporting. Biological Diversity Protocol (BD Protocol) Lead at the Endangered Wildlife Trust and a Senior Research Fellow at the Albert Luthuli Leadership Institute (University of Pretoria), he undertakes research, capacity building, policy analysis and advisory work for both the private and public sectors. Over the past 12 years, he has supported more than 40 organisations in addressing sustainability challenges. He was a Technical Group member of the WBCSD-led consortium in charge of drafting the Natural Capital Protocol, and an expert working on several assessments of the Intergovernmental Platform on Biodiversity and Ecosystem Services (IPBES).

Emine Isciel joined Storebrand Asset Management in 2008. She is leading Storebrand Asset Management's work on climate and environment and also responsible for coordinating and undertaking strategic engagements with investee companies and sovereigns on a range of environmental issues. Prior to joining Storebrand, Isciel worked for the Norwegian Ministry of Climate and Environment with multilateral environmental agreements related to biodiversity advising the government on sustainability policies and strategies and leading the work on implementing the UN SDGs. She is currently a member of the Informal Working Group, Taskforce on Nature-related Financial Disclosures.

Nicolas Jacob is currently thematic equity fund manager at ODDO BHF Asset Management. He started his career at IXIS Asset Management in 2001 before joining the Franco-German bank ODDO BHF in 2005. During the last five years, Nicolas took in charge the broad implementation of the ESG integration policy across the different asset classes. For the past 10 years, Nicolas also taught sustainable finance at the University of Paris Dauphine and IAE Lyon.

Magdalena Kettis is Active Ownership Director at Nordea Asset Management. She is a member of the IPDD Advisory Council and leads on Nordea's participation the IPDD engagement on Brazil. She is also a member of the Pharmaceutical Supply Chain Advisory Panel and CDP Water Advisory Council and was previously on the steering committee and advisory council of the Corporate Human Rights Benchmark. Magdalena holds a PhD in international political economy.

Mira Lieberman is a Grantham Scholar at the Grantham Centre for Sustainable Futures and a PhD researcher at the Sheffield University Management School. She has an MA in Sociocultural Linguistics from Goldsmiths College, University of London. She is a co-convenor for the International Ecolinguistics Association and is on the organising committee of the IFear4theFuture seminar series on extinction accounting.

Sonya Likhtman currently works in EOS, the stewardship and engagement team at Federated Hermes. She focuses primarily on engaging with companies across Asia and emerging markets. Previously, Sonya worked as a sustainability consultant in London and Barcelona. She holds a Bachelor of Arts degree in Geography from the University of Cambridge and was a Herchel Smith Scholar at Harvard University.

Martina Macpherson is President of the Network of Sustainable Financial Markets, a NextGen think tank in sustainable finance. She is also Head of ESG Strategy and an ExCo member for ODDO BHF Asset Management & Private Equity and a visiting fellow in sustainable finance at the University of Zurich and Henley Business School. Martina has held several global leadership roles in ESG strategy, product development and innovation including Senior Vice President, ESG and Engagement Strategy at Moody's, Global Head of ESG Index Products and Research at S&P DJI, Managing Director of Sustainable Investments Partners Ltd. and Vice President of ESG Solutions at MSCI. Prior to this, she worked in (ESG) product, research and engagement roles at Insight Investment, F&C AM and Deutsche Bank AG. She is a public speaker and global expert in sustainable investing and has co-authored a range of ESG and Fintech books, including *The AI Book* (Wiley, 2020), *Handbook on Species Extinction Accounting and Biodiversity* (Routledge, 2021) and *ESG in Portfolio Construction* (RiskBooks, 2022).

Warren Maroun is a professor at the School of Accountancy. He teaches courses on auditing, financial reporting and integrated reporting at an undergraduate and postgraduate level. Warren served at PricewaterhouseCoopers in different roles from 2010 to 2018. He consults widely on corporate reporting issues. His research interests include financial accounting, integrated reporting, external audit and corporate governance with a specific focus on the functioning of mechanisms of accountability. Warren has produced over 50 academic publications. He has produced technical and practitioner-focused reports for the Association of Certified Chartered Accountants and the South African Institute of Chartered Accountants. Warren has contributed to several books, including two on integrated thinking and reporting. He is a SAICA and CIMA member and holds a PhD from King's College London.

Peta Milan is CEO and co-founder of Jade Eli Technologies, CEO and founder of venture studio Transcendent Media Capital and an author and international speaker. She sits on the international advisory board of The World Sustainable Development Forum and is a founding council member of The Digital Economist and Associate Fellow of The World Academy of Art and Science and a member of two UN working groups in transforming global energy and agriculture and global leadership in the 21st century. Peta is also an inaugural member of Future Capital and founding advisor for 100 Women @Davos, a multinational group advocating for diversity, inclusion and greater presence of women in leadership.

Shân Millie is a Board Advisor for national rewilding charity Heal. A founder, advisor, coach, voice of authority and Knowledge Communicator on FinTech's role in AI/Data, Corporate Digital Governance, Open Finance, and Financial Inclusion, Shân is deeply interested in how StoryTelling enables Innovation and change, in all sectors, especially Civic Society Organisations (CSOs) and community-based change-makers.

Omar Mowafi is Assistant Professor at Accounting Department in the School of Business, the University of Jordan. His research interest is governance and accountability in developing countries. He received his Bachelor degree in Accounting from Yamouk University and his Master's in accountancy from Bridgewater State University and his PhD in Accounting from Sheffield University. Moreover, he is a Certified Management Accountant (CMA). You can visit him at http://eacademic.ju.edu.jo/O.Mowafi/default.aspx

M. Murison was the National Biodiversity and Business Network of South Africa Manager at the Endangered Wildlife Trust (EWT). She is now a Public and Media Relations Officer at EWT. She leads and develops communication campaigns, managed media and public relations, and supported the business through logistics and strategic planning.

Hannah Needham is Operations Director and a member of the founding team at Heal, the rewilding charity. Her background is in habitat management, livestock care, leading practical volunteers and environmental planning. She previously worked as a Rivers Project Officer with Groundwork South and a heathland

Warden with Natural England. She completed a conservation traineeship with the Berkshire, Buckinghamshire and Oxfordshire Wildlife Trust. She has a BSc in Human Biology and an MSc in Molecular and Cellular Biosciences.

My-Linh Ngo has spent over two decades in the field of sustainable/ESG investing working on incorporating ESG considerations into ESG dedicated as well as conventional portfolios. She is currently at BlueBay Asset Management, with previous ESG roles at Schroders Investment Management and Henderson Global Investors. My-Linh holds two master's degrees and a degree in the field of sustainability/ESG from Middlesex University/Forum for the Future, as well as the University of East Anglia.

Nnamdi Okolo is a qualified accountant under the ACCA and works as a doctoral associate with the University of Sheffield, UK. His research focuses on accountability of social impact investments in welfare, humanitarian services and conservation of wildlife. He also volunteers as the treasurer of BAFA-SIGCG.

Gunnar Rimmel holds the Chair in Accounting & Corporate Reporting and is the Director of The Henley Centre of Accounting Research & Practice (HARP) at Henley Business School, University of Reading, UK. He is an expert in sustainability reporting and is a member of CSEAR Executive Council, EAA Stakeholder Reporting Committee, European Financial Advisory Group (EFRAG) and the BAFA FAR SIG Advisory Board. His research areas include sustainability reporting and governance, especially biodiversity reporting and extinction accounting.

Nick Robins is Professor in Practice for Sustainable Finance at the Grantham Research Institute for Climate Change and the Environment at the London School of Economics. He is co-chair of the International Network for Sustainable Finance Policy, Insights, Research and Exchange (INSPIRE) and co-chairs the joint NGFS–INSPIRE Study Group on Biodiversity and Financial Stability. The focus of his work is on how to mobilise finance for climate action in ways that support a just transition, promoting the role of central banks and regulators in achieving sustainable development and investigating how the financial system can support the restoration of nature. Nick is co-founder of Carbon Tracker and Planet Tracker and has previously worked at UNEP, HSBC, Henderson Global Investors and the European Commission. For more information, see https://www.lse.ac.uk/granthaminstitute/profile/nick-robins/

Mohamed Saeudy is acting Principle Lecturer in Accounting and Finance and Director of Research Centre for Contemporary Accounting, Finance and Economics (Res CAFE). His research interest focuses on how business organizations use innovative accounting and finance tools to manage the contemporary challenges of sustainable development. It involves the ambition to develop organizational lenses to explore how sustainability may allow or help organizations to improve their triple bottom line impact. He argues the possibility to create innovative social and environmental impact from the economic activities of business organizations. He helps designed many courses to help students to learn how to use accounting and finance tools to manage the contemporary challenges of sustainable development such as climate change, modern slavery, UN SDGs, human rights and ecological biodiversity. He develops social media tools e.g. blogs to help students to explore how business organisations could make business opportunities and profit from considering social and environmental activities. He also developed innovative academic courses on DBA, Green Accounting, Sustainable Finance and Financial Entrepreneurship. These courses covered many contemporary topics ranging from corporate governance to sustainable business strategies and policies. In addition, Dr Saeudy provides professional consultancies for many business organisations in the UK and overseas in the field of sustainable business solutions, entrepreneurial finance, green finance, risk management and virtual business innovation.

Mxolisi Sibanda is an ecologist working on natural resource management and conservation covering individual species such as black rhinos and ecosystems (marine and terrestrial), climate change, human development and livelihoods. He is keenly interested in the science–policy–practice nexus in natural resources management which is critical for the transfer of knowledge and learning from research into practice and vice versa. He has previously worked in various roles in WWF as a Research Fellow (Ecology) for a large multi-country programme in southern Africa, Design and Impact Adviser, Senior Programme Advisor and more recently as Advisor, Climate Change for the Commonwealth Secretariat. He is also a Biodiversity Fellow at the University of Oxford's Interdisciplinary Centre for Conservation Science (ICCS).

Clarisse Simonek is a Director and Head of Responsible Investment for Ossiam. She is the academic advisor of the ESG Investing certification and a member of S&P's Scientific Council for Sustainable Finance. Clarisse holds a joint MBA-MSc on sustainability from HEC Paris/FGV and a Bachelor of Economics and Political Science from Swarthmore College.

Krystyna Springer is a Financial Sector Research Analyst at ShareAction. She authored the recent report 'Point of No Returns Part IV – Biodiversity An assessment of asset managers' approaches to biodiversity', published by Share-Action. Prior to joining ShareAction, Krystyna worked as a finance analyst at Amazon. She holds an MA with Distinction in International Political Economy from King's College London.

Jan Stannard is a founder trustee and acting CEO of the national rewilding charity Heal, which is raising money to buy land in England for nature recovery, climate change action and wellbeing. She is also a non-executive on the board of

Bookmycharge, the bookable EV charging service. She moved into the charity sector after 40 years' experience in business, having served on company boards in the strategic communications and digital marketing sectors. She is a qualified coach and resilience specialist.

Carmen Thissen is an Associate at Business for Nature, which is a global coalition that drives nature-positive business action and policy ambition. Prior to her work at Business for Nature, Carmen studied the climate impacts of ranching as well as corporate valuations of natural capital at the University of Montana.

Steve Trent has over 30 years' experience in campaigning on issues at the intersection of environmental and human rights, creating effective advocacy and leading investigations in over 40 countries. He is founder and CEO of the Environmental Justice Foundation and co-founded WildAid, serving as president and leading the organisation's work in China and India.

Eva Zabey leads Business for Nature coalition that drives nature-positive business action and policy ambition. Previously, Eva spent 15 years at the World Business Council for Sustainable Development (WBCSD), leading work on natural, social and human capital measurement and valuation for business decision-making and disclosure, including the Natural Capital Protocol.

Longxiang Zhao is a Research Associate in Sustainable Accounting & Finance at Loughborough University, working as part of the UKRI National Circular Economy Research Hub. He holds a PhD degree from the University of Sheffield, researching on biodiversity accounting and accountability in China.

Anna Zubets-Anderson is a Vice President – ESG Analyst at Moody's ESG Solutions Group. Anna's work is focused on establishing thought leadership in sustainable finance markets. Anna supports the development of environmental, social and governance (ESG) research at Moody's and represents the firm at conferences and in conversations with investors, media, standard setters and the academic community. Prior to her current role, Anna served on the green bonds team and was a member of Moody's Global ESG Working Group, focused on exploring how ESG risks impact the global credit markets. After joining Moody's in 2009, she spent several years covering a portfolio of companies within basic industries. Prior to joining Moody's, Anna was an accounting litigation consultant at Marks Paneth & Shron LLP and worked at KPMG LLP as an audit manager and a member of their International Standards Group in London, UK. Anna is a Certified Public Accountant and holds a Bachelor of Science in Business Administration from San Francisco State University. She is fluent in Russian and English.

FOREWORD

The book that you are holding is a gigantic inter- and multidisciplinary effort drawing from several fields such as financial accounting, ecology, conservation science, accounting, business finance, sustainability science and business governance for our time. It proposes a framework for acting on species extinction in a transformative and emancipatory manner at such a momentous time of human existence and history. It is transformative and emancipatory in that it appreciates the possibility of using business and its practices such as accounting, ESG and good governance to overcome the destructive pathways that our current system of capital and industry has been locked into for centuries and creates a better world out of it.

This is vital as our world faces several crises – three current and major ones among these are the COVID-19 pandemic, the biodiversity and climate crisis. Notably these are interlinked and feed off each other with huge implications for species around the world as well as human existence as we know it. Starting in Wuhan in December 2019, the coronavirus is thought to have jumped from a wildlife host to humans. Since then, across the world, millions have died from the COVID-19 caused by the virus, and though vaccines have been produced at unprecedented speeds, the full-scale impact of the COVID-19 crisis on human health, economies and more will reverberate for many years to come. For many years, experts warned that the destruction of the natural world exposes human communities to new strains of viruses that may cause untold damage. Clearly the COVID-19 pandemic illustrates how material, the loss of nature is to our health, businesses, economies and interaction in this home we call earth.

Unfortunately, this destruction of nature – the biodiversity crisis – has continued across the world at rates of 1,000 to 10,000 times beyond the natural rate of species loss from the past raising the risk of future pandemics of this sort and scale shown by COVID-19. Reversing this trend of biodiversity loss is vital to stopping the potential disruptions and enabling future prosperity for nature and people. This should be easy to understand when we realise that the world's biodiversity is the bedrock of our lives – whether one looks at our medicines, livelihoods, wellbeing and inspiration and material for innovative solutions of the future among many goods and services we derive from it.

The third crisis that our world faces is the climate one. Industrialisation, beginning in Europe and North America and now at full throttle in countries such as China and India, has been driven on the back of industrial processes that use unsustainably produced energy and resource extraction that spews carbon into the atmosphere. We have built our modern civilisation on this, and its unbridled generation of carbon emissions is coming to haunt us. In a space of less than 50 years, estimates of the carbon concentrations in the atmosphere have moved from 370 ppm to reach 415 ppm today. If this trajectory continues, global mean temperature will rise beyond 2°C which will cause devastating changes to our climate, leading to further species loss and ultimately putting our own future as humans in jeopardy. This march towards a natural apocalypse is already happening with impacts such as changes in temperature and precipitation, increased frequency of climate-related extreme events like storms, flooding and hazardous fires being witnessed across the world.

These crises call for action from the world's governments, businesses and citizens. This book, a third in a series that Jill Atkins and her collaborators have produced, provides new light of looking at the problem and the role of business and specifically accounting and business in addressing this challenge. The authors make a case for businesses to move from tokenistic and greenwashing activities to real transformative action. The various chapters examine species extinction, business and potential solutions from various perspectives including ecology, justice, business risk and profitability. Topics covered include rewilding, the role of investors, financial markets, ESG ratings, green bonds, lending and banking.

In so doing, the book enables the reader to see, feel and touch the "elephant" in the room from different angles. This is particularly helpful as we know that singular stories and understandings often lead to poor diagnosis to problems and therefore inadequate strategies or solutions. At this critical juncture, when the world's governments and businesses are set on "building back" after the COVID-19 pandemic, this handbook makes a much-needed contribution. It reminds readers that what is needed is not a programme of making slight improvements to our past ways but new ways of rebuilding centred on restoring nature, transforming our systems of production including food and agriculture, and ramping up renewable energy production among other green actions. This kind of transformative action has accountability and better social purpose embedded in it.

While the book is aimed at institutional investors and accounting and fund managers, it is a valuable resource to leaders and professionals from sustainability departments in businesses, practitioners working in corporate governance and conservation and policy makers. In my view, it is a tour de force for anyone keen on not only understanding the financial material risk of species extinction but also what to do about it in a pragmatic manner. You will find examples of innovations being applied such as the green bonds, ESG reporting or extinction banking.

My hope is that this handbook receives the response it deserves: genuine engagement on the subject it discusses, bold action against species extinction and a real contribution to stopping the destructive extinction of species and degradation of habitats and species extinction we are witnessing. In the words of the authors, "it should not be business as we know it".

Students, professionals, investors and frankly all people will make a good investment out of engaging with the material in this book to enlighten themselves and arm themselves with the understanding and tools that are vastly needed for our present challenges. Failure to do so means that we remain on a destructive path as a species and bequeath future generations a world that none of us can live in. That is unacceptable on any account.

I am therefore very delighted to offer this foreword to a book that if taken seriously will make a much-needed difference to our present and future world. I am sure many future generations will build on its foundations and be grateful for its insights. I highly commend it.

Mxolisi Sibanda,
Senior Programme Advisor, WWF UK
April 2021

PREAMBLE

This is a finance book. And a book for financial services professionals.

Like all finance textbooks, it covers various aspects of investment and capital markets instruments, is aimed at institutional investors and fund managers, provides guidance around investor engagement and dialogue and captures many other areas and sectors where ESG and, more specifically, biodiversity, natural habitat and species protection are emerging as systemic risks and opportunities such as insurance, banking, stock market indexes, corporate ratings, financial analysis, corporate accounting and reporting, and corporate governance.

Unlike finance texts, this book is inter- and multidisciplinary. We weave our way through cutting-edge science on biodiversity, ecology, ecosystems and species extinctions, bringing issues of species and biodiversity protection into the very heart of octane finance.

This is also an accounting and governance book. And a book for accounting and auditing professionals.

Like all accounting and governance books, this handbook provides accounting and reporting frameworks, policy developments and a framework for corporate governance best practices.

Unlike other accounting and governance texts, this adopts an interdisciplinary and ecological approach. We integrate ecological issues, biodiversity, natural habitat and species protection into the heart of integrated reporting and governance frameworks.

COVID-19 has changed the world. COVID-19 has catapulted concerns around biodiversity and habitat loss onto centre stage as we increasingly perceive the linkages between transmission of disease from wild animals to humans, and diminishing habitat for wildlife, the invasion of humans into pristine rainforest and wild spaces, wildlife trafficking and consumption of endangered species.

The world is on the brink of ecological disaster. With around one million species at risk of extinction and rainforest continuing to disappear at an alarming rate, tragedy is on the horizon, and urgent action is required.

Urgent action is not only required from conservationists, ecologists, zoologists and biologists. They cannot fix the planet alone. Business activity and the capitalist system have created the mess we are now faced with: pollution, land use, extraction, agriculture, climate change and global warming. The financial markets created to assist businesses and companies the world over in their profitable endeavours by providing much-needed finance and capital investment are the instruments feeding the fire. Without an interdisciplinary approach that combines conservation, ecology, finance, accounting and business, realistic and practicable solutions will not be found.

Over the last couple of years, there has been a surge of interest across the global finance and accounting communities in addressing and integrating biodiversity into various financial instruments, mechanisms and reporting frameworks. Climate change has until now eclipsed biodiversity as an environmental issue in accounting and finance. Biodiversity collapse and species extinctions, connected to potential ecosystem collapse, are threats to the natural world and the balance of nature. They are also threats to human health and survival. As COVID-19 has demonstrated in a truly horrifying way, protection of endangered species and enhancement of biodiversity, nature and natural habitat could prevent further pandemics. Biodiversity should no longer be classified as merely an environmental issue: it is increasingly obvious that it is a financial, social and governance issue.

An earlier book, *Around the World in 80 Species: Exploring the Business of Extinction*,[1] provided a substantial overview of the causes and symptoms of the current mass extinction crisis in which we find ourselves, with a focus on species, conservation and the state of the planet. The concepts of extinction accounting and extinction engagement were introduced, and there were contributions from academics and practitioners exploring these concepts in a variety of situations, sectors and countries. This book develops the earlier book by focusing entirely on the financial markets, especially the concepts of extinction accounting, extinction finance, extinction engagement and extinction governance. We do not intend to provide an in-depth overview of the state of nature and refer readers to the detailed coverage in the earlier book.

In this book, we explore developments and initiatives across financial and capital markets, corporate reporting and corporate governance which are seeking to integrate biodiversity. We begin this book by presenting our Species Protection Action Plan for the Financial Markets. Our approach involves summarising the latest scientific research into biodiversity loss and extinction and connecting it to the most innovative, forward-thinking and enlightened finance practice. We then offer an Extinction Governance framework that brings together frameworks for extinction accounting, extinction engagement and extinction finance into the heart of corporate governance and accountability. The rest of this text explores a wide range of new financial instruments and mechanisms, across sectors, approaches and asset classes, including investor engagement on biodiversity (and species extinction), integration of biodiversity into sustainability ratings, green and blue bonds that incorporate biodiversity, integration of biodiversity into financial analysis, and species impact bonds. Exploring and assessing these new and exciting forms of finance allows us to identify gaps in practice and to offer insights on where further initiatives may be developed.

Our message, as with all messages, comes with a warning. Capture by consultants needs to be avoided. Proliferation of frameworks for financial gain and competitive advantage will only result in short-term gains, leading to a potential green bubble and ultimately to a race to the bottom.

The world needs a finance that does not protect the status quo but is transformative. We need a finance that is emancipatory, which drives change towards social and environmental betterment. An emancipatory finance is essential if we are to turn around the current march towards biodiversity and ecosystem collapse. This book provides the frameworks, the tools, the rationale for the continuous development of such an emancipatory finance, emancipatory governance and emancipatory accounting and offers hope for a better, safer, healthier and more beautiful planet.

It's finance... but not as we know it. And we need more of it.

Jill Atkins and Martina Macpherson

Note

1 See Akins and Atkins (2019).

Reference

Atkins, J. and Atkins, B. (2019) (eds.) *Around the World in 80 Species: Exploring the Business of Extinction*, Routledge, UK.

INTRODUCTION

Why Are Species Extinction and Biodiversity Collapse Relevant to the Financial Markets, Accounting and Governance?

Jill Atkins and Martina Macpherson

The planet is currently experiencing a mass extinction event, with human and business activity being the root cause of species loss and habitat destruction.[1] Pervasive human-driven pollution, climate change, an ever-increasing use of land and over-consumption are just some of the determining factors contributing to this dangerous loss of biodiversity, natural habitat and species, which in turn results in the overall loss of ecosystem services.

Recent scientific research finds that from a sample of almost half vertebrate species, 32% are decreasing in population size and range as a result of habitat loss, overexploitation, invasion by alien species, pollution and global warming.[2] As well as species 'going extinct', populations of species are diminishing and disappearing. Population extinctions refer to local extinctions of a species, but such local extinctions are a prelude to species extinctions, such that

> The massive loss of populations is already damaging the services ecosystems provide to civilization .... All signs point to ever more powerful assaults on biodiversity in the next two decades, painting a dismal picture of the future of life, including human life.[3]

The IUCN Red List provides the most up-to-date information and research available on species threatened with extinction. Around 90% of the world's large ocean fish have been lost due to overfishing.[4] In addition, the BGCI's[5] Threat-Search database provides the only global database of all known conservation assessments of plants. The accelerating global collapse in biodiversity accompanying species extinctions is similarly of grave concern. Given the extinction crisis we currently find ourselves in, making connections between species extinction and our global capitalist system is crucial to driving conservation and species protection. By identifying species loss and extinction as a financially material risk

DOI: 10.4324/9781003045557-1

pervasive across all aspects of business, finance and accounting, we also identify an urgent need for action. Our response is to offer a *Species Protection Action Plan* for the financial sector, in Chapter 1:

> Given this looming environmental disaster, the accounting and business community cannot simply assume that a scientific solution will be found to prevent extinction and the associated risks which it poses to humanity.[6]

A recent book, '*Around the World in 80 Species: Exploring the Business of Extinction*', focused on investigating two avenues leading to integration of species protection into the heart of business, finance and accounting. The research underpinning this book led to the development of an extinction accounting framework and an extinction engagement framework for responsible investment, and this text is a development from the earlier book. We outline these in more detail in Chapter 1.

Given the ongoing extinction crisis, there have been substantial efforts across interdisciplinary boundaries to develop valuations for ecosystem services. These valuations provide an essential insight into how significant our reliance on ecosystems and 'natural capital' is. Ecosystem services and their valuation allow us to understand how critical these natural gifts are to our survival. Such valuations simultaneously provide an insight into the value of their decline, or disappearance. From another angle, the loss of an ecosystem service or of any aspect of 'natural capital' represents a significant financial loss. The value is often arrived at by considering how much it would cost to replace the naturally occurring ecosystem service, where there is a viable replacement. The actual figure of valuation is not the important focus of the valuation; rather, it is the magnitude of this value and often its irreplaceability. Where an ecosystem service disappears and cannot be replaced by some artificial alternative, then that service has become *INvaluable*. In attempting to value species loss, we have to consider the value at risk were a species to go extinct. Irreplaceable ecosystem services do not hold a value per se but rather represent a significant and material financial risk to business and society. This material financial risk is a real and imminent risk for many ecosystems. The contribution of each and every species to the healthy functioning, and indeed continuance, of every ecosystem is generally scientifically unknown, until a species disappears. The loss of any one species can lead to the collapse of an ecosystem – or it may not. Given the millions of species of flora and fauna on the planet, it is impossible to know comprehensively which species are keystone species, which species could have little impact on an ecosystem were they to disappear and which are crucial to an ecosystem's survival. Many of these are known but by no means not all. Ecosystem collapse implies the collapse of ecosystem services. It is the *interconnectedness of species* that presents business, finance and accounting with a massive challenge, as species protection is suddenly recognised as a core and essential component of risk management systems and internal control.

Any material financial risk requires risk management tools, disclosure, audit, accountability and monitoring. Any part of the financial system that does not incorporate biodiversity, natural habitat, species protection and extinction prevention into the heart of its risk management, mitigation and adaptation strategy is failing to acknowledge the massive potential financial losses that could arise were certain species to go extinct. It is helpful to consider some cases that serve to illustrate the crucial role each and every species has to the continuance and survival of healthy ecosystems, and to the sustainability of business and finance, within the context of the Ecological Transition. Indeed, in order to communicate the enormity of the financial risks attached to species loss and extinction, we need to consider illustrations that people in business, finance and accounting can relate to at both a personal level and the level of employment and work-related responsibilities.

Bee Decline, Finance and Accounting

Bee, and pollinator decline, provides an easily communicable example of how species loss can affect, and is affecting, the value chain, businesses, finance and investment. Worrying scientific and economics-based research has provided staggering figures relating to the value of pollination services provided by bees for some years now.

One recent report produced by the Intergovernmental Science-Policy Platform on Biodiversity and Ecosystem Services (IPBES)[7] stated that the value of agricultural crop production ($2.6 trillion in 2016) has increased approximately threefold since 1970, but also asserts that between $235 billion and $577 billion in annual global crop output is at risk as a result of pollinator loss.[8] Estimates of the impact of pollinator decline globally average around £130 billion per year.[9]

Bee populations are declining globally due to the lack of floral biodiversity, pesticide use, habitat degradation and reduction, mono-agriculture and global warming arising from climate change. A recent red list showed that out of a total of 1,101 species, about 15% of bees in the EU are threatened or near-threatened with extinction.[10] Recent statistics for the USA estimate around 42% annual loss in commercial bee colonies. Further, there has been a loss of around 96% in four wild bumblebee species in North America over the last 20 years. Both commercial and wild bee populations are affected. There has been an increase in bee loss across France, Italy, Belgium, the UK, Sweden, Spain and elsewhere.

A previous book, *The Business of Bees*,[11] reviewed the current state of bee decline globally and highlighted the links to controversial company activities in the chemical industry[12], considered how this was affecting businesses and proposed frameworks for addressing bee decline, and pollinator decline more broadly, throughout the stakeholder value chain (including corporates, investors, policy makers, NGOs and consumers). This book brought together views from academic research into corporate representation of bee-related risks through accounting with the views of responsible investor practitioners who are dealing with these issues in collaborative dialogue with investee companies, NGOs and policy makers, across the globe. Essentially, decline in bee populations, both of wild bees and commercial bees, represents a significant material financial risk for businesses for the food industry but also in other sectors such as cotton production and the luxury perfume market.

The Business of Bees also includes a framework for incorporating bee decline and initiatives to protect and enhance bee populations within responsible investment, from a practitioner's perspective.[13] This framework has been used as the basis for investor engagements on pollinator decline.

Material Financial Risk through the Interconnectedness of Species: Durian and Fruit Bats

An exotic fruit, the durian, provides a salient example of potential loss of value arising from species loss as well as of the critical balance of interrelationships that necessitate the healthy functioning of ecosystems and the provision of ecosystem services. The fruit is farmed primarily in Indonesia, Thailand and Malaysia. An article published in Geographical online in April this year highlights some imminent problems facing durian farming which have the potential to impact on business, investors and consumers, as well as the broader Malaysian society.[14]

The Guardian in December last year featured an article about how the durian, a 'foul smelling fruit', could make millions for Malaysia.[15] China is the world's largest importer of durian with imports of around 292 million kg in 2016 and a share of up to 80% of global imports, with an anticipated growth of up to 15% in future years. Total trade in durian is expected to reach 4.5 billion kg by 2030 (currently total trade is around 1.6 billion kg). Global durian consumption has recently been valued at $14 billion annually, and it is growing rapidly.

There is also a substantial tourist industry that has built up around durian, for people wishing to visit the plantations.[16] However, another Guardian article raised concerns about how the increasing demand from China is leading to a surge in large-scale durian farming involving destruction of habitat that is home to the critically endangered Malayan tiger.[17]

The IUCN Red List website states that the estimated nationwide population has continued to decline from roughly 3,000 in the 1950s, to 500 between 1990 and 2003 to an estimate of between 80 and 120 mature tigers today.[18] However, the rush to develop more and more durian plantations is not only threatening endangered jungle species such as tigers, elephants, monkeys and birds, but is also leading to a decline in fruit bats (flying foxes) and other critically important pollinator species. Indeed, the future survival of the durian tree is considered to be threatened by the decline in flying foxes.[19]

A recent scientific study provided evidence that giant fruit bats (flying foxes) are very active and effective in pollinating durian trees. Until this study was published, it was commonly thought that these huge bats were destructive and only the smaller, nectar-feeding bats were key pollinators. They are already classified as endangered on Malaysia's Red List and are threatened by deforestation and habitat loss, as well as by hunting as bushmeat and killed as potential pests rather than seen as helpful pollinators. This research highlights the critical nature of interrelationships between species of flora and fauna, habitat and human-focused ecosystem services:[20]

> Given the potential importance of flying foxes in ensuring the continued reproductive success of durian trees, the economic implications for the durian fruit industry should not be ignored. The conservation value of such an economic role is obvious. It is particularly significant given that some commercial durian farmers, such as in southern Thailand, have resorted to artificial cross-pollination by hand in the absence of natural pollinators - a laborious, time-consuming, costly, and dangerous method.
>
> *(Aziz et al., 2017, p. 8682)*

Is it realistic to see human pollination as an alternative to natural pollination by fruit bats?

A recent market report on Durian concludes that

> The obstacle facing Musang King [the largest and most popular durian strain] will not be one of demand as its demand is evident. Instead it will be on finding the correct balance between supply and price in order to optimise the fruits profitability.

Clearly, this financial and economic assessment fails to acknowledge risks to durian production arising from key pollinator loss due to continuous increasing habitat destruction. This is a material financial risk to the business arising from species decline and potential extinction that should be incorporated into any business model. An approach to fruit production that fails to incorporate these ecological risks ensures only a short-term and unsustainable profitability that will result over the medium to long term in a collapse in the business with no fruit and no forest.

The report indicates that profits from durian are expected to outstrip those from palm oil production – and look what that has done to orang-utan. They are on the very brink of extinction. In summary, for any financial institution involved in financing durian farming and development of plantations and any investor considering investing in durian agricultural companies that appear to have an extremely promising future of financial growth, these ecological risks arising from species interrelationships and decline in pollinators should be core to financial decision-making. From a purely financial and business perspective, it is critically important to invest in conservation and protection of key pollinator species such as flying foxes. From a deep ecology perspective, these creatures are beautiful, charismatic species with intrinsic value and are surely worth saving from extinction.

Luxury Foods: Truffle Industry, Caviar

Thousands more examples linking financial materiality and species extinction can be found. Here we discuss just two from the luxury food sector: truffles and caviar. White truffles are found in the north-western region of Piedmont, and these specific truffles *(Tuber magnatum)* are dubbed 'white gold' or 'white diamonds'. They are incredibly expensive with 100 grams (3.5 ounces) of white truffle costing between 300 and 450 euros. Over the past 25 years, there has been a 30% decrease in truffle production. Indeed, all truffles are at risk from extinction for a range of reasons: climate change (due to changes in rainfall and temperature/humidity); drought and heat; the extension of vineyards in the region; and invasive species (e.g. locust tree). The warmer and drier climate in the region is especially a concern although habitat is a major extinction threat.

Caviar is also potentially under threat. The highest quality caviar consists of the roe from sturgeon. Current estimates suggest that 85% of sturgeon, one of the most ancient fish species, are at risk of extinction, making them the most threatened group of animals on the IUCN Red List. Indeed, all 18 species of sturgeon from all over Europe and Asia are threatened. Of course, sturgeon are farmed for caviar, but there are always concerns around whether farmed fish are sustainable. Against this extinction issue, the world market for caviar is expected to grow by 5.7% annually and is expected to reach US$500 million in 2023, rising from 360 million US$ in 2017[21]. But what would happen were sturgeon to disappear?

Species Extinction, Species Interrelationships and Material Financial Risk

There have been numerous attempts to estimate the value of ecosystem services that include provisioning services, regulatory services, supporting services and cultural services. Ecosystem services worldwide were estimated to be annually worth *$33 trillion,*[22] almost twice the global GNP at an estimated *$18 trillion.* Such 'valuing' of global ecosystem services is clearly immensely complicated and can at best only result in a very rough estimate. Research concludes that changes in global land use between 1997 and 2011 have resulted in a loss of ecosystem services of between *$4.3 and $20.2 trillion* per year.[23] The authors further estimated total global ecosystem services in 2011 to be *$125 trillion per year* or *$145 trillion per year,* using slightly different measures. These figures are alarming, yet the paper stresses that the estimates are conservative. It is not the size of the estimates that matters, rather the magnitude and enormity of our reliance, as a species, on all other species and their interdependence. As we cannot easily understand the contribution of each endangered species to the functioning of the ecosystem as a whole, as seen from discussion of the scientific literature above, the loss of one species could be represented by a *pro rata* proportion of $145 trillion a year, or could equal a substantial amount, if not all, of $145 trillion, if it is found to be a keynote species.[24]

The 2019 IPBES report provides (with varying levels of certainty according to probability estimates) a range of the latest information relating to species decline and the impact of extinction threat on human life, in their new report. An average of around *25%* of species across the many terrestrial, freshwater and marine vertebrate, invertebrate and plant groups are currently considered to be threatened with extinction, and the threat of extinction is accelerating. More than 40% of amphibian species, almost a third of reef-forming corals, sharks and shark relatives and over a third of marine mammals are currently threatened. The proportion of insect species threatened with extinction is a key uncertainty, but available evidence supports a tentative estimate of 10%. Overall, it is estimated that of an estimated 8 million animal and plant species (75% of which are insects), around 1 million are threatened with extinction. The report also states that around 9% of the world's estimated 5.9 million terrestrial species — more than 500,000 species — have insufficient habitat for long-term survival and are committed to extinction, many within decades, unless their habitats are restored.

Meat from wild animals forms a critical contribution to food sources and livelihoods in many countries with high levels of poverty and food insecurity — monkeys, tapirs, antelopes, pigs, pheasants, turtles and snakes. Not only are wild flora and fauna at risk, but also farmed and domestic species are threatened due to reducing gene pools. An increasing proportion of marine fish stocks are over-fished (33% in 2015), including economically important species, while 60% are maximally sustainably fished and only 7% are underfished. Approximately 100 million metric tons of aquatic organisms, including fish, molluscs and crustaceans, are taken from the wild every year and represent a vital contribution to world food security.

Tourism and specifically ecotourism also represent significant and substantial contributions to economies often in developing countries. Ecotourism is likely to be under threat from species extinction: who would visit the Kruger Park in South Africa were the Big Five to disappear? Human health is also under threat from plant species decline. An estimated 50,000–70,000 plant species are used in traditional and modern medicine worldwide.

The value creation process should take cognisance of interconnection between different types of capital (including financial, manufactured, intellectual, environmental, human and social and relationship capital) in the context of the entity's strategy, risks and operating model.[25] In theory, this integrated thinking framework should be well suited for framing how biodiversity should be understood and reported on by organisations. However, the equal treatment of the six capitals could be called into question when we consider that 'natural' capital represents life on earth and the ecosystem, without which the other five are rendered meaningless.

In summary for a company, the financial materiality of biodiversity decline and species loss arises from the following: interdependencies between nature and business; legal fines for adverse impacts of business activities on species;

rehabilitation of land; unavailability of natural capital and ecosystem services (such as pollination); and reputational damage due to accidents or incidents.[26] As explained by Trent in Chapter 9, the ongoing biodiversity crisis, as an imminent threat to humanity, society and business, is at least as significant as the climate crisis. For investment institutions, mirroring these factors, biodiversity loss and species extinctions represent a similar financially material risk across their investments in companies. As we show in the following chapter, not only are all parts of the financial markets and all financial institutions susceptible to biodiversity and species extinction risk, but also they represent hefty mechanisms of governance, financing and accountability that can be re-tuned to saving species and biodiversity. Instead of adding to a global cacophony of broken, atonal, unsynchronised sounds of dying creatures, the financial markets could begin to write and conduct a harmonious pastoral symphony.

Notes

1 Ceballos, García, and Ehrlich (2010); Ceballos et al. (2015); Kolbert (2014).
2 Ceballos, Ehlrich, and Dirzo (2017).
3 Ceballos et al. (2017, p. 6095).
4 See the discussion in Trent, Chapter 9.
5 Botanic Gardens Conservation International.
6 Maroun and Atkins (2018).
7 The IPBES is the intergovernmental body that assesses the state of biodiversity and of the ecosystem services it provides to society, in response to requests from decision-makers.
8 IPBES Report, Summary for policymakers of the global assessment report on biodiversity and ecosystem services of the Intergovernmental Science-Policy Platform on Biodiversity and Ecosystem Services, May 2019.
9 Stathers (2016).
10 Nieto et al. (2014).
11 Atkins and Atkins (2016)
12 Macpherson and Biehl, Bees and Accountability in Germany: A Multi-Stakeholder Perspective, in: Atkins and Atkins (2016).
13 Herron, Pollinators as a Portfolio Risk: Making the Case for Investor Action, in: Atkins and Atkins (2016)
14 https://geographical.co.uk/people/development/item/3129-durian-fruit.
15 https://www.theguardian.com/world/2018/dec/02/durian-foul-smelling-fruit-make-malaysia-millions-export-china.
16 These data were taken from the Durian Global Market Report produced by MK Durian Harvest Sdn. Bhd., Kuala Lumpur, Malaysia.
17 https://www.theguardian.com/world/2018/oct/24/chinas-appetite-for-stinky-durian-fruit-threatening-endangered-tigers.
18 Kawanishi (2015); Kawanishi and Sunquist (2004); Topani (1990).
19 https://www.conservationjobs.co.uk/articles/durian-tree-threatened-by-decline-of-flying-foxes/.
20 Aziz et al. (2017).
21 Global Caviar Market by Manufacturers, Regions, Type and Application, Forecast to 2023 | Orbis Research.
22 Constanza et al. (1997).
23 Constanza et al. (2014); Constanza (2006).
24 This argument is taken from Atkins and Maroun (2018).

25 Eccles and Krzus (2010); Eccles and Saltzman (2011).
26 See an excellent summary of the financial materiality of a company's biodiversity footprint in Chapter 16: Lehman and Zubets Anderson.

References

Atkins, J. F. and Atkins, B. C. (eds.) (2016) *The Business of Bees, An Integrated Approach to Bee Decline*, June, Greenleaf Publishers.

Atkins, J. F. and Maroun, W. (2018) "Integrated Extinction Accounting and Accountability: Building an Ark", *Accounting, Auditing & Accountability Journal*, Vol. 31, No. 3, pp. 1–41.

Aziz, S. A., Clements, G. R., McConkey, K. R., Sritongchuay, T., Saifful, P., Muhammad Nur Hafizi, A. Y., Campos-Arceiz, A., Forget, P.-M. and Bumrungsri, S. (2017). "Pollination by the Locally Endangered Island Flying Fox (Pteropus hypomelanus) Enhances Fruit Production of the Economically Important Durian (Durio zibethinus)", *Ecology and Evolution*: doi: 10.1002/ece3.3213

Ceballos, G., Ehrlich, P. R., Barnosky, A. D., García, A., Pringle, R. M. and Palmer, T. M. (2015). "Accelerated Modern Human-Induced Species Losses: Entering the Sixth Mass Extinction", *Science Advances*, Vol. 1, e1400253.

Ceballos, G., Ehrlich, P. R. and Dirzo, R. (2017). "Biological Annihilation via the Ongoing Sixth Mass Extinction Signaled by Vertebrate Population Losses and Declines", *Proceedings of the National Academy of Sciences*.

Ceballos, G., García, A. and Ehrlich, P. R. (2010). "The Sixth Extinction Crisis: Loss of Animal Populations and Species", *Journal of Cosmology*, Vol. 8, 1821–1831.

Constanza, R. (2006). "Nature: Ecosystems without Commodifying Them", *Nature*, Vol. 443, p. 749.

Constanza, R., dArge, R., de Groot, R., Farber, S., Grasso, M., Hannon, B., Limburg, K., Naeem, S., O'Neill, R. V., Paruelo, J., Raskin, R. G., Sutton, P. and van den Belt, M., (1997). "The Value of the World's Ecosystem Services and Natural Capital", *Nature*, Vol. 387, pp. 253–260.

Constanza, R., de Groot, R., Sutton, P., van der Ploeg, S, Anderson, S. J., Kubiszewski, I., Farber, S. and Turner, K. (2014). "Changes in the Global Value of Ecosystem Services", *Global Environmental Change*, Vol. 26, pp. 152–158.

Eccles, R. G. and Krzus, M. P. (2010). "Integrated Reporting for a Sustainable Strategy", Available: http://www.financialexecutives.org/KenticoCMS/Financial-Executive-Magazine/2010_03/Financial-Reporting-Feature-March-2010.aspx#axzz48iuAkAHV. Accessed 26 November 2012.

Eccles, R. and Saltzman, D. (2011). "Achieving Sustainability through Integrated Reporting", *Stanford Social Innovation Review*. Available: http://202.154.59.182/mfile/files/Jurnal/MIT%202012-2013%20(PDF)/Achieving%20Sustainability%20Through%20Integrated%20Reporting.pdf.

Kawanishi, K. (2015). *Panthera tigris ssp. jacksoni. The IUCN Red List of Threatened Species* 2015: e.T136893A50665029. http://dx.doi.org/10.2305/IUCN.UK.2015-2.RLTS.T136893A50665029.en. Downloaded on 26 May 2019.

Kawanishi, K. and Sunquist, M. E. (2004). "Conservation Status of Tigers in a Primary Rainforest of Peninsular Malaysia", *Biological Conservation*, Vol. 120, No. 3, pp. 329–344.

Maroun, W. and Atkins, J. F. (2018) "The Emancipatory Potential of Extinction Accounting: Exploring Current Practice in Integrated Reports", *Accounting Forum*, Vol. 42, pp. 102–118.

Nieto, A., Roberts, S. P. M., Kemp, J., Rasmont, P., Kuhlmann, M., García Criado, M., Biesmeijer, J. C., Bogusch, P., Dathe, H. H., De la Rúa, P., De Meulemeester, T., Dehon, M., Dewulf, A., Ortiz-Sánchez, F. J., Lhomme, P., Pauly, A., Potts, S. G., Praz, C., Quaranta, M., Radchenko, V. G., Scheuchl, E., Smit, J., Straka, J., Terzo, M., Tomozii, B., Window, J. and Michez, D. (2014) *European Red List of Bees*. Luxembourg: Publication Office of the European Union.

Stathers, R. (2016). "The Bee and the Stock Market: An Overview of Pollinator Decline and Its Economic and Corporate Significance", chapter 6 in Atkins, J. and Atkins, B. (2016) *The Business of Bees: An Integrated Approach to Bee Decline and Corporate Responsibility*, Greenleaf Publishers Limited, Saltaire, UK, pp. 110–131.

Topani, R. (1990). "Status and Distribution of Tiger in Peninsular Malaysia", *Journal of Wildlife Parks (Malaysia)*, Vol. 9, pp. 71–102.

PART I

Defining Extinction Governance, Extinction Accounting and Extinction Finance

1

EXTINCTION ACCOUNTING, FINANCE AND ENGAGEMENT

Implementing a Species Protection Action Plan for the Financial Markets

Jill Atkins and Martina Macpherson

This book could be neither timelier, nor more necessary. We aim to present cutting-edge developments in the finance industry with contributions from market leaders and academics so as to enable the development of a toolkit, or framework, that incorporates current best practice. The World Economic Forum's *Annual Risk Report* 2020 ranks biodiversity loss as the third most impactful risk facing the global economy, and the fourth most likely to occur.[1] At Abu Dhabi in the United Arab Emirates, an urgent call was launched in 2019 to massively scale up species conservation action in response to the escalating biodiversity crisis.[2] The Abu Dhabi Call for Global Species Conservation Action appeals to the world's governments, international agencies and the private sector to halt species decline and prevent human-driven extinctions by 2030, and to improve the conservation status of threatened species, with a view to bringing about widespread recovery by 2050. The UK is taking a leading role in addressing biodiversity decline as well as climate change, being the host of the UN Climate Change Conference (COP26) in 2021 (see Box 1.1). The WWF states that the UK Government must now align financial sector regulation with climate and nature goals.[3] Further, the UK's Dasgupta Review, published in February 2021, leaves us in no doubt of the urgent need to address biodiversity loss and species extinction. Policymakers, regulators and financial institutions the world over have a key role to play in addressing the ongoing extinction crisis, as do businesses and other organisations worldwide. Indeed, the Dasgupta Review represents one of many calls from international bodies and organisations for the financial markets to act urgently to preserve nature. The 2019 IPBES Report also identified economic and financial systems as crucial to the fight against the degradation of ecosystems, equally calling for transformative action in the financial sector, stating,[4]

DOI: 10.4324/9781003045557-3

BOX 1.1 THE EUROPEAN COMMISSION COP, BIODIVERSITY AND FINANCE

What Is the Link between Finance and Biodiversity?

There is a section on the European Commission's website specifically devoted to the link between biodiversity and finance, focusing on what the EU Community of Practice (CoP), a header platform with a number of subdivisions established in 2016, is doing to engage with, and educate, financial institutions on how they can integrate schemes centred around natural capital into their portfolios. The CoP aims to provide a 'forum of dialogue between financial institutions to share experiences, raise awareness and promote best practices at EU level on how to integrate biodiversity and natural capital into mainstream financial activities and foster investments in natural capital as a new asset class' by advocating the implementation of biodiversity-centric policies and investments at multiple levels, which will support 'the transition towards a sustainable financial sector'.

See more at https://ec.europa.eu/environment/biodiversity/business/workstreams/finance/index_en.htm

Contributed by Zoe Solomon

Decision makers have a range of options and tools for improving the sustainability of economic and financial systems. Achieving a sustainable economy involves making fundamental reforms to economic and financial systems .... Trade agreements and derivatives markets could be reformed to promote equity and prevent deterioration of nature, although there are uncertainties associated with implementation. ...... Structural changes to economies are also key to shifting action over long time scales, including technological and social innovation regimes and investment frameworks that internalize environmental impacts such as externalities of economic activities, including by addressing environmental impacts in socially just and appropriate ways.

The Dasgupta Review also calls for a Global Standard for the international financial system. It is our hope that the summary mapping contained in Table 1.1 in the final chapter, that consolidates the innovations and mechanisms showcased in chapters contributed by financial institutions, academics and other nature-related organisations, can assist in developing such a Global Standard. The Review ends with calls for action, and our book provides a full and detailed response to this call. In this chapter, we weave some of the commentary from the Dasgupta Review into our discussion in order to integrate some of the most recent developments, and to elucidate and highlight the discussion around the chapters in the rest of the text. A critically important initiative for the business

TABLE 1.1 Targets, tools, methods and measures for biodiversity

Tool/Measurement	Acronym	Organisation	Comments
Tools for the Finance Industry			
Exploring Natural Capital Opportunities, Risks and Exposure	ENCORE	Natural Capital Finance Alliance	Helps users understand how businesses across all sectors depend on nature and how these dependencies may represent business risk
Biodiversity Footprint for Financial Institutions	BFFI	ASN Bank	Not based on exposure of financial institutions to biodiversity-related risks (except for reputational and litigation) rather attribution of financial activity to negative biodiversity impacts
Species Threat Abatement and Recovery Metric	STAR	IUCN	Metric to understand whether investments achieve conservation outcome
Tools for Companies and the Finance Industry			
Global Biodiversity Score	GBS	CDC Biodiversité Club for Positive Biodiversity Businesses Club B4B+	Focuses on financial portfolio and corporate assessments for internal uses and external reporting Uses the MSA[a]
Tools for Companies			
Corporate Ecosystem Valuation	CEV	World Business Council for Sustainable Development (WBCSD)	Process for business to value natural ecosystems, including biodiversity A process to make better-informed business decisions by explicitly valuing both ecosystem degradation and the benefits provided by ecosystem services

(Continued)

Tool/Measurement	Acronym	Organisation	Comments
Biodiversity Footprints for Companies and Products			
Biodiversity Footprint Calculator		Plansup	A free calculation tool that assesses current and future biodiversity footprint of a company or a product
Product Biodiversity Footprint	PBF	icare&consult	Assesses impact of products on biodiversity
Sector-Specific Tools			
Agrobiodiversity Index		Biodiversity International	
Biodiversity and Ecosystem Services Fundamentals	IPIECA	IPIECA	Biodiversity impacts/risks for the oil and gas sector
Biodiversity Indicator and Reporting System	BIRS	IUCN	Biodiversity monitoring for the cement and aggregates sector
Biodiversity Indicators for Monitoring Impacts and Conservation Actions		The Energy and Biodiversity Initiative	Method for assessing biodiversity impacts
Business Impact on Biodiversity			
Environmental Profit and Loss	EP&L	Kering	Sharing with companies in the luxury sector – and others
ICMA harmonised Framework for Impact Reporting	ICMA (2019)		
IFC Operating Principles for Impact	IFC		
Healthy Ecosystem Framework/ Biodiversity Impact Metric		CISL – Cambridge Institute for Sustainability Leadership	Metric to calculate business impact on biodiversity

Tool/Measurement	Acronym	Organisation	Comments
Human Impact on Biodiversity			
Biodiversity Intactness Index	BII	Biodiversity Indicators Partnership	
Reporting Methods and Reporting Frameworks			
GRI Standards 304	GRI	Global Reporting Initiative (GRI)	Method for disclosing biodiversity information
SASB	Sustainability Accounting Standards Board (SASB) (Conceptual Framework) (2017)		
SASB Materiality Map 2018	SASB		
CDP (Climate)	CDP (Climate Disclosure Project) (Climate Change) 2002		
CDP (Forests)	CDP (Forests) 2011		
CDP (Water)	CDP (Water Security) 2009		
Biological Diversity Protocol	BD Protocol	Output from Biodiversity Disclosure Project (BDP), managed by National Biodiversity and Business Network (NBBN) South Africa, hosted by Endangered Wildlife Trust (EWT)	Developed through online consultation with a wide range of stakeholders
Extinction accounting framework	Atkins and Maroun (2018), Atkins and Atkins (2019)	Accounting Academia	
Universal Biodiversity Data Providers			
Integrated Biodiversity Assessment Tool	IBAT	IBAT Alliance	Planning tool, providing data on existing biodiversity

(Continued)

Tool/Measurement	Acronym	Organisation	Comments
Nature Map Explorer		Nature Map Initiative. Developed jointly by the International Institute for Applied Systems Analysis (IIASA), the Instituto Internacional para Sustentabilidade (IIS), the UN Sustainable Development Solutions Network (SDSN) and the UN Environment Programme World Conservation Monitoring Centre (UNEP-WCMC). Royal Botanic Gardens Kew is supporting the analysis of plant taxa. The project is funded by Norway's International Climate and Forest Initiative (NICFI).	Global map of terrestrial biodiversity and ecosystem carbon stocks. Freely accessible by the UN Biodiversity Lab.
	GLOBIO	https://www.globio.info/what-is-globio	Modelling framework to calculate the impact of environmental drivers on biodiversity for past, present and future

a **MSA for Mean Species Abundance** = *Observed Biodiversity (Species)/Undistributed Biodiversity (Species)* as a percentage. The unit of the GBS: *km²MSA = MSA% × Surface*. 1 km² MSA loss is equivalent to the destruction of 1 km² of undisturbed natural areas. The MSA assesses the increase/decrease in species and expresses the fraction of naturally present biodiversity remaining.

community is the Business for Nature (BfN) coalition launched in July 2019, as they are mobilising companies to protect biodiversity, as outlined by Zabey and Thissen in Chapter 4.

This chapter seeks to provide an overview of all the areas of the financial markets where initiatives can be, or are being, implemented to prevent extinctions and biodiversity loss, as well as setting out our *Species Protection Action Plan for the Financial Markets*. We now turn to providing an overview of some of the most significant initiatives implemented across the financial markets, although many of these – and others – will be the focus of later chapters. Our aim here is to give a flavour of the veritable explosion of activity that is currently underway.

We begin by considering the burgeoning financial market for ratings, indexes, tools, methods being developed and/or in use for measuring biodiversity, or at least for attempting to assess the impact of biodiversity decline and species loss on financial markets, as well as the impact of financing, investment and business activity on biodiversity and species. Then, we consider extinction finance, extinction engagement and extinction accounting.

Extinction Governance: Targets and Tools for Measuring Biodiversity

As actors across the financial markets begin to recognise and acknowledge the need to incorporate biodiversity into their assessments of companies as well as the impacts of their own financial activities and decisions on biodiversity, a demand for measures and methods of assessment has been created. Into what could only be described as a vacuum of information, or at least an extremely inefficient market for biodiversity information, have poured a diverse and expanding array of initiatives, measures and tools. The financial markets are always frenetic, characterised by talented individuals of the highest intellect. The competitive nature of the financial markets and the need for institutions to outthink each other to stay ahead spawn innovative practices at lightning speed. In the same way the pharmaceutical industry has risen immediately to the challenge of finding, producing and distributing vaccines for COVID-19 in record time, the financial industry is now responding in a fast and furious manner to the sudden realisation that the sixth mass extinction threatens their own survival. Indeed, there are substantial connections between the two crises, that are explored in Chapters 26 and 30, but also mentioned throughout this book. In Chapter 14, Borgeaud, Chatain and Preudhomme introduce the proximity indicator as a novel measure.

Resonating with the explosion of biodiversity initiatives and concepts discussed above, there is a commensurate surge in interest in developing metrics, tools, methods to attempt to measure biodiversity in order to service the finance industry, corporate needs and those of many other related users and clients. The Cambridge Institute for Sustainability Leadership (CISL) states that the three main approaches to estimating the monetary value of biodiversity are the cost of restoring biodiversity once it has been degraded; the volume of biodiversity finance available; and totalling the value of the economic outputs of industries identified as being dependent on nature.[5]

CISL[6] compiled a list of 16 prominent tools, targets, methods and measures for biodiversity. In Table 1.1, we include these and some additional ones, categorising them according to Tools for the Finance Industry; Tools for Companies and the Finance Industry; Biodiversity Footprints for Companies and Products; Sector-Specific Tools; Business Impact on Biodiversity; Human Impact on Biodiversity; Reporting Methods and Reporting Frameworks; and Universal Biodiversity Data Providers. The very wide array and diversity of these represents one of the essential challenges to addressing biodiversity loss and species extinctions in any urgent manner: too many, lack of consistency, incomparability. This challenge is raised in Chapter 13[7] where they conclude that the current situation is characterised by inadequate public biodiversity disclosure, inadequate company-level data, a proliferation of ESG assessment methods and the overarching voluntary environment for biodiversity and species information. These factors provide significant challenges for asset managers.

Overall, most of the tools in Table 1.1 focus on the biodiversity impact of business operations. This considers the dependence of sectors on natural capital. We are not going to discuss these exhaustively but make a few comments below on points of interest.

The categorisations are only suggestions, but they attempt to plot some contours through this evolving landscape. The two major universal data providers are extremely interesting. IBAT seems especially interesting, as it claims on its website to offer a 'one-stop shop' data search services for those seeking authoritative global biodiversity information and draws on data relating to 120,372 IUCN Red List Species, 235,136 protected areas and 16,312 key biodiversity areas.[8] They provide reports to clients, at a price, and provide a list of users,[9] which is impressive. IBAT hosts and maintains the three global biodiversity databases: the IUCN Red List of Threatened Species, World Database on Protected Areas and World Database of Key Biodiversity Areas. They state that it costs US$6.5 million per year to maintain these databases. Alternately, Nature Map Explorer seems to offer some similar information from the Nature Map Initiative but is free to users.

As well as assessing companies' biodiversity footprint, we can also see the Product Biodiversity Footprint as an interesting and essential innovation. Their website states that the baseline principle is to co-develop a method and a tool that quantify a product's impacts on biodiversity throughout the product's life cycle stages. This is a neat way of assessing biodiversity impact through the supply chain and to separate products and their development from the activities of an individual business, thereby providing a different layer of vision.

Reflecting on the current tools and methods available reveals, for us at least, a gap: the lack of a universally applicable species extinction-related marker. The BFFI and the GBS do integrate the MSA measure, as discussed in Table 1.1. The MSA does provide a means of assessing any increase or decrease in species, as it expresses the fraction of naturally present biodiversity remaining. However, it is a complex and not easily understandable term for wide audiences. Perhaps a more focused and simpler target would be helpful. We explore a possible solution below.

A New Species Extinction-Based Measure?

One of the aims of this book and the extinction accounting project in paris to bring together research and ideas from different disciplines, as an

interdisciplinary approach is essential if we are to address the urgency of the mass extinction crisis. We therefore turn to the latest science research to draw inspiration for additional or even alternative measures and tools.

A science paper published in 2020 argues that we need a,

> ... clear global goal for biodiversity, that can be readily communicated to galvanize both political will and public support.[10]

They argue that in the same way as a single indicator[11] and target[12] have been established for climate change, as a basis for policy action, we now need an indicator for biodiversity. The authors propose a target based on *Extinction Rate*. Their justifications for an extinction rate-based target are as follows: (i) species extinction is irreversible whereas decline in species populations, abundance or ecological communities may be recoverable, as, '... extinction fully incorporates the most fundamental aspect of biodiversity loss'[13]; (ii) 'Extinction of species is widely understood and easy to communicate'.[14]

In the same way as the academic accounting literature has argued that the concept of extinction accounting communicates the urgent need to act due to the ongoing extinction crisis, this approach communicates the urgency and also provides a simple and easily understood measurement, focusing on extinction of species rather than vague and obfuscated biodiversity measures.

This is in keeping with the intentions of extinction accounting, extinction finance and extinction engagement, which focus on species protection and extinction prevention rather than what some may construe as generalisations such as 'biodiversity protection'. Specifically, the science paper proposes a,

> .... Measurable, near-term target of keeping described species extinctions to well below 20 per year over the next 100 years[15] across all major groups[16] ... and across all ecosystem types.[17,18]

Reflecting on this target, losing less than 20 species a year really brings home the raw, naked fact of species extinction – total permanent disappearance – and cuts through any potentially euphemistic targets that effectively (although unintentionally) obscure the true losses associated with failure to stem biodiversity decline. The paper states that the target has the great advantage of being communicable to a non-science audience.

The authors do not intend this to be the only measure to be used but that it should be a necessary element of any biodiversity policy target as they emphasise changes in biodiversity can affect the flow of ecosystem services. Again, this is the basis of the extinction governance framework for the financial markets discussed throughout this book – species extinction should be an explicit factor and element of reporting, investor engagement, governance and finance – as well as biodiversity, ecosystems and habitats. The focus of the paper is for a target that is applicable at country, or national, level. We suggest such a target could be applied at company, or organisational level, in extinction accounting or in extinction engagement. This target could form the basis of investor engagement discussions with investee companies. For a company for example, a local extinction rate could be set – say 10 species becoming extinct in the areas upon which they operate. Or even one species could be enough in a local area? Given the discussion in the Introduction around population loss, local extinctions are the precursor to species extinctions. Its application in accounting and finance reflects the views of the scientific authors that,

> We recognise that a single indicator cannot capture the multiple dimensions of complex systems … however, we need to catalyse both policy and public support for biodiversity and its preservation – we need an indicator and target that readily communicate the urgency of the problem to multiple audiences and enable the monitoring of progress.[19]

Extinction Ratings and Indexes

One area of innovative initiatives that has taken off vertically over the last year or so is that of sustainability assessments, or ESG ratings, terms that may be employed synonymously. These ratings attempt to distil a veritable mess of ESG data into a more readily understandable and accessible form. This is a youthful market but one which is evolving at a pace. We refer to the nascent ratings and indexes that focus specifically on biodiversity as Extinction Ratings and Extinction Indexes. VE (formerly Vigeo Eiris) is a distinctive leader in this new area, as we can see from Montagnon and Zanella's discussion in Chapter 12 where they discuss their pioneering biodiversity index.

Extinction Finance

Overview of Initiatives Implemented across the Financial Markets

We view 'extinction finance' as the integration of species protection, extinction prevention and biodiversity enhancement into financial market mechanisms: sustainability/ESG ratings, financial analysis, bonds, indexes, bank lending and banking more broadly. Investor engagement, direct dialogue between investors and investees, can also focus on species extinction and biodiversity, and this is termed, for our purposes, 'extinction engagement', which may be interpreted as a subset of extinction finance. Extinction finance includes extinction banking and the new Extinction Bond framework presented by Macpherson and Biehl in Chapter 11, as discussed below.

There has been a proliferation of initiatives aimed at heightening the profile of biodiversity in the international financial community over the past two years, or so, that we interpret as the emergence of extinction finance. Indeed, social media, especially LinkedIn, Facebook and Twitter, are filled on a daily basis with posts and commentary relating biodiversity, nature and efforts to integrate these into the activities of financial institutions such as banks and institutional investors, as well as pressures from lobby groups on companies to reduce their impacts on biodiversity. The latest version of the Equator Principles published in 2020 points to a significant shift towards incorporating biodiversity into the heart of the Principles.

The European Initiative, TEG, represents a pioneering and substantial shift towards incorporating biodiversity, as well as other sustainability factors, into the finance industry.[20] Another salient initiative driving extinction finance, in our view, is the Partnership for Biodiversity Accounting Financials (PBAF). This partnership of financial institutions explores opportunities and challenges around the assessment and disclosure of the impact on biodiversity associated with their loans and investments, with the aim of developing a set of harmonised principles. The ultimate objective is to contribute to the development of a harmonised biodiversity accounting approach in the financial sector.[21]

Public Extinction Finance: Government/ Sovereign Investment/Lending

The recent Dasgupta Review on 'Finance for Sustainable Engagement with Nature' discusses trends in public and private finance towards a more proactive approach to nature.[22] In relation to public finance, the Review states that governments are key financial investors in domestic and foreign natural assets and explains how public funds which are devoted to addressing environmental issues are currently focused primarily on climate change with only 3% of those funds being allocated to biodiversity and ecosystems.[23] As a case in point, Dasgupta mentions green and blue bonds and especially discusses the Seychelles Blue Bond. This is addressed by NGO in Chapter 19.

The WWF, in their response to the Dasgupta Review, stated that the UK Government should take 'urgent, transformative and impact-multiplying actions', with one focus being to promote the greening of sovereign debt markets in a way that protects biodiversity, inter alia.[24] Further, the WWF highlighted the development of new nature performance bonds (NPBs)[25] as new financial instruments that could provide a reduction in interest payable or the principal over time in return for nature-based outcomes, including protection of forests, restoring wetlands and protecting species. At country level, these could be attractive as they would provide cheaper finance for indebted economies due to the lower rate of return on the debt. This could assist in protecting threatened species and habitats at country level and also hopefully lead to further incentives and further initiatives to assist in biodiversity and species protection.

Most chapters in this book are devoted to extinction finance, as we are referring to efforts from the financial services community to address biodiversity decline and species loss, focusing on initiatives and approaches being developed by private finance institutions and organisations. However, we suspect that public sector finance can learn and transfer cutting-edge practice from the private sector into their own practice. This has been noted as typical in corporate governance, for example, where codes of best practice in governance and accountability around the world have been developed initially for financial markets and for the corporate sector and have then been adapted and transmuted into public finance.[26]

The Dasgupta Review suggests that there is a huge potential which is currently not being tapped for public funds to be channelled more effectively and in a more targeted manner into saving biodiversity and, by implication, species. We explore this process in Chapters 17 and 20.

Private Extinction Finance: Banks, Institutional Investors

The lion's share of finance that is currently being channelled into biodiversity-related investments comes from the private sector. Financial institutions have been called to sign the Finance for Biodiversity Pledge.[27] The Pledge's stated mission is, '*We as financial institutions recognize that the Earth's biosphere is the foundation of human resilience and progress and that it is under increasing stress. We are calling for and commit to take ambitious action on biodiversity*'. The Pledge was launched through collaboration between 26 financial institutions, and by December 2020, there were 37 signatories representing 4.8 trillion euros in assets under management.

The Dasgupta Review emphasises how more substantial private finance is than public finance.

This underlines the importance of refocusing financial institutions urgently on biodiversity and species extinction given the weight of their potential influence. Worryingly, from our perspective, estimates of the current flows of private finance to businesses and activities that are driving biodiversity loss and by implication species extinctions are immense. In 2019, the world's largest financial institutions channelled more than US$2.6 trillion of loans and underwriting services to high biodiversity impact sectors.[28] Indeed, an estimated US$44 million are being poured into business activities and companies directly or indirectly involved in deforestation.[29] Certainly, fast food is fast becoming a salient issue for concern due to the increasing encroachment of land, effectively habitat, for the production of 'animal protein', an uncomfortable term for mass beef- and chicken-intensive agricultural activities. In terms of financial institutions channelling private finance into activities which are deemed to have positive impacts on biodiversity, and by implication on species, the figures are relatively dismal, with estimates of only between US$6.6 and 13.6 billion.

This imbalance needs to be addressed urgently if the financial markets are going to contribute to saving biodiversity and species rather than the reverse. Only by informing and educating the financial sector, and by increasing investment into activities and businesses that have a positive effect on biodiversity and species protection, can these patterns of fund flows be reversed. It is our intention for this book to act as a driving force of such change and transformation across the global financial sector. To summarise, finance, both private and public, needs to be redirected to biodiversity enhancing and conservation-leading business sectors and activities and away from those that do harm. However, we also advocate a focus which has greater granularity, namely a focus on species, a species–specific finance, species accounting and species governance. This extinction approach needs to target specific species as well as biodiversity more broadly if transform-ative emancipatory accounting and finance are to be genuinely operationalised.

Extinction Banking

Extinction Finance Initiatives by Banks

As in other areas of the financial markets, the banking sector is currently wit-nessing a veritable explosion of interest and initiatives around biodiversity pro-tection. We refer to these efforts as extinction banking. A salient illustration of what we refer to as extinction banking is that of ABN AMRO.[30,31] In 2017, the bank conducted stakeholder dialogue on natural resources and biodiversity. This formed part of their sustainability banking strategy. The dialogue aimed to explore the ways in which financial institutions have an impact on biodiversity and how this could be better measured. An overall aim was to establish actions for ABN AMRO to address their impact on biodiversity across three areas of the bank's operations: loans, clients' investments and the bank's own operations. There is a potential to have a negative or positive impact on biodiversity through the bank's lending decisions, given the substantial lending by ABN AMRO of euros 263 billion in 2016. Equally, there is substantial negative or positive im-pact on biodiversity from their investments which were over euros 152 billion in 2016. The outcome recommendations included ensuring a high-level vision, exploring best practice and considering current policies, engaging in dialogue with clients on biodiversity.

Over the last 18 months, examples of biodiversity initiatives within the bank-ing sector abound. See, for example, Box 1.2, which discusses Barclays and their partnership with the Blue Marine Foundation.

BOX 1.2 BARCLAYS AND THE BLUE MARINE FOUNDATION

Barclays' website, which has a section devoted to their stance on climate change, details their partnership with the Blue Marine Foundation (BLUE). They have established a 5 million pound partnership for three years to ad-vance conservation of the world's ocean. The programmes endorsed by the economic partnership focus on protection, as they aim to protect 30% of the ocean by 2030 by further strengthening the 'Blue Belt' of effective marine protected areas (MPAs); sustainable management of the other 70% by developing models based on collaborative conservation of sustainable, low-impact fishing that benefits both the ecosystem and fishers, while working to restore stocks in overfished waters; and restoration, with the development of five key projects that will work to 'revive and protect vulnerable and threatened species and sequester carbon (…), mitigate the effects of climate change, and establish best practice (with) scalable, replicable templates'.

More information at https://home.barclays/society/our-position-on-climate-change/a-partnership-to-protect-the-ocean/*a partnership to protect the ocean*

Contributed by Zoe Solomon

The EU Taxonomy, published in March 2020, is a tool aimed at helping investors, companies and issuers, and project promoters to focus on sustainability. The Taxonomy is built on the basis of making a substantial contribution to at least one of six environmental objectives of which 'protection and restoration of biodiversity and ecosystems' is the sixth. This is coupled with doing 'no significant harm' to the rest of the six objectives.

Another illustrative example of leadership in extinction banking is presented in Box 1.3, where we discuss the approach adopted by ASN Bank, a Dutch bank founded in 1960 as part of the Volksbank Group.[32] ASN initiated the PBAF collaboration, mentioned earlier in relation to extinction finance, which produced their first Common Ground Report on biodiversity impact assessment in 2020 that establishes an agenda for a harmonised biodiversity accounting metric for the financial sector.[33] The Report states that, 'With this common ground paper this group of frontrunners is paving the way to address the following key challenges: (1) suggesting ways to blend (potential) impacts on biodiversity and ultimately the value of nature into "traditional" management and investment information processes; (2) contributing to the need for better comparability of natural capital and biodiversity information produced by different companies; (3) ensuring that biodiversity is the central pillar of this from the outset'. This collaborative approach demonstrates an emancipatory form of extinction finance and extinction banking and initially involved ASN partnering with ACTIAM, Triodos Bank, Robeco and FMO. PBAF's strategy includes aligning PBAF footprinting with the Product Environmental Footprint, the EU Taxonomy and the Taskforce for Nature Related Financial Disclosure (TNFD). As of March 2021, 26 organisations, managing over 3 trillion euros in assets, have committed to the biodiversity impact and disclosure pledge to set targets and reporting on biodiversity and to put pressure on world leaders to reverse nature loss.

Another leading initiative comes from HSBC who are effectively restorying the way we understand and interpret nature and natural capital by treating

BOX 1.3 EXTINCTION BANKING IN PRACTICE: BIODIVERSITY AND ASN BANK

ASN Bank addresses biodiversity as one of its three sustainability pillars.[34] The bank recognises their role in biodiversity loss by explaining that the savings and investments of their customers are in enterprises, countries and projects that do place a burden on biodiversity and hence result in a loss of biodiversity. The bank states that they started their biodiversity journey in 2014 and that the process has been challenging. ASN cooperated with CDC Biodiversité, ACTIAM and Finance in Motion. The bank expresses in their online documentation their desire to prevent any further loss of biodiversity such that by 2030 they will be actively contributing to the enhancement of wildlife within and outside of the Netherlands. They are adopting a two-pronged approach, seeking to reduce negative impacts on biodiversity while simultaneously investing in wildlife conservation. This approach allows them to achieve a net positive impact as the positive effects of their investments will outweigh losses. As we can see from Table 1.1, ASN used the BFFI. They also implement the PDF measure, the Potentially Disappeared Fraction of Species, defined as a metric used to assess the potential decline in species richness in an area over a time period, where larger PDF values indicated a higher level of impact for the activity. The PDF allows the bank to assess the grandeur of biodiversity loss for each of its investments. They summarise biodiversity impact across different asset classes showing that equities and residential construction have the most substantial negative impacts. Their modelling addresses terrestrial biodiversity loss, marine water damage and freshwater damage. ASN also used Exiobase,[35] that defines itself as a global, detailed Multi-Regional Environmentally Extended Supply-Use Table and Input-Output Table, developed by harmonising and detailing supply-use tables for a large number of countries, estimating emissions and resource extractions by industry. ASN stated in their online documentation that they aim to achieve a net positive effect on biodiversity as a result of all their loans and investments by 2030. This is a tall order for a bank, but as we can see from this discussion, their strategy and target are underpinned by substantial policies and actions.

biodiversity and nature as an asset class. This approach and the underlying rationale are outlined in Box 1.4.

In Chapter 21, Doni *et al.* provide a fascinating insight into extinction finance at an Italian bank as well as outlining recent research findings at earth portfolio on banks and biodiversity. This section has sought to provide a flavour of the innovative and far-reaching approaches being instigated by banks but is by no means exhaustive.

BOX 1.4 NATURAL CAPITAL – REBIRTH OF AN ASSET CLASS

HSBC and Biodiversity

Natural capital provides a string of services to mankind, which together are essential to the preservation of life on earth. Yet natural capital has always been undervalued and has been destroyed at an unprecedented rate. That said, advances are being achieved that may rekindle 'natural capital' as an asset class, allowing for some restoration and enhancement of these assets. Governments are realising that protecting natural capital achieves a double win – protecting biodiversity and slowing climate change. Because deforestation and soil tilling are responsible for 18% of CO_2 emissions, a policy to preserve biodiversity will also help to slow climate change. Metrics are being developed to measure biodiversity. The Mean Species Abundance (MSA) metric quantifies the impact of humans on biodiversity: 100% represents a pristine original nature state, 0% means wholly depleted. Such metrics allow investors to monitor the quality of their asset. The rising number of firms and states making net zero carbon commitments may also see funds flow to projects capturing carbon and projects nurturing natural capital too. 'Net zero' planning will combine emissions cuts with nature-based solutions (or carbon capture and storage).

Economists are reappraising natural capital. One hundred years ago, natural capital was recognised as one of the three means of production alongside capital and labour.[36] For much of the period since, economists and policymakers have ignored natural capital; yet today, economists are re-examining the topic: Dasgupta estimates that up to USD6 trillion per year of subsidies damage nature.[37] Some natural capital owners are learning to 'stack' the cash flows derived from their assets: monetising several natural capital services from one site. In addition to timber or agricultural cash flows from sustainable or regenerative management, owners may secure funds from 'informal' carbon markets and the nascent biodiversity credit market.[38] Sites can benefit from ecotourism. Input costs fall as fertilisers and pesticides are given up, and water is used more efficiently.

In 2020, HSBC Asset Management and Pollination partnered to create the world's largest dedicated natural capital asset management company: **HSBC Pollination Climate Asset Management** intends to establish a series of natural capital funds, investing in a diverse range of activities that preserve, protect and enhance nature over the long term, and address climate change. HSBC Pollination Climate Asset Management will work with agriculture and forestry innovators challenging today's industrialised approach, raising profit and resiliency via improved soil quality, water efficiency and carbon capture. The upsize is large if we eventually see appropriate pricing for carbon, biodiversity, water and appropriate fines or taxes for pollution or excessive use of chemicals. Natural capital investments also could serve as an excellent hedge to investors and operators with exposure to highly carbon-intensive portfolios.

Contributed by Melissa McDonald and Dr. Michael Ridley,
HSBC Asset Management

Extinction Bonds and Framework Mapping

The market for green bonds, and more recently for blue bonds, has grown significantly in recent years, as discussed by de Zijl *et al.* in Chapter 16. They focus on prioritising environmental and sustainability incentives and outcomes and biodiversity issues are often included in their mandate. However, the Dasgupta Review[39] reports that the only estimates currently available suggest that biodiversity conservation receives only 4% of bond proceeds through green bonds. Chapter 19 focuses on the need to heighten biodiversity and species extinction as a core aspect of green bonds. Further, Okolu, in Chapter 17, explores the newly developed Rhino Impact Bond, the first impact bond to be constructed with the sole purpose of increasing rhinoceros populations. There is great potential for growth in this area that can assist conservation efforts through innovative financial market mechanisms.

An innovative biodiversity taxonomies and metrics mapping, and conceptual framework for 'Extinction Bonds' are presented by Macpherson and Biehl in Chapter 11, that sets an agenda for the development of bonds that involve conservation of species and biodiversity. Macpherson and Biehl note that the EU Taxonomy 2020 stipulates that if financial products, such as bonds, do not have sustainable investment objectives, then issuers must include a negative disclosure statement. This is effectively a mandatory disclosure statement and as such can have an emancipatory effect, as issuers would not wish to appear negligent on sustainability. The introduction of this statement resonates with the 2000 move to mandate all UK occupational pension funds to disclose in their Statement of Investment Principles (SIPs) the extent to which (if at all) they applied socially responsible investment criteria to their pension fund decision-making as part of their fiduciary duty. This disclosure requirement was effective as the majority of pension fund trustees had incorporated a social, ethical and environmental statement into their SIPs by the following year.[40] There is huge potential for financial products and instruments such as bonds to evolve that have a positive rather than a negative impact on species and nature. There is now huge potential for biodiversity to be increasingly incorporated into the whole gamut of sustainability-linked bonds, sustainability-linked loans and sustainable bonds, as discussed in Macpherson and Biehl, Chapter 11.

As we can see from this discussion, one of the most significant challenges in the biodiversity and species space is a lack of comparability between institutional practice, between reporters and preparers, between rating agencies. There is sub-stantial activity, as we can see from the contributors' chapters in this book, with a proliferation of innovative methods and tools to integrate biodiversity, in every part of the financial markets. Yet there is little consistency. This situation ur-gently needs to change if we are to see effective and transformative shifts across global financial markets.

Extinction Engagement (Private Extinction Accounting)

If we now turn to the role of institutional investors in enhancing governance and accountability, then investor engagement and dialogue can also contribute significantly to species protection and extinction prevention. Investor engage-ment in the form of direct dialogue may be defined as the process of one-on-one meetings held between institutional investor representatives and directors of their investee companies, as encouraged by the original Cadbury Report. In the academic accounting literature, this process is also referred to as private reporting, due to the private nature of information flows. Such engagement ac-tivity is identified as a key mechanism of holistic governance and stakeholder accountability.[41] In 2010, the Stewardship Code was published which establishes a framework for institutional investor activism and advocacy, with a focus on engagement and dialogue. The 2020 version of the Stewardship Code includes a substantial focus on social and environmental issues. Research into the devel-opment of private reporting on environmental issues showed that a two-way dialogue was evolving around the turn of the century which was beneficial to both the investment institutions and their investee companies.[42] Indeed, it has been recognised for some time that financial institutions, such as pension funds, that do not take account of ESG issues in their decision-making and portfolio management are in breach of their fiduciary duty, as ESG issues are deemed material.[43] Engagement on climate change started to develop around 2010, and research found increasingly detailed information being discussed in private meetings, focused entirely on the materiality of climate change risk and risk management. The main reason for the evolution of private reporting channels was investors' view that publicly available information in companies' reports and other disclosures was inadequate. In a similar way, as the financial materiality of biodiversity is becoming increasingly evident across the global asset management industry, private reporting mechanisms are evolving quickly to compensate for inadequate, incomparable and inconsistent biodiversity-related information on investees.[44] COVID-19 has acted as a catalyst encouraging institutional investors to focus on biodiversity, and the last 18 months have seen biodiversity and species loss appearing on the radar of investors worldwide.

An important driver in this area is the Global Sustainable Investment Alli-ance (GSIA)[45] which is encouraging growth in 'sustainable investing'.[46] Their latest report provides a snapshot of sustainable investing across Europe, the USA, Japan, Canada, Australia and New Zealand and includes data on Africa and Latin

America.[47] The report states that sustainably invested assets globally across the five major markets were $30.7 trillion at the start of 2018, demonstrating an increase of 34% from their report published two years earlier. Corporate engagement and shareholder action represents one of seven mechanisms of sustainable investment discussed in their analysis.[48] In Part IV of this book, we focus on that subsection of engagement devoted to protecting biodiversity and species, and we are especially concerned with direct engagement, or private reporting.[49]

As an 'E' but also an 'S' and 'G' factor, biodiversity loss and species extinction need to be incorporated into sustainable investment. Arguments have been made in the academic accounting literature to demonstrate the financial materiality of biodiversity loss and species extinctions such that by implication institutional investors have to take account of them as part of their fiduciary duty, and companies have to report on them.[50] The University of Cambridge Institute for Sustainability Leadership[51] emphasises the financial materiality of biodiversity in their recent report. As an illustration of the substantial growth in what we would refer to as extinction engagement, almost 250 investors engaged collaboratively in 2019 (representing a total of US$17.5 trillion in assets) to pressurise investee companies to increase efforts to eliminate deforestation from supply chains.[52] There are many more similar examples of recent shareholder activism discussed throughout the rest of this book, for example Chapters 23, 24 and 25. Another poignant issue connected to deforestation, which is attracting increasing attention, is land degradation and soil health. CISL considers tools and data for measuring land degradation.[53] According to the CISL Report, factors examined in measuring land degradation include vegetation cover and soil studies. Efforts to provide information and assessment include the following:

GLASOD 1988–1991 global assessment of human-induced soil degradation
UN FAO mapping of land degradation 1981–2003
Imhoff et al. (2004) and Haberl et al. (2007), satellite images
Global forest change. This has been updated for 2000–2018
An integrated extinction accounting framework for reporting on soil health has
    been published in the social and environmental accounting literature which
    provides a pivot for organisations to assess, act on and improve soil health.[54]

Given the growing awareness around material risks arising from deteriorating soil health to the agricultural and food sectors, this is a ripe area for investor engagement. A framework for extinction engagement that is emancipatory between responsible investors, companies and other actors in the financial markets presents one way forward, as presented in Table 1.2. The Dasgupta Review states that,

> There is some evidence that engagement by investors with businesses in relation to sustainability issues can influence business activities and processes.
> *(p. 480)*

TABLE 1.2 A framework for investor engagement on extinction prevention

- How do you inform yourselves about species decline and extinction threats in relation to your business (strategy, operations, transactions), investment or capital markets activities?
- In what ways is your supply/value chain, both upstream and downstream, likely to be affected by species loss?
- Have you commissioned any studies to determine which species threatened with extinction on the IUCN Red List are directly or indirectly affected by your operations, or those of organisations within your supply/value chain?
- If you have commissioned studies, what were the outcomes? Have you identified which species are most at risk and what the financial (and other: reputational, social responsibility, ethical, moral) consequences of decline and extinction of these species are for your organisation or investment decision-making?
- Are you engaging, or partnering, with any wildlife organisation or industry association regarding species threatened with extinction, for example the WWF? If so what are the targets and outcomes of these engagements/partnerships?
- Are you engaging with service provides (rating houses/stock exchanges) and intermediaries (investment consultants) on species protection issues?
- Are you engaging with reference benchmarks (e.g. WBA), investable index (e.g. MSCI, FTSE, S&P, Nasdaq) and passive product providers (e.g. ETF managers) on species protection issues?
- What contingency measures, risk scenarios, mitigation and adaptation strategies have you considered regarding species decline and extinction?
- What measures are you taking to reduce and limit the impact of your operations or investments on the ecosystem?
- What initiatives, policies and strategies have you implemented in order to prevent species extinction?
- Have you assessed the impact of these initiatives, policies and strategies on species populations?
- Have your assessments led to alterations and improvements in your policies and strategies and initiatives/transactions?
- If they have, in what ways has your extinction prevention strategy altered?

An earlier version of this framework was published in Atkins and Maroun (2018, p. 773).

This in our view somewhat understates current activity among institutional investors as well as the potential outcomes from these activities. Indeed, we can see from Box 1.5 the substantial efforts being made by AXA in this area of growing importance. Chapter 22 authored by Krystyna Springer from ShareAction summarises the findings of the survey referenced several times by the Dasgupta Review. Despite the ShareAction Report finding little evidence of asset managers engaging on biodiversity or requesting biodiversity-related reporting from companies, we provide significant evidence in this book to suggest that since that survey was carried out, in December 2019, there has been a substantial shift across the financial markets in this area. Indeed, we have witnessed a veritable explosion of interest and activity across the international financial markets in the area of biodiversity and species extinctions. This shift is reflected in Springer's chapter as she discusses the latest findings from a 2021 ShareAction Report.

BOX 1.5 AXA INVESTMENT MANAGERS AND BIODIVERSITY

An excellent example of a financial institution designing and implementing initiatives aimed at enhancing biodiversity and by default saving species is AXA Investment Managers. They have reinforced over the last few years their efforts to better integrate biodiversity considerations into their research, engagement and investment processes. Three biodiversity-related publications at AXA IM, the AXA/WWF Report and the AXA Research Fund Biodiversity guide, presented in 2019, focused on the need for more biodiversity-related data, as well as more defined metrics and targets. One of the key messages of the AXA/WWF Report is a call for a TNFD (Taskforce for Nature-related Financial Disclosure), similar to the TCFD for climate. In order to support these efforts, AXA IM launched early 2020, together with Mirova, BNPP AM and Sycomore AM, a Call for Expression of Interest to find partners to develop and implement a tool measuring the impact of investments on biodiversity. The goal was to find a player capable of measuring companies' impact on biodiversity on a large scale. It has then been supported by an investor statement. In September 2020, the selection of IDL-ICC has been announced and the consortium started receiving biodiversity impact data early 2021. As in 2019, AXA IM published a dedicated biodiversity research paper in 2020 that discusses the agriculture-related activities impacts and dependencies on biodiversity.

An Illustration of Extinction Engagement

AXA IM also engaged over 30 companies on biodiversity issues. In line with research findings, this engagement notably focuses on commodity traders. Six traders control around 60% of all soy exports from Brazil which is identified for deforestation risks. In collaboration with other investors, AXA asked traders to increase efforts on no-deforestation commitments, traceability and reporting. AXA IM, together with its parent company AXA Group, is currently extending its 2014 palm oil policy to broaden this policy, which aims at avoiding deforestation, to other deforestation risks commodities such as soy, cattle and timber. In line with their work within the EU Finance@ Biodiversity working group, AXA Group signed the Finance for Biodiversity Pledge, which aligns with its biodiversity objectives. AXA also reaffirmed its commitment to support biodiversity-related metrics through Act4Nature International.

Contribution from Julien Foll,
AXA Investment Managers

We are now seeing a significant shift in 'extinction engagement', or 'private extinction accounting', with institutional investors engaging with companies to force them (or to gently encourage them) to move away from any involvement in activities that lead to biodiversity loss, as outlined in Part IV of the book, specifically Chapters 22–26. The Dasgupta Review does mention the need to integrate nature-related considerations into financial institutions which is what we are exploring throughout this text.

Extinction Accounting

The latest 'KPMG Survey of Sustainability Reporting 2020' explored corporate reporting on risks from biodiversity loss for the first time in the history of these important reports. The Survey finds that less than a quarter of companies deemed 'at risk' from biodiversity loss were reporting, with mining being the only at-risk sector where most companies were accounting for biodiversity. The report also discusses biodiversity as being represented by the SDGs[55] and found that few companies were reporting on the biodiversity-related SDGs.

> Biodiversity is an all-encompassing term for what many regard as nature-related risk … Today our concern is climate risk; tomorrow it will be about biodiversity and everything that is beyond carbon.[56]

The statement above is important from our perspective as it highlights one of the significant problems with biodiversity from an accounting and transparency point of view: the term itself is a problem.[57] The all-encompassing, 'kitchen sink' nature of the term 'biodiversity' renders it too easy to ignore, misinterpret. Its meaning is evasive to non-scientists which leads to biodiversity slipping through the fingers of accountants, as well as other key actors in finance and governance. It lends itself to being bandied about as a feel-good word, contributing to greenwash and impression management. This is the reason we choose to focus our discussion around extinction accounting and species accounting. A species is easily identifiable and understandable, to hold and to save. According to the KPMG Survey, predictions are that,

> … reporting on biodiversity risk will follow the climate trend – with initial use of the framework [TNFD] being voluntary, followed by disclosure mandates and regulation by governments to protect and replenish nature.[58]

Current treatments of species extinction and biodiversity loss within reporting frameworks and the GRI principles go some way towards dealing with biodiversity loss and species loss. However, it may be argued that they are not generally emancipatory, or transformational. They could result solely in a 'fossil record' of species, merely reporting on species extinctions in habitats under the control of organisations on an annual basis. Indeed, the majority of 'extinction accounts' have been found to be descriptive with little or no emancipatory elements.[59] We therefore propose a disclosure/reporting framework that seeks to incorporate species protection and extinction prevention in a more emancipatory manner.

The extinction accounting framework was developed through analysing integrated reporting and sustainability reports in order to identify best practice in accounting for species. The framework is providing a springboard for international academic research. It has also been used to inform responsible investment practice as it assists in the formulation of questions for investor engagement with investee companies. Indeed, the frameworks have been used to develop engagement strategies on bees and pollinators by leading investment institutions such as Hermes EOS.[60]

Academic research into the practice and incidence of what is now termed 'extinction accounting' is burgeoning. Extinction accounting as a concept and as a framework differentiates from biodiversity accounting in a number of ways and especially because of its transformative nature. The academic research into accounting for biodiversity has generally concluded that it is characterised by tokenism, or by financial risk motivations, or by impression management and greenwash.[61] Extinction accounting, however, is emancipatory and involves the reporting organisation making significant efforts to stem species extinction and enhance biodiversity, reporting regularly to demonstrate positive (or negative) impacts of their species protection and biodiversity strategies and policies. Table 1.3 summarises the differences between accounting for biodiversity and the recently emerging extinction accounting. Applying a framework for extinction accounting can assist an organisation to focus on species protection, biodiversity conservation and enhancement, habitat protection.

The shift from accounting for biodiversity to extinction accounting is an evolution in corporate disclosure practice that was first identified as a new form of accounting, distinct from philanthropic accounting in accounting for the rhinoceros.[62] Indeed, extinction accounting emerged from extensive research into corporate reporting practice that identified best practice in the form of disclosures that demonstrate transformative, emancipatory elements. There were elements in the rhinoceros reporting that differed distinctly from an accounting driven entirely by financial risk considerations: there were emotional elements and concerns about cultural heritage which acknowledged motivations far removed from merely philanthropic giving. Indeed, extinction accounting does not always seem to be motivated by financial materiality, as is the case for accounting for biodiversity. Different motivations for extinction accounting are reflected throughout this book as we see cultural and political causes of extinction that could motivate an extinction governance (see Chapter 7 on camel extinction), as well as religious motivations (Chapter 8 on extinction in the Middle East) and a deep ecology perspective. Emancipatory extinction accounting elements were detected in South African listed company reports, with illustrative examples such as toad accounting that demonstrated transformative positive change in toad populations over time due to the company's actions and initiatives.[63] Further, emancipatory

TABLE 1.3 Differentiating between accounting for biodiversity and extinction
accounting

Characteristics of accounting for biodiversity	Characteristics that differentiate extinction accounting from accounting for biodiversity
Biodiversity accounting is inadequate because of the term 'biodiversity' itself, as it is not '…immediately understandable, sounds scientific and does not perhaps convey either the notion of accountability for species and wildlife, nor does it communicate the urgency of species extinction being overly scientific' (Jones and Solomon, 2013, p. 683)	The term 'extinction' itself focuses the reader and preparer on the urgency of species loss and biodiversity decline. By focusing on species rather than 'biodiversity', there is less vagueness of potential for obfuscation (Atkins and Maroun, 2018)
Biodiversity accounting tends to be largely descriptive (Jones and Solomon, 2013	Extinction accounting goes further than description and incorporates reporting on action taken, strategies implemented and partnerships with conservation NGOs (Maroun and Atkins, 2018)
Biodiversity accounting tends to be entirely anthropocentric in nature (Jones and Solomon, 2013; Atkins et al., 2014; Adler et al., 2018)	Extinction accounting combines anthropocentric with non-anthropocentric intentions and elements (Maroun and Atkins, 2018). Indeed, extinction accounting is species-specific and species-centric (for example the bee accounting framework in Atkins and Atkins, 2016). Species accounting is a dominant element in extinction accounting as it focuses on preventing species extinction and hones in on accounting for impacts on specific species as well as efforts to conserve them
Little if any emancipatory potential evident in biodiversity accounting (Jones and Solomon, 2013, Atkins et al., 2014)	Extinction accounting displays elements of an emancipatory nature where the organisation is making efforts to save species and be transformative in their operations (Maroun and Atkins, 2018)
Biodiversity accounting is imbued with impression management and greenwash (Hassan et al., 2020)	Extinction accounting is not motivated only by reputational issues or impression management efforts (Atkins and Atkins, 2019)
Biodiversity accounting is generally narrative (Jones and Solomon, 2013)	Extinction accounting is hybrid in form incorporating quantitative, qualitative and even pictorial elements (Atkins and Maroun, 2018; 2020)
Biodiversity accounting tends to be driven by Codes of Practice such as GRI and represents compliance with minimum disclosure recommendations (Atkins and Maroun, 2018)	Extinction accounting goes further than complying with best practice and disclosure recommendations (Atkins and Maroun, 2018)

Characteristics of accounting for biodiversity	Characteristics that differentiate extinction accounting from accounting for biodiversity
Biodiversity accounting is motivated entirely by legitimacy or by financial materiality and risk management concerns (Jones and Solomon, 2013)	Extinction accounting reveals motivations in addition to legitimacy, reputation and financial materiality including cultural heritage, emotional elements and deep ecology motivations (Atkins et al., 2018)
Accounting for biodiversity tends to be static often with information repeated in boilerplate fashion year on year (Jones and Solomon, 2013)	Extinction accounting is dynamic, demonstrating transformational change year on year, with an emphasis on the impact of initiatives and strategies which have positive (but sometimes disappointingly negative) effects (Atkins and Maroun, 2020)
Species treated as part of a broad environmental impact assessment	Species need to be treated as stakeholders to whom the company has an accountability (Hassan et al., 2020)

and transformative policies aimed at protecting specific species and enhancing biodiversity were found in Chinese mining company reports.[64] An important development in the extinction accounting framework is to consider the reporting of species absence by organisations, in other words, disclosing which species have disappeared as a direct (or indirect) result of their activities and operations from the habitats affected by their actions. This is represented in the extended extinction accounting framework in Table 1.4. At present, a species that has disappeared could be as easily absent from the disclosures as from their previous habitat: step 8, were it to be mandatory, addresses this loophole in species accounting.

This may be summarised in diagrammatic form as follows (Figure 1.1):

The potential for accounting to be emancipatory and to drive positive change is always there, as,

> … an appreciation of accounting's emancipatory possibilities implies seeing accounting as at least potentially aiding (and being integral to) or giving further help to an emancipatory project. Critical researchers thus envisage accounting as functioning to help overcome repressive obstacles so that a better state is realised …A vision of accounting as an emancipatory force is consistent with seeing accounting as a communicative social practice that functions as a system of informing that renders transparent and enlightens with the effect of social betterment.[65]

The emancipatory nature of this framework cannot be over-emphasised. Environmental, ecological or biodiversity reporting that simply underlines the status quo and ensures business as usual is quite literally a waste of time in a situation of urgency given the rate and speed of species loss. Many studies have concluded that accounting for biodiversity in its current form is driven by PR motives, by

TABLE 1.4 The extinction accounting framework for disclosure on species protection and extinction prevention

Stages

1 Record a list of plant and animal species, identified as endangered by the IUCN Red List, whose habitats are affected by the company's activities

   Report where, geographically, the company's activities pose a threat to endangered plant and animal species, as identified by the IUCN Red List, and assess habitat status

   Report potential risks/impacts on these specific species arising from the company's operations

   (equivalent to the existing GRI principles to this point)

   Incorporate images (photographs or drawings, for example) of threatened species which are affected by the company's operations and which the company needs to protect and explain how these have been integrated into the company's internal control system, business model, business strategy and operational plans

   Report full details (narrative as well as financial figures) relating to any fines or ongoing claims relating to endangered species legislation including the names of species and a summary of losses suffered with causes identified

   Report corporate expressions of moral, ethical and/or emotional motivations for preserving species and preventing extinction with a consideration of ecosystem-level effects, including normative reflective self-accounts of the company's impact on threatened and endangered species

2 Report actions/initiatives taken by the company to avoid harm to, and to prevent the extinction of, endangered plant and animal species

3 Report partnerships between wildlife/nature/conservation organisations and the company which aim to address corporate impacts on endangered species and report the outcome/impact of engagement/partnerships on endangered species as well as the outcome of engagement with the responsible investment community (respecting investor confidentiality where appropriate)

4 Report assessment and reflection on outcome/impact of engagement/partnerships and decisions taken about necessary changes to policy/initiatives going forward

5 Report regular assessments (audit) of species populations in areas affected by corporate operations

6 Report assessment of whether or not corporate initiatives/actions are assisting in the prevention of species extinction

7 Report strategy for the future development and improvement of actions/initiatives: an iterative process

   Ensure that the whole process of 'extinction accounting' is integrated into corporate strategy and is incorporated into the company's integrated report, not resigned to separate sustainability reports or websites, including species-specific information.

   Report potential liabilities relating to future possible legal fines/claims relating to endangered species impacts.

   Include a discussion of ways in which the company is working to prevent future liabilities related to harming endangered species.

   Provide a pictorial representation of success in conservation

8 Report absence of species that were previously present and that have disappeared from the habitats where the organisation's activities have an impact as a direct or indirect result of that activity

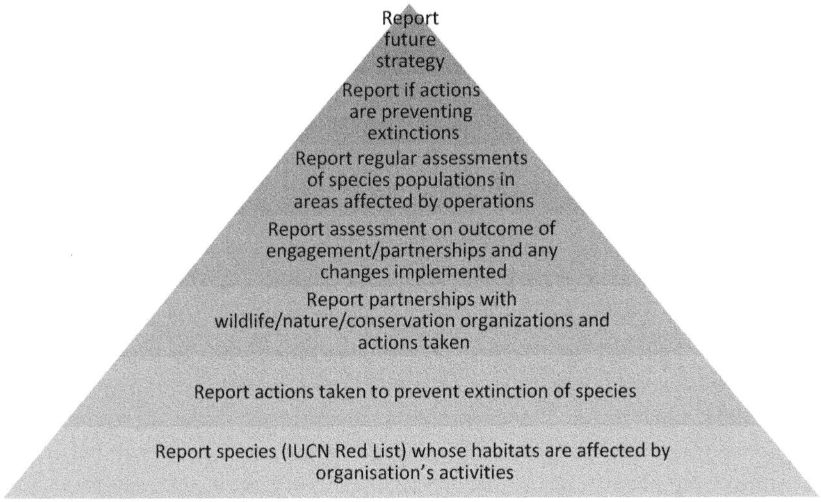

Report
future
strategy

Report if actions
are preventing
extinctions

Report regular assessments
of species populations in
areas affected by operations

Report assessment on outcome of
engagement/partnerships and any
changes implemented

Report partnerships with
wildlife/nature/conservation organizations and
actions taken

Report actions taken to prevent extinction of species

Report species (IUCN Red List) whose habitats are affected by
organisation's activities

FIGURE 1.1   The emancipatory extinction accounting framework.

impression management inclinations and not by desire for change. Any attempt to implement extinction accounting needs to be transformative and progressive, as,

> .... unless extinction accounting is emancipatory, or at least progressive in nature, extinctions will not be prevented at either population or species level and all of the worst predictions about the future of the planet will be borne out. In other words, by prioritising an emancipatory extinction accounting, businesses will transform their ethos, activities and business strategy to slow and stop extinction trends.[66]

The explosion of interest in biodiversity-related issues that has occurred since the beginning of 2020 within the international investment community, discussed in the previous section, is being mirrored by a commensurate surge of interest in accounting for biodiversity. This shift in attitude among preparers as well as users is most clearly evidenced by the latest KPMG Report, as mentioned earlier.[67]

The extinction accounting framework provides a basis for any organisation to report on how their operations are impacting on species but also how species are impacting on them through risk. It is a dynamic framework that requires companies to explain what they are doing to lessen these impacts, to improve biodiversity and ultimately to save species from extinction, for example by forming partnerships with conservation NGOs and organisations such as the WWF. In this way, the framework intends to be transformational and emancipatory as the reporting should feed into changes in behaviour and practice.

Interestingly, the Dasgupta Review does not focus to a great extent on the role of the accounting function in addressing the biodiversity and extinction crises: at least, only in a partial manner, as providing information to financial institutions and in developing and maintaining reputation. There is no recognition or acknowledgement of accounting as having a potentially emancipatory impact. Understandably as an economics–driven review, the focus is on economic modelling and economic theory rather than accounting and finance although there is substantial discussion around the role of finance globally in transforming the current situation. Accounting price is discussed throughout the Review as a way of understanding how an effective tax may assist in providing funds for conservation as well as perhaps deterring excessive use of natural assets of flora and fauna. We, however, see accounting and reporting as critically important elements of an overarching extinction governance model that operationalises every part of the financial markets and capitalist system into saving nature from imminent destruction.

Certainly, the Dasgupta Review does not mention extinction accounting and does not appear to recognise that accounting as a function can have an emancipatory impact and ultimately assist in saving species, as part of a broader extinction governance and extinction finance framework. We want to highlight the importance of accounting and reporting, and specially the importance and relevance of extinction accounting as an essential and potentially powerful emancipatory element in this framework. Indeed, one of the foci of this book is to highlight the potentially powerful role that accounting, reporting and disclosure can play in addressing the biodiversity and species extinction crises.

In terms of geographic analysis, there has to date been no research at all into extinction accounting in Middle Eastern countries. Chapters 8 and 7 address this gap in the literature by providing an overview of species extinction threat in Saudi Arabia and Jordan, and in Israel, respectively. Further, there is existing work on some specific species, such as rhinoceros, bees, panda and even toads, as mentioned above, but this leaves scope for further species accounting research. In Chapter 7, Lieberman focuses on camels and an evolving camel extinction accounting framework.

Dual and Dynamic Materiality

An important concept that is sweeping through the sustainability reporting and especially the biodiversity reporting space is that of dual (and increasingly, dynamic) materiality. This dual materiality concept, as enshrined in the GRI's methodology and in the revised EU NFRD (2014/95) regulation, is an intrinsic element of the discussions throughout this book, especially in Chapters 15 and 13.[68] As explained in Chapter 13, accounting fails to value the natural habitat and natural capital consumed by industrial processes. No reporting mechanism recognises obligations to, or impact on, other species than us. The authors argue that reporting mechanisms need to give cognisance in reporting to:

1. Factors that have a material financial impact on company's long-term value
2. Factors that relate to company's impact on ecosystems

The following diagram clarifies the concept nicely (Figure 1.2):

Biodiversity and species with material financial impact on a company **Company's impact on biodiversity and species**

FIGURE 1.2 Dual materiality.

Indeed, dual materiality seeks to go beyond the financial materiality of species loss and biodiversity decline, as outlined in the Introduction, in order to integrate the impact of a company's business activities on biodiversity, resonating with the outcomes for natural capital in the IIRC's integrated reporting framework. However, despite double materiality appearing in frameworks, the reporting remains voluntary.[69]

The Biological Diversity Protocol (BD Protocol),[70] launched in March 2021, outlines a framework for species accounting that depends upon an organisation selecting species that are material to them, from a double materiality perspective: i.e. those whose loss or decline materially impacts the company's operations, or those that are negatively impacted by the organisation's operations. It is meant to complement the Natural Capital Protocol and the work of the Capitals Coalition, which are discussed in Chapter 27 by Gough. The Protocol recognises that species accounting is far more complex than accounting for ecosystems and biodiversity more generally,

> .... assessing impacts on taxa (i.e. species and sub-species) should be undertaken only for taxa that are material for the business and/or its stakeholders (e.g. highly threatened bird species, with a decreasing local population due to business activities). Several options are also available to your business for each step of the impact measurement process for taxa. The BD Protocol does not prescribe a comprehensive list of approaches suitable for different taxa. Instead, it highlights the issues to consider for selecting the most appropriate, cost-effective method to meet accounting and reporting principles given your business context. However, you should note that this selection process is more challenging than the one for ecosystems.
>
> *(BD Protocol, p. 56)*

This framework is presented and discussed by Houdet and the Endangered Wildlife Trust in Chapter 28.

Illustrations of Emancipatory Extinction Accounting in Practice

Interestingly, from prior research, the finance industry in South Africa is producing extinction accounts. We feel this often derives in part from the emotional connection some senior directors have with the South African national parks and their endangered species. A paper entitled, '*From the Big Five to the Big Four*',[71] analysed an extensive sample of corporate reports in relation to rhinoceros under extinction threat. The research found many cases of 'rhinoceros accounting', with some examples of 'extinction accounting' that seemed to demonstrate an emancipatory element. For example, Investec Ltd. stated in their 2013 integrated report that they partnered with scientific experts to launch Investec Rhino Life-line. The stated aim of this initiative was to raise awareness of the rhinoceros' crisis and respond through education, rescue and prevention initiatives. Specifically, Investec emphasised that this partnership is motivated by recognition of the '... *intensity of the rhino issue in Southern Africa*'.[72] Further, Investec stated that they were, '... *proud to be associated with a number of non-profit organisations that are working hard toward creating a sustainable future and preserving the future security of the world's rich cultural and national heritage*'[73] and that,

> Given Investec's African roots, we are passionate about ensuring the continued existence of a number of African species. We, therefore, fund three biodiversity projects which are focused around rhinos, wild dogs and the impact of renewable energy on local birdlife. These initiatives allow Investec to give back to the environment and help ensure the sustainable existence of South African wildlife.[74]

Also, in the Sustainability Report, Investec stated that,

> South Africa loses rhinos on a daily basis. The rhino crisis has become the most significant conservation issue faced by the country. Poaching attacks represent lawlessness, a lack of political will, human greed, and a disregard for the wellbeing of animals in spite of the most dramatic public response in our conservation history.[75]

This seems to go far further than impression management or reputation-building type disclosures. The above extract displays a genuine desire to contribute to avoiding rhinoceros' extinction and to enhance South Africa's wildlife due to a love for the country's heritage. In the authors' views, the comments are too passionate to be motivated purely by impression management. This disclosure also seems to portray a corporate form of accounting which adopts a moral high ground and takes a purely ethical stance. The 'reality' being constructed and communicated through this corporate reporting is one which appears to hold rhinoceros protection and extinction prevention at a premium. The corporate website states that,

> South Africa is losing rhinos daily, through poaching. It is the most significant conservation issue faced by the country and time is running out. In 2012 Investec established Investec Rhino Lifeline to respond to this crisis ... By working closely with our trusted partners and supporters, and

by taking a hands-on approach, we believe that we can make a difference in saving the rhino and ensuring its long-term survival.[76]

This does not seem to coincide with public relations–driven disclosure aimed at building corporate reputation and managing impressions. Rather, it appears to be a form of accounting driven by the realisation of imminent extinction of a species. Again, there is impassioned language used in this 'extinction accounting'. For example, '*Rhinos are at the centre of a violent, well-organised series of poaching attacks in South Africa due to rampant trade in rhino horn*'. This depicts a form of corporate reporting which is characterised by sincere, emotional, rhetoric, which is quite the opposite of traditional accounting rhetoric based on calculative rationalities. An example of what we felt was emancipatory extinction accounting for rhinoceros is embedded here,

> Realising the need for greater support on the prevention side, Investec partnered with Wilderness Foundation in their Vietnamese demand reduction campaign which started in April 2014 when they hosted two Vietnamese pop stars in South Africa on a rhino experience. Through their extensive influence in the media, they are educating and raising awareness about the properties of rhino horn as well as the impact on rhino populations in Vietnam, the biggest market for rhino horn.[77]

This represents an emancipatory extinction accounting as it provides evidence of an innovative means of strangling the demand for horns using Vietnamese social icons who may be able to reach a large part of the population and change minds and hearts. This, for us, represents an attempt at providing disclosures which seek to transform and change behaviours and an illustration of pragmatic emancipatory accounting. Species accounting may be understood as a subgroup of extinction accounting, where the reporting and accounting by an entity or organisation focus on one or more specific species. Accounting for the rhinoceros by Investec is an outstanding illustration of species accounting in practice.

From an academic perspective, there is a significant potential for further research into extinction accounting. Chapter 29 by Lieberman provides a detailed method and approach for both academics and practitioners to analyse extinction accounts from practice, namely the application of ecolinguistic analysis. This chapter provides the ultimate 'go-to' toolkit for extinction accounting research. Tentative extinction accounting frameworks for a wide variety of species and sectors have now been developed by academics, through stakeholder consultation, interviews with businesses and conservation organisations and discussion with practitioners. These include frameworks for panda[78] and hedgehogs.[79] *Around the World in 80 Species*[80] also explores accounting for polar bears by Russian oil companies, accounting for extinction by European zoos, accounting for belugas by aquaria, and extinction accounting by the South African National Parks. The plight of the orangutan is the focus of Chapter 6.

Incorporating Extinction Accounting into Reporting Frameworks

One way of operationalising an emancipatory extinction accounting framework is to incorporate it into integrated reporting or into other reporting and disclosure frameworks (IFRS included) as a necessary core element. Further, the relatively recent creation of the United Nation's Sustainable Development Goals, the SDGs, provides another means of pushing for species protection at all levels: governmental, regional, national and international. Extinction accounting can also be incorporated into integrated reporting and other reporting frameworks specifically via the two SDGs, 14 and 15, namely: 'Conserve and sustainably use the oceans, seas and marine resources for sustainable development' (life under water) and 'Protect, restore and promote sustainable use of terrestrial ecosystems, sustainably manage forests, combat desertification, and halt and reverse land degradation' (life on land).

Nowadays, it is common for organisations to be concerned about their impact on stakeholders and accounting and reporting are motivated by a need to satisfy the information requirements of a wide group of stakeholders, as well as to discharge an accountability to them. It has long been acknowledged that non-human species are stakeholders as well as the traditional stakeholder groups such as employees, suppliers and financial stakeholders.[81] Adopting a holistic governance approach that is stakeholder inclusive requires an accounting that discharges accountability to non-human species, and extinction accounting provides such a framework. Further, a company's value creation process should take cognisance of interconnection between different types of capital (including financial, manufactured, intellectual, environmental, human and social and relationship capital) in the context of the entity's strategy, risks and operating model.[82] In theory, this integrated thinking framework should be well suited for framing how biodiversity should be understood and reported on by organisations. However, the equal treatment of the six capitals could be called into question when we consider that 'natural' capital represents life on earth and the ecosystem, without which the other five are rendered meaningless. As mentioned above, the work of the Natural Capital Coalition, now the Capitals Coalition, has been instrumental in raising the profile of natural capital globally, and the Capitals Coalition and journey are explained by Gough in Chapter 27. The integrated reporting framework, first developed by the King Committee in South Africa and implemented as mandatory for South African listed companies in the third Code of Governance, King III, epitomises a holistic governance approach couched in the six capitals and in value creation. We explore this further in the next chapter where we explore extinction governance.

As discussed earlier, the new Biological Diversity Protocol outlined in Chapter 28, and launched in March 2021, draws from the extinction accounting framework and proposes ways for organisations to report on species, a form of extinction accounting in our view, as well as on biodiversity more broadly. This is the first standardised framework for reporting on biodiversity.

Species Protection Action Plan

Considering extinction finance, extinction engagement and extinction accounting represents three steps towards integrating species protection into the financial
markets. In an event hosted by Investec on 30 May 2019, we explored how these
concepts may be implemented into practice. Our intention was to consider ways
of incorporating species protection and extinction prevention into other mechanisms of the financial markets such that species protection becomes embedded in
the heart of our global financial system. At the event, we launched a Species Protection Action Plan, as shown below, which could provide the basis for integrating species protection into the banking sector, into stock indexes, into corporate
ratings, into financial analysis. The innovative tools and techniques that need to
be developed require imagination, 'thinking outside the box', 'blue sky thinking'
perhaps. At this urgent point in human history where the extinction crisis is at
a critical stage, we cannot rely on existing approaches. Never have imagination
and innovative thinking been more necessary and urgent. The development of
such mechanisms, tools and techniques across the financial markets and throughout business value chains leads us to an extinction governance model that embeds
species protection into the heart of capitalism.

BOX 1.6 SPECIES PROTECTION ACTION PLAN FOR THE FINANCIAL MARKETS

Why Extinction represents a Material Financial Risk for a Sustainable Finance Sector?

Our world is in the grip of a mass extinction crisis with extinction of flora
and fauna caused by a variety of factors arising from industrial activity and
increasing human populations, including global warming, climate change,
habitat loss, pollution and use of pesticides. Most extinctions are linked to
industrial and business activity either directly or indirectly. Business, society
and the financial markets rely on the healthy functioning of the ecosystem.
Each and every species has a unique role to play in our ecosystem. Through
the interconnectedness of all life on earth, every extinction diminishes and
weakens these relationships. This **Species Protection Action Plan** aims to
form the basis for the development of tools, techniques, models and other
initiatives to protect and enhance value, mitigate material financial risks from
species loss and extinctions, and save the planet – and ourselves.

Why Does Extinction Matter to the Corporate Sector?

Species extinction can impact value creation and threaten supply chains, production and profits

What Should Companies Do?

Implement emancipatory extinction accounting, incorporating species protection into integrated reports

Explore and identify means of assuring/verifying extinction accounting to provide confidence

Incorporate species extinction risk through risk management, internal control systems and internal audit

Develop KPIs to measure success/failure in species protection and extinction prevention

Why Does Extinction Matter to Banking?

Species loss and extinctions affect company value and corporate clients could suffer losses, default on loans. There are also potential markets and untested clients relating to species protection

What Should Banks Do?

Including species protection in substantial lending decisions (incorporate into Equator Principles)

Incorporate species protection into green and blue bonds

Develop innovative bonds such as 'insect apocalypse bonds', 'bee bonds', 'chocolate protection bonds'

Innovate with personal accounts/personal credit cards that contribute to species protection

Why Does Extinction Matter to Institutional Investors?

Corporate value affected by species extinction represents a material financial risk for the investment industry

What Should Institutional Investors Do?

Practise extinction engagement and engage with investee companies on species protection

Why Does Extinction Matter to Pension Fund Trustees and Fund Managers?

Risk to investment return and pension fund value from species extinction

What Should Trustees and Fund Managers Do?

Include species protection on agendas for trustee meetings and in fund managers' mandates so they practise emancipatory extinction engagement and communicate with pension fund members on relevance of species protection to the fund and future benefits

Why Does Extinction Matter to Analysts?
Corporate value is affected by the way companies protect species through their value chain

What Should Analysts Do?
Integrate corporate performance in preventing extinctions and protecting species into financial analysis

Why Does Extinction Matter to Stock Indexes?
Species loss and extinction affect company value that is reflected through indexes

What Should Stock Indexes Include?
Incorporate species protection into the specific indexes such as the FTSE4Good

Why Does Extinction Matter to Sustainability Ratings?
Species loss and extinction affect company value and therefore need to be reflected in any sustainability ratings

What Sustainability Ratings Need to Include?
Incorporate species protection as a primary factor in any rating model relating to sustainability

Saving Nature, Wildlife, Species and Biodiversity

Naturally, the Species Protection Action Plan can only achieve success by complementing interdisciplinary efforts: finance, business and accounting cannot be the only answers. Indeed, the world of business and finance can assist conservation organisations and other initiatives from the ecological, conservation and wildlife areas. In this book, the WWF perspective is provided in Chapter 3 by Sibanda. Further, critically important initiatives to save habitat from destruction, as habitat loss is one of the most significant drivers of biodiversity loss and species extinction, are discussed throughout this book. For example, rewilding efforts through a land ownership model are outlined in Chapter 5 by Heal. Rewilding is such an important element of any national or international attempt to address habitat loss. Heal's work is currently focused on the South East of England but is sure to expand as the charity develops. Rewilding projects are also underway in Scotland.[83] There are also efforts to reintroduce species that have gone extinct in the UK. For example, an ongoing project to reintroduce lynx in Scotland provides a fascinating case study, highlighting the challenges but also the advantages of this form of reintroduction.[84]

The Impact of COVID-19 on Awareness around Biodiversity Loss

The investment industry and corporate internal control processes and all actors across the financial markets are rapidly becoming aware of a human health-motivated reason to protect biodiversity and species. New academic research conducted interviews with leading experts during March and April 2020 in the ESG investment and governance space and found that COVID-19 is acting as a catalyst, raising awareness of connections between biodiversity loss and pandemics.[85] Further, the interviewees indicated that as a result, investor engagement on biodiversity and related issues would escalate in the wake of the pandemic, which would have consequences for corporate reporting, with an increased demand from the institutional investment community for biodiversity and species-related information. The paper provides a framework for rendering pandemic risk implicit in investor engagement which is presented in Chapter 26, where the full study is discussed in detail. COVID-19 has also led to a proliferation in professional reports into the linkages between biodiversity loss and pandemic risk. For example, in an online article entitled, '*Pandemic: The Inextricable link between human, animal and ecosystem health and the emergence of communicable disease*', M&G Investments explains that,

> We believe our clients and customers need us to evidence that we have understood the inextricable link between human, animal and ecosystem health and that our company engagements are now far-reaching and exploratory in a way that we have never engaged before.[86]

COVID-19 has changed every area of our lives, the way we work, the way we socialise. Everything from moving house, to seeing a doctor, to getting married, or attending a funeral has been turned upside down by the pandemic. There are evident impacts on attitudes within the financial markets. However, the wider impacts on our feelings and perceptions of biodiversity loss, extinction and COVID-19 on societal and individual well-being are immense. Chapter 30, '*Extinction, Biodiversity Loss and Covid-19: Searching for Meaning*', provides a helpful glimmer of hope. Written by a mental health counsellor, this chapter explores the ways we can respond to these gargantuan crises and may offer some assistance to readers in coping with current events.

Summary

In this book, we explore how we can operationalise a whole raft of financial mechanisms, capital market instruments and accounting to address species loss. In so doing, the financial system can be geared to protect natural capital that is so critical to our planet as a going concern, to our future survival and, from a sustainability perspective, for future generations. The UN SDGs are entirely consistent with this approach, and our aim is to ensure technical pathways to protect and enhance life on land and life in water. Reducing the financial risk to businesses and potential financial losses arising from species extinction is, from a purely financial rent-seeking perspective, a core argument for our approach. Happily, this motivation walks hand in hand with ethical and deep ecology desires to preserve species for their individual and intrinsic value. It is a classic '-win-win' scenario. A deep ecology perspective on extinction and species often coincides with an anti-capitalist stance. We choose to take a more constructive approach which attempts to work *within* our global system of financial markets and business. Our approach involves exploring ways in which species protection and extinction prevention can and must be integrated into every mechanism of business, investing, finance, accounting and services. This represents an extinction governance – a conceptualisation of governance across all countries, all sectors, all segments (retail and institutional) and all financial markets that places preservation of the natural world at the heart and develops mechanisms both simple and complex to ensure the continuation of life on earth and humanity. Figure 1.3 provides a landscape graphic of our Species Protection Action Plan for the Financial Markets that identifies the contributions to this book, highlighting the aspect of the financial markets being addressed and the element contributed to the whole.

We can see from this landscape the flows of information, flows of finance and pressures for change, as expressed via arrows from one group to another, as follows.

Information Flows

There are information flows to finance providers from framework providers, namely public reporting, or extinction accounting.[87] As can be ascertained from the contributors to this book, such public information flows regarding biodiversity are inadequate for financial decision-making as well as for other purposes.

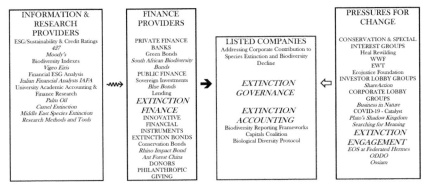

FIGURE 1.3   A species protection action plan for the financial markets extinction governance, finance, engagement and accounting.

Therefore, we are witnessing rapidly evolving private channels of information flows between institutional investors and their investee companies in the form of extinction engagement. In addition to public and private disclosure channels, there is also the proliferation of information and research providers including biodiversity-focused ratings, indexes, analysis and also academic research, which is playing an increasingly important role.

Flows of Finance

Flows of finance pass from the finance providers: private and public finance providers, as well as from the global asset management industry. However, we are also seeing the emergence of new innovative financial instruments such as the Rhino Impact Bond (see Chapter 17) which channels finance from private and public finance providers, including donors, towards conservation organisations. This new form of intermediary instrument may provide solutions to the species extinction crisis that are far more effective in both enhancing species populations and demonstrating effectiveness than other initiatives. Further, 'Ant Forest' is an interesting means of channelling finance into conservation, as outlined in Chapter 18 by Zhao.

Pressures for Change

We present pressures for integration of biodiversity and extinction prevention into financial market mechanisms on the right-hand side of the landscape graphic. This is not meant to represent an exhaustive set of pressures, as it does not incorporate societal level factors, ethical drivers or the countless initiatives in place around the world to save species. Rather, we seek here to capture the pressures identified throughout this book in relation to financial market initiatives covered by the contributors. As a detailed and urgent response to the recent IPBES Report, that represents a call for action, we believe this book is timely and calls for efforts to develop further innovative and imaginative solutions within the financial sector specifically, connecting to broader governance frameworks, which in an increasingly interdisciplinary and inter-sectoral environment can assist in protecting species from extinction.

Any hopes of success in preventing further extinctions require an interdisciplinary, inter-sectoral and intergovernmental approach. Saving species from extinction is not the remit of one group, such as government, but is a responsibility to be borne by every member of society at every level including governmental, financial, corporate, community and individual.

In relation to this text, a critical section of the Dasgupta Review,[88] devoted to the global financial system, states that,

> ... far more global support is needed for initiatives directed at enhancing the understanding and awareness among financial institutions of [such]

nature-related risks, learning and building on the advances on climate-related financial risks.

(p. 494)

This is certainly one intention of our book: to raise awareness and enhance understanding among financial institutions in this urgently important area. The next chapter presents an extinction governance framework.

Notes

1 See CISL (2020).
2 https://www.iucn.org/commissions/species-survival-commission/get-involved/abu-dhabi-call-global-species-conservation-action.
3 See WWF Response to the Dasgupta Review at https://www.wwf.org.uk/sites/default/files/2021-02/WWF_UK_response_Dasgupta%20Review_1_2_21.pdf.
4 This is adapted from paragraph 40 of IPBES (2019).
5 CISL (2020).
6 CISL (2020).
7 Moody's ESG Solutions group discussion by Zubets Anderson on the 'Growing Need for Comprehensive and Reliable Biodiversity Impact Data'.
8 https://www.ibat-alliance.org/.
9 They list: A Rocha Ghana – Asian Development Bank – Allianz – Bangor Agricultural University – Cambridge Institute for Sustainability Leadership – European Investment Bank – French Development Agency – General Motors – Harvard University – International Finance Corporation – Ministry of Environment Cameroon – Nature Fiji – Pew Charitable Trusts – Shell – Swedish Export Credit Agency – University of Cambridge – World Bank – WWF.
10 Rounsevell et al. (2020, p.1193).
11 i.e. Global mean temperature change.
12 i.e. maximum 2 degrees, or more recently 1.5 degrees centigrade rise relative to pre-industrial levels.
13 Rounsevell et al. (2020, p. 1194).
14 Rounsevell et al. (2020, p. 1194).
15 The 20 species a year is derived from the threshold of 10 per million species years adopted by the planetary boundaries framework.
16 By groups, they are referring to fungi, plants, invertebrates and vertebrates.
17 By ecosystem types, they are referring to marine, freshwater and terrestrial.
18 Rounsevell et al. (2020, p. 1193).
19 Rounsevell et al. (2020, p. 1195).
20 https://knowledge4policy.ec.europa.eu/publication/sustainable-finance-teg-final-report-eu-taxonomy_en.
21 See PBAF Netherlands, Paving the way towards a harmonised biodiversity accounting approach for the financial sector, September 2020.
22 See Dasgupta Review Chapter 20.
23 See p. 466.
24 See the WWF Response to the Dasgupta Review at https://www.wwf.org.uk/sites/default/files/2021-02/WWF_UK_response_Dasgupta%20Review_1_2_21.pdf.
25 https://www.wwf.org.uk/sites/default/files/2021-02/WWF_UK_response_Dasgupta%20Review_1_2_21.pdf.
26 Solomon (2021).
27 See https://www.financeforbiodiversity.org/.

28 Primary sectors with the most significant impact on biodiversity were highlighted as food, forestry, mining and fossil fuels.

29 The Dasgupta Review.

30 ABN AMRO is a Dutch bank serving retail, private and corporate banking clients. Their primary focus is on Northwest Europe.

31 https://assets.ctfassets.net/1u811bvgvthc/7tzfyzr1vFqzXoHSi6lA5E/1e75c383883e7fe2567214388e3b2837/ABN_AMRO_Stakeholder_dialogue_on_biodiversity_-_October_2017.pdf.

32 See more information at Netto positive effect on biodiversity in 2030 - ASN Bank.

33 PBAF Report: 'Paving the Way towards a Harmonised Biodiversity Accounting Approach for the Financial Sector'.

34 See more information at https://www.asnbank.nl/algemeen/duurzaamheid/duurzaamheidsbeleid/biodiversiteit/no-net-loss-of-bd-in-.

35 See: Exiobase - Home at https://www.exiobase.eu/.

36 'The three requisites of production, as has been so often repeated, are labour, capital and land: understanding....by land, the materials and instruments supplied by nature, whether contained in the interior of the earth, or constituting its surface'. 'The Economics of Welfare', A C Pigou, 1920.

37 'The Economics of Biodiversity'; the Dasgupta Review, 2 February 2021.

38 Biodiversity offsets are being tested in the UK and Australia: 'Natural England Biodiversity Credits Scheme Pilot – call for Projects', CIEEM, 6 July 2020; 'Biodiversity credits', New South Wales Environment, Energy and Science, 21 April 2020.

39 Dasgupta Review (2021).

40 See Solomon (2021, p 259).

41 See Solomon (2021).

42 See Solomon and Solomon (2006).

43 See Freshfields Bruckhaus Deringer (2005); Solomon (2007; 2013; 2021).

44 See Chapter 26 for research findings supporting this statement.

45 The Global Sustainable Investment Alliance (GSIA) is an international collaboration of membership-based sustainable investment organisations, with a stated mission to deepen and expand the practice of sustainable investment through intentional international collaboration.

46 The GSIA defines sustainable investing as an investment approach that considers ESG factors in portfolio selection and management.

47 The data are collated from Eurosif, Japan Sustainable Investment Forum, Responsible Investment Association Australasia, RIA Canada, US SIF, African Investing for Impact barometer and the PRI.

48 The others are negative/positive screening, norms-based screening, ESG integration, sustainability themed investing and impact/community investing.

49 Corporate engagement is defined as '...the use of shareholder power to influence corporate behaviour, including through direct engagement (communicating with senior management and/or boards of companies), filing or co-filing shareholder proposals, and proxy voting guided by comprehensive ESG guidelines'.

50 Atkins and Maroun (2018); Atkins and Atkins (2019).

51 CISL (2020).

52 See Dasgupta Review (2021) p. 480 on Zero-Deforestation Policies.

53 CISL (2020).

54 Maroun and Atkins (2020).

55 Specifically SDGs 14 and 15, life below water, life on land, respectively.

56 KPMG (2020, p. 24).

57 See Jones and Solomon (2013).

58 KPMG (2020, p. 34).

59 This argument and the following extinction accounting framework are taken from Maroun and Atkins (2018).

60 See, for example, https://www.beekblog.co.uk/environment/threats-to-bees/bee-welfare-more-at-stake-than-just-honey/.
61 See Hassan et al. (2020).
62 See Atkins et al. (2018).
63 See Maroun and Atkins (2018).
64 See Zhao and Atkins (2021).
65 Gallhofer and Haslam (2003, p. 7).
66 Maroun and Atkins (2018).
67 KPMG (2020) 'The Time Has Come: The KPMG Survey of Sustainability Reporting, 2020', KPMG Impact, December.
68 Zubets Anderson and Lehman, and Gasperini and Artuso.
69 See Chapter 18: Gasperini and Artuso.
70 See the following link to the BD Protocol: https://www.nbbnbdp.org/uploads/1/3/1/4/131498886/biological_diversity_protocol__bd_protocol_pdf.
71 See Atkins et al. (2018).
72 Investec, Integrated Report, 2013, p. 110.
73 Investec, Integrated Report, 2013, p. 110.
74 Investec, Sustainability Report, 2013, p. 25.
75 Investec, Sustainability Report, 2013, p. 25.
76 This is from the company website; https://www.investec.co.za/about-investec/sustainability/planet/investec-rhino-lifeline.html.
77 Investec, Sustainability Report, 2015.
78 This framework was developed by Longxiang Zhao for his doctoral thesis and is published in *Around the World in 80 Species*, Chapter 19.
79 A framework for companies in the agrochemical industry to report on hedgehogs (or absence of hedgehogs) is being developed by Mira Lieberman for her doctoral research.
80 Atkins and Atkins (2019).
81 Wheeler and Sillanpää (1997); Hassan et al., 2020; Solomon, 2021.
82 Eccles and Krzus (2010); Eccles and Saltzman (2011).
83 See the Scottish Rewilding Alliance's aims and objectives for a rewilding nation at https://www.rewild.scot/.
84 Hetherington (2018).
85 The paper has been presented at a number of virtual events including the Egyptian Online Seminar in Accounting Series and at Excel College, Nepal, in May and June 2020, respectively (Atkins et al., 2020).
86 This quotation is from McBain (2020, p. 20).
87 Interestingly, the Dasgupta Review considered that reporting and disclosure on biodiversity was intended for financial institutions and to build and maintain reputation. Certainly, this is represented in our landscape graphic by an arrow flowing from extinction accounting leftwards towards financial institutions. However, this is a myopic view of extinction accounting and reporting on biodiversity, as we would argue strongly that there are far more stakeholder groups interested in, and needful of, this information, such as conservation organisations. As mentioned earlier, we would also emphasise the emancipatory potential of extinction accounting to elicit transformations in behaviour and genuine change.
88 Specifically Section 21.3.2.

References

Atkins, J. and Atkins, B. (2019) (eds.) *Around the World in 80 Species: Exploring the Business of Extinction*, Routledge, London, UK.
Atkins, J. F. and Atkins, B. C. (eds.) (2016) *The Business of Bees, An Integrated Approach to Bee Decline*, June, Greenleaf Publishers, Saltaire, UK.

Atkins, J., Gräbsch, C. and Jones, M. J. (2014) "Biodiversity Reporting: Exploring its Anthropocentric Nature" chapter in Jones (eds.) *Accounting for Biodiversity*, Routledge, UK.

Atkins, J. F. and Maroun, W. (2018) "Integrated Extinction Accounting and Accountability: Building an Ark", *Accounting, Auditing & Accountability Journal*, Vol. 31, No. 3, pp. 1–41.

Atkins, J. F., Maroun, W., Atkins, B. C. and Barone, E. (2018) "From the Big Five to the Big Four? Exploring Extinction Accounting for the Rhinoceros?", *Accounting, Auditing & Accountability Journal*, Vol. 31, No. 2, pp. 1–31.

Atkins, J. F. and Maroun, W. (2020) "The Naturalist's Journals of Gilbert White: Exploring the roots of accounting for biodiversity and extinction accounting", *Accounting, Auditing & Accountability Journal*, Vol.33 (8), pp.1835-1870.

Eccles, R. G. and Krzus, M. P. (2010). Integrated Reporting for a Sustainable Strategy. Available: http://www.financialexecutives.org/KenticoCMS/Financial-Executive-Magazine/2010_03/Financial-Reporting-Feature-March-2010.aspx#axzz48iuAkAHV. Accessed 26 November 2012.

Eccles, R. and Saltzman, D. (2011). Achieving Sustainability through Integrated Reporting. *Stanford Social Innovation Review*. Available: http://202.154.59.182/mfile/files/Jurnal/MIT%202012-2013%20(PDF)/Achieving%20Sustainability%20Through%20Integrated%20Reporting.pdf.

Freshfields Bruckhaus Deringer (2005) A Legal Framework for the Integration of Environmental, Social and Governance Issues into Institutional Investment, UNEP Finance Initiative, produced for the Asset Management Working Group of the UNEP Finance Initiative, October.

Gallhofer, S. and Haslam, J. (2003) *Accounting and Emancipation: Some Critical Interventions*. London and New York: Routledge.

Haberl, H., Erb, K.H., Krausmann, F., Gaube, V., Bondeau, A., Plutzar, C., Gingrich, S., Lucht, W., & Fischer-Kowalski, M. (2007). Quantifying and mapping the human appropriation of net primary production in earth's terrestrial ecosystems. PNAS, 104(31): 12942–12947

Hassan, A., Roberts, L. and Atkins, J. (2020) "Exploring Factors Relating to Extinction Disclosures: What Motivates Companies to Report on Biodiversity and Species Protection?" *Business Strategy and the Environment*, January, Vol. 19(3) pp. 1–18.

Hetherington, D. (2018) "The Lynx and Us", The Big Picture, Scotland, ww.scotlandbigpicture.com.

Imhoff, M.L., Bounoua, L., Ricketts, T., Loucks, C., Hariss, R., & Lawrence, W.T. (2004). Global patterns in human consumption of net primary production. Nature, 429: 870–873.

IPBES (2019) IPBES Report, Summary for policymakers of the global assessment report on biodiversity and ecosystem services of the Intergovernmental Science-Policy Platform on Biodiversity and Ecosystem Services, May 2019.

Jones, M. J. and Solomon, J. F. (2013) "Problematising accounting for biodiversity," *Accounting, Auditing & Accountability Journal*, Vol.26, Issue 5, pp. 668-687

Jones, M. J. and Solomon, J. F. (2013) "Problematising Accounting for Biodiversity," *Accounting, Auditing & Accountability Journal*, Vol. 26, No. 5.

McBain, A. (2020) "Pandemic: The Inextricable Link between Human, Animal and Ecosystem Health and the Emergence of Communicable Disease", https://www.mandg.co.uk/investor/articles/the-inextricable-link-between-human-animal-and-ecosystem-health-and-the-emergence-of-communicable-disease/

Maroun, W. and Atkins, J. F. (2018) "The Emancipatory Potential of Extinction Accounting: Exploring Current Practice in Integrated Reports", *Accounting Forum*, Vol. 42, pp. 102–118.

Maroun, W. and Atkins, J. (2020) "A Practical Application of Accounting for Biodiversity: The Case of Soil Health", *Social and Environmental Accountability Journal*, Vol.41, No.1-2, pp.37-65.

Rounsevell, M. D. A., Harfoot, M., Harrison, P. A., Newbold, T. Gregory, R. D. and Mace, G. M. (2020) "A Biodiversity Target based on Species Extinctions", *Science*, Vol. 368, No. 6496, pp. 1193–1195.

Solomon, J. F. (2007) *Corporate Governance and Accountability*, 2nd edition, John Wiley Inc. Chichester, UK.

Solomon, J. F. (2013) *Corporate Governance and Accountability*, 4th edition, John Wiley & Sons Inc. Chichester, UK.

Solomon, J. F. (2021) *Corporate Governance and Accountability*, 5th edition, John Wiley & Sons Inc. Chichester, UK.

Solomon, J. F. and Solomon, A. (2006) "Private Social, Ethical and Environmental Disclosure", *Accounting, Auditing & Accountability Journal*, Vol.19, No.4, pp. 564–591.

University of Cambridge Institute for Sustainability Leadership (CISL 2020). Biodiversity Loss and Land Degradation: An Overview of the Financial Materiality.

Wheeler, D. and Sillanpää, M. (1997) *The Stakeholder Corporation*. London: Pitman.

World Economic Forum (WEF). (2020, January) *Nature Risk Rising: Why the Crisis Engulfing Nature Matters for Business and the Economy*, p. 8. Retrieved from: https://www.weforum.org/reports/nature-risk-rising-why-the-crisis-engulfing-nature-matters-for-business-and-the-economy.

Zhao, L. and Atkins, J. (2021) "Assessing the Emancipatory Nature of Chinese Corporate Reporting on Conservation and Biodiversity", *Social and Environmental Accountability Journal*, Vol.41(1-2), pp.8-36

2

EXTINCTION GOVERNANCE

Establishing a Framework for Extinction Accounting, Accountability and Finance

Mervyn E. King, Jill Atkins and Warren Maroun

Introduction

Interest in emerging forms of environmental accounting and reporting is growing. Examples include biodiversity reporting [1], ecological accounting [2] and extinction accounting [3]. In addition to these academic endeavours, the Global Reporting Initiative [4, 5] provides suggested biodiversity disclosures for inclusion in sustainability reports. While not dealing with biodiversity directly, the International Integrated Reporting Council [6] outlines an approach for managing and reporting on multiple types of capitals, including natural resources. Most recently, the United Nations [7] endorsed a set of environmental accounting experiments focused on delineating the spatial and biological properties of biodiversity and accounting for changes in assigned financial values. What has not been considered is how biodiversity and the risk posed by a loss of species should be incorporated as part of an organisation's broader approach to corporate governance and long-term sustainability.

As explained by Solomon [8],

> corporate governance is the system of checks and balances, both internal and external to companies, which ensures that companies discharge their accountability to all their stakeholders and act in a socially responsible way in all areas of their business activity.

Protecting biodiversity is an integral part of this stakeholder–accountability paradigm. Organisations operate in a broader societal context and are legally separate from their financial capital providers. Their status as 'corporate citizens' accords them the right to provide goods and services in exchange for fair compensation

DOI: 10.4324/9781003045557-4

and corresponding obligations to avoid compromising the ability of future generations to meet their needs [Institute of Directors in Southern Africa [IOD], 9]. This includes access to the ecosystems which are an integral part of modern economies and essential for humanity's very existence.

In the above context, we outline an 'extinction governance framework' which places biodiversity protection and ecological issues at the centre of a stakeholder-inclusive approach to how organisations are directed and managed [10, 11]. Specifically, we define extinction governance as *the system of checks and balances, both internal and external to an organisation, which ensures that the organisation discharges accountability to all their stakeholders and acts in a socially responsible way, whilst explicitly integrating the protection of biodiversity and non-human species into all areas of the organisation's activity.*

The framework demonstrates how well-established principles and practices in South Africa's King codes on corporate governance may evolve to incorporate specifically with the dangers posed by biodiversity loss; enable transformative types of environmental accounting and reporting; and, ultimately, prevent the extinction of species. Although these issues are currently implicit within the King IV framework, our intention is to render them explicit.

In other words, it may be argued that the 'governance of extinction' is addressed indirectly by King IV's broader corporate governance framework and the advancement of integrated reporting. The urgency and critical nature of the extinction and interrelated climate crisis make it necessary to deal with these issues explicitly. Given the financial, ecological and sociocultural consequences of biodiversity decline [12, 13], species, habitat, ecosystem and other natural capital issues need to become part of the boardroom discourse and a central feature of how organisations are operated and managed. Before examining the features of the proposed extinction governance framework in more detail, we briefly discuss the trends in and the business case for preventing the extinction of species.

Extinction of Species and the Associated Implications

Climate change is now an explicit element in reporting and governance frameworks and has attracted substantial attention from financial markets and accounting bodies worldwide. Biodiversity and species loss, however, have been eclipsed by the growing dominance of climate change within environmental agendas. The current mass extinction crisis and its ramifications for business, ecosystem services and the financial business risks associated with species loss and decline in biodiversity make, at least, an equal focus on extinction prevention and species protection a matter of urgency.

As many are now aware, the planet is experiencing a mass extinction event, with human and business activity being the root cause of species loss and habitat destruction [12]. A recent report by the IPBES [14] estimates that 25% of species across terrestrial, freshwater and marine vertebrate, invertebrate and plant groups are threatened with extinction. Overall, it is estimated that, of 8 million animal and plant species, as many as 1 million are threatened with extinction. The report also states that around 9% of the world's estimated 5.9 million terrestrial species have insufficient habitats to ensure their long-term survival.

There have been substantial interdisciplinary efforts to value species and the ecosystems of which they form a part. These valuations reveal the billions of dollars which ecosystem services contribute directly or indirectly to the global economy annually [see 7, 15]. Valuations are often calculated by considering how much it would cost to replace a naturally occurring ecosystem service, such as pollination, with an alternative assuming that such a replacement is possible. These calculations suffer from technical limitations [e.g. 2, 16], but they provide, at least, some sense of the magnitude of the financial losses which may be incurred if biodiversity decline continues. Perhaps most important is the realisation that many ecosystem services cannot be replicated with existing technologies and are, effectively, invaluable from an economic and an ecological perspective.

It is easy to prioritise the financial case for protecting species and overlook the intrinsic value of nature. There are also strong moral, ethical and philosophical grounds for conserving plant and animal species. Many of these are an integral part of humanity's social, cultural and religious identity. As a result, the extinction of species cannot be understood in only financial terms [17, 18] or as a type of exposed position which can be cleverly hedged [13]. Biodiversity loss is a real and significant risk to business, society and, possibly, human existence. As explained by Atkins and Macpherson [19]:

> humans are also a species and as such are part of nature. As a species, we are as reliant on the rest of nature as any other species.

This is especially true when considering that the biological impact of extinction is often unquantifiable. Each species' contribution to the healthy functioning of every ecosystem is unknown until a species disappears. At one extreme, the demise of a single species may have negligible consequences. At the other, extinction can result in ecosystem collapse. Given the millions of species of flora and fauna, it is impossible to know which are keystone species and precisely how their removal will impact other species, including people. As we are now acutely aware, there is also an imminent human health (and potential human extinction) motivation for enhancing biodiversity, protecting habitats and preserving species. The links between biodiversity loss, endangered species, habitat loss and transmission of diseases from animals to humans are increasingly obvious and, in turn, linked to business activities and the decisions made by financial institutions.

Given the above context, it will be difficult for an organisation's governing body to argue that the impact of biodiversity loss on their business model and long-term sustainability is immaterial. An organisation which does not incorporate species protection and extinction prevention into the heart of its strategy development, risk management and control environment is left vulnerable. Its governing body will be failing to acknowledge potentially massive losses which can result if species go extinct. An unresponsive organisation will also be assuming that it will never be held responsible for contributing directly or indirectly to biodiversity decline. From a different perspective, proactively managing the risks posed by extinction can yield important benefits such as a stronger competitive advantage, access to new markets, technological advancements, improved stakeholder relationships and, ultimately, long-term sustainability. These cannot be realised if those charged with an organisation's governance ignore or overlook the urgent need to prevent the loss of species. A governing body must, therefore, appreciate the fact that its organisation is inherently and undeniably dependent on nature and take an inclusive approach to ecological awareness and a proactive stance on extinction governance.

The Principles of Good Governance

The prior research acknowledges the importance of the internal controls, management systems and monitoring functions of governing bodies in promoting environmental accountability [20–22]. If the benefits of extinction governance are to be fully realised, measures to protect biodiversity must form an integral part of an organisation's business model and operations [11]. To assist with achieving this objective, South Africa's codes on corporate governance are particularly useful.

South Africa is well-regarded as a pioneer in corporate governance [8, 23]. The country has a long history of applying stakeholder-centric governance models which focus on balancing economic, environmental and social objectives [see 24–26]. This has contributed to advances in corporate social responsibility and sustainability reporting. The most recent development is integrated reporting which South Africa was first to adopt as an integral part of its approach to good governance [27–29].

South Africa's codes on corporate governance take the position that financial performance cannot be the sole measure of value creation [10]. Aligned with the IIRC's [6, 30] recommendations, King IV calls for an integrated approach to business management based on the interconnections among economic, environmental and social capitals; an organisation's strategic position; and how its business model is executed [9]. To avoid a legalistic approach to governance, it calls for 'mindful application' of governance principles which are operationalised by specific practices tailored according to an organisation's circumstances. The principles:

> embody the aspirations of the journey towards good corporate governance. They guide on what organisations should strive to achieve by the application of governance practices. Principles build on and reinforce one another;

they are phrased so that they are fundamental to good corporate governance and hold true across all organisations.

[9]

The principles are summarised in Table 2.1, and their application in the context
of an extinction governance model is discussed in Section 'Towards Ecologically
Motivated Boardrooms'.

TABLE 2.1 Principles of King IV

Code	Principle	Explanation
P1	Principle 1:	The governing body should lead ethically and effectively.
P2	Principle 2:	The governing body should govern the ethics of the organisation in a way that supports the establishment of an ethical culture.
P3	Principle 3:	The governing body should ensure that the organisation is seen to be a responsible corporate citizen.
P4	Principle 4:	The governing body should appreciate that the organisation's core purpose, its risks and opportunities, strategy, business model, performance and sustainable development are all inseparable elements of the value creation process.
P5	Principle 5:	The governing body should ensure that reports issued by the organisation enable stakeholders to make informed assessments of the organisation's performance and its short-, medium- and long-term prospects.
P6	Principle 6:	The governing body should serve as the focal point and custodian of corporate governance in the organisation.
P7	Principle 7:	The governing body should comprise the appropriate balance of knowledge, skills, experience, diversity and independence for it to discharge its governance role and responsibilities objectively and effectively.
P8	Principle 8:	The governing body should ensure that its arrangements for delegation within its structures promote independent judgement and assist with balance of power and the effective discharge of its duties.
P9	Principle 9:	The governing body should ensure that the evaluation of its performance and that of its committees, its chair and its members support continued improvement in its performance and effectiveness.
P10	Principle 10:	The governing body should ensure that the appointment of, and delegation to, management contribute to role clarity and the effective exercise of authority and responsibilities.
P11	Principle 11:	The governing body should govern risk in a way that supports the organisation in setting and achieving its strategic objectives.
P12	Principle 12:	The governing body should govern technology and information in a way that supports the organisation in setting and achieving its strategic objectives.

Code	Principle	Explanation
P13	Principle 13:	The governing body should govern compliance with applicable laws and adopted, non-binding rules, codes and standards in a way that supports the organisation being ethical and a good corporate citizen.
P14	Principle 14:	The governing body should ensure that the organisation remunerates fairly, responsibly and transparently to promote the achievement of strategic objectives and positive outcomes in the short, medium and long term.
P15	Principle 15:	The governing body should ensure that assurance services and functions enable an effective control environment and that these support the integrity of information for internal decision-making and of the organisation's external reports.
P16	Principle 16:	In the execution of its governance role and responsibilities, the governing body should adopt a stakeholder-inclusive approach that balances the needs, interests and expectations of material stakeholders in the best interests of the organisation over time.
P17	Principle 17:	The governing body of an institutional investor organisation should ensure that responsible investment is practised by the organisation to promote good governance and the creation of value by the companies in which it invests.

Ref. [9].

Towards Ecologically Motivated Boardrooms

The proposed extinction governance framework aims to conserve and enhance biodiversity from the perspective of financial risk management but also recognises the importance of preventing extinction due to the intrinsic value of nature. We also take account of the need to discharge accountability for an organisation's impact on threatened species and biodiversity due to a dual materiality approach, as defined in Chapter 1. A deep ecology perspective on extinction and species often coincides with an anti-capitalist stance. We choose to take a more constructive approach which attempts to work *within* our global system of financial markets and business. The approach involves exploring ways in which species protection and extinction prevention can and must be integrated into every mechanism of business, investing, finance and accounting. Recommendations are organised according to the principles in Table 2.1 and discussed in more detail below.

Ethical and Responsible Leadership

In many jurisdictions, directors are obligated by statute or common law to act in the best interest of their companies [31], a position iterated by a responsibility to lead ethically and effectively (P1) per King IV (IOD, 2016). This can no longer be understood as maximising financial value for shareholders:

> Stakeholder inclusivity means that the board considers other stakeholders not merely as instruments to serve the interests of shareholders, but as having intrinsic value for decision-making in the best interests *of the company* over time.
>
> *[9, emphasis added]*

As discussed in Section 'Extinction of Species and the Associated Implications', a loss of biodiversity is not just an ecological concern. It represents an impairment of natural capital with direct and indirect implications for how an organisation generates value, its relationship with stakeholders and its long-term sustainability [for details, see 13, 32, 33]. There are also important moral, social and cultural reasons for protecting biodiversity [17, 34]. As a result, mitigating an organisation's direct and indirect environmental impact and working proactively to prevent extinction can be understood as an integral part of boards' fiduciary duties and imperative for ensuring that their organisations act ethically (P2) and as responsible corporate citizens (P3). Broad recommendations include:

- Ensuring the highest ethical standards when it comes to evaluating and managing an organisation's relationship with biodiversity;
- Addressing the extinction of species as a material ethical risk in an organisation's codes of conduct and best practice;
- Outlining responsibilities for protecting biodiversity;
- Monitoring how an organisation's processes, activities and outputs affect biodiversity

[adapted from 9]

An Integrated Approach to Addressing Extinction: Principles 4 and 5

According to Principle 4 of King IV, an organisation's strategy, risks and opportunities, business model, performance and sustainable development are inseparable parts of the value creation process [9]. To discharge their extinction governance responsibilities, governing bodies should ensure that the loss of species is actively managed. For example:

- An organisation's responsibility for protecting species and habitats should be understood from a regulatory and stakeholder perspective taking into consideration the economic, ecological and social case for wanting to prevent the extinction of species. The consequences for actual or perceived unresponsiveness to extinction for an organisation's immediate and long-term credibility must also be addressed [see 3].

- At the strategic level, a governing body should reflect on how its objectives, operations and position in the value chain are affected by a decline in biodiversity. This can include how the loss of species may impact other resources on which the organisation is dependent, its ability to generate value for stakeholders and its relationship with stakeholders [see 11].
- Related to the above, climate change, habitat destruction and over-utilisation of natural resources are contributing to the loss of species. Extinction must be internalised as a significant business risk and evaluated in terms of the timing and magnitude of the impact on an organisation's strategy and business model [see 35, 36].
- Plans for mitigating the impact of extinction must be developed and implemented. The governing body should review any biodiversity protection policies, monitor their execution and ensure that managers are held accountable for failing to achieve environmental objectives [see 21, 22]. An ecological value officer (EVO) (see also Section 'The Roles and Responsibilities of the Governing Body: Principles 6–10') can assist by providing the technical expertise required to evaluate and develop appropriate responses to biodiversity loss.
- An organisation's management should be tasked with executing policies and plans developed to mitigate the risk of extinction. Performance should be reviewed over the short, medium and long term paying attention to the positive and negative outcomes of its anti-extinction measures [see 11]. To assist with this process, suitable performance indicators should be developed and tracked. Examples of ecologically orientated key performance indicators include:
  - Annual % reduction in financial risk estimated to arise from species loss/ climate change
  - The estimated decrease in the cost of capital arising from reduced risks from climate change/species loss
  - Annual % increase in endangered species populations in habitat affected by business operations
  - Annual % reduction in fines/legal liabilities arising from environmental damage/habitat loss/endangered species loss
  - Year-on-year improvement in habitats and ecosystems affected by business operations
  - Evaluation of successful engagement/partnership with wildlife/climate change NGOs
  - Annual % increase in spending on conservation, species protection and habitat preservation
- Preventing extinction will require different resources. The capitals needed to implement biodiversity policies should be evaluated including dedicated funding (financial capital), multi-disciplinary teams to execute initiatives (human capital) and research to inform new plans for protecting biodiversity (intellectual capital) [see 5, 6].

[adapted from 9]

In the interest of transparent reporting on an organisation's value creation process, details on how biodiversity is being managed should be included in integrated and sustainability reports. As explained by the IIRC [6] and the GRI [4, 5], an integrated or a sustainability report should be used to explain how an organisation's value creation process is impacted by its external environment, relationship with stakeholders and a combination of financial and non-financial resources including natural capital.

As discussed in Section 'Extinction of Species and the Associated Implications', the loss of species can have a material impact on an organisation and its business model from financial, social and ethical perspectives. The risks and strategic implications of a decline in biodiversity cannot be ignored [13, 19, 37]. To remain strategically viable and ensure long-term sustainability, the responsible management and protection of natural capital must be incorporated as part of a holistic approach to management and governance informed by an integrated thinking philosophy [11, 33]. Reporting on biodiversity can also be used to reinforce accountability for environmental performance; build legitimacy in the eyes of material stakeholders; and drive continuous improvement to anti-extinction measures [see 2, 3, 5, 37].

The extinction accounting model outlined by Atkins and colleagues [3, 13, 32, 38] can assist a governing body discharge their reporting responsibilities (see Principle 5). Extinction accounting builds on earlier research by Jones [39, 40] dealing with natural capital inventories and recommended biodiversity disclosures for environmental and sustainability reports in the academic [41, 42] and professional [4, 5] literature.

The extinction accounting model draws on the potential for existing technologies of accounting and accountability to delineate an organisation's activity, define its performance and identify areas for improvement. Applied in the context of the broader sustainable development movement, extinction accounting should raise awareness of the importance of protecting biodiversity and provide a basis for explaining the steps organisations are taking to prevent the loss of species. When implemented as part of corporate governance mechanisms, including the preparation of integrated reports, extinction accounting is a direct method for bringing species, ecosystem and habitat protection into the heart of corporate reporting. The key 'elements' of an extinction account are summarised in Table 2.2.

Information on the species, habitats and ecosystems affected directly or indirectly by an organisation's activities provides context [see 5, 39, 44] and is important for explaining the importance of protecting the environment from both ecological and economic perspectives [33, 43]. To ensure that reporting does not become generic, action-specific disclosures are emphasised. Details are provided on the partnerships formed to combat extinction, key performance indicators, favourable and unfavourable variances and resulting changes to environmental policies and initiatives [see 13]. Drawing on the guidance provided by the International Integrated Reporting Council [6], the measures taken to protect species

TABLE 2.2 Elements in an extinction accounting framework

#	Element	Purpose	Elements
1	Extinction accounting context	Describe the extinction risk in the context of the organisation's business and the diverse reasons for wanting to address this risk	• Record a list of plant and animal species, identified as endangered by the IUCN Red List, whose habitats are affected by the company's activities • Report where, geographically, the company's activities pose a threat to endangered plant and animal species, as identified by the IUCN Red List • Report potential risks/impacts on these specific species arising from the company's operations (equivalent to the existing GRI principles to this point) • Incorporate images (photographs or drawings, for example) of threatened species which are affected by the company's operations and which the company needs to protect • Report full details (narrative as well as financial figures) relating to any fines or ongoing claims relating to endangered species legislation • Report corporate expressions of moral, ethical, emotional, financial and reputational motivations for preserving species and preventing extinction (to respond to diverse needs and requirements of different stakeholders/readers)
2	Action-focused reporting	Explain the actions the company takes and plans to take to reduce extinction risk	• Report actions/initiatives taken by the company to avoid harm to, and to prevent the extinction of, endangered plant and animal species
3	Partnership reporting	Complement action-focused reporting by explaining broader partnerships/initiatives formed to combat/reverse extinction trends	• Report partnerships/engagement between wildlife/nature/conservation organisations and the company which aim to address corporate impacts on endangered species and report the outcome/impact of engagement/partnerships on endangered species
4	Analysis and reflection	Evaluation of extinction prevention initiatives against aims/targets to inform changes to actions and partnerships	• Report assessment and reflection on outcome/impact of engagement/partnerships and decisions taken about necessary changes to policy/initiatives going forward

(Continued)

#	Element	Purpose	Elements
5	Assessment	Audit of affected species/populations/biomes	• Report regular assessments (audit) of species populations in areas affected by corporate operations
6	Reporting	Provide an account of the progress made to date on preventing or mitigating extinction, planned future actions and risk exposure	• Report assessment of whether or not corporate initiatives/actions are assisting in the prevention of species extinction • Report strategy for the future development and improvement of actions/initiatives: an iterative process • Ensure that the whole process of 'extinction accounting' is integrated into corporate strategy and is incorporated into the company's integrated report, the company's business plan, corporate strategy and risk management/internal control system not resigned to separate sustainability reports or websites. • Potential liabilities relating to future possible legal fines/claims relating to endangered species impacts. • Discussion of ways in which the company is working to prevent future liabilities related to harming endangered species. • Provide a pictorial representation of success in conservation – and failure (i.e. species loss)

Refs. [3, 43].

are supported by an explanation of how different types of resources or capitals are used to support anti-extinction measures and are affected by an organisation's broader environmental policies [3]. These include, in alphabetical order:

- financial capital – debts and equity financing available for producing goods and rendering services;
- human capital – the 'competencies, capabilities and experiences' of the individuals working under an organisation's control or direction;
- intellectual capital – 'knowledge-based' intangibles such intellectual property and 'tacit knowledge, systems, procedures and protocols';
- manufactured capital – the physical objectives and resources used in the production or supply of goods and services;
- natural capital – 'renewable and non-renewable environmental resources and processes that provide goods or services that support the past, current or future prosperity of an organisation';

- social and relationship capital – 'the institutions and the relationships within and between communities, groups of stakeholders and other networks, and the ability to share information to enhance individual and collective well-being'.

[6]

The prior research finds historically low levels of reporting dealing generally with biodiversity [e.g. 41, 42, 45]. The possibility that this type of reporting will be used by some companies as part of an impression management strategy cannot be precluded [consider 16, 46–48]. Nevertheless, more recent studies point to an uptake in interest in extinction accounting and its application by preparers [33, 49] and the investor community [19]. There are also several examples of variations of the extinction accounting framework (as outlined in Table 2.1) being used to make a case for the conservation of different species [see, for example, 33, 50–56].

The Missing Link in the Extinction Accounting Framework: Accounting for Absence

It seems that an important adjustment and addition to the extinction accounting framework outlined above is to incorporate 'accounting for absence'. In other words, as well as reporting on species threatened by extinction that are affected by an organisation's operations, it is also necessary to report on species that have disappeared. If this is not required by the extinction accounting framework, then organisations do not have to discharge an accountability for local species extinctions that have occurred as a result of their business activities. This can be interpreted as reporting on failure in this area, but we suggest that specific reporting of species that have become extinct in specific habitats be a mandatory requirement for all organisations.

The extinction rate measure proposed in Chapter 1 could provide a useful tool for such reporting on absence, as it would be relatively easy to incorporate information relating to extinction rates into accounts and disclosures, especially from an integrated reporting perspective. This would be a form of species accounting. Species accounting, as discussed in Chapter 1, represents a crucial element of extinction accounting, especially where keystone species are involved that have a demonstrable financial materiality for the organisation.

The Roles and Responsibilities of the Governing Body: Principles 6–10

A board of directors should provide strategic direction and oversee the executions of any strategies, policies and plans developed and executed by management [8]. As discussed in Section 'An Integrated Approach to Addressing Extinction: Principles 4 and 5', they should provide 'accountability for organisational performance by means of, among others, reporting and disclosure' [9]. In the interest of enabling extinction governance:

- Any charter documenting a board's role and responsibilities should deal explicitly with extinction accounting and provide for the instances where board members or committees of the board should defer to environmental experts when developing and executing policies dealing with the prevention of extinction.
- The nomination, election and appointment of board members should take cognisance of the need for expertise in and experience with managing environmental challenges, including the loss of species. The important role which non-executive directors play in driving ethical and responsible business practices is iterated.
- The portfolio of social and environmental, risk or other equivalent committees can be expanded to deal specifically with the identification and management of the risk of extinction, internal controls, reporting protocols and stakeholder engagement. To ensure efficiency, the responsibilities of different committees concerning biodiversity-related issues should be delineated. Where applicable, a member of the audit and/or risk committee may need to serve on any sub-committees tasked specifically with combatting extinction.
- Delegation of responsibility for developing and executing anti-extinction measures to management is essential. The respective management body should have the necessary experience, expertise and standing in the organisation to discharge their duties. An EVO can be appointed who should have direct access to the relevant committees and the board.
- The EVO should support the functions of the chief value officer (CVO). As suggested by King and Atkins [11], an executive director concerned exclusively with financial performance (typically a chief financial or executive officer) is inconsistent with an integrated approach to managing economic, environmental and social concerns. The CVO should champion a broader approach to strategy development, risk governance, operational management and stakeholder engagement which recognises the importance of preventing the loss of species. The EVO will preside over ensuring value creation and avoiding value destruction or erosion from biodiversity and species loss.
- A board should have access to professional and independent advice when dealing with biodiversity matters including related regulatory and ethical concerns. This can be provided by the EVO or a suitably qualified external party.
- The board's performance evaluation should include measures of how well it has managed its responsibilities for overseeing the extinction governance framework.

[adapted from 9]

Functional Aspects of Extinction Governance: Principles 11–15

Per Principle 11 of King IV, the governing body should govern risk in a way that supports the organisation in setting and achieving its strategic objectives [9].

This would include an assessment of the risks associated with extinction from both business *and* ecological perspectives [32]. Opportunities arising from biodiversity management and protection should also be addressed. For example, restoring damaged habitats or supporting the efforts of an NGO to protect an endangered species can be used to differentiate a company from its competitors, establish its credibility as an environmentally responsible entity and decrease the risk associated with the loss of that species [adapted from 5, 9].

As discussed in Section 'An Integrated Approach to Addressing Extinction: Principles 4 and 5', management should develop an appropriate response to mitigating material risks which the relevant committee of the board reviews, assisted by the CVO. The outlines of an ecological risk management and internal control matrix derived from the Turnbull Framework and Grabsch et al. (2014) are presented in Figure 2.1.

Figure 2.1 starts from the position that extinction must be avoided to mitigate material business risks and prevent a loss of value. Addressing the risk of extinction will also improve resilience against risks throughout the financial markets including business continuity risks in the face of emerging pandemics.

The value assessment would be conducted from a financial and non-financial perspective which stresses the economic and ecological importance of protecting biodiversity [13]. A risk management strategy would be developed (see Section 'An Integrated Approach to Addressing Extinction: Principles 4 and 5') supported by specific initiatives to protect species. This would include an assessment of the different capitals (such as financial, intellectual and human capital) required. The emphasis is on the species most at risk of extinction; stakeholder collaboration to avoid the loss of species; and the minimisation of species-related liabilities or costs. As discussed in Section 'An Integrated Approach to Addressing Extinction: Principles 4 and 5', performance against planned targets or assessments should be assessed regularly and included in integrated reports. A process of continuous improvement, informed by performance reviews and stakeholder engagement, ensures that the organisation refines its anti-extinction measures.

Focusing specifically on companies, directors owe their duties to their companies in terms of statute and/or common law. They should report to the company and, through the company, to stakeholders. In the interest of inclusivity, transparency and proactivity, a governing body should be ready to receive feedback from its stakeholders. This will require formal mechanisms for identifying material stakeholders, managing associated risks and resolving any disputes [9]. (Stakeholder engagement is discussed in more detail in Section 'Stakeholder Engagement: Principles 16–17'.)

Information technology can play a key role in the broader risk management and reporting process. For example, new technologies in imaging and mapping can be used to track the ecological health of habitats and how this changes over time. Developments in data collection and analytics can allow an organisation to expand the scope of its existing accounting system to include different environmental performance indicators such as habitat sizes, number of species, reduction

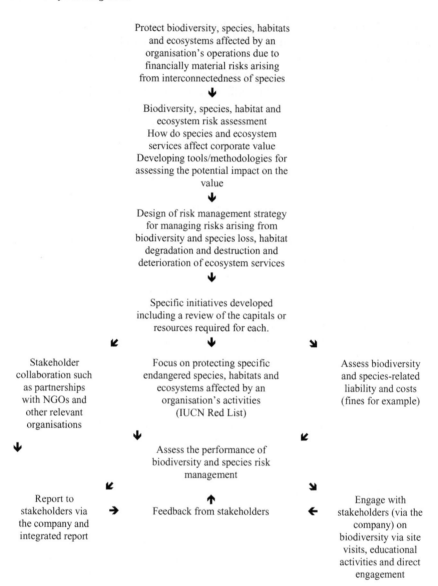

FIGURE 2.1 System of ecological risk management and internal control.

in pollution levels or increases in biomass. Cloud computing, blockchain and social media can be used to aggregate information from multiple organisations to provide a consolidated perspective on how the risks posed by extinction are being managed. Governance considerations include:

• developing guidelines for integrating technology solutions, extinction risk assessments and associated management plans;

- proactive monitoring to ensure the integrity of data and systems;
- ensuring compliance with applicable laws and regulations;
- integrating the use of technology with codes on ethics to ensure responsible application and
- developing frameworks for sharing data with other firms, non-governmental organisations and research institutions to enable a coordinated approach to prevent extinction.

[adapted from 9]

As environmental concerns continue to mount, national and supra-national bodies are developing laws, regulations and recommended practices to promote more sustainable business. The governing body should keep abreast of these developments and ensure compliance with applicable requirements [adapted from 9]. Levels of compliance and overall measures of performance against environmental targets in the short, medium and long term (see Section 'An Integrated Approach to Addressing Extinction: Principles 4 and 5') should be incorporated in remuneration policies to promote accountability and reinforce the need for improvements to anti-extinction efforts [adapted from 9].

Finally, the governing body should consider the use of assurance [33, 43]. Recommendations include:

- Developing an appropriate accounting and management system to enable internal decision-making and reporting to stakeholders;
- Active monitoring and review by the committee overseeing the application of extinction accounting;
- Tasking internal and external auditors to test systems, business processes and controls dealing directly or indirectly with extinction accounting;
- Verification of specific disclosures included in an integrated or sustainability report by internal auditors, external auditors and panels of expert stakeholders;
- Appointing in-house specialists to assist with the development, execution and review of environmental policies;

[adapted from 9]

Stakeholder Engagement: Principles 16–17

A governing body should reflect on how stakeholders can be co-opted in the identification and mitigation of extinction-related risks (see also Sections 'Ethical and Responsible Leadership' and 'Functional Aspects of Extinction Governance: Principles 11–15'). For example:

- Providers of financial capital can offer much-needed access to funds for conservation projects and raise awareness of the need to protect species and habitats.

- Partnerships with environmental bodies and NGOs can provide technical support for extinction prevention initiatives.
- Universities can be engaged in researching new approaches to managing and reporting on the risks associated with extinction.

[adapted from 9]

Institutional investors also have a key role to play. The UN Principles for Responsible Investment [57] and Equator Principles [58] already deal with the importance of incorporating environmental factors as part of the investment analysis and appraisal process. This would include details on how organisations are identifying and managing the risks posed by the loss of biodiversity. The large investment houses have the experience and influence to champion more comprehensive disclosure of extinction-related issues and provide feedback to companies on how to enhance their management of and reporting on the risks posed by the extinction of species. A preliminary framework for investor engagement on preventing extinction is adapted from Atkins, Maroun [33] and presented in Table 2.3:

TABLE 2.3 Investor engagement suggestions

- How do you inform yourselves about species decline and extinction threats concerning your business activities?
- In what ways is your supply chain, both upstream and downstream, likely to be affected by species loss?
- Have you commissioned any studies to determine which species threatened with extinction on the IUCN Red List are directly or indirectly affected by your operations or those of organisations within your supply chain?
- If you have commissioned studies, what were the outcomes? Have you identified which species are most at risk and what the financial (and other: reputational, social responsibility, ethical, moral) consequences of decline and extinction of these species are for your organisation?
- Are you engaging, or partnering, with any wildlife organisation regarding species threatened with extinction, for example, the WWF? If so what are the outcomes of these engagements/partnerships?
- What contingency measures, risk scenarios and mitigation strategies have you considered regarding species decline and extinction?
- What measures are you taking to reduce and limit the impact of your operations on the ecosystem?
- What initiatives, policies and strategies have you implemented to prevent species extinction?
- Have you assessed the impact of these initiatives, policies and strategies on species populations?
- Have your assessments led to alterations and improvements in your initiatives, policies and strategies?
- If they have, in what ways has your extinction prevention strategy altered?

The suggestions in Table 2.3 can be complemented by a species protection action plan which involves incorporating the risk of extinction of species in financial analysis, credit ratings, fund management mandates and the pension fund trustee's agendas. Active investor engagement to combat extinction must form part of a formal approach to responsible investment and be supported by a proactive implementation of extinction accounting in the public and private sectors [19].

Summary and Conclusion

Figure 2.2 outlines the application of King IV's principles in the context of 'extinction governance'.

Starting from the left, King IV calls for ethical and effective leadership by a governing body which necessitates:

- providing strategic direction for the organisation and guidance on how different aspects of governance are operationalised;
- approving the policies and plans developed by management to give effect to the organisation's strategy;
- monitoring and reviewing management's performance and
- ensuring accountability.

[9]

To discharge these responsibilities, King IV outlines 15 principles. These deal with leadership strategy and reporting, the roles and responsibilities of the board, functional governance areas and stakeholder engagement. Each of these is applied to give effect to the 'governance of extinction'. The result is:

- a culture of ethics which incorporates the ecological, social and moral responsibility for protecting species and habitats;
- improved sustainability performance because of a more comprehensive approach to assessing and managing environmental risk;
- a robust system of internal control which ensures efficient and effective utilisation of the resources required to implement extinction accounting and governance frameworks and
- long-term credibility based on a genuine commitment to conserving natural capital.

[adapted from 9]

In summary, it is essential that all organisations incorporate biodiversity loss and species extinction into every aspect and mechanism of their governance model and accountability. The model we propose in this chapter provides a blueprint (or greenprint) for organisations to develop their governance with biodiversity and species protection at its heart. Biodiversity loss and species extinction, whether

Leadership

P1 – Governing body leads ethically and effectively
P2 – The governance of ethics
P3 – The organisation is and is seen to be a responsible corporate citizen

Application

Application of highest ethical standards for managing the organisation's relationship with biodiversity reinforced by active monitoring by the board
Responsibility for Extinction of species to be acknowledged and dealt with explicitly on codes of ethics

Strategy and performance

P4 – Integrated strategies
P5 – Integrated reporting

Application

Biodiversity and loss of species to be dealt with directly in an organisation's strategy and risk assessment;
Policies and plans to mitigate biodiversity loss to be developed and implemented by management with appropriate review by the board
Transparent reporting on how an organisation is working to prevent loss of species

Roles & resp. of the gov. body

P6 – Focal point for governance
P7 – Composition
P8 – Committees
P9 – Performance evaluation
P 10 – Delegation of responsibilities

Application

Board charters and membership to take extinction of species into consideration; appropriate committees tasked wit managing extinction accounting
Delegation of responsibility for extinction accounting to appropriate management body;
Appointment of a CBO or equivalent
Board's performance includes measures relating to extinction accounting

Functional areas

P11 -Risk governance
P12-Techology governance
P13-Compliance governance
P14-Remuneration governance
P15-Assurance

Application

Integration of extinction in entry-wide approach to risk identification and management
Capitalising on technological developments to expand the scope of accounting for and management of extinction of species
Awareness of and compliance with regulatory, governance and reporting developments; Use of different sources of assurance to ensure the integrity of extinction accounting

Stakeholders

P16– Stakeholder engagement
P17– Institutional investors

Application

Co-option of stakeholders in assessing and mitigating extinction risk
Transparent reporting to stakeholders on extinction-related issues

Leadership by the governing body

Steers and sets strategic direction

Approves policies and plans

Ensures accountability

Oversees and monitors

Outcomes

Ethical culture

Good performance

Effective control

Legitimacy

FIGURE 2.2 Summarised extinction governance model.

financial material to the organisation, or an area where the organisation has an impact, must be an item on the agenda of every meeting and every discussion at board level in order for these critically important issues to filter down through every level of the organisation and its value chain. Only by developing an extinction governance which integrates ecological issues into the heart of governance and accountability can we address the biodiversity emergency that faces humans and non-human species today.

References

1. Jones, M.J. and J.F. Solomon, *Problematising accounting for biodiversity.* Accounting, Auditing & Accountability Journal, 2013. **26**(5): p. 668–687.
2. Russell, S., M.J. Milne, and C. Dey, *Accounts of nature and the nature of accounts: Critical reflections on environmental accounting and propositions for ecologically informed accounting.* Accounting, Auditing & Accountability Journal, 2017. **30**(7): p. 1426–1458.
3. Atkins, J. and W. Maroun, *Integrated extinction accounting and accountability: Building an ark.* Accounting, Auditing & Accountability Journal, 2018. **31**(3): p. 750–786.
4. GRI *Consolidated set of GRI sustainability reporting standards (2016).* 2016.
5. GRI *Biodiversity: A GRI reporting resource.* 2007.
6. IIRC *The International Framework: Integrated Reporting.* 2013.
7. United Nations. *SEEA Experimental Ecosystem Accounting Revision.* 2019 1 March 2020; Available from: https://seea.un.org/content/seea-experimental-ecosystem-accounting-revision.
8. Solomon, J., *Corporate Governance and Accountability, Fourth Edition.* 2013, West Sussex: John Wiley and Sons Ltd.
9. IOD, *King IV Report on Corporate Governance in South Africa.* 2016: Lexis Nexus South Africa, Johannesburg, South Africa.
10. King, M., *Integrated reporting and corporate governance in South Africa.* 2018, IRCSA Annual Conference, The Johannesburg Stock Exchange, South Africa.
11. King, M. and J. Atkins, *The chief value officer. Accountants can save the planet.* 2016, Abingdon, Oxon: Greenleaf Publishing Limited.
12. Ceballos, G., P.R. Ehrlich, and R. Dirzo, *Biological annihilation via the ongoing sixth mass extinction signaled by vertebrate population losses and declines.* Proceedings of the National Academy of Sciences, 2017. **114**(30): p. E6089–E6096. Published by National Academy of Sciences.
13. Atkins, J. and B. Atkins, *Around the world in 80 species. Exploring the business of extinction.* Around the World in 80 Species. 2019, London: Routledge. 434.
14. IPBES *Global Assessment Report on Biodiversity and Ecosystem Services for the Americas.* 2019.
15. United Nations *The Sustainable Development Goals Report 2019.* 2019.
16. Gray, R., *Is accounting for sustainability actually accounting for sustainability...and how would we know? An exploration of narratives of organisations and the planet.* Accounting, Organizations and Society, 2010. **35**(1): p. 47–62.
17. Samkin, G., A. Schneider, and D. Tappin, *Developing a reporting and evaluation framework for biodiversity.* Accounting, Auditing & Accountability Journal, 2014. **27**(3): p. 527–562.
18. Christian, J., *Bombus terrestris. A personal deep ecological account,* in *The Business of Bees: An Integrated Approach to Bee Decline and Corporate Responsibility,* K. Atkins and B. Atkins, Editors. 2016, Greenleaf Publishers: Sheffield, UK. p. 89–107.

19. Atkins, J. and M. Macpherson, *Developing a Species Protection Action Plan – An Integrated Approach for Taxonomies, Reporting and Engagement for the Financial Services Sector*. 2019, Concept Paper circulated and presented at Investec Bank's Natural Capital, Species Extinction & Sustainable Financial Markets Event, 30th May.
20. Milne, M.J., *On sustainability; the environment and management accounting*. Management Accounting Research, 1996. **7**(1): p. 135–161.
21. Alrazi, B., C. De Villiers, and C.J. van Staden, *A comprehensive literature review on, and the construction of a framework for, environmental legitimacy, accountability and proactivity*. Journal of Cleaner Production, 2015. **102**: p. 44–57.
22. Gray, R. *The Greening of Accountancy*. The Profession after Pearce, ACCA, London, 1990. 198.
23. Solomon, J., *Directions for Corporate Governance*, ACCA, Editor. 2009, Certified Accountants Educational Trust: London.
24. IOD, *The King Code of Governance for South Africa (2009) and King Report on Governance for South Africa (2009) (King-III)*. 2009: Lexis Nexus South Africa, Johannesburg, South Africa.
25. IOD, *The King report on corporate governance in South Africa – 2002 (King-II)*. 2002: Lexis Nexus South Africa, Johannesburg, South Africa.
26. IOD, *The King report on corporate governance (King-I)*. 1994: Lexis Nexus South Africa, Johannesburg, South Africa.
27. Atkins, J. and W. Maroun, *Integrated reporting in South Africa in 2012: Perspectives from South African institutional investors*. Meditari Accountancy Research, 2015. **23**(2): p. 197–221.
28. De Villiers, C., L. Rinaldi, and J. Unerman, *Integrated reporting: Insights, gaps and an agenda for future research*. Accounting, Auditing & Accountability Journal, 2014. **27**(7): p. 1042–1067.
29. Maroun, W. and D. Cerbone, *Corporate Governance in South Africa*. Vol. 2. 2020: Walter de Gruyter GmbH & Co KG.
30. IIRC *Integrated Thinking & Strategy: State of play report*. 2019.
31. Esser, I. and J. Du Plessis, *The stakeholder debate and directors' fiduciary duties*. SA Mercantile Law Journal, 2007. **19**(3): p. 346–363.
32. Atkins, J. and B. Atkins, *The business of bees: An integrated approach to bee decline and corporate responsibility*. 2016: Routledge.
33. Atkins, J., et al., *From the big five to the big four? Exploring extinction accounting for the rhinoceros*. Accounting, Auditing & Accountability Journal, 2018. **31**(2): p. 674–702.
34. Naess, A. and G. Sessions, *The basic principles of deep ecology*. The Trumpeter, 1986. **3**(4): p. 1–39.
35. KPMG *The road ahead. The KPMG Survey of Corporate Responsibility Reporting 2017*. 2017.
36. Van Zijl, W., C. Wöstmann, and W. Maroun, *Strategy disclosures by listed financial services companies: Signalling theory, legitimacy theory and South African integrated reporting practices*. South African Journal of Business Management, 2017. **48**(3): p. 73–85.
37. Buchling, M. and J. Atkins, *Chapter 29: Reporting on more than just natural capital*, in *The Routledge Handbook of Integrated Reporting*, C. De Villiers, P.-C.K. Hsiao, and W. Maroun, Editors. 2020, Routledge: London pp. 440–455.
38. Atkins, J., et al., *'Good' news from nowhere: Imagining utopian sustainable accounting*. Accounting, Auditing & Accountability Journal, 2015. **28**(5): p. 651–670.
39. Jones, M.J., *Accounting for biodiversity: A pilot study*. The British Accounting Review, 1996. **28**(4): p. 281–303.

40. Jones, M.J., *Accounting for biodiversity: Operationalising environmental accounting.* Accounting, Auditing & Accountability Journal, 2003. **16**(5): p. 762–789.

41. van Liempd, D. and J. Busch, *Biodiversity reporting in Denmark.* Accounting, Auditing & Accountability Journal, 2013. **26**(5): p. 833–872.

42. Rimmel, G. and K. Jonäll, *Biodiversity reporting in Sweden: Corporate disclosure and preparers' views.* Accounting, Auditing & Accountability Journal, 2013. **26**(5): p. 746–778.

43. Maroun, W. and J. Atkins, *The emancipatory potential of extinction accounting: Exploring current practice in integrated reports.* Accounting Forum, 2018. **42**(1): p. 102–118.

44. Cuckston, T., *Ecology-centred accounting for biodiversity in the production of a blanket bog.* Accounting, Auditing & Accountability Journal, 2017. **30**(7): p. 1537–1567.

45. Mansoor, H. and W. Maroun, *An initial review of biodiversity reporting by South African corporates - The case of the food and mining sectors.* South African Journal of Economic and Management Sciences, 2016. **19**(4): p. 592–614.

46. Boiral, O., *Accounting for the unaccountable: Biodiversity reporting and impression management.* Journal of Business Ethics, 2016. **135**(4): p. 751–768.

47. Maroun, W., K. Usher, and H. Mansoor, *Biodiversity reporting and organised hypocrisy: The case of the South African food and retail industry.* Qualitative Research in Accounting & Management, 2018. **15**(4): p. 437–464.

48. Tregidga, H., M. Milne, and K. Kearins, *(Re)presenting 'sustainable organizations'.* Accounting, Organizations and Society, 2014. **39**(6): p. 477–494.

49. Hassan, A.M., L. Roberts, and J. Atkins, *Exploring factors relating to extinction disclosures: What motivates companies to report on biodiversity and species protection?* Business Strategy and the Environment, 2020. **29**(3): p. 1419–1436.

50. Jonäll, K. and G. Rimmel, *Corporate bee accountability among Sweedish companies,* in *The Business of Bees: An Integrated Approach to Bee Decline and Corporate Responsibility,* K. Atkins and B. Atkins, Editors. 2016, Greenleaf Publishers: Sheffield, UK. p. 212–230.

51. Jonäll, K. and S. Sabelfeld, *Accounting for survival of polar bears: An artic icon on thin ice,* in *Around the World in 80 Species. Exploring the Business of Extinction,* K. Atkins and B. Atkins, Editors. 2019, Routledge: London, UK. p. 201–219.

52. Lanka, S.V., *An ecological auto-ethnography of a monarch butterfly,* in *Around the World in 80 Species. Exploring the Business of Extinction,* K. Atkins and B. Atkins, Editors. 2019, Routledge: London, UK. p. 201–219.

53. Nicolov, S., *Recovered species? The eastern North Pacific grey whale unusual mortality event, 1999–2000,* in *Around the World in 80 Species. Exploring the Business of Extinction,* K. Atkins and B. Atkins, Editors. 2019, Routledge: London, UK. p. 133–141.

54. Sibanda, M. and M. Mulama, *Business contributions to extinction risk mitigation for black rhino in Laikipia, Kenya,* in *Around the World in 80 Species. Exploring the Business of Extinction,* K. Atkins and B. Atkins, Editors. 2019, Routledge: London, UK. p. 192–200.

55. Solomon, A. and M. Clappison, *Accounting for captive belugas: A whale of a business,* in *Around the World in 80 Species. Exploring the Business of Extinction,* K. Atkins and B. Atkins, Editors. 2019, Routledge: London, UK. p. 289–323.

56. Zhao, L. and J. Atkins, *Panda accounting and accountability: Preventing giant panda extinction in China,* in *Around the World in 80 Species. Exploring the Business of Extinction,* K. Atkins and B. Atkins, Editors. 2019, Routledge: London, UK. p. 201–219.

57. Principles for Responsible Investment. *What Are the Principles for Responsible Investment?* 2019 1 March 2020; Available from: https://www.unpri.org/pri/an-introduction-to-responsible-investment/what-are-the-principles-for-responsible-investment.

58. Equator Principles Association *Equator Principles - EP4.* 2019.

PART II

The Urgent State of Nature

Addressing Extinction and
Biodiversity Decline

3

BUSINESS, EXTINCTION AND THE FUTURE OF SPECIES

Moving from Good Intention to Action against Species Extinction

Mxolisi Sibanda

Introduction

The catastrophic decline of nature has now been widely recognised as evidenced by agreement among geologists that we have entered an age of mass extinction due to human activity (Barnosky et al., 2011). This is the sixth in the geological history of the earth. While extinction events in the past could be regarded as part of natural evolution, the present crisis is particularly significant due to the increased rate of extinctions that we are witnessing. Estimates are that extinctions are between 1,000 and 10,000 times above the background rate that would be expected due to natural environmental change (Pimm et al. 1995, Sodhi et al, 2009). The loss of individual species while important has even more devastating results which have been less highlighted in discussions or studies. These include trophic cascades associated with food chains, effects of co-extinctions such as in the case of hosts and parasites, disruption of ecological processes and the loss of varied social, economic and ecosystem benefits associated with biodiversity (Balmford et al. 2002, Estes et al., 2011, Valiente-Banuet et al., 2015).

Various studies have illustrated the ongoing species declines and extinctions across different taxa as well as the erosion of ecosystem services and other benefits. The IUCN Red List, which assesses probability of extinction for species, estimates that 38,500 species are at risk of extinction which is 28% of all species. When one considers that we still have many unknown species (Purvis and Hector, 2000), it seems fair to imagine that there will be many more species that go extinct before discovery. This is likely to be already the case in places like Africa where there is still need for more effort to catalogue biodiversity (Daniels et al., 2020).

Unfortunately, many places that are rich repositories of biodiversity are also experiencing massive scales of species extinctions (Myers et al., 2000). These hot

DOI: 10.4324/9781003045557-6

spots occur across the world from Brazil's Cerrado to Tanzania's Eastern Arc Mountains. They also cut across ecosystem types from the terrestrial to freshwater and marine environments. This happens because of the compounding impact of threats that drive extinction such as habitat loss, life history traits that make species vulnerable to extinction, restricted range and endemism. Research on mammals, plants, birds, amphibians, reptiles, fish and corals demonstrates this crisis (Garner et al., 2016, Le Roux et al., 2019, Davis et al., 2019, WWF, 2021). Data from WWF's Living Planet Index, 2020, indicate that from 1970, there has been a decrease of 68% in abundance of wildlife populations across these different taxa (mammals, birds, amphibians, reptiles and fish). Smaller populations increase vulnerability to extinction.

These figures of decline have been a clarion call for action to the world's governments, businesses and communities. The 1992 Rio Earth Summit was an important collective moment for the world's governments to seriously address the biodiversity and climate crises. Since then, intergovernmental forums and agreements such as the Convention on Biological Diversity (CBD), UN Framework Convention on Climate Change (UNFCCC), Kyoto Protocol and the Paris Agreement have taken steps to address this emerging challenge of our times. The CBD's Aichi Target 12 specifically aims to "prevent extinctions of known threatened species".

Lately young people around the world and civil society groups, moved by the impact of climate change, have joined environmental groups like WWF to demand action on both the biodiversity and climate crises. The fight for our world has taken a moral and justice form in view of the fact that the younger generation has had no part in causing the climate and biodiversity/extinction crisis as well as the recognition that the world's poorer people, who largely depend on nature, will suffer the most from the impact of these crises.

For business, the case for action has been framed around the economics associated with the climate crisis and more recently the biodiversity crisis (Dasgupta Review, 2021). The topic has also gained traction, beyond corporate social responsibility, as exemplified by several initiatives, key businesses and investors who have made commitments focused on climate, nature risk among others. Yet with all these efforts, it is apparent that more needs to be done. A systemic shift in the way that capital operates must be found to ensure that businesses deliver a fair, just and sustainable world for their shareholders and all. Evidence from the global coronavirus disease (COVID-19) pandemic, which is thought to have come from a viral infection moving from animals to humans, illustrates how a business-as-usual or minimal contribution approach devastates business and all (Dobson et al., 2020, Jones et al., 2008). Sustainable business lies in an environmentally sustainable approach. That vision can also deliver sustainable profit for businesses and investors as well as reduce material risk to profitability and sustainability of enterprise. A proper accounting framework for contributions from business needs to be at the fore of this so that extinction mitigation becomes a core part of the strategy and execution that businesses carry out.

Starting Point for Extinction Migration – Understanding the Threats to Species

In order to make real progress towards promoting mitigative actions against extinction by business, efforts should be directed at the direct threats to species persistence which we know drive and cause extinctions. While there may be a variety of ways to do so, the IUCN unified classification of threats with an attendant hierarchy is ideal for this (Rodrigues et al., 2006, Salafsky et al., 2008). The system has 12 categories of threats covering a global range of threats. Using these categories, a business, be it tertiary, secondary or primary, is able to situate where its greatest direct contribution to a threat might lie or choose where it might want to prioritise its mitigation from local sites to global scale. Table 3.1 presents the IUCN threat system used for the Red List system and examples of businesses that may be thought to have a direct contribution to some of the threats. The examples are not an exhaustive list by any means.

TABLE 3.1 The IUCN hierarchical threat system used for the Red List

Threat		Second tier level	Examples of business with direct relevance
1. Residential and commercial property development	1.1	Housing and urban areas	Infrastructure developers
	1.2	Commercial and industrial areas	Hoteliers
	1.3	Tourism and recreation areas	Tourism industry
2. Agriculture and aquaculture	2.1	Shifting agriculture/smallholder farming/agro-industry farming	Agro-industry
			Livestock
	2.2	Wood and pulp plantations	Industrial chemicals
	2.3	Livestock farming and ranching	Paper
	2.4	Marine and freshwater aquaculture	Food
			Water sports
3. Energy productions and mining	3.1	Oil and gas drilling	Oil and gas companies
	3.2	Mining and quarrying	Energy
	3.3	Renewable energy	Mining
4. Transportation and service corridors	4.1	Roads and railroads	Construction
	4.2	Utility and service lines	Shipping
	4.3	Shipping lanes	Air travel
	4.4	Flight paths	Tourism
5. Biological resource use	5.1	Hunting and collecting terrestrial animals	Hunting
			Tourism
	5.2	Gathering terrestrial plants	Décor
	5.3	Logging and wood harvesting	Furniture
	5.4	Fishing and harvesting aquatic resources	Construction
6. Human intrusions and disturbance	6.1	Recreational activities	Tourism
	6.2	War, civil unrest and military exercises	International contractors
	6.3	Works and other activities	

(Continued)

Threat	Second tier level		Examples of business with direct relevance
7. Natural system modifications	7.1	Fire and fire suppression	Fire
	7.2	Dams and water management/use	Chemical industry
			Water
8. Invasive and other problematic species, genes and diseases	8.1	Invasive non-native/alien species/diseases	Flower
			Forest
	8.2	Problematic native species/diseases	Paper and pulp industry
			Biochemistry industry
	8.3	Introduced genetic material	Pesticides/chemicals
	8.4	Problematic species/diseases of unknown origin	
	8.5	Viral/prion-induced diseases	
	8.6	Disease of unknown cause	
9. Pollution	9.1	Domestic and urban wastewater	Water
	9.2	Industrial and military effluents	Military enterprises
	9.3	Agricultural and forestry effluents	Forestry companies
	9.4	Garbage and solid waste	Agricultural companies
	9.5	Airborne pollutants	Waste disposal
	9.6	Excess energy	Car
			Air travel
10. Geological events	10.1	Volcanoes	Construction
	10.2	Earthquake/tsunamis	Tourism
	10.3	Avalanches/landslide	Planning
11. Climate change and weather events	12	Habitat shifting and alteration	Oil and gas
	13	Droughts	Travel
	14	Temperature extremes	Agriculture
	15	Storms and flooding	Construction
16. Other	The threats classification scheme is intended to be comprehensive, but as there are often new and emerging threats, this option allows for these new threats to be recorded		

For those businesses that are based on products or services that are a direct threat to species, understanding their impact should lead to a desire to transition their model to a more sustainable one. A typical example of this is commercial farming which through land use change and methane production by cattle is causing huge reductions in biodiversity, accentuating climate change and species extinction (Rojas-Downing et al., 2017). The oil and gas industry is another example where a threat is directly the result of production (Grasso, 2019). In addition to changing their models, these kinds of companies should be at the fore of developing new technologies and solutions that replace the unsustainable and mitigate impact that causes extinctions. Investors in these or any business for that matter need to also look at how their resources can be better used to support these kinds of transitions or more competitive and sustainable products than currently produced in these industries (PRI, 2021).

Looking at extinction threats and their mitigation this way also enables not just a reflection on one specific business impact but can be extended to value chains from source to market. Similarly, an investor can look at their investment portfolio and be able to understand the threats that he or she may be inadvertently supporting against species extinction.

These data on threats can also be looked at in a different way to help businesses explore how they support mitigation against specific taxon groups like birds, mammals or corals. For various taxon groups, information exists that analyses the key direct threats for those groups. Table 3.2 shows an example illustrating the direct threats for birds, mammals, fish and amphibians. These can be drawn from specific publications looking at threats and standardised to the lexicon of the IUCN unified classification. Consequently, direct actions can then be formulated that address specific groups in a variety of contexts.

Doing this kind of analysis also yields results on which threats occur most frequently across various taxon groups which can be weighted or ranked accordingly. From the above example, this could be climate change or overexploitation (unsustainable trade) and a good target for corporate action.

This direct threat approach can be used across multiple scales and for individual species of interest. A global analysis for a company can, if necessary, have vested elements that cover different spatial scales, taxon groups or ecosystems (Stephenson and Carbone, 2021). There are already data and information on many species which can be harvested to support decision-making and monitoring.

What Actions Then?

Identifying the direct threats to develop actions against is just the beginning, what matters most for species at risk of extinction are the actions that are taken

TABLE 3.2 Ranked direct threats causing species extinction according to taxa

Drivers	Birds	Mammals	Fish	Corals	Amphibians
Agriculture					
Overexploitation					
Pollution					
Climate change					
Residential and commercial development					
Logging					
Diseases					
Invasives					

This is based on publications covering taxon groups including BirdLife International (2018), Carpenter et al. (2008), WWF International (2021), Wake and Vredenburg (2008) and Ripple et al. (2017).

to reduce and ultimately stop species extinction as well as those that help restore their populations. There is an urgent need for action and therefore accountability among businesses to their customers and investors (IPBES, 2019). However big or small a business, there are multiple ways to act to protect species, enable restoration of their populations and secure the future while making profit for investors and delivering value for employees and society. The increasing calls for this mean that business should do it for their survival and in readiness for tighter regulatory frameworks in line with changing attitudes among governments.

Many companies already have sustainability units that help formulate biodiversity strategies for them. Stephenson and Carbone, 2021, have developed guidance on how to do this covering four critical stages from understanding of a business' impact on nature; prioritising species, habitats and ecosystems for a company; developing a vision, goals and objectives and selecting appropriate strategies and activities; and measuring and reporting implementation of the strategies. Mitigation of species extinction should be part of such biodiversity strategies, and an appropriate objective associated with extinction mitigation should be developed in line with the analysis and prioritisation of what species or threat a business aims to target.

Once that is clear, strategies to achieve the extinction mitigation goal or objective must then be developed. Arlidge and others (2018)'s mitigation hierarchy for biodiversity conservation could be considered in the process of developing extinction mitigation strategies. The hierarchy has four elements: avoiding negative action (in this case these would be actions that increase threat); minimising impact (if threats cannot be eliminated); remediating; and lastly offsetting in that order. Adopting such an approach would lead to clear objectives particularly on actions related to the business' direct actions. In addition to these, business should also add other actions that they take to support direct reduction of threats along their value chain, corporate donations to organisations delivering on specific extinction mitigation. All these can be captured in real terms as species extinction mitigation expenditure similar to a biodiversity expenditure. This would be loosely defined as "any expenditure whose purpose is to have a positive impact or to reduce or eliminate" threats to species at risk of extinction (Seidl et al., 2021: 532). In this way, business can move from ambition to clear contribution to species extinction mitigation that can be accounted for and reported in real terms. Extinction mitigation must now move from ambition to reality.

Conclusion

The state of the extinction crisis is now established, and business must be engaged and actively seek to reverse it together with the biodiversity and climate crises (IPBES, 2019). It makes business sense for this to be done as a responsible moral, just and vital contribution to society and the future. There is a dire need for business to show in real terms investments against biodiversity extinctions. Using the IUCN threat system makes sense as it is global and scalable. It can be adapted to suit the objective of business entity from a small business to a large global corporation in any industry. Its advantage is that it directs actions towards specific targeted threat reduction. Other actions that may positively contribute to increments in species populations should be added to those aimed at reducing threat. The mitigation hierarchy can be adopted as an approach for these extinction mitigations. With such clarity of what is being done, businesses can then move towards calculating and reporting in real terms their investments against species extinction.

References

Arlidge, W. N. S., Bull, J. W., Addison, P. F. E. *et al.* (2018). A global mitigation hierarchy for nature conservation. *BioScience* **68**(5), 336–347.

Balmford, A., et al. (2002). Economic reasons for conserving wild nature. *Science* **297**. 9 August 2002, 950–953. 10.1126/science.1073947

Barnosky, A., Matzke, N., Tomiya, S. *et al.* (2011) Has the Earth's sixth mass extinction already arrived?. *Nature* **471**, 51–57.

BirdLife International (2018) *State of the World's Birds: Taking the Pulse of the Planet.* Cambridge: BirdLife International.

Carpenter, K. E., Abrar, M., Aeby, G. *et al.* (2008) One-third of reef-building corals face elevated extinction risk from climate change and local impacts. *Science* **321** (5888), 560–563.

Daniels, S. R., Bittencourt-Silva, G. B., Muianga, V., Bayliss, J. (2020) Phylogenetics of the freshwater crab (*Potamonautes* MacLeay, 1838) fauna from 'sky islands' in Mozambique with the description of a new species (Brachyura: Potamoidea: Potamonautidae). *European Journal of Taxonomy* 716: 1–23.

Dasgupta, P. (2021) *The Economics of Biodiversity: The Dasgupta Review.* Abridged Version. London: HM Treasury.

Davis, A. P., Chadburn, H., Moat, J. J. et al. (2019) High extinction risk for wild coffee species and implications for coffee sector sustainability. *Science Advances* **5**: eaav3473.

Dobson, A. P., Pimm, S. L., Hannah, L. et al. (2020). Ecology and economics for pandemic prevention. *Science* **369** (6502): 379–381.

Estes, J. A., Terbogh, J., Brashares, J. S. et al. (2011) Trophic downgrading of planet earth. *Science* **333**: 301–306.

Garner, T. W., Schmidt, B. R., Martel, A. et al. (2016). Mitigating amphibian chytridiomycoses in nature. *Philosophical Transactions of the Royal Society of London. Series B, Biological Sciences* **371**(1709): 20160207.

Grasso, M. (2019) Oily politics: A critical assessment of the oil and gas industry's contribution to climate change. *Energy Research and Social Science* 50: 106–115.

IPBES. (2019). Summary for policymakers of the global assessment report on biodiversity and ecosystem services of the Intergovernmental Science-Policy Platform on Biodiversity and Ecosystem Services. Díaz S., Settele J., Brondízio E. S., Ngo H. T., Guèze M., Agard J., ... Zayas C. N., (Eds.). Bonn, Germany: IPBES Secretariat.

Jones, K. E., Patel, N. G., Levy, M. A. et al. (2008). Global trends in emerging infectious diseases. *Nature* **451**(7181): 990–993.

Le Roux, J. L., Hui, C., Castillo, M. L. et al. (2019) Recent Anthropogenic Plant Extinctions Differ in Biodiversity Hotspots and Coldspots, *Current Biology* **29**(17): 2912–2918.e2.

Myers, N. R., Mittermeier, R. A., Mittermeier, C. G. et al. (2000) Biodiversity hotspots for conservation priorities. *Nature* **403**: 853–858.

Pimm, S. L., Russel, J., Gittleman, J. L., T. M. Brooks. (1995). The future of biodiversity. *Science* **269**: 347–350.

Pimm, S. L, and John, H. (1998) Planning for Biodiversity. *Science,* **279**(5359): 2068–2069, American Association for the Advancement of Science, http://www.jstor.org/stable/2896262.

PRI (2021) *Investor action on biodiversity: discussion paper.* London. Available at https://www.unpri.org/download?ac=11357

Purvis, A., and Hector, A. (2000) Getting the measure of biodiversity. *Nature* **405**: 212–219.

Ripple, W. J., Wolf, C., Newsome, T. M. et al (2017) Vertebrate species extinction risk. *Proceedings of the National Academy of Sciences* **114**(40): 10678–10683.

Rodrigues, A. S., Pilgrim, J. D., Lamoreux, J. F. et al. (2006). The value of the IUCN Red List for conservation. *Trends in Ecology & Evolution* **21**(2): 71–76.

Rojas-Downing, M. M., Nejadhashemi, A. P., Harrigan, T. and Woznicki, S. A. (2017) Climate change and livestock: Impacts, adaptation, and mitigation. *Climate Risk Management* **16**: 145–163.

Salafsky, N., Salzer, D., Stattersfield, A. J. et al. (2008). A standard lexicon for biodiversity conservation: Unified classifications of threats and actions. *Conservation Biology* **22**(4): 897–911.

Seidl, A., Mulungu, K., Arlaud, M. et al. (2020) Finance for nature: A global estimate of public biodiversity investments. *Ecosystem Services* **46**: 101216.

Sodhi, N. S., Brook, B. W., Bradshaw, C. J. A. (2009). Causes and consequences of species extinctions in *The Princeton Guide to Ecology,* ed. S. A. Levin. Princeton, NJ: Princeton University Press, 514–520.

Stephenson, P. J., Carbone, G. (2021). *Guidelines for Planning and Monitoring Corporate Biodiversity Performance.* Gland, Switzerland: IUCN.

Valiente-Banuet A., Aizen, M. A., Alcantara, J. M. et al. (2015) Beyond species loss: the extinction of ecological interactions in a changing world. *Functional Ecology* **29**: 299–307.

Wake, D. B., Vredenburg, V. T. (2008) Are we in the midst of the sixth mass extinction? A view from the world of amphibians. *Proceedings of the National Academy of Sciences* **105**: 11466–11473.

WWF International (2021) *The World's Forgotten Fishes.* Gland, Switzerland.

4

BUSINESS FOR NATURE

How Businesses Can Save Species and Preserve Biodiversity

Eva Zabey and Carmen Thissen

Introduction

Nature is at a tipping point. More than 1 million species are threatened by extinction, 75% the world's land and 66% of the marine environment is significantly altered by humans, and global temperatures are expected to rise between 2.6°C and 3.9°C (IPBES, 2019). The natural materials and ecosystems that power businesses, underpin economies and support healthy societies are under massive strain. The science is clear – the nature crisis must be tackled within this decade if we are to build a thriving future.

Destructive business practices and an economic and financial system that prioritizes efficiency have in part been responsible for intense degradation of nature and the extinction of many species. A 2016 study showed that agricultural practices threaten 5,407 species, and unsustainable logging harms more than 4,000 forest-dwelling species. This will continue unless the business community does its part to halt and reverse nature and biodiversity loss throughout this decade, giving all parts of society the chance to become more resilient and to thrive within, not beyond, nature's limits. While focus for many companies has been on climate impacts, it is critical that we open the conversation to include nature and biodiversity, and recognize that climate action alone is insufficient to tackle the crisis happening in nature. We must simultaneously address the other drivers of nature loss including land and sea use change, resource exploitation, pollution and invasive species.

The *Dasgupta Review*, published in early 2021, emphasizes the need for transformational change and the acceptance of the "simple truth" that economies exist within and are dependent upon the natural world. Businesses have a critical role to play in reversing nature loss, protecting biodiversity and preserving species, and business action is about more than responsibility – there are real and

DOI: 10.4324/9781003045557-7

material risks associated with nature's decline. Businesses depend on a healthy planet to provide a stable operating environment, customers and workforces, and the natural resources necessary for production – food, fibre, water, minerals, building materials and more. Nature also provides ecosystem services worth at least US$125 trillion/year globally which businesses benefit from at no cost, for example through waste decomposition, flood control, pollination of crops, water purification, carbon sequestration and climate regulation. These services yield significant value; it is estimated that US$235 billion–US$577 billion (5–8%) of current global crop production is directly attributable to animal pollination and that the supply of free water reached €16 billion a year at European level for the consumption of economic sectors and households.

Losing nature means losing these services, creating extra costs and vulnerability for businesses. In fact, more than half of the world's GDP – an estimated US$44 trillion of economic value generation – is moderately or highly dependent on nature and its services, and between 1997 and 2011, land use change alone generated an economic loss of between US$4.3 and 20.2 trillion/year. WWF estimates that the unprecedented loss of ecosystem services, for example through coastal erosion and the decline of natural renewable resources such as fisheries and forests, could cost our global economy as much as US$10 trillion by 2050.

The impacts of nature loss are already becoming more than just financial projections and are showing up on business balance sheets. Just ask US utility firm PG&E, which accumulated billions of dollars in liabilities from wildfires in California in 2019. Physical risks present themselves to companies in the form of damage to facilities, disruption of supply chains and availability of commodities. For example, 60% of coffee varieties face extinction due to disease and deforestation, threatening the very future of coffee production. Mangrove forests, which provide critical coastal protection and flood prevention during tropical storms, have lost 35% of their original littoral cover, leaving seaside operations vulnerable to damage.

Faced with the crisis of nature and biodiversity loss, businesses have an opportunity to take action by changing the way they manage and use natural resources, and creating clean jobs (as many as 395 million jobs by 2030). They can formulate specific pathways to help "bend the curve" of nature loss within the decade by halting nature's loss, working to restore what has been lost and contributing to achieving net zero emissions by mid-century through smart nature-based solutions.

However, businesses cannot address this global crisis on their own. To scale and speed up business action, leading businesses are calling on governments to work together to create a positive policy feedback loop that levels the playing field and encourages further business actions. The year 2020 was supposed to be a "Super Year" for Nature. Key negotiations were planned, and world leaders prepared to make international agreements to reverse nature loss similar to the 2015 Paris Agreement on climate change. Though many of these key negotiations for nature have been postponed, business ambition for nature remains high, and the COVID-19 pandemic has highlighted the interconnectedness of our global

CREATING A **POSITIVE FEEDBACK** LOOP

POLICY
AMBITION

BUSINESS
ACTION

TRANSFORMED ECONOMY
THAT VALUES NATURE

BUSINESS
FOR NATURE

FIGURE 4.1   Creating a positive business policy feedback loop.
Adapted from ambitionloop.org.

systems – the nature, climate, human health and social inequality crises cannot be addressed in isolation (Figure 4.1).

Business for Nature

The Business for Nature (BfN) coalition launched in July 2019 to champion radical collaboration to unite the vast network of business initiatives for nature, with the goal of demonstrating credible business leadership on nature and amplifying a powerful leading business voice calling for governments to adopt policies now to reverse nature loss in this decade. The BfN coalition's model was based on We Mean Business, who brought the voice of business together in the run-up to the 2015 Paris Climate Agreement.

The BfN coalition is comprised of 60 partner organizations, a Strategic Advisory Group and a core secretariat. Partners include international actors such as the World Economic Forum, the World Business Council for Sustainable Development, the International Chamber of Commerce, WWF, the International Union for Conservation of Nature and the Nature Conservancy, as well as national and regional organizations such as the Japan Business Initiative for Biodiversity and the Brazilian Business Council for Sustainable Development (CEBDS).

BfN is the only global coalition unifying the leading business voice to give policymakers the courage and comfort to make ambitious agreements on nature. This is achieved by encouraging businesses around the world, from all sectors and of all sizes, to commit and act to reverse nature loss, and advocate for greater policy ambition. The following sections provide a current snapshot of business action and advocacy for nature and biodiversity, following the high-level steps outlined on the Business for Nature website (Figure 4.2).

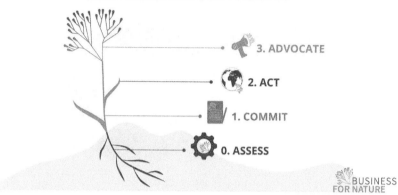

BECOMING NATURE-POSITIVE

3. ADVOCATE

2. ACT

1. COMMIT

0. ASSESS

BUSINESS
FOR NATURE

FIGURE 4.2 This figure represents Business for Nature's iterative and high-level steps for companies as they strive to become nature-positive. To succeed in this journey, companies can start by conducting an assessment of their impacts and dependencies on nature, which forms the roots and support for ambitious commitments and resulting actions. Companies can build on these commitments and actions by advocating for ambitious nature policies, which encourage a nature-positive future by creating a level playing field and stable operating environment for business.

Assess

To set informed commitments and take decisive action that is grounded in a deep understanding of a company's environmental and ecological footprint, many leading businesses have chosen to measure their impacts and dependencies on nature, or "natural capital." For an in-depth look at how companies are valuing natural capital, please see the chapter from the Natural Capital Coalition by Gough, Chapter XX, and the Natural Capital Protocol. BfN encourages companies to conduct comprehensive assessments of their impacts, dependencies and risks related to nature loss and to prioritize commitments and actions that will tackle their most material impacts and dependencies, ensuring that action in one area does not negatively impact any of the other Sustainable Development Goals (SDGs). One often-cited example of a corporate natural capital assessment is Kering's development of an Environmental Profit and Loss (EP&L) framework for measuring, monetizing and communicating about their impacts on nature.

Commit

Setting commitments is a critical step companies may take towards tackling nature loss. BfN knows of at least 530 businesses that have already made commitments to help reverse nature loss by halting deforestation, reducing plastic production, replenishing water sources, protecting oceans, converting to sustainable agricultural practices and more, across over ten platforms. These platforms can be international, regional or sectoral and include:

- International: The New York Forest Declaration aims to end deforestation by 2030 and is endorsed by over 50 of the world's biggest companies.
- Regional: Thirteen companies have committed to reversing nature loss through the Brazilian Business Commitment on Biodiversity.
- Sectoral: The Fashion Pact unites over 60 fashion and textile brands to commit in three areas: stopping global warming, restoring biodiversity and protecting the oceans.
- Cross-cutting: Companies participating in Act4Nature International have signed ten common commitments as well as Specific, Measurable, Attainable, Relevant and Time-bound (SMART) individual commitments at CEO level.

In addition to the business commitments above, companies are setting ambitious climate targets through BfN's partner We Mean Business and working closely with the Science Based Targets Network (SBTN) to prepare to set informed targets around the interrelated systems of biodiversity, land, freshwater and oceans. According to SBTN, "We must adhere to the limits of all Earth's systems as set out by science… This will help them go from doing 'a little better' to doing 'at least enough' to stay within these limits."

Act

For transformational change to occur, businesses must do more than commit to change – they must act in real and meaningful ways to reduce their negative impact on the planet. Companies can take action through specific projects, across their operations, through their supply chains or collaboratively within their sector. They can tackle different drivers of nature loss, on land or at sea, in ways that, for example:

- Reduce their negative impact on nature;
- Invest in protecting and restoring nature;
- Innovate and scale up products and technologies with a lower impact.

Together with PwC and the Cambridge Institute for Sustainability Leadership, BfN has analysed corporate nature action case studies and has identified over 1,200 companies acting for nature. This estimate is based on a review of case studies either collected in databases developed by other organizations, or actions submitted directly to BfN. Databases include the Convention on Biological Diversity's Business and Biodiversity case study library, NaturalCapital.community Solutions from MVO Nederland and the Water Action Hub from UN Global Compact.

TABLE 4.1 Innovative business actions to tackle nature loss

Natura & Co's commitment to life in Brazil	*Danone's investment in regenerative agriculture*	*SUEZ's ecologically inspired approach to wastewater treatment in China*
Cosmetics-giant Natura & Co has long been a leader in climate and biodiversity action. Moving forward, they are expanding Amazon protection across their operations to reach zero deforestation by 2025 and to deliver on the 1.5° climate goal ahead of the UN commitment, making gains on packaging and formula circularity, and setting Science Based Targets for biodiversity.	Food-products company Danone is developing and implanting better agricultural practices which bolster soil biodiversity and support farmers. Danone utilizes strategies such as crop rotation, tilling reduction and limited chemical use and supports farmers in these efforts through the development of long-term relationships, and access to training, equipment and financing, for example through their Livelihoods Fund.	Utility company SUEZ is tackling the issue of micropollutants by installing artificial wetlands, "Zone Libellule" (Dragonfly Zone), downstream of wastewater treatment plants. These wetlands support critical biodiversity and help remove micropollutants that remain following traditional treatment. The largest industrial Zone Libellule opened in China in 2018.

Many companies are finding strength in collaboration and are increasingly working together to facilitate knowledge sharing and collective action. Example partnerships include the One Planet Business for Biodiversity coalition, which brings together over 20 companies driving transformative change in regenerative agriculture, and the Value Balancing Alliance, a collaboration between companies working to create a standard for monetizing and disclosing impacts.

We need to scale and speed up action for nature including by making it front and centre in business decision-making. This must happen across all sectors to move forward towards the Convention on Biological Diversity's 2050 Vision of Living in Harmony with Nature, and the private sector must lead this transformation to trigger a global sustainable business movement.

Advocate

While the current level of business action is promising, voluntary action on its own is not enough and businesses need political leadership. Policies must be ambitious and transformative to deliver the change the science tells us is necessary and create a level playing field so that all businesses are required to do their part to protect, restore and safeguard nature for future generations. By aligning policy frameworks and using economic and financial systems to drive this change,

WE ARE CALLING FOR POLICIES TO **ACCELERATE** BUSINESS **ACTION**

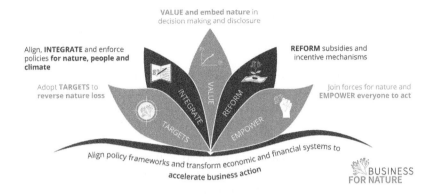

FIGURE 4.3   Business for Nature's five policy recommendations.

governments can make a substantial difference in nature protection and help accelerate business action around the world.

BfN led an intensive and effective consultation on the development of high-level policy recommendations, to which over 200 businesses contributed. The resulting recommendations provide a road map for the types of policies governments can and should adopt (Figure 4.3).

Business for Nature's five recommendations for policymakers:

1. **Adopt targets to reverse nature loss: Provide direction and ambition.** Businesses need long-term certainty to invest in changing business models. Concrete evidence-based targets informed by science are needed to provide clear direction and ambition for business action to reverse nature loss by 2030. These targets should be relevant and translatable from the global to the local level. Policy action is required to:

   a   Publicly recognize the planetary emergency and commit to both reversing nature loss by 2030 and keeping global warming below 1.5 degrees Celsius.

   b   Adopt global targets and indicators informed by science to reverse the loss of nature and provide direction for business actions, including to (a) significantly reduce production and consumption footprints; (b) halt and reverse the loss of habitat and species and restore their resilience; (c) conserve ecosystem services; and (d) protect natural areas appropriately respecting the rights, practices and wishes of indigenous peoples and local communities.

   c   Adopt strong implementation and ratchet mechanisms informed by science to increase action and ambition in the Post-2020 Global Biodiversity Framework of the Convention on Biological Diversity (CBD).

2. **Align, integrate and enforce policies for nature, people and climate: Ensure coherence.** Climate change, nature loss and social inequality need to be solved together to achieve a just transition. Policy coherence and efficient implementation and enforcement at global, national and local levels are needed to create a level playing field that supports business action. Policy action is required to:

   a   Bring the UN Framework Convention on Climate Change (UNFCCC), the Convention on Biological Diversity (CBD) and the UN Convention to Combat Desertification (UNCCD) into alignment ahead of Rio +30 in coherence with the SDGs and the 2030 Agenda for Sustainable Development.

   b   Pursue an integrated approach to Nationally Determined Contributions (NDCs), National Biodiversity Strategies and Action Plans (NBSAPs) and National Action Programmes (NAPs) to combat desertification that recognizes the synergies, co-benefits and trade-offs to enable a just transition.

   c   Mainstream nature into all relevant policies, ministries and finance regulators' mandates, addressing the major direct threats to nature identified by the Intergovernmental Science-Policy Platform on Biodiversity and Ecosystem Services (IPBES) (i.e. land/sea use change, direct exploitation of organisms, climate change, pollution, overexploitation and invasive species), and stimulating investment and job creation.

   d   Ensure the adoption and effective enforcement of environmental laws and standards, including by providing capacity building to countries worldwide.

3. **Value and embed nature in decision-making and disclosure: Go beyond short-term profit and GDP.** The value of nature for people and the economy needs to be visible and considered in decision-making. The valuation may be qualitative, quantitative or monetary, to reflect the importance, value and utility of natural capital, recognizing that nature's intrinsic value cannot be fully captured in economic terms. Policy action is required to:

   a   Develop and implement frameworks to integrate the value of nature in decision-making and global market mechanisms, including pricing the use of natural resources and ecosystem services, and penalizing the destruction of nature, while recognizing that the value of nature can never be fully quantified.

   b   Produce adequate national metrics such as a natural capital index or gross ecosystem product (GEP) to better enable countries to go beyond GDP and track progress on the SDGs by assessing and accounting for their impacts and dependencies on nature.

   c   Support and require business to internalize environmental externalities and integrate their impact and dependencies on nature in decision-making, risk management, supply chain management and external disclosure. This will require (a) standardizing metrics, tools and guidance to undertake robust corporate natural capital assessments and accounting; (b) promoting guidance on nature-related financial disclosures; and (c) providing contextual natural capital data from national statistical systems.

4. **Reform subsidies and incentive mechanisms: Finance a just transformation.** The transformative change needed to reverse nature loss; climate change and inequality cannot be achieved without proper incentives and financial mechanisms. A systemic change is required in subsidies and incentives to reward business leadership to design innovative, circular and profitable business models that deliver positive long-term outcomes on nature. Policy action is required to:

   a   Review, disclose and shift away from direct and indirect subsidies and tax policies that incentivize the degradation and overexploitation of nature and redirect them towards sustainable use, resilience, restoration and circularity.

   b   Adopt mechanisms and quantifiable indicators to value ecosystem services delivery and reward sustainable natural resources management.

   c   Integrate nature and nature-based solutions into public procurement policies and infrastructure development guidelines and promote net gain requirements with adherence to the mitigation hierarchy for all major development sectors.

   d   Promote the rapid development and implementation of innovative financial solutions such as green financing, large public funds and blended finance schemes to finance nature including small- and large-scale nature-based solutions.

5. **Join forces for nature and empower everyone to act: Engage, enable and collaborate.** Transformative change requires that all public, private and civil society actors work together to deliver on commitments for nature and to implement solutions. Governments play an important role in empowering society to collaborate and act for nature. Policy action is required to:

   a   Integrate business commitments and sectoral plans on nature in national commitments.

   b   Conduct well-informed spatial planning and Strategic Environmental Assessments, incorporating important natural areas, including Key Biodiversity Areas, and inform national and sub-national development plans with specific consideration for the needs of vulnerable groups and local communities.

   c   Implement jurisdictional and landscape approaches through innovative multi-stakeholder collaboration models.

d   Promote supply chain and/or sectoral collaboration mechanisms such as multi-stakeholder and multi-sectoral platforms and joint action plans, in particular for high-impact sectors.

In addition to these policy recommendations, more than 700 companies have called for ambitious government policies through the Call to Action, "Nature is Everyone's Business," which was released at the same time as the 75th UN General Assembly declaration's call for multilateral engagement to protect our planet and in the run-up to the UN Biodiversity Summit. Representing 54 countries, from all sectors and over $4.3 trillion USD in combined annual revenue, these companies made the following appeal:

Nature is everyone's business
Healthy societies, resilient economies and thriving businesses rely on nature.
   Governments must adopt policies now to reverse nature loss in this decade.
   Together let's protect, restore and sustainably use our natural resources.

Signatories to the Call to Action include Walmart, Citigroup, Microsoft, JD.com, Hitachi, IKEA, Unilever, AXA, Mahindra Group and H&M. The Call to Action has the backing of more than 30 NGOs and international organizations and aligns with other joint calls across society letting political leaders know that a healthy, nature-positive world remains a priority for all of us. See the public statements ahead of the UN Biodiversity Summit and the G20.

   Through these advocacy efforts, BfN aims to give policymakers the courage and comfort to adopt an ambitious Post-2020 Global Biodiversity Framework that sets the world on track to reverse nature loss by 2030. By providing a unified business voice, businesses can help influence policies that promote sustainable growth, halt the decline of biodiversity and stop climate change.

   As well as galvanizing a large group of businesses calling for stronger nature policies, BfN works directly with leading businesses who can directly and indirectly influence governments.

   For example:

-   Senior representatives from Gucci, H&M, Yara, Rabobank and COFCO International, and many more in the audience, convened at the World Economic Forum's annual meeting in Davos, Switzerland, to champion BfN's policy recommendations (listed above).
-   Companies joined BfN at the Convention on Biological Diversity's second Open-Ended Working Group in Rome. Alongside business representatives, BfN's Executive Director Eva Zabey delivered two statements (available here and here) contributing to the zero draft of the Post-2020 Framework, and championing the need for policymakers to "create a level playing field

and stable operating environment for business," "unlock further business opportunities and innovation, such as accelerating the uptake of nature-based solutions," and "transform our economic and financial systems in a way that places nature at the heart of global decision-making." BfN also called for a more ambitious Post-2020 Framework, stating that the then draft did not meet the urgency of the crisis.

- Corporate leaders demonstrated the growing bridges between business leaders and policymakers, at "Building Business Resilience," an event hosted by BfN, the World Economic Forum, the World Business Council for Sustainable Development, the International Chamber of Commerce, the United Nations Global Compact and the International Union for Conservation of Nature. Speakers included both business and government representatives, such as Elizabeth Maruma Mrema, Executive Secretary of the Convention Biological Diversity, and Emmanuel Faber, CEO of Danone. Over 2,200 participants were online, of which over half were from business.

- Business came out in full force to push the nature agenda around the United Nations General Assembly and UN Summit on Biodiversity in September 2020. On the same day as the UN General Assembly adopted its 75th Declaration to protect nature, hundreds of companies urged governments to adopt policies to reverse nature loss in this decade. CEOs from AXA and Sintesa spoke at the Summit, highlighting the need for business and governments to work together. Danone and BfN both came out in support of the Leaders' Pledge for Nature, which at the time included commitments by over 75 governments to reverse nature loss by 2030.

- Over 100 companies headquartered across 31 countries gave inputs and helped to shape BfN's position on the zero draft of the Convention on Biological Diversity's Post-2020 Framework. This position was shared directly with Parties.

Nature Is Everyone's Business – a Post-2020 Global Biodiversity Framework to Accelerate Action

The fifteenth meeting of the Conference of the Parties to the Convention on Biological Diversity (CBD COP15) represents a significant moment to chart an ambitious path forward to address the crisis happening in nature. Governments have the responsibility to adopt a Post-2020 Global Biodiversity Framework (GBF) that includes a clear and concise road map on how the world will protect, restore and sustainably use our natural resources.

Businesses need to make a positive contribution in designing and implementing the GBF as its objectives cannot be achieved without the sector's meaningful and constructive engagement. They play a critical role beyond committing and acting within their direct sphere of influence. It is no longer enough for businesses to be "less bad" – they must actively reverse the damage which destructive practices have caused. Business is a source of investment, a driver of innovation and technological development and a key engine of economic prosperity and employment. The GBF should promote sectoral collaboration across and within sectors, as well as encourage Parties to recognize and reward companies that protect or enhance biodiversity and stop harmful practices.

Conclusion

Forward-thinking businesses are starting to change the way they operate, but this is still the exception rather than the norm. Businesses are ready to engage with policymakers in 2021 and beyond, and business and political leadership is needed now to:

- transform our economic and financial systems in a way that places nature at the heart of global decision-making;
- create a level playing field and stable operating environment for business; and
- unlock further business opportunities and innovation, such as accelerating the uptake of nature-based solutions.

Leading companies are starting to realize that financial performance is irrelevant on a dead planet and are calling on governments to ensure that collectively we can "build back (or forward) better" to create healthy societies, resilient economies and thriving businesses.

Case study: Unilever

> The science on nature loss is terrifying. Nature underpins everything on this planet. An ambitious post-2020 Global Biodiversity Framework that brings transformative change to our relationship with our planet is absolutely critical. Business should be at the fore of calling for this change.–
>
> Alan Jope, CEO

Unilever, one of the world's largest consumer goods companies, is committing, acting and advocating for nature.

Commit

Unilever has made commitments to reversing nature loss across a host of platforms, including CSA100, the New Plastics Global Economy Commitment and the CEO Water Mandate. Unilever's national branches are also committing through regional platforms – Unilever UK is part of the Courtauld Commitment, and Unilever France has signed up to the French initiative Act4Nature. In addition to these commitments, eight of Unilever's brands – including

---

Seventh Generation, Pukka Herbs and Ben & Jerry's – are certified B Corps, meaning that they're *legally required* to incorporate the environment in decision-making. Unilever has also set its own commitments:

- Net zero emissions for all products by 2039.
- A deforestation-free supply chain by 2023.
- Empowering a new generation of farmers and smallholders to protect and regenerate their environment.
- A new Regenerative Agriculture Code for all suppliers.
- Water stewardship programmes to 100 locations in water-stressed areas by 2030.
- Investing €1 billion in a new Climate & Nature Fund, which will be used by Unilever's brands over the next ten years to take meaningful and decisive action.

Act

To put these commitments into action, Unilever is contributing to reversing nature loss by reducing environmental impact by half by 2030. Compared to 2008 levels, Unilever is drawing down impacts related to production – CO_2 emissions have been cut by 65%, water use by 47% and waste generation by 96%. Sixty-two per cent of agricultural raw materials were sustainably sourced in 2019, with the goal of 100% by 2020. Unilever's suppliers are also acting in concerted ways to support and replenish biodiversity, for example by protecting migration routes, creating habitat and establishing breeding grounds for birds, bats and pollinators, and turning to natural predators – rather than chemicals – for pest management. During summer 2020, Unilever released their €1 billion Climate & Nature Fund. This fund will be used over the next ten years to protect and regenerate nature, for example through projects related to reforestation, protection of wildlife, and restoration and protection of lands and waters.

These environmental actions are part of Unilever's Sustainable Living Plan, which also includes strategies for improving human health and well-being through hygiene, health and nutrition programmes, and enhancing livelihoods through workplace fairness, inclusive business and opportunities for women.

Advocate

Unilever is a strong advocate for ambitious nature policies. Alongside more than 700 companies with combined revenue of US$ 4.3 trillion including Walmart, Citigroup, Microsoft, JD.com, Hitachi, IKEA, AXA, Mahindra Group and H&M Group, Unilever is urging governments to adopt policies now to reverse nature loss in this decade. Unilever's CEO, Alan Jope, has spoken out in support of ambitious policies, at events such as Building Business Resilience in June 2020, and around the UN Summit on Biodiversity in September 2020.

References

Dasgupta, P. (2021), *The Economics of Biodiversity: The Dasgupta Review*, UK Government Report: https://www.gov.uk/government/publications/final-report-the-economics-of-biodiversity-the-dasgupta-review

Intergovernmental science-policy platform on biodiversity and ecosystem services - IPBES, 2019. *Intergovernmental science-policy platform on biodiversity and ecosystem services.* [online] *IPBES*, Available at: http://bit.ly/IPBESReport [Accessed 16 Jul. 21].

5

HEAL REWILDING

A Landowning Model for Species Recovery

Jan Stannard, Hannah Needham and Shân M. Millie

Introduction

What role can civic activism play in offering financial markets new options for a meaningful role in species protection? Heal is a young UK-based social enterprise offering a species recovery solution – rewilding – organised in an innovative way: it is the first charity in Europe, possibly the world, dedicated to being a rewilding **landowner**, with a business model built on financially sustainable operations that includes engaging with the financial markets in new ways.

In shaping Heal as an organisation, the founders were acutely aware of the acute sense of anxiety and powerlessness amongst individuals around the climate emergency and biodiversity loss. In the UK, government targets are 30 years away. Activism by Greta Thunberg, the school climate strikers and Extinction Rebellion have intensified feelings of helplessness – people are making personal changes but know those are not enough. The Heal team saw that a direct and tangible involvement in practical action to rewild land would give them a sense of hope and optimism, a feeling that they are *doing* something collectively at a scale they cannot achieve as individuals.

But we also know that collective efforts from within civic society, however well-organised and passionate, will not be enough to meet the urgent and enormous challenges of stemming and reversing biodiversity loss. Our insight is that financial market capital is essential: the job of shaping 'offers' that are attractive to these key players is a key founding focus of Heal. A significant driver in our funding approach, alongside crowd-funding, is to find and develop (new) ways to engage with financial institutions that combine well-known vehicles like donation and sponsorship with emerging ones coming out of ideas of Natural Capital.

Although we are a young charity, we believe we have touched a 'collective nerve' indicative of an accelerating appreciation and understanding of the value

DOI: 10.4324/9781003045557-8

of nature, which has been amplified further by the COVID pandemic. What were the innovative ways we went about stimulating and channelling this into specific support for Heal?

Here, we share what we believe to be this and other key elements of our story so far in the hope that our progress to date (and in the future) stands as a useful, live case study of working with and through financial markets to deliver a meaningful chance for nature – and human – recovery in the 2020s. This piece has five sections:

- Why rewilding?
- Why do we need to be a landowner?
- The Heal concept (1) Youth and Diversity (2) Site location and function (3) Finance and business model (4) Our metrics: (a) human impacts and wellness (b) biodiversity (c) carbon capture
- Our progress
- Conclusion

Why Rewilding?

Heal[1] is an organisation born of ecological and climate crises that offers a low-input, nature-based resolution to species declines: rewilding.

The state of nature in the UK is amongst the worst on the planet, ranking 189th of 218 countries analysed for biodiversity intactness.[2] Biodiversity loss in the UK is continuing at a shocking rate – 41 percent of species have declined since 1970[3] and now, in 2020, nearly a thousand species are threatened with extinction.[4] Among the worst hit species are insects, the backbone of functioning ecosystems, with populations declining 75 percent over the last 27 years.[5] These declines are a result of the widespread destruction of habitats over centuries, intensifying over the last 50 years, exacerbated by excess atmospheric nitrogen, climate change and a counterintuitive farming subsidy system which rewards intensive, environmentally destructive practices. Habitat changes include:

- More ancient woodlands lost in the 40 years than in the previous 400 years
- 13% of woodland cover, compared with the European average of 37%[6]
- 90% of wetlands lost since the start of the industrial revolution[7] in 1760 when at least a quarter of Britain was once wetlands
- Around 75% (more than a million) of Britain's ponds lost over the last hundred years[8]
- 97% of wild flower meadows replaced with grasses for livestock cropping[9]
- Reductions in soil organic carbon – a study showed that in comparison with allotments (public plots for growing flowers or vegetables), soil in arable fields had on average 32% less organic carbon and 36% lower carbon-to-nitrogen ratios and was significantly more compact.[10]

Rewilding is an approach to managing land involving the reinstatement of natural processes and, where appropriate, missing species, allowing them to shape the landscape and the habitats within, leading to the restoration of fully functioning ecosystems. Through this process of healing, species have been shown to be protected, to thrive and to reappear after long periods of absence and have been successfully reintroduced.

Rewilding has become a major focus of interest over the last 20 years; a recent study observed that 'traditional conservation has been based on stewardship [using] protectionist policies to preserve biodiversity *in situ*, characterised by high levels of management, target orientation and a static nature.[11] However, as Peter Taylor crucially notes, this approach is **not** working[12] and the question has arisen: 'How have we lost so much while we have protected so much?'.[13] Rewilding is now a new 'layer' of larger-scale land management in response to this realisation.

There is a key difference between rewilding approaches and classic conservation projects, however. Rewilding is an emergent process driven by nature. Nature does not work to goals and aims, and unexpected natural events may occur. This is a challenge given the history of funding for conservation work which is usually predicated on numbers, measures and 'successes'. The ecological aspects of rewilding projects will not have key performance indicators, stretch targets or SMART[14] objectives.

The nature-driven basis of rewilding has also fed into new hypotheses on the composition of landscape habitats. The most influential of these comes from the Dutch scientist, Frans Vera, who argues that landscapes like the English lowlands were not a continuous forest but rather wood pasture with a range of habitats, created by the actions of browsing, grazing and rootling animals like aurochs (cattle), tarpans (ponies), wild boar and deer, each acting in particular ways upon vegetation, resulting in a changing mosaic of habitats: grassland, scrub (such as hawthorn and blackthorn) and regenerating trees, along with wet and bare areas.[15] Rewilding sites now use proxies for these ancient species of 'ecosystem engineers' – cows, ancient pony breeds and pigs along with deer (Figure 5.1).

The rewilding project at the privately owned Knepp estate in Sussex, a southern English county, adopted Vera's approach, with free-roaming, full-time herbivores (see Figure 5.2). The estate has experienced a range of process effects that have supported biodiversity improvement.[16] There have been spectacular species gains:

- 19 male nightingale territories in 2019
- More lesser whitethroat and blackcaps ringed in six weeks than in the previous 30 years
- Land now a stronghold for turtle doves, with 16 singing males recorded on 1,100 acres of the southern estate in 2017, compared with three on the whole estate in 1999
- 13 species of bats

- 57 species of bird in 2018 including 22 red list species of high conservation concern and 21 amber list species of medium conservation concern
- 36 species of butterfly seen since 2005, including the largest population of Purple Emperors in the UK (388 individuals counted in 2018)
- Peregrine falcons and lesser spotted woodpeckers now breeding on site
- Doubling in soil organic carbon in rewilded areas in comparison to arable control
- More than 600 invertebrate species recorded
- Doubling of bank vole population from 2005 to 2016

Rewilding works. We believe it will deliver key environmental benefits including helping meet the UK government's stated aim to return more land – an

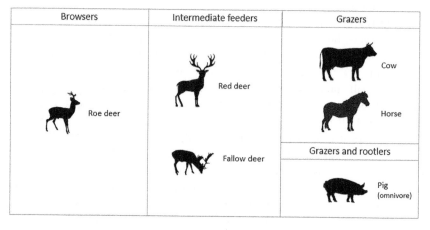

FIGURE 5.1   Different feeding styles of large herbivore/omnivore species deployed in many rewilding projects (adapted from Vera, 2002, ibid).

FIGURE 5.2   Herbivores, management intensity and area.

additional 500,000 hectares – to 'wildlife-rich habitat' in nature networks across the country.[17] Rewilding is hugely important for restoring biodiversity loss at all levels of the country's ecosystems.[18] It is also vital to deliver the UK's legally binding commitment to achieve net-zero emissions by 2050. Rewilding land draws carbon from the atmosphere, storing it in trees, vegetation and in the soil and allows for the natural regeneration of plants that lock in more carbon as they grow. Moreover, it has a significant role to play in:

- improving the health of our depleted soils
- helping land to recover from prolonged periods of intensive farming
- supporting water retention in soil and flood risk management
- contributing to clean air

Why Do We Need To Be a Landowner?

Rewilding is rapidly growing as a land management approach in the UK with, for example, 24 large-scale (>1,000 acres) English rewilding projects underway, according to Rewilding Britain.[19] However, most of these are run by private landowners without public involvement or access. Those who own the land decide how it is used, so for nature recovery to succeed, there need to be more landowners dedicated to nature's well-being. And we believe that public involvement, indeed ownership, is integral to the success of both individual projects and the system change we are working for. Heal is a way for everyone to be involved in rewilding in an urgent, practical way.

The Heal Concept

Inspired by rewilding success stories in the UK and mainland Europe, the Heal team have modelled its rewilding approach with a focus on the English lowlands. The organisation's mission aligns with the UK Government's land-use change goal for wildlife habitats. Rewilding is about far more than land use – it has become a synonym for hope. Heal will invite the public to visit their land as it rewilds, providing experiences for people from all backgrounds to connect with nature. Heal hopes to inspire its visitors to return to their communities with a determination to create more space for wildlife and make changes that will address the biodiversity and climate emergency.

The team behind Heal comes from outside the conservation sector, with backgrounds in business, finance, management consultancy, communications, marketing, technology and journalism, but all with a passion for nature and intense concern about extinctions and species declines – sometimes lifelong, sometimes newly awakened. This blend of experience, perspectives and skills made us think differently about how best to organise ourselves as a social enterprise to achieve our goals, to be a non-profit landowner funded through individual crowdfunding, corporate support and other, newer forms of financing.

We think that there are key elements that make us distinctive:

1. Youth & diversity
2. Site location and function
3. Finance and business model
4. Our metrics: (a) human impacts and wellness, (b) biodiversity, (c) carbon capture

Youth and Diversity

The Heal team is acutely aware of the legacy that will be left for the next generation. Young people are becoming increasingly engaged in climate change activism, primed by David Attenborough documentaries and social media narratives. To embed this energy, enthusiasm and perspective, we created Heal Future, a network for the under 30s, led by a youth advisory panel who provide input to the Heal Trustee Board.

Just as greater biodiversity leads to better ecosystem health, Heal understands that diversity of cultures and ideas leads to better organisation function and stronger outcomes. Therefore, Heal took significant steps to ensure that its youth panel is representative of varying ages (15–26), backgrounds and ethnicities and is made up of individuals with different professions, skills and interests. The panel members are passionate about making Heal's rewilding work accessible to all in society, particularly ethnic minorities, young people and low-income families.

IMAGE 5.1 Members of the Heal Future Panel.

Site Location and Function

Heal's founding vision is to create a strategic chain of rewilded landholdings across the UK, which also support climate change mitigation and well-being through public access to nature. All the rewilding activity will be underpinned by scientific research, and Heal is already developing links with academics at the Universities of Sussex, Sheffield and Exeter. Education is also a primary driver for the general public and for professionals.

The Heal approach is to acquire landholdings of 200 hectares or more in locations which can act either as wildlife 'reservoirs' linking out through surrounding land or as stepping stones close to existing/planned landscape-scale areas for nature recovery, restoration or conservation (see Figure 5.3).

Some parts of Heal's land will remain permanently closed except to staff and volunteers to give wildlife the seclusion it needs, but the rest will be accessible for visitors to explore and enjoy.

Regenerating vegetation and trees on Heal sites will sequester increasing amounts of carbon.[20] Sites not only protect natural capital resources but also build them, including improved water retention and better soil health and support for pollinators. As well as Heal generating revenues to make sites self-supporting, the ecotourism growth will bring economic benefit to communities, creating new jobs and attracting money into a locality. From the outset, experts and trained volunteers will establish biodiversity baselines across animal groups (amphibians, birds, fish, invertebrates, mammals, and reptiles) and plant groups, along with soil metrics. As the project progresses, changes, gains and losses in biodiversity and soil health will be monitored as indicators of how well the ecosystem is functioning.

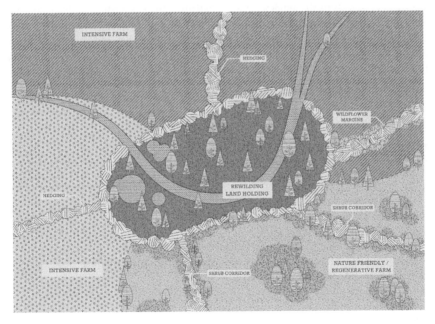

FIGURE 5.3 Heal site acts as a wildlife reservoir with blue and green corridors into the surrounding land.

The site model comprises:

- Rewilding land area, with around half publicly accessible
- Large animal ecosystem engineers 'managing' the site all year round
- A large indoor space for conferences
- Smaller buildings for classrooms
- Café for lunches and teas
- Shop
- Accommodation in buildings and a campsite
- Wild camping field for visitors and volunteers
- Sustainable energy use
- Allotments (food growing areas) for use by the project and also the local community
- A demonstration urban wildlife garden

Finance and Business Model

As noted, Heal is the first charity in Europe, possibly the world, dedicated to being a rewilding **landowner**, with a business model built on financially sustainable operations that includes engaging with the financial markets in new ways. Crowdfunding is very important to us: our innovative 3×3 scheme (see below) offers a brand-new way for public support that translates into a more personal 'ownership' of specific bits of land, as well as the rewilding site as a whole. Alongside this, from the outset, we are focusing efforts on finding and developing (new) ways to engage with financial institutions that include well-known vehicles like donation and sponsorship with emerging ones coming out of ideas of Natural Capital. We asked ourselves the question: is there something that sits between donation and sponsorship, a returns-based instrument, for example, that is attractive to patient (green) capital?

Site Acquisition

TABLE 5.1 Sources of funding for site acquisition

Loans: commercial; patient capital
Corporate support and sponsorship
Biodiversity credits (in certain circumstances)
Carbon offsetting
Natural capital finance, as systems and values become developed
UK government land-use funding and other special government funding
National crowdfunding donations – Heal 3×3
Wealthy supporter donations
Friends of Heal scheme
Grants
Legacies

Heal 3×3

Heal 3×3 is our unique crowdfunding (donating) scheme linking a £20 donation to the sponsorship of a specific 3m × 3m square of land, using the what3words system. Once Heal land is acquired, donors can be told exactly where their Heal 3×3 square is by searching for its three words in the what3words app or at what-3words.com. They then have the option of visiting the Heal rewilding site they have helped to create.

Corporate Engagement

Heal is at an early stage with corporate engagement. A London-based asset manager, TT International, has set up a new global equities fund with a remarkable founding principle – to use one-third of its fund management fee to make a direct and practical difference to climate change action and nature recovery.

Figure 5.4 shows how we're structuring potential support at the time of writing:

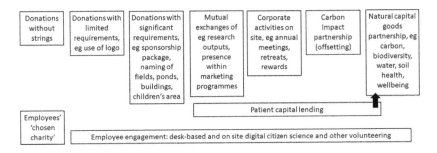

FIGURE 5.4   Heal and its partners.

Progress to date suggests that there is interest in financial institutions in evaluating Heal as a venue for sponsorship, and donations, to address their developing offset, biodiversity and employee wellness objectives; and also as a route to offer their own clients options for patient capital. As a not-for-profit able to create and deliver public goods and natural capital resources as a form of return, particularly in biodiversity net gain and carbon offsetting, Heal also hopes that newly developing creative and innovative green instruments will become a funding option. Rewilding land increases its natural capital value, fast becoming an essential component of economic systems. In economist Professor Dieter Helm's seminal book 'Green and Prosperous Land',[21] he sets out a 'blueprint for rescuing the British countryside' from an economic perspective, using 'sound mainstream economic principles like public money for public goods, polluter pays and net environmental gain'.[22] Helm makes a strategic case for the environment being at the core of an economy and describes 'underlying critical natural infrastructures [...] every bit as important as man-made infrastructure is in energy and transport'. By taking action to protect and enhance these renewables, our prosperity increases. Indeed, he says that 'economic gains from enhancing the natural infrastructure are considerable and may be greater than some of those projected for physical infrastructure'.

Site Operations

Sites will be run in perpetuity as ongoing rewilding projects. In the 'rewilding gap' before income from ecotourism has become established, education will be a key income source. The income model for ongoing site operations includes:

- Land sponsorship
- Carbon offsetting
- Accommodation – buildings and campsite
- Rental income from business units and houses
- Café
- Corporate training and meeting facility
- Education programme
- Ecotourism
- Merchandise and sponsorship
- Agri-funding
- Livestock sponsorship
- Local crowdfunding donations
- Local membership package

Our Metrics

Human Impacts and Wellness

National well-being is arguably as important as any economic concern and strongly links to healthier, happier citizens, and more productive employees. However, almost all of the UK's population is nature-deprived, a pattern repeated across developed nations. At the same time, indices for well-being in the UK, particularly mental health, are declining. One in four adults and one in ten children experience mental illness.[23]

There is a wealth of evidence linking exposure to nature to well-being.[24,25,26] Numerous studies have demonstrated that experiencing nature is associated with psychological well-being including decreases in mental distress.[27] Providing access to quiet space in nature for people is central to Heal's mission. Metrics for these are being developed and we hope will begin to answer questions including:

- what 'prescriptions' for time in nature are most effective?
- how are different genders and age groups affected?
- can people learn and apply 'nature connectedness' techniques effectively?

Biodiversity

Biodiversity metrics will include:

- species variety
- species abundance
- species returns
- soil organic and microbiome changes
- water quality

Carbon Capture

Heal is developing a 'carbon sequestration calculator' designed by a PhD student specialising in ecosystem carbon and verified by a professor working in the same discipline. It calculates the carbon capture on land undergoing ecological succession, which increasingly sequesters carbon as it re-vegetates. Our calculator uses data from existing studies estimating the carbon capture potential of individual habitat types undergoing ecological succession.

Our Progress So Far

There has been a significant response to our launch. Within a few months, we had over 6,000 social media followers, more than 170 volunteers on board, a small but growing base of individuals donating regularly, a flow of one-off donations and early support from a number of businesses including partnerships with several small online retail sites for profits to go to Heal.

Conclusion

We believe we have developed a model which has the potential for adoption in any country where nature is already heavily depleted and we encourage readers to support national and local rewilding initiatives as a vital option for species recovery.

We see Heal as a critical element in the context of any 'Extinction Governance' framework. Our strategic and systematic approach to land acquisition and its dedicated use for rewilding and nature recovery, climate change action and well-being can function as a progressive and action-oriented form of extinction governance. As a charity, we are in a position to be a delivery partner for business, finance and society who wish to take action for humanity – to achieve social betterment as well as extinction prevention, biodiversity enhancement and growth in species populations, especially those that are endangered locally and nationally.

Notes

1 www.healrewilding.org.uk.
2 www.rspb.org.uk/globalassets/downloads/documents/conservation-projects/state-of-nature/state-of-nature-uk-report-2016.pdf.
3 Ibid.
4 *State of Nature, 2019.*
5 https://tinyurl.com/y6lwpepd.
6 https://www.theguardian.com/commentisfree/2018/nov/26/wildwoods-britain-climate-change-northern-forest.
7 https://www.wwt.org.uk/news/2018/09/27/global-wetland-crisis-the-lowdown/15493.
8 http://adlib.everysite.co.uk/adlib/defra/content.aspx?id=000HK277ZW.09SUFIY DQ4SEB6.
9 https://www.kew.org/read-and-watch/meadows-matter.
10 https://publications.parliament.uk/pa/cm201617/cmselect/cmenvaud/180/180.pdf p36 and https://www.fwi.co.uk/news/only-100-harvests-left-in-uk-farm-soils-scientists-warn.
11 Anonymous (2009) Rewilding: New Constructions of Nature in Conservations Biology, the Knepp Castle Estate, West Sussex. Oxford University.
12 Taylor, P. (2005) *Beyond Conservation: A Wildland Strategy*, Routledge, UK.
13 Foreman, D. (1995, p. 10) Wilderness: From Scenery to Nature. *Wild Earth*, 5(4): 9–16.
14 Specific Measurable Achievable Relevant Timebound.
15 Vera, F.W.M. (2002) The Dynamic European Forest. *Arboricultural Journal*, 26: 179–211.
16 Eg https://knepp.co.uk/yearly-surveys.
17 The 25-Year Environment Plan aims to roll out a Nature Recovery Network [providing] an additional 500,000 hectares of wildlife-rich habitat.
18 Whitbread, T. (2018) Biodiversity successes at Knepp; fitting it into the bigger picture. In Rewilding: Perspectives and Applications Conference 2018, Royal Agricultural University, Cirencester.
19 https://twitter.com/alidriveruk/status/1308439910920212481?s=21.
20 Taylor, C. (unpublished study). Carbon sequestration calculations in a rewilding setting.
21 Helm, D. (2019) *Green and Prosperous Land: A Blueprint for Rescuing the British Countryside.* William Collins, London.
22 Ibid., p. 265.
23 https://www.england.nhs.uk/mental-health/.
24 Ulrich, R.S. View through a window may influence recovery from surgery. *Science*, 1984 Apr 27; 224(4647): 420–421.
25 Li, Q et al., Visiting a forest, but not a city, increases […] expression of anti-cancer proteins. *International Journal of Immunopathol and Pharmacology* 2008 Jan-Mar; 21(1): 117–127.
26 Mao G.X. et al. Therapeutic effect of forest bathing on human hypertension in the elderly. *Journal of Cardiology* 2012; 60(6): 295–502.
27 Gregory N. et al. Nature and mental health: An ecosystem service perspective. *Science Advances* 24 Jul 2019: 5(7): Nature and mental health: An ecosystem service perspective - PubMed (nih.gov).

6

OIL PALM INDUSTRY AND BIODIVERSITY LOSS

Enhancing Governance through the Sustainability Policy Transparency Toolkit (SPOTT)

Gunnar Rimmel and Maizatulakma Abdullah

Introduction

Worldwide demand for palm oil has risen sharply over the past decade, resulting in an increase in global palm oil production. In 1990, palm oil was produced on a small scale, with global palm oil production of around 11 million metric tonnes. In 2020, the United States Department of Agriculture (USDA) reports that global production increased to 72.2 million metric tonnes. This increase has led to an expansion of the oil palm plantation area. As of November 2020, USDA data estimated the total area of oil palm plantations all over the world to be now up to 24.093 million hectares, which is a little less than the size of New Zealand.

According to USDA, oil palm is currently grown in 28 countries, Indonesia has the largest hectarage under cultivation for palm oil which accounted for a total land use of 11.950 million hectares as of 2020. It is estimated to reach 17 million hectares by 2025 for Indonesia alone.[1] The country with the second-largest hectarage under palm oil cultivation is Malaysia, where it accounts for a total land use of 5.74 million hectares, mainly located in Sabah and Sarawak, in the northern part of the island of Borneo. It has been documented[2] that oil palm has caused up to 60% of forest loss in that region between 1972 and 2015. In another study,[3] it has been observed that 45% of sampled oil palm plantations in Southeast Asia came from areas that were forests in 1989.

Africa and Latin America have the greatest potential for oil palm expansion after Southeast Asia.[4] In Africa, it has been observed that the most massive deforestation between 1989 and 2013 occurred in Cameroon and Ghana.[5] In Latin America, the majority of the suitable land area is located in the Amazon rainforest area, which has a wide variety of rare flora and fauna,[6] with estimates as high as 238 million hectares of suitable lands in Brazil alone.[7] A detailed regional study in the Peruvian Amazon forest found that oil palm plantations have destroyed

DOI: 10.4324/9781003045557-9

about 84,500 hectares of the forest area between 2000 and 2015.[8] Another study shows that 72% of new oil palm plantations in Peru expanded into the Amazon rainforest areas.[9] In Tumaco, Colombia, 60% of oil palm plantations is located in the primary forest and resulted in the loss of biodiversity and increased extinction risk.[10,11]

Despite being blamed for environmental degradation in the tropics, oil palm is more efficient at producing oil than alternatives such as rapeseed and sunflower, which needs less land to produce the same amount of oil.[12,13] Replacing palm oil with the alternatives would lead to greater land conversion, causing more deforestation, biodiversity loss, and heightened extinction risk.[14,15] Besides, palm oil is now ubiquitous and used in so many products that boycotts or negative campaigns against it are unlikely to succeed. According to Voora, Larrea, Bermudez, and Baliño (2019), the negative campaigns have not registered significant implications on the total export of palm oil as there exists massive demand from the largest palm oil-consuming countries like India and the Republic of China. Thus, the best solution is to help the palm oil industry to develop and expand sustainably.

This chapter is dedicated to presenting one of the external governance initiatives implemented in the industry, namely the Sustainability Policy Transparency Toolkit (SPOTT). This toolkit may help in promoting the development of a sustainable palm oil industry by tracking transparency and creating awareness among stakeholders about the problems of biodiversity loss and extinction risks caused by the industry. Before discussing the SPOTT, this chapter begins with a discussion on the environmental impacts of the industry and the weaknesses in the current governance that justifies the need for other initiatives.

Has the Oil Palm Industry Really Caused Biodiversity Loss and Increased Extinction Risk?

Previous studies provide evidence that the extensive conversion of natural forest to oil palm plantation increases biodiversity loss and increases the extinction risk of highly valued species, mainly through forest clearing and the use of slash-and-burn practices to prepare the land for oil palm plantation. For example, a million hectares of a forest clearing in eastern Sabah, Malaysia has severely affected Bornean orangutan populations, which is classified as critically endangered according to the International Union for the Conservation of Nature and Natural Resources (IUCN) Red List of Threatened Species.[16] Extensive oil palm development in that region has forced them to take refuge in the surrounding fragmented forest area. A study found that some of them were unable to disperse and have become isolated and overcrowded in remnant forest patches.[17] The size of the forest patches matters for their survival.[18] The smaller the size, the lower the survival chance because of high competition for resources.[19,20]

Additionally, when only very few of them are left in an isolated area, the population may not be viable and go extinct over one or several generations. The loss of habitat and limited resources may also increase human–orangutan contact and conflict, leading to conflict-motivated killing by humans,[21] thus increasing their extinction risk.[22] It is estimated about 651,757 hectares of forest loss in Peninsular Malaysia between 1988 and 2012 and threatened critically endangered species like the tiger (*Panthera tigris jacksoni*), the rhino (*Dicerorhinus sumatrensis*) and the elephant (*Elephas maximus*).[23] The forest loss has also caused a loss of 46 species of forest birds.[24]

A similar situation has arisen in Indonesia in The Tripa swamp forest area in Aceh.[25] Oil palm development has had a substantial negative impact on more than 3,000 Sumatran orangutans and other countless animal and plant species in that area, among others, tigers,[26] white-winged wood duck, otter civets, storm's stork and the masked finfoot and saltwater crocodile.[27] Oil palm plantations are also expanding massively in Kalimantan's forest in Borneo island, which is the home of 12,000 species of flowering plants, 3,000 species of trees, 44 localised mammals such as the rhino and elephants, 100 species of endemic amphibian, 47 species of lizard and 41 species of snake.[28] Evidence shows that excessive use of pesticides and fertilizers affects over 160 species of fish in freshwater biodiversity in that area.[29] The oil palm has also led to the loss of butterfly and birds species.[30,31]

Although deforestation in the Latin America region is less severe than it has been in Southeast Asia, evidence shows that flora and fauna diversity and abundance in the Amazon rainforest have started to be affected, especially in the Colombia region. It is one of the most biodiverse-rich countries in the world, yet is the largest palm oil producer in Latin America.[32] Oil palm plantations are expanding exponentially in the region, especially in the Tumaco forest and has destroyed species diversity. An activist from Tumaco said, '*we saw the animals crossing the river, fleeing from the forest*'.[33] Obviously, the oil palm industry results in harmful effects on the ecosystem and biodiversity.

What Are the Main Drivers of Biodiversity Loss?

Government Policy and Incentives

Oil palm is expanding rapidly in Southeast Asia and Latin America, mainly driven by government support.[34,35] It is understandable that governments support this industry because it can significantly boost the economy of their nations and increase employment opportunities.[36] According to previous records, there were 3.5 million households or about 14 million people who earn a living from oil palms in Indonesia.[37] The Malaysian Palm Oil Council reported that there were 860,000 people in Malaysia who made a living from this industry in 2015, and this is estimated to have increased further. The IUCN estimates that one worker is hired per every eight hectares of oil palm plantation.[38]

Although this industry makes a significant economic contribution to the producing countries, as discussed previously, the land area used to plant the oil palms is often cleared at the expense of natural forest and biodiversity. Government policy and incentives drive oil palm expansion in Indonesia. For example, in the late 1990s, the government of Indonesia made a decision to open up its oil palm industry to foreign investors because of limited capital and technology to expand oil palm production.[39] Due to limited available land area for oil palm cultivation, the governments of Malaysia and Singapore then took the opportunity and provided financial support to their oil palm companies and financial institutions to establish plantations in Indonesia.[40,41,42,43] Malaysia also brought significant palm-oil-specific technology into Indonesia[44,45] such as the continuous sterilisation system, which allows the sterilisation process of fresh fruit bunches (FFB) to become less labour-intensive[46]; as a result, oil palm production has increased exponentially in Indonesia.[47] As palm oil production has increased, so has the land conversion and habitat loss.

Besides, in the early 1980s, the government of Indonesia granted extensive new concessions to private oil palm companies.[48,49] Due to weak land registration and poor government, the concession maps and land ownership were not correctly and accurately recorded,[50,51] which has created an opportunity for unscrupulous oil palm growers to clear forest area.[52,53] Without accurate concession maps and land ownership, it is difficult to address the actors responsible for forest fires and clearance.[54]

In Latin America, the governments of Brazil, Peru, and Colombia declared the oil palm industry to be in the national interest, and much effort has gone into promoting this industry. Various economic incentives were put in place, in Peru, for example, the government introduced at least 14 laws promoting this industry, and one of them was tax relief programs for investments in oil palm expansion in the Amazon forest.[55,56] The three countries have also created biofuel programs that mandate mineral diesel to contain a certain level of palm oil–based biodiesel.[57] Subsidies for the consumption of palm oil–based biodiesel were also put into place in Colombia as a way to boost the palm oil industry in the country.[58,59] As a result, almost half of palm oil production in Colombia is now geared to the biodiesel market,[60] and land conversion to oil palm is expected to continue to fulfil the growing demand, as well as the destruction of the ecosystems and biodiversity.

Oil Palm Producer Groups

Governments grant concessions to oil palm producer groups to give them rights to clear land and plant palm oil trees. They can be categorised into three types: (1) industrial plantations, (2) medium-scale operators, and (3) smallholder plantations. An industrial plantation is usually managed by a company which possesses its own palm oil mill and operates across thousands of hectares.[61] Medium-scale operators often operate medium-to-large plantations (generally greater than 25 hectares in Indonesia, but up to several thousand hectares) without formal company status. Smallholder plantations are usually run as family farms, rely on other actors for processing their FFB, and occupy smaller areas, typically less than 50 ha, as defined by the Roundtable on Sustainable Palm Oil. Smallholders can operate independently or collaborate in a company scheme if they have no facilities to process FFB. In the Southeast Asia region, smallholders usually manage about 35–40% of planted oil palm,[62,63] and their impact on biodiversity is significant if they fail to get support to produce palm oil sustainably. Due to limited expertise, capacity, resources, access to finance, information, and support services, they usually use the most cost-efficient way to clear land in forested and peat areas to get the lands ready for planting.[64]

It was reported that more than 2.6 million hectares of forested area was burnt in the provinces of Riau, Kalimantan, South Sumatra, Papua, and Jambi in 2015.[65] Another report by Greenpeace[66] shows that more than 3.7 million hectares of forested land in Indonesia burnt between 2015 and 2018. The massive fires caused serious destruction of vegetation and biodiversity loss in the affected areas. Greenpeace's report[67] identified 21 industrial plantation companies which they claimed were responsible for the fire crisis between 2015 and 2018. In 2019, Indonesia's Supreme Audit Agency (BPK) announced that 81% of industrial plantations operating in Indonesia violated at least one of the laws or mandatory management standards they were required to comply with.[68] Violations reported include operating illegally in forest areas, operating outside concession areas, operating without relevant permits and failing to develop smallholdings for local people as required.[69]

Are There Any Governance Mechanisms in Place to Mitigate and Monitor the Oil Palm Industry's Impact on Biodiversity?

Due to intense pressure from stakeholder groups especially environmental non-governmental organisations (NGOs), the governments of producing countries as well as oil palm producer groups have started to work towards sustainable oil palm production by improving country-level and organisational-level governance, which is a complex task.

Country-Level Governance

The governments of producing countries take various initiatives such as improving regulatory policies and mandating certification standards.[70] Given various and numerous initiatives which have been implemented by the governments from different countries, this subsection only discusses a few examples in the context of Indonesia.

Moratorium

In 2011, the central government declared a moratorium which prohibits district and provincial governments from issuing new concession licenses. The main objectives of the moratorium are to reduce the deforestation rate and preserve ecosystems. However, many parties, particularly activists, are sceptical about the effectiveness of the implementation of a moratorium.[71,72] Deforestation and forest fires were reported to continue and in fact reached their highest level in 2012, despite the moratorium already being put into place.[73] There are many cases reported on the failure of the district or provincial governments to implement the central government policy.[74] For example, in August 2011, the governor of Aceh signed a new permit for PT Kallista Alam to clear part of the Tripa swamp forest within the moratorium area. In 2012, the company set more than 90 fires to clear thousands of hectares of forest area which was the home of orangutans, rhinos, tigers and elephants. The forest fires caused lasting environmental damage. The Indonesian Ministry of Environment and Forestry filed a charge against the company and, in 2014, the court ordered the company to pay fines of $27 million. However, as far as we know, the fines remained unpaid and in fact, in July 2019, this company filed a lawsuit challenging the legality of the court decision.[75] Due to insufficient enforcement, many other similar cases were reported in other districts and provinces which challenge the central government in realising their objectives.[76]

Certification

In 2011, the government of Indonesia introduced its own national certification standard, namely the Indonesian Sustainable Palm Oil (ISPO), which was later made compulsory for all Indonesian oil palm companies. In 2022, this standard will become compulsory for all Indonesian smallholders too. Analysis from previous studies revealed serious doubts on its potential contribution to protecting biodiversity, mainly because of vagueness in its definition of high conservation values (HCVs) and its identification procedures.[77,78] The ISPO only prohibits companies from cultivating in particular protection zones because the government defines these zones as areas that contain HCVs, whereas HCVs can be any areas that contain HCVs, including in the existing concession area.[79] ISPO requires companies to cultivate their entire concession area even if this area contains HCVs, and failing to do this will lead to the cancellation of their concession permit.[80] Thus, the certification has limited contribution to conserving biodiversity.

Organisational-Level Governance

Organisational governance is important to monitor the policies, actions, practices and decisions of the management of companies to align the interests of all stakeholders. The management should not only be able to create long-term shareholder value but also sustainable value for the environment and the communities. According to Chain Reaction Research as of 2020, nearly all oil palm growers, traders and consumer good companies in the global oil palm supply chain have committed to implement No Deforestation, Peat, and Exploitation (NDPE) policy in their organisations. Core to this policy is a commitment to ensure that there is no development of high carbon stock (HCS) forest and HCV areas, no burning, no development on peat and no exploitation of people and local communities.[81]

Effective governance mechanism is a key to the NDPE's success. Governance mechanisms can be implemented in many forms, such as the establishment of a board system, creating whistleblowing policies and so forth. The mechanisms also vary across producing countries. For example, Indonesia adopts a two-tier board system, which consists of a board of directors and a board of commissioners. The former manages the company, while the latter supervises the former. Malaysia, on the other hand, adopts a one-tier board system which has a single body of directors that monitors the top management of the company. Both board systems can work well as long as directors that serve the board are capable of discharging their roles effectively. However, Varkkey[82] questions whether directors in oil palm companies can be effective monitors of the companies' management. It is because directors have limited resources to perform an effective monitoring role, they are often appointed because of their political capacity.

The close patronage relationships between the government elites and oil palm companies have been described as hampering the effort to resolve the problem of deforestation and biodiversity loss in Indonesia and Malaysia.[83,84,85,86] The government elites tend to use their political influence to provide protection and defend their oil palm companies especially when threatened with legal actions.[87] The support and protection the companies received have rendered them 'untouchable'.[88]

Based on the above discussions, it is clear that an ineffective board system and deficiencies in the government initiatives (as well as problems in their implementation) resulted in the failure of attempts to resolve the problem of forest clearance and biodiversity loss. Internal monitoring does not seem to work effectively and that could be one of the reasons why consumer markets in the global north and environmental NGOs exert their pressures on the Southeast Asian oil palm industry. Pressure from European Union (EU) investors can positively affect the environment-related information disclosure of Indonesian oil palm companies.[89] They also found that neither Singaporean nor Malaysian investors could influence information transparency. However, generalisation of study results is limited because it only measures the influence of investors based on ownership percentage and does not consider other investment initiatives such as Support Asia for Sustainable Palm Oil (SASPO). The power of the financial institutions may be used towards resolving the problem of deforestation and eventually help in reducing the risks of biodiversity loss and extinction. However, what is the best way to go about this? The next section will discuss the SPOTT), which is an initiative developed by the Zoological Society of London (ZSL), a conservation and science charity based in London.

How Does the SPOTT Help in Improving the Current Oil Palm Governance Weaknesses?

Although the current oil palm governance shows signs of progress in terms of initiatives, policies and commitment (for example through NDPE commitment uptake), as discussed earlier, the implementation on the ground is still problematic. Investors and other stakeholders especially from other international palm oil-producing countries need to intervene and play their monitoring roles to ensure the oil palm supply chains make progress towards meeting commitments and walking the talk.[90] However, the biggest challenge they face is to obtain information from the oil palm producers or companies,[91] especially when they are separated geographically and face language barriers.[92]

The ZSL's SPOTT is an initiative that is created to incentivise transparency of reporting and the implementation of best practices of oil palm companies. Unlike other reporting standards, which provide reporting guidelines without industry-specific contents, SPOTT provides oil palm-specific disclosure expectations through its detailed indicator and scoring criteria frameworks. The frameworks are reviewed through the feedback it gathers from investors and other stakeholders in order to ensure that they reflect the latest developments in environmental, social and governance transparency and reporting expectations. SPOTT then assesses companies and gives them a score based on the public disclosures. They are not penalised for non-disclosure of irrelevant items, for example, a processor or a trader company is not penalised if there is no disclosure about commitment to zero deforestation. SPOTT then reaches out to companies assessed for comments and after this review period where companies can choose to publish more or better information, the results are made available publicly on its website.

Besides, SPOTT provides a unique solution in helping address the weaknesses in the current palm oil governance through its annual monitoring of disclosures by oil palm companies to measure progress over time towards its targets and implementation of its policies and commitments on the ground.[93] For example, SPOTT requires companies to give evidence for monitoring deforestation. On indicators such as this one, which it calls 'practice indicators', SPOTT gives the highest score for information that is externally verified and a lower score if a company gives evidence without external verification. This scoring method increases the reliability of the information given.

Investors, banks, suppliers and other stakeholders can get benefit from the results to inform their processes or decisions. For example, banks can use the results to make decision on financial alternatives or products that can be offered to oil palm companies that show good progress and effort in reducing deforestation, such as issuing green bonds to companies to finance their sustainable agriculture or alternatives to deforestation practices.[94] Investors can also use the results to make an investment decision (whether to hold, buy or sell their stake) if companies from their investment portfolio show unethical behaviour and harm biodiversity.[95]

How Does the SPOTT Help in Addressing the Problems of Biodiversity Loss and Extinction Risk?

SPOTT requires oil palm companies to report under three types of disclosure, which are: (i) organisation, (ii) policy, and (iii) practice. Under the organisation category, a company is expected to disclose information regarding its operations, assets and management structure. For the policy category, a company is expected to disclose information regarding the policies, commitments and processes it uses to guide its operations and practices on the ground. While under the practice category, a company is expected to disclose information regarding activities it undertakes in order to actively progress towards its targets and implement its policies and commitments on the ground. For each type, there are several indicators that are identified to relate directly to the effort in monitoring and preventing biodiversity loss and extinction, and this is illustrated in Figure 6.1.

Information about Organisation Indicators

SPOTT highlights the importance of certain kinds of disclosures and best practices for oil palm companies, like the relevance of reporting on the existence of a high-level position of responsibility for sustainability. Among others, this information could help stakeholders to understand if the company is committed to tackling sustainability issues. For example, company X reported that it has appointed a chief strategy and sustainability officer, who is responsible for

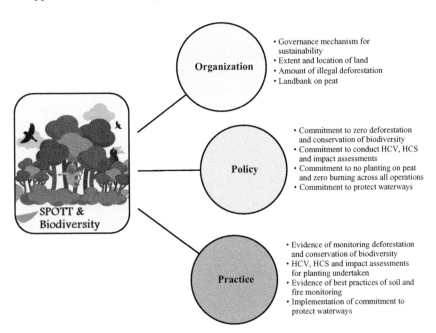

FIGURE 6.1   SPOTT indicator framework that relates to biodiversity and extinction.

monitoring its suppliers for illegal deforestation activities in their supply base when company Y has not. In addition, an oil palm company is expected to be transparent on the extent and locations of its landholdings. SPOTT reports that the depth of disclosure of this information varies across oil palm companies with some providing detailed information on total landbank, planted areas, unplanted areas and areas set aside for conservation. According to a report published in 2017, many companies were not revealing sufficient information to understand risks that the company may be facing as a result of the location, development stage or nature of its landholdings.[96] The information is important for stakeholders to monitor whether companies are adequately mitigating the environmental impacts associated with different land uses and addressing the biodiversity-related risks. One such requirement is that companies disclose the details of hotspots in company estates and the amount of illegal deforestation in its own or its supplier operations – and this is one of the aspects of palm oil operations which pose the highest threat to biodiversity.

Information about Policy

SPOTT expects that oil palm companies show their commitment to zero deforestation or zero conversion of natural ecosystems by placing specific policies on this. The policies must not only apply to a particular company but also across its supply chain and to its suppliers. SPOTT expects all companies to show their commitment to the restoration of the non-compliant deforestation or conversion, commitment to biodiversity conservation and commitment to no hunting or only sustainable hunting of species. Companies also need to disclose information on their use of HCV and HCS methodologies and the publication of related assessment reports. To further protect biodiversity, SPOTT results highlight the importance of information on companies' commitment to no planting on peat of any depth, to zero burning, to protecting natural waterways through buffer zones and to minimising the use of chemicals, including pesticides and chemicals that can harm marine biodiversity.

Information about Practice

The core problem in current practice in relation to environment-related reporting is that companies may use this reporting for their own benefits, for example to manage stakeholders impressions[97] or as a legitimacy tool.[98,99] Companies tend to report on 'soft' information which consists of policies and commitments without evidence of implementation.[100,101] One of the unique aspects of SPOTT is that besides comparing companies with peers (like other scorecards) its scoring specificities also drive oil palm companies to report on verifiable and reliable information.

To benchmark and encourage best practices on deforestation issues, SPOTT requests companies to give evidence of monitoring deforestation, which is specifying how deforestation is being monitored including the extent of the area monitored and timeframe. To benchmark and encourage the best practice on biodiversity protection, SPOTT requests companies to report if they take the step of identifying species of conservation concern, referencing international or national systems of species classification, which means identifying whether species are, for example rare, threatened or endangered, referencing an appropriate system of classification such as the IUCN Red List. Companies also need to reveal how the HCV, HCS and impact assessments for planting are undertaken in their plantation areas, as well as give evidence of the implementation of the commitment to no planting on peat of any depth, best management practices for soils and peat and to fire monitoring and management. SPOTT also requests companies to show evidence of implementation of a commitment to protecting natural waterways and evidence of measures undertaken by companies.

The Examples of Using SPOTT to Help in Addressing the Problems of Deforestation and Biodiversity Loss

SPOTT publishes the full results of the analysis on its website (https://www. spott.org/) and is free for everyone to access. The website has a user-friendly interface that allows stakeholders to choose the information they need for making decisions. For example, stakeholders can choose the results by disclosure types or by indicator categories, as depicted in Figures 6.2 and 6.3 respectively.

Average scores by types

Disclosure types

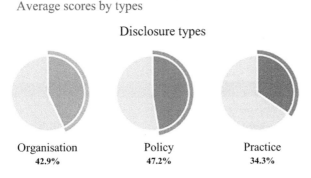

Organisation	Policy	Practice
42.9%	47.2%	34.3%

FIGURE 6.2 Average score by disclosure type as of November 2020.
Source: the SPOTT website.

> Deforestation and biodiversity		38.1%
> HCV, HCS and impact assessments		41.7%
> Peat, fire and GHG emissions		41.5%
> Water, chemical and pest management		36.9%

FIGURE 6.3 Average total score by indicator categories as of November 2020.
Source: the SPOTT website.

As Figure 6.2 illustrates, oil palm companies tend to disclose more information about organisation and policy rather than information about practice. This result is consistent with prior studies[102,103] which show that companies are likely to disclose 'soft' information which is unverifiable and subjective. Policies and commitment information can be easily mimicked, and any company can claim that it is committed towards sustainability. Figure 6.3 indicates that companies provide very low disclosure levels of 'deforestation and biodiversity' information, as well as 'water, chemical and management' information. Further information provided on the SPOTT's website (as illustrated in Figure 6.4) shows that the low disclosure score of 'deforestation and biodiversity' is due to the failure of companies in providing clear evidence of monitoring deforestation and committing to restoring illegal deforestation/conversion they have committed. Inadequate evidence of information raises the alarm about the possibility that companies may not be walking the talk and may only use disclosure for impression management or manipulating stakeholders.[104]

SPOTT also allows stakeholders to understand the policies, commitments and practices within a company. For further explanation, we chose one company as an example.

Astra Agro Lestari is an Indonesian-based company that is engaged in oil palm cultivation and processing of FFB into crude palm oil and palm kernel. Figures 6.5 and 6.6 show that this company lacks transparency in all four indicator categories. The category with the least information available was information regarding water, chemical and waste management, where it only reported 4 out of 22 in 2019 and 5.5 out of 25 in 2020. Figure 6.6 indicates that the company did not improve its disclosure on the HCV, HCS and impact assessment as compared to the previous year, and it keeps on communicating its commitment to

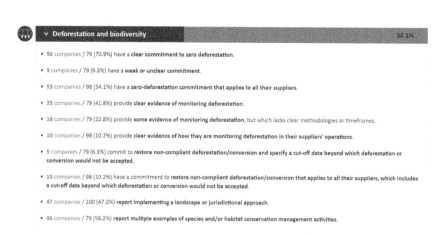

FIGURE 6.4 Detailed results for deforestation and biodiversity indicator as of November 2020.

Source: the SPOTT website.

> Deforestation and biodiversity	9 / 18	50%
> HCV, HCS and impact assessments	4.5 / 14	32.1%
> Peat, fire and GHG emissions	11.25 / 20	56.3%
> Water, chemical and pest management	4 / 22	18.2%

FIGURE 6.5 Average total score by indicator categories for Astra Agro Lestari as of October 2019.

Source: the SPOTT website.

> Deforestation and biodiversity	9 / 17	52.9%
> HCV, HCS and impact assessments	4.5 / 14	32.1%
> Peat, fire and GHG emissions	11.75 / 20	58.8%
> Water, chemical and pest management	5.5 / 25	22%

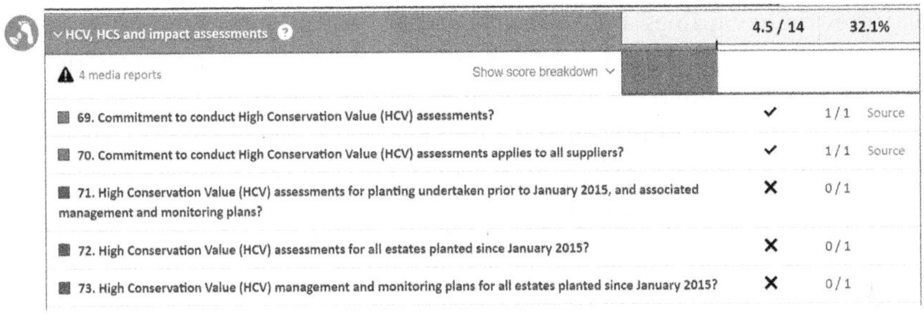

FIGURE 6.6 Average total score by indicator categories for Astra Agro Lestari as of November 2020.

Source: the SPOTT website.

∨ HCV, HCS and impact assessments		4.5 / 14	32.1%
⚠ 4 media reports	Show score breakdown ∨		
69. Commitment to conduct High Conservation Value (HCV) assessments?	✓	1 / 1	Source
70. Commitment to conduct High Conservation Value (HCV) assessments applies to all suppliers?	✓	1 / 1	Source
71. High Conservation Value (HCV) assessments for planting undertaken prior to January 2015, and associated management and monitoring plans?	✗	0 / 1	
72. High Conservation Value (HCV) assessments for all estates planted since January 2015?	✗	0 / 1	
73. High Conservation Value (HCV) management and monitoring plans for all estates planted since January 2015?	✗	0 / 1	

FIGURE 6.7 Detailed results for HCV, HCS and impact assessments as of November 2020.

Source: the SPOTT website.

conduct HCV assessments without providing clear evidence of the implementation. Without reporting on the implementation of biodiversity conservation-related commitments, it may be difficult for stakeholders to understand whether a company is taking adequate steps to mitigate its operations' impact on biodiversity (Figure 6.7).

Based on the above explanation, it seems that SPOTT can help to actively track the progress of oil palm companies in fulfilling their no deforestation, peat, and exploitation commitments and highlighting important areas for engagements. Stakeholders can drive transparency by requiring companies to coherently disclose more information on the areas needed.

Conclusion

Palm oil has become one of the important industries that significantly contributes to the economic growth of its producing countries. However, unsustainable palm oil production has caused tremendous negative impacts on local biodiversity and ecosystems. This chapter explains how deforestation for oil palm cultivation has caused habitat and biodiversity loss, which eventually contribute to extinction dynamics. Some evidence of forest loss and species under threat in the Southeast Asian and Amazonian regions are presented in the second section of this chapter. The third and fourth sections of this chapter focus on governance issues, which is believed to be the main driver of unsustainable practices in the industry. While governments appear to make progress in improving their governance practices, such as through establishing moratoriums and developing national certification schemes, there have been issues in the past around the legality of companies publishing their concession maps that led to the lack of transparency and accountability of oil palm producer companies.

Due to intense pressure from stakeholders, oil palm producer companies are now working to improve their accountability and transparency. However, the existing internal governance system does not seem to work effectively, impeding their effort. The last section of this chapter presents one of the external governance initiatives that is being implemented by ZSL, namely SPOTT. This toolkit measures the companies' transparency in terms of three aspects, which are: (i) organisation, (ii) policy, and (iii) practice. One of the important contributions of SPOTT is the scoring framework that allows companies to get a higher score for externally verified information and a lower score for self-reported information. This scoring system could benefit stakeholders as they can retrieve more reliable information on the progress the oil palm companies have made in preserving the ecosystems and biodiversity. This could eventually help them to make better decisions and to play a more active role in ensuring the oil palm industry develop and expand sustainably.

Notes

1 Teh, B. S. C. (2016). Availability, use, and removal of oil palm biomass in Indonesia. Report prepared for the International Council on Clean Transportation.
2 Meijaard, E., Garcia-Ulloa, J., Sheil, D., Wich, S. A., Carlson, K. M., Juffe-Bignoli, D., & Brooks, T. M. (2018). Oil palm and biodiversity: A situation analysis by the IUCN Oil Palm Task Force. Retrieved from Gland, Switzerland: 10.2305/IUCN.CH.2018.11.en.
3 Vijay, V., Pimm, S. L., Jenkins, C. N., & Smith, S. J. (2016). The impacts of oil palm on recent deforestation and biodiversity loss. *PLoS ONE*, 11(7), 1–19. Retrieved from https://doi.org/10.1371/journal.pone.0159668.
4 Vijay, Pimm, Jenkins, and Smith (2016).
5 Vijay, Pimm, Jenkins, and Smith (2016).
6 Yui, S., & Yeh, S. (2013). Land use change emissions from oil palm expansion in Pará, Brazil depend on proper policy enforcement on deforested lands. *Environmental Research Letters*, 8(4). Retrieved from https://doi.org/10.1088/1748-9326/8/4/044031.

7 Benami, E., Curran, L. M., Cochrane, M., Venturieri, A., Franco, R., Kneipp, J., & Swartos, A. (2018). Oil palm land conversion in Pará, Brazil, from 2006-2014: Evaluating the 2010 Brazilian Sustainable Palm Oil Production Program. *Environmental Research Letters*, 13(3). Retrieved from https://doi.org/10.1088/1748-9326/aaa270.

8 Vijay, Reid, Finer, Jenkins, & Pimm, 2018 Vijay, V., Reid, C. D., Finer, M., Jenkins, C. N., & Pimm, S. L. (2018). Deforestation risks posed by oil palm expansion in the Peruvian Amazon. *Environmental Research Letters*, 13(11). Retrieved from https://doi.org/10.1088/1748-9326/aae540.

9 Gutiérrez-Vélez, V. H., DeFries, R., Pinedo-Vásquez, M., Uriarte, M., Padoch, C., Baethgen, W., ... Lim, Y. (2011). High-yield oil palm expansion spares land at the expense of forests in the Peruvian Amazon. *Environmental Research Letters*, 6(4), 044029. Retrieved from https://doi.org/10.1088/1748-9326/6/4/044029.

10 Meijaard et al. (2018.)

11 Mol, H. (2017). Preparing the ground. In *The Politics of Palm Oil Harm: A Green Criminological Perspective* (pp. 123–160). Cham: Palgrave Macmillan. Retrieved from https://doi.org/10.1007/978-3-319-55378-8.

12 Grayson, J., & Stampe, J. (2012). *Palm Oil Investor Review: Investor Guidance on Palm Oil. The role of Investors in Supporting the Development of a Sustainable Palm Oil Industry.* World Wide Fund for Nature (WWF).

13 Wilcove, D. S., & Koh, L. P. (2010). Addressing the threats to biodiversity from oil-palm agriculture. *Biodiversity and Conservation*, 19(4), 999–1007. Retrieved from https://doi.org/10.1007/s10531-009-9760-x.

14 Cattau, M. E., Marlier, M. E., & DeFries, R. (2016). Effectiveness of Roundtable on Sustainable Palm Oil (RSPO) for reducing fires on oil palm concessions in Indonesia from 2012 to 2015. *Environmental Research Letters*, 11(10). Retrieved from https://doi.org/10.1088/1748-9326/11/10/105007.

15 Meijaard et al. (2018).

16 Seaman, D. J. I., Bernard, H., Ancrenaz, M., Coomes, D., Swinfield, T., Milodowski, D. T., ... Struebig, M. J. (2019). Densities of Bornean orang-utans (Pongo pygmaeus morio) in heavily degraded forest and oil palm plantations in Sabah, Borneo. *American Journal of Primatology*, 81(8). Retrieved from https://doi.org/10.1002/ajp.23030.

17 Seaman et al. (2019).

18 Yue, S., Brodie, J. F., Zipkin, E. F., & Bernard, H. (2015). Oil palm plantations fail to support mammal diversity. *Ecological Applications*, 25(8), 2285–2292.

19 Ancrenaz, M., Ambu, L., Sunjoto, I., Ahmad, E., Manokaran, K., Meijaard, E., & Lackman, I. (2010). Recent surveys in the forests of Ulu Segama Malua, Sabah, Malaysia, show that Orang-utans (P. p. morio) can be maintained in slightly logged forests. *PLoS ONE*, 5(7). Retrieved from https://doi.org/10.1371/journal.pone.0011510.

20 Santika, T., Ancrenaz, M., Wilson, K. A., Spehar, S., Abram, N., Banes, G. L., ... Meijaard, E. (2017). First integrative trend analysis for a great ape species in Borneo. *Scientific Reports*, 7(1), 1–16. Retrieved from https://doi.org/10.1038/s41598-017-04435-9.

21 Davis, J. T., Mengersen, K., Abram, N. K., Ancrenaz, M., Wells, J. A., & Meijaard, E. (2013). It's not just conflict that motivates killing of Orangutans. *PLoS ONE*, 8(-10). Retrieved from https://doi.org/10.1371/journal.pone.0075373.

22 Corlett, R. T. (2007). The impact of hunting on the Mammalian Fauna of Tropical Asian Forests. *Biotropica*, 39(3), 292–303.

23 Shevade, V. S., & Loboda, T. V. (2019). Oil palm plantations in Peninsular Malaysia: Determinants and constraints on expansion. *PLoS ONE*, 14(2), 2010–2017. Retrieved from https://doi.org/10.1371/journal.pone.021062.

24 Koh, L. P., Miettinen, J., Liew, S. C., Ghazoul, J., & Ehrlich, P. R. (2011). Remotely sensed evidence of tropical peatland conversion to oil palm. *Proceedings of the National Academy of Sciences*, 108(12), 5127–5132. Retrieved from https://doi.org/10.1073/pnas.

25 Tata, H. L., van Noordwijk, M., Ruysschaert, D., Mulia, R., Rahayu, S., Muly-outami, E., ... Dewi, S. (2014). Will funding to Reduce Emissions from Deforest-ation and (forest) Degradation (REDD+) stop conversion of peat swamps to oil palm in orangutan habitat in Tripa in Aceh, Indonesia? *Mitigation and Adap-tation Strategies for Global Change*, 19(6), 693–713. Retrieved from https://doi.org/10.1007/s11027-013-9524-5.

26 Meijaard et al. (2018).

27 Tata et al. (2014).

28 Khan, T. (2014). Kalimantan's biodiversity: Developing accounting models to pre-vent its economic destruction. *Accounting, Auditing and Accountability Journal*, 27(1), 150–182. Retrieved from https://doi.org/10.1108/AAAJ-07-2013-1392.

29 Khan (2014).

30 Ginoga, L. N., Santosa, Y., & Mutmainnah, A. R. (2019). The loss, gain, and diver-sity of butterfly species due to the development of PT PKWE oil palm plantation, West Kalimantan Province. IOP Conference Series: Earth and Environmental Sci-ence, 336(1). Retrieved from https://doi.org/10.1088/1755-1315/336/1/012025.

31 Yudea, C., & Santosa, Y. (2019). How does oil palm plantation impact bird species diversity? A case study from PKWE Estate, West Kalimantan. *IOP Conference Series: Earth and Environmental Science*, 336(1). Retrieved from https://doi.org/10.1088/1755-1315/336/1/012026.

32 Ocampo-Peñuela, N., Garcia-Ulloa, J., Ghazoul, J., & Etter, A. (2018). Quantifying impacts of oil palm expansion on Colombia's threatened biodiversity. *Biological Con-servation*, 224(May), 117–121. Retrieved from https://doi.org/10.1016/j.biocon.2018.05.024.

33 Mol (2017).

34 Varkkey, H., Tyson, A., & Choiruzzad, S. A. B. (2018). Palm oil intensification and expansion in Indonesia and Malaysia: Environmental and socio-political factors influencing policy. *Forest Policy and Economics*, 92(July), 148–159. Retrieved from https://doi.org/10.1016/j.forpol.2018.05.0022018.

35 Vijay et al. (2018).

36 Singagerda, F. S., Hendrowati, T. Y., & Sanusi, A. (2018). Indonesia growth of eco-nomics and the industrialization biodiesel based CPO. *International Journal of Energy Economics and Policy*, 8(5), 319–334.

37 Choiruzzad, S. A. B. (2019). Save Palm Oil, Save the Nation: Palm Oil Companies and the Shaping of Indonesia's National Interest. *Asian Politics and Policy*, 11(1), 8–26. Retrieved from https://doi.org/10.1111/aspp.12431.

38 Meijaard et al. (2018).

39 Varkkey et al. (2018).

40 Varkkey, H. (2012). Patronage politics as a driver of economic regionalisation: The Indonesian oil palm sector and transboundary haze. *Asia Pacific Viewpoint*, 53(3), 314–329. Retrieved from https://doi.org/10.1111/j.1467-8373.2012.01493.x.

41 Varkkey, H. (2013). Malaysian investors in the Indonesian oil palm plantation sector: Home state facilitation and transboundary haze. *Asia Pacific Business Review*, 19(3), 381–401. Retrieved from https://doi.org/10.1080/13602381.2012.748262.

42 Varkkey et al. (2018).

43 Wilcove and Koh (2010).

44 Cramb, R., & McCarthy, J. F. (2016). Characterising Oil Palm Production in Indo-nesia and Malaysia. In R. Cramb & J. F. McCarthy (Eds.), *The Oil Palm Complex: Smallholders, Agribusiness and the State in Indonesia and Malaysia* (pp. 27–77). Singa-pore: NUS Press. Retrieved from https://doi.org/10.2307/j.ctv1xz0km.7.

45 Varkkey et al. (2018).

46 Kandiah, S., Halim, R. M., Basiron, Y., Rahman, Z. A., & Ma Ah Ngan. (2002). Continuous sterilization of fresh fruit bunches. *MPOB Information Series Malaysia*, 148, 1–4.

47 Bruno, L. C. (2017). Palm oil plantation productivity during the establishment of the Malaysian refinery sector, 1970–1990. *Economic History of Developing Regions*, 32(3), 221–269. Retrieved from https://doi.org/10.1080/20780389.2017.1343660.

48 Gaveau, D. L. A., Locatelli, B., Salim, M. A., Yaen, H., Pacheco, P., & Sheil, D. (2018). Rise and fall of forest loss and industrial plantations in Borneo (2000–2017). *Conservation Letters*, (November 2018), 1–8. Retrieved from https://doi.org/10.1111/conl.12622.

49 McCarthy and Cramb (2009).

50 Alisjahbana, A. S., & Busch, J. M. (2017). Forestry, forest fires, and climate change in Indonesia. *Bulletin of Indonesian Economic Studies*, 53(2), 111–136. Retrieved from https://doi.org/10.1080/00074918.2017.13654042017.

51 Lee, J. S. H., Jaafar, Z., Tan, A. K. J., Carrasco, L. R., Ewing, J. J., Bickford, D. P., … Koh, L. P. (2016). Toward clearer skies: Challenges in regulating transboundary haze in Southeast Asia. *Environmental Science and Policy*, 55, 87–95. Retrieved from https://doi.org/10.1016/j.envsci.2015.09.008.

52 Greenpeace (2018). World's largest palm oil trader linked to rainforest destruction twice the size of Paris. Retrieved 20 August 2020, from https://www.greenpeace.org/international/press-release/17248/worlds-largest-palm-oil-trader-linked-to-rainforest-destruction-twice-the-size-of-paris/.

53 Jacobson (2018).

54 Lee et al. (2016).

55 Bennett, A., Ravikumar, A., & Paltán, H. (2018). The political ecology of Oil Palm Company-Community partnerships in the Peruvian Amazon: Deforestation consequences of the privatization of rural development. *World Development*, 109(September), 29–41. Retrieved from https://doi.org/10.1016/j.worlddev.2018.04.001.

56 Gutiérrez-Vélez et al. (2011).

57 Furumo, P. R., & Aide, T. M. (2017). Characterizing commercial oil palm expansion in Latin America: Land use change and trade. *Environmental Research Letters*, 12(2). Retrieved from https://doi.org/10.1088/1748-9326/aa5892.

58 Castiblanco, C., Etter, A., & Ramirez, A. (2015). Impacts of oil palm expansion in Colombia: What do socioeconomic indicators show? *Land Use Policy*, 44, 31–43. Retrieved from https://doi.org/10.1016/j.landusepol.2014.10.007.

59 Castiblanco, C., Moreno, A., & Etter, A. (2015). Impact of policies and subsidies in agribusiness: The case of oil palm and biofuels in Colombia. *Energy Economics*, 49, 676–686. Retrieved from https://doi.org/10.1016/j.eneco.2015.02.025.

60 Meijaard et al. (2018).

61 Meijaard et al. (2018).

62 Gaveau, D. L. A., Sheil, D., Husnayaen, Salim, M. A., Arjasakusuma, S., Ancrenaz, M., … Meijaard, E. (2016). Rapid conversions and avoided deforestation: Examining four decades of industrial plantation expansion in Borneo. *Scientific Reports*, 6(June), 1–13. Retrieved from https://doi.org/10.1038/srep32017.

63 Meijaard et al. (2018).

64 Purnomo, Ramdani, R., Agustiyara, Tomaro, Q. P. V., & Samidjo, G. S. (2019). Land ownership transformation before and after forest fires in Indonesian palm oil plantation areas. *Journal of Land Use Science*, 14(1), 37–51. Retrieved from https://doi.org/10.1080/1747423X.2019.1614686.

65 Purnomo, H., Shantiko, B., Sitorus, S., Gunawan, H., Achdiawan, R., Kartodihardjo, H., & Dewayani, A. A. (2017). Fire economy and actor network of forest and land fires in Indonesia. *Forest Policy and Economics*, 78, 21–31. Retrieved from https://doi.org/10.1016/j.forpol.2017.01.001.

66 Greenpeace (2019). *Burning Down the House*.

67 Greenpeace (2019).

68 Nugraha, I., & Jong, N. H. (2019, August 27). Audit BPK Temukan Banyak Perkebunan Sawit Besar Bermasalah. *Mongabay News*. Retrieved 1 August 2020 from

https://www.mongabay.co.id/2019/08/27/audit-bpk-temukan-banyak-perkebunan-sawit-besar-bermasalah/.

69 Greenpeace (2019).
70 Firdaus, M., Kamello, T., Saidin, O. K., & Sunarmi. (2020). Obligations of Indonesian Sustainable Palm Oil (ISPO) certification for oil palm plantation companies in North Sumatera to support sustainable development. *IOP Conference Series: Earth and Environmental Science*, 452(1). Retrieved from https://doi.org/10.1088/1755-1315/452/1/012100.
71 Jong, H. N. (2019). Indonesia forest-clearing ban is made permanent, but labeled 'propaganda'. Retrieved 30 October 2020, from https://news.mongabay.com/2019/08/indonesia-forest-clearing-ban-is-made-permanent-but-labeled-propaganda/.
72 Sloan, S. (2014). Indonesia's moratorium on new forest licenses: An update. *Land Use Policy*, 38, 37–40. Retrieved from https://doi.org/10.1016/j.landusepol.2013.10.018.
73 Cramb and McCarthy (2016).
74 Jong (2019).
75 Greenpeace (2019).
76 Jong (2019).
77 Efeca. (2015). *Comparison of the ISPO, MSPO and RSPO Standards*. Efeca.
78 Hidayat, N. K., Offermans, A., & Glasbergen, P. (2018). Sustainable palm oil as a public responsibility? On the governance capacity of Indonesian Standard for Sustainable Palm Oil (ISPO). *Agriculture and Human Values*, 35(1), 223–242. Retrieved from https://doi.org/10.1007/s10460-017-9816-6.
79 Timmins, H. (2017). Opsi legal perlindungan hutan in indonesia pada lahan zona pertanian di indonesia. Retrieved from https://www.earthworm.org/uploads/files/OPSI-LEGAL-PERLINDUNGAN-HUTAN-IN-INDONESIA-PADA-LAHAN-ZONA.pdf.
80 Hidayat et al. (2018).
81 Proforest. (2020). Understanding commitments to no deforestation, peat and exploitation. Retrieved from https://proforest.net/proforest/en/publications/infonote_04_introndpe.pdf.
82 Varkkey (2012).
83 Hidayat et al. (2018).
84 Lee et al. (2016).
85 Varkkey (2012).
86 Varkkey (2013).
87 Varkkey (2012).
88 Varkkey (2013).
89 Abdullah, M., Hamzah, N., & Abd Rahman, I. M. (2020). Pengaruh Pemilikan Asing ke atas Pendedahan Maklumat Alam Sekitar dalam Industri Sawit di Indonesia (The Influence of Foreign Ownership towards Environmental Information Disclosure in the Oil Palm Industry in Indonesia). *Asian Journal of Accounting and Governance*, 14, 1–14.
90 Grayson and Stampe (2012).
91 Abdullah, M., Hamzah, N., Mohd-Ali, H., Tseng, M., & Brander, M. (2020). The Southeast Asian haze : The quality of environmental disclosures and firm performance. *Journal of Cleaner Production*, 246, 1–11. Retrieved from https://doi.org/10.1016/j.jclepro.2019.118958.
92 Huafang, X., & Jianguo, Y. (2007). Ownership structure, board composition and corporate voluntary disclosure: Evidence from listed companies in China. *Managerial Auditing Journal*, 22(6), 604–619. Retrieved from https://doi.org/10.1108/02686900710759406, 2007.
93 SPOTT: ZSL. (2020). Indicators and scoring criteria for assessing palm oil producers, processors and traders – November 2020. Retrieved from https://www.spott.org/wp-content/uploads/sites/3/2019/10/SPOTT-Palm-oil-scoring-criteria-2019.pdf.

94 The Sustainable Finance Platform. (2020). A guideline on the use of deforestation risk mitigation solutions for financial institutions from the sustainable finance platform mitigation sources for financial institutions content. Retrieved from https://www.dnb. nl/binaries/DNB Deforestation Guideline Document_ASN_21_08 DNB_tcm46-390356.pdf.
95 The Sustainable Finance Platform, 2020.
96 Abdullah, Hamzah, and Abd Rahman (2020).
97 Higgins and Walker (2012).
98 Michelon, Pilonato, and Ricceri (2015).
99 Qian and Schaltegger (2017).
100 Abdullah, Hamzah, Mohd-Ali, et al. (2020).
101 Clarkson, Overell, and Chapple (2011).
102 Clarkson, Fang, Li, and Richardson (2013).
103 Clarkson, Li, Richardson, and Vasvari (2008).
104 Higgins and Walker (2012).

References

Abdullah, M., Hamzah, N., & Abd Rahman, I. M. (2020). Pengaruh Pemilikan Asing ke atas Pendedahan Maklumat Alam Sekitar dalam Industri Sawit di Indonesia (The influence of Foreign Ownership towards environmental information disclosure in the Oil Palm Industry in Indonesia). *Asian Journal of Accounting and Governance*, 14, 1–14.

Abdullah, M., Hamzah, N., Mohd-Ali, H., Tseng, M., & Brander, M. (2020). The Southeast Asian haze : The quality of environmental disclosures and firm performance. *Journal of Cleaner Production*, 246, 1–11. Retrieved from https://doi.org/10.1016/j.jclepro.2019.118958

Alisjahbana, A. S., & Busch, J. M. (2017). Forestry, forest fires, and climate change in Indonesia. *Bulletin of Indonesian Economic Studies*, 53(2), 111–136. Retrieved from https://doi.org/10.1080/00074918.2017.1365404

Ancrenaz, M., Ambu, L., Sunjoto, I., Ahmad, E., Manokaran, K., Meijaard, E., & Lackman, I. (2010). Recent surveys in the forests of Ulu Segama Malua, Sabah, Malaysia, show that Orang-utans (P. p. morio) can be maintained in slightly logged forests. *PLoS ONE*, 5(7). Retrieved from https://doi.org/10.1371/journal.pone.0011510

Benami, E., Curran, L. M., Cochrane, M., Venturieri, A., Franco, R., Kneipp, J., & Swartos, A. (2018). Oil palm land conversion in Pará, Brazil, from 2006–2014: Evaluating the 2010 Brazilian Sustainable Palm Oil Production Program. *Environmental Research Letters*, 13(3). Retrieved from https://doi.org/10.1088/1748-9326/aaa270

Bennett, A., Ravikumar, A., & Paltán, H. (2018). The political ecology of Oil Palm Company-Community partnerships in the Peruvian Amazon: Deforestation consequences of the privatization of rural development. *World Development*, 109(September), 29–41. Retrieved from https://doi.org/10.1016/j.worlddev.2018.04.001

Bruno, L. C. (2017). Palm oil plantation productivity during the establishment of the Malaysian refinery sector, 1970–1990. *Economic History of Developing Regions*, 32(3), 221–269. Retrieved from https://doi.org/10.1080/20780389.2017.1343660

Cabedo Semper, D., & Tirado Beltrán, J. M. (2014). Risk disclosure and cost of equity: The Spanish case. *Contaduría y Administración*, 59(4), 105–135. Retrieved from https://doi.org/10.1016/S0186-1042(14)70157-3

Castiblanco, C., Etter, A., & Ramirez, A. (2015). Impacts of oil palm expansion in Colombia: What do socioeconomic indicators show? *Land Use Policy*, 44, 31–43. Retrieved from https://doi.org/10.1016/j.landusepol.2014.10.007

Castiblanco, C., Moreno, A., & Etter, A. (2015). Impact of policies and subsidies in agribusiness: The case of oil palm and biofuels in Colombia. *Energy Economics*, 49, 676–686. Retrieved from https://doi.org/10.1016/j.eneco.2015.02.025

Cattau, M. E., Marlier, M. E., & DeFries, R. (2016). Effectiveness of Roundtable on Sustainable Palm Oil (RSPO) for reducing fires on oil palm concessions in Indonesia from 2012 to 2015. *Environmental Research Letters*, 11(10). Retrieved from https://doi.org/10.1088/1748-9326/11/10/105007

Choiruzzad, S. A. B. (2019). Save Palm Oil, save the nation: Palm Oil Companies and the Shaping of Indonesia's National Interest. *Asian Politics and Policy*, 11(1), 8–26. Retrieved from https://doi.org/10.1111/aspp.12431

Clarkson, P. M., Fang, X., Li, Y., & Richardson, G. (2013). The relevance of environmental disclosures: Are such disclosures incrementally informative? *Journal of Accounting and Public Policy*, 32(5), 410–431. Retrieved 29 November 2014 from https://doi.org/10.1016/j.jaccpubpol.2013.06.008

Clarkson, P. M., Li, Y., Richardson, G. D., & Vasvari, F. P. (2008). Revisiting the relation between environmental performance and environmental disclosure: An empirical analysis. *Accounting, Organizations and Society*, 33(4–5), 303–327. Retrieved from https://doi.org/10.1016/j.aos.2007.05.003

Clarkson, P. M., Overell, M. B., & Chapple, L. (2011). Environmental reporting and its relation to corporate environmental performance. *Abacus*, 47(1), 27–60. Retrieved from https://doi.org/10.1111/j.1467-6281.2011.00330.x

Corlett, R. T. (2007). The impact of hunting on the Mammalian Fauna of Tropical Asian Forests. *Biotropica*, 39(3), 292–303.

Cramb, R., & Mccarthy, J. F. (2016). Introduction. In R. Cramb & J. F. McCarthy (Eds.), *The Oil Palm Complex: Smallholders, Agribusiness and the State in Indonesia and Malaysia* (pp. 1–26). Singapore: NUS Press. Retrieved from https://doi.org/10.2307/j.ctv1xz0km

Cramb, R., & McCarthy, J. F. (2016). Characterising Oil Palm Production in Indonesia and Malaysia. In R. Cramb & J. F. McCarthy (Eds.), *The Oil Palm Complex: Smallholders, Agribusiness and the State in Indonesia and Malaysia* (pp. 27–77). Singapore: NUS Press. Retrieved from https://doi.org/10.2307/j.ctv1xz0km.7

Davis, J. T., Mengersen, K., Abram, N. K., Ancrenaz, M., Wells, J. A., & Meijaard, E. (2013). It's not just conflict that motivates killing of Orangutans. *PLoS ONE*, 8(10). Retrieved from https://doi.org/10.1371/journal.pone.0075373

Efeca. (2015). *Comparison of the ISPO, MSPO and RSPO Standards*. Efeca. https://www.efeca.com/

Firdaus, M., Kamello, T., Saidin, O. K., & Sunarmi. (2020). Obligations of Indonesian Sustainable Palm Oil (ISPO) certification for oil palm plantation companies in North Sumatera to support sustainable development. *IOP Conference Series: Earth and Environmental Science*, 452(1). Retrieved from https://doi.org/10.1088/1755-1315/452/1/012100

Forsyth, T. (2014). Public concerns about transboundary haze: A comparison of Indonesia, Singapore, and Malaysia. *Global Environmental Change*, 25(1), 76–86. Retrieved from https://doi.org/10.1016/j.gloenvcha.2014.01.013

Furumo, P. R., & Aide, T. M. (2017). Characterizing commercial oil palm expansion in Latin America: Land use change and trade. *Environmental Research Letters*, 12(2). Retrieved from https://doi.org/10.1088/1748-9326/aa5892

Gaveau, D. L. A., Locatelli, B., Salim, M. A., Yaen, H., Pacheco, P., & Sheil, D. (2018). Rise and fall of forest loss and industrial plantations in Borneo (2000–2017). *Conservation Letters*, (November 2018), 1–8. Retrieved from https://doi.org/10.1111/conl.12622

Gaveau, D. L. A., Sheil, D., Husnayaen, Salim, M. A., Arjasakusuma, S., Ancrenaz, M., ... Meijaard, E. (2016). Rapid conversions and avoided deforestation: Examining four decades of industrial plantation expansion in Borneo. *Scientific Reports*, 6(June), 1–13. Retrieved from https://doi.org/10.1038/srep32017

Ginoga, L. N., Santosa, Y., & Mutmainnah, A. R. (2019). The loss, gain, and diversity of butterfly species due to the development of PT PKWE oil palm plantation, West Kalimantan Province. *IOP Conference Series: Earth and Environmental Science*, 336(1). Retrieved from https://doi.org/10.1088/1755-1315/336/1/012025

Gode, D., & Mohanram, P. (2003). Inferring the cost of capital using the Ohlson-Juettner model. *Review of Accounting Studies*, 8(4), 399–431. Retrieved from https://doi.org/10.1023/A:1027378728141

Grayson, J., & Stampe, J. (2012). *Palm Oil Investor Review: Investor Guidance on Palm Oil. The Role of Investors in Supporting the Development of a Sustainable Palm Oil Industry.* World Wide Fund for Nature (WWF). https://www.rspo.org/file/Palm%20Oil%20Investor%20Review%20Web%20Version.pdf

Greenpeace (2018). World's largest palm oil trader linked to rainforest destruction twice the size of Paris. Retrieved 20 August 2020, from https://www.greenpeace.org/international/press-release/17248/worlds-largest-palm-oil-trader-linked-to-rainforest-destruction-twice-the-size-of-paris/

Greenpeace (2019). *Burning Down the House.* Retrieved from https://storage.googleapis.com/planet4-international-stateless/2019/11/5c8a9799-burning-down-the-house-greenpeace-indonesia-fires-briefing.pdf [Last Accessed: 09 Jan 2022]

Gutiérrez-Vélez, V. H., DeFries, R., Pinedo-Vásquez, M., Uriarte, M., Padoch, C., Baethgen, W., ... Lim, Y. (2011). High-yield oil palm expansion spares land at the expense of forests in the Peruvian Amazon. *Environmental Research Letters*, 6(4), 044029. Retrieved from https://doi.org/10.1088/1748-9326/6/4/044029

Hidayat, N. K., Offermans, A., & Glasbergen, P. (2018). Sustainable palm oil as a public responsibility? On the governance capacity of Indonesian Standard for Sustainable Palm Oil (ISPO). *Agriculture and Human Values*, 35(1), 223–242. Retrieved from https://doi.org/10.1007/s10460-017-9816-6

Higgins, C., & Walker, R. (2012). Ethos, logos, pathos: Strategies of persuasion in social/environmental reports. *Accounting Forum*, 36(3), 194–208. Retrieved from https://doi.org/10.1016/j.accfor.2012.02.003

Huafang, X., & Jianguo, Y. (2007). Ownership structure, board composition and corporate voluntary disclosure: Evidence from listed companies in China. *Managerial Auditing Journal*, 22(6), 604–619. Retrieved from https://doi.org/10.1108/02686900710759406

Jacobson, P. (2018). Revealed: Paper giant's ex-staff say it used their names for secret company in Borneo. Retrieved from https://news.mongabay.com/2018/07/revealed-paper-giants-ex-staff-say-it-used-their-names-for-secret-company-in-borneo/

Jong, H. N. (2019). Indonesia forest-clearing ban is made permanent, but labeled 'propaganda'. Retrieved 30 October 2020, from https://news.mongabay.com/2019/08/indonesia-forest-clearing-ban-is-made-permanent-but-labeled-propaganda/

Kandiah, S., Halim, R. M., Basiron, Y., Rahman, Z. A., & Ma Ah Ngan. (2002). Continuous sterilization of fresh fruit bunches. *MPOB Information Series Malaysia*, 148, 1–4.

Khan, T. (2014). Kalimantan's biodiversity: Developing accounting models to prevent its economic destruction. *Accounting, Auditing and Accountability Journal*, 27(1), 150–182. Retrieved from https://doi.org/10.1108/AAAJ-07-2013-1392

Koh, L. P., Miettinen, J., Liew, S. C., Ghazoul, J., & Ehrlich, P. R. (2011). Remotely sensed evidence of tropical peatland conversion to oil palm. *Proceedings of the National Academy of Sciences*, 108(12), 5127–5132. Retrieved from https://doi.org/10.1073/pnas

Lee, J. S. H., Jaafar, Z., Tan, A. K. J., Carrasco, L. R., Ewing, J. J., Bickford, D. P., … Koh, L. P. (2016). Toward clearer skies: Challenges in regulating transboundary haze in Southeast Asia. *Environmental Science and Policy*, 55, 87–95. Retrieved from https://doi.org/10.1016/j.envsci.2015.09.008

McCarthy, J. F., & Cramb, R. A. (2009). Policy narratives, landholder engagement, and oil palm expansion on the Malaysian and Indonesian frontiers. *Geographical Journal*, 175(2), 112–123. Retrieved from https://doi.org/10.1111/j.1475-4959.2009.00322.x

Meijaard, E., Garcia-Ulloa, J., Sheil, D., Wich, S. A., Carlson, K. M., Juffe-Bignoli, D., & Brooks, T. M. (2018). *Oil palm and biodiversity: A situation analysis by the IUCN Oil Palm Task Force*. Retrieved from Gland, Switzerland: 10.2305/IUCN.CH.2018.11.en

Michelon, G., Pilonato, S., & Ricceri, F. (2015). CSR reporting practices and the quality of disclosure: An empirical analysis. *Critical Perspectives on Accounting*, 33, 59–78. Retrieved from https://doi.org/10.1016/j.cpa.2014.10.003

Mol, H. (2017). *The Politics of Palm Oil Harm: A Green Criminological Perspective* (pp. 123–160). Cham: Palgrave Macmillan. Retrieved from https://doi.org/10.1007/978-3-319-55378-8

Nugraha, I., & Jong, N. H. (2019, August 27). Audit BPK Temukan Banyak Perkebunan Sawit Besar Bermasalah. *Mongabay News*. Retrieved 1 August 2020 from https://www.mongabay.co.id/2019/08/27/audit-bpk-temukan-banyak-perkebunan-sawit-besar-bermasalah/

Ocampo-Peñuela, N., Garcia-Ulloa, J., Ghazoul, J., & Etter, A. (2018). Quantifying impacts of oil palm expansion on Colombia's threatened biodiversity. *Biological Conservation*, 224(May), 117–121. Retrieved from https://doi.org/10.1016/j.biocon.2018.05.024

Proforest (2020). Understanding commitments to no deforestation, peat and exploitation. Retrieved from https://proforest.net/proforest/en/publications/infonote_04_introndpe.pdf

Purnomo, H., Shantiko, B., Sitorus, S., Gunawan, H., Achdiawan, R., Kartodihardjo, H., & Dewayani, A. A. (2017). Fire economy and actor network of forest and land fires in Indonesia. *Forest Policy and Economics*, 78, 21–31. Retrieved from https://doi.org/10.1016/j.forpol.2017.01.001

Purnomo, E. P., Ramdani, R., Agustiyara, Tomaro, Q. P. V., & Samidjo, G. S. (2019). Land ownership transformation before and after forest fires in Indonesian palm oil plantation areas. *Journal of Land Use Science*, 14(1), 37–51. Retrieved from https://doi.org/10.1080/1747423X.2019.1614686

Qian, W., & Schaltegger, S. (2017). Revisiting carbon disclosure and performance: Legitimacy and management views. *The British Accounting Review*, 49(4), 365–379. Retrieved from https://doi.org/10.1016/j.bar.2017.05.005

Santika, T., Ancrenaz, M., Wilson, K. A., Spehar, S., Abram, N., Banes, G. L., … Meijaard, E. (2017). First integrative trend analysis for a great ape species in Borneo. *Scientific Reports*, 7(1), 1–16. Retrieved from https://doi.org/10.1038/s41598-017-04435-9

Seaman, D. J. I., Bernard, H., Ancrenaz, M., Coomes, D., Swinfield, T., Milodowski, D. T., … Struebig, M. J. (2019). Densities of Bornean orang-utans (Pongo pygmaeus morio) in heavily degraded forest and oil palm plantations in Sabah, Borneo. *American Journal of Primatology*, 81(8). Retrieved from https://doi.org/10.1002/ajp.23030

Shevade, V. S., & Loboda, T. V. (2019). Oil palm plantations in Peninsular Malaysia: Determinants and constraints on expansion. *PLoS ONE*, 14(2), 2010–2017. Retrieved from https://doi.org/10.1371/journal.pone.0210628

Singagerda, F. S., Hendrowati, T. Y., & Sanusi, A. (2018). Indonesia growth of economics and the industrialization biodiesel based CPO. *International Journal of Energy Economics and Policy*, 8(5), 319–334.

Sloan, S. (2014). Indonesia's moratorium on new forest licenses: An update. *Land Use Policy*, 38, 37–40. Retrieved from https://doi.org/10.1016/j.landusepol.2013.10.018

SPOTT: ZSL. (2020). Indicators and scoring criteria for assessing palm oil producers, processors and traders – November 2020. Retrieved from https://www.spott.org/wp-content/uploads/sites/3/2019/10/SPOTT-Palm-oil-scoring-criteria-2019.pdf

Tata, H. L., van Noordwijk, M., Ruysschaert, D., Mulia, R., Rahayu, S., Mulyoutami, E., … Dewi, S. (2014). Will funding to Reduce Emissions from Deforestation and (forest) Degradation (REDD+) stop conversion of peat swamps to oil palm in orangutan habitat in Tripa in Aceh, Indonesia? *Mitigation and Adaptation Strategies for Global Change*, 19(6), 693–713. Retrieved from https://doi.org/10.1007/s11027-013-9524-5

Teh, B. S. C. (2016). *Availability, use, and removal of oil palm biomass in Indonesia. Report prepared for the International Council on Clean Transportation*. Retrieved from https://theicct.org/publications/availability-use-and-removal-oil-palm-biomass-indonesia [Last Accessed 09 Jan 2022].

The Sustainable Finance Platform. (2020). A guideline on the use of deforestation risk mitigation solutions for financial institutions from the sustainable finance platform mitigation sources for financial institutions content. Retrieved from https://www.dnb.nl/binaries/DNB Deforestation Guideline Document_ASN_21_08 DNB_tcm46-390356.pdf

Timmins, H. (2017). Opsi legal perlindungan hutan in indonesia pada lahan zona pertanian di indonesia. Retrieved from https://www.earthworm.org/uploads/files/OPSI-LEGAL-PERLINDUNGAN-HUTAN-IN-INDONESIA-PADA-LAHAN-ZONA.pdf

Varkkey, H. (2012). Patronage politics as a driver of economic regionalisation: The Indonesian oil palm sector and transboundary haze. *Asia Pacific Viewpoint*, 53(3), 314–329. Retrieved from https://doi.org/10.1111/j.1467-8373.2012.01493.x

Varkkey, H. (2013). Malaysian investors in the Indonesian oil palm plantation sector: Home state facilitation and transboundary haze. *Asia Pacific Business Review*, 19(3), 381–401. Retrieved from https://doi.org/10.1080/13602381.2012.748262

Varkkey, H., Tyson, A., & Choiruzzad, S. A. B. (2018). Palm oil intensification and expansion in Indonesia and Malaysia: Environmental and socio-political factors influencing policy. *Forest Policy and Economics*, 92(July), 148–159. Retrieved from https://doi.org/10.1016/j.forpol.2018.05.002

Vijay, V., Pimm, S. L., Jenkins, C. N., & Smith, S. J. (2016). The impacts of oil palm on recent deforestation and biodiversity loss. *PLoS ONE*, 11(7), 1–19. Retrieved from https://doi.org/10.1371/journal.pone.0159668

Vijay, V., Reid, C. D., Finer, M., Jenkins, C. N., & Pimm, S. L. (2018). Deforestation risks posed by oil palm expansion in the Peruvian Amazon. *Environmental Research Letters*, 13(11). Retrieved from https://doi.org/10.1088/1748-9326/aae540

Voora, V., Larrea, C., Bermudez, S., & Baliño, S. (2019). Global market report : Palm Oil. *International Institute for Sustainable Development*. Retrieved from https://www.iisd.org/system/files/publications/ssi-global-market-report-palm-oil.pdf

Wilcove, D. S., & Koh, L. P. (2010). Addressing the threats to biodiversity from oil-palm agriculture. *Biodiversity and Conservation*, 19(4), 999–1007. Retrieved from https://doi.org/10.1007/s10531-009-9760-x

Yudea, C., & Santosa, Y. (2019). How does oil palm plantation impact bird species diversity? A case study from PKWE Estate, West Kalimantan. *IOP Conference Series: Earth and Environmental Science*, 336(1). Retrieved from https://doi.org/10.1088/1755-1315/336/1/012026

Yue, S., Brodie, J. F., Zipkin, E. F., & Bernard, H. (2015). Oil palm plantations fail to support mammal diversity. *Ecological Applications*, 25(8), 2285–2292.

Yui, S., & Yeh, S. (2013). Land use change emissions from oil palm expansion in Pará, Brazil depend on proper policy enforcement on deforested lands. *Environmental Research Letters*, 8(4). Retrieved from https://doi.org/10.1088/1748-9326/8/4/044031

Zoological Society of London -ZSL. (2017). Hidden Land, Hidden Risks ? London. Retrieved from http://www.spott.org/wp-content/uploads/sites/3/2017/05/Hidden-Land_Hidden-Risks.pdf

7

CULTURAL AND RELIGIOUS ASPECTS OF EXTINCTION GOVERNANCE IN THE MIDDLE EAST

Accounting for Camels in the Israeli Context

Mira Lieberman

Introduction

Although Israel is a small country of about 20,000 km^2, it resides at the junction of three continents and is rich in diversity of wildlife.[1] Long and narrow, Israel is approximately 470 kilometres long and approximately 135 kilometres wide at its widest point. The total area of the state of Israel – including Judea and Samaria (the West Bank) and the Golan Heights – is 22,145 sq. km., of which 2.1% is water.[2] Israel is densely populated, exceeding 6 million, yielding an average density of about 300 persons/km^2. The majority of the population in Israel comprises Jews (74.8%) and Arabs (20.8%), of which 84.7% are Muslims.[3]

Israel is quite conservation-minded with strict wildlife protection laws. The dromedary camel, not native to Israel, has now become an icon of the Arab Middle East.[4] About 60% of the world's camel population is found in Somalia, Sudan, Ethiopia and Kenya.[5] In Israel, it is thought that the camel population is declining, although the sector is unregulated and it is therefore difficult to pinpoint an exact census.[6]

Camels have had a close relationship with humans, with the very first event where this intriguing species is mentioned in the Hebrew Bible dealing with Abraham's sojourn in Egypt (Gen 12:11–13).[7] In Israel, the main community which has had a close relationship with camels are the Bedouin, a nomadic Muslim Arab population with cultural, historical and social uniqueness. While non-Bedouin Muslim Arabs who live in villages spread around the country, mostly in the northern and central part of Israel, do not own camels, many of the Bedouin who live in southern Israel do own dromedary camels and consume camel products.[8]

DOI: 10.4324/9781003045557-10

However, breeding camels present health risks. Dromedary camels in the region have been found to be highly seropositive for hepatitis E (HEV[9]), with camels in Egypt similarly reported to carry the disease.

Culturally, the dromedary camel is associated with 'backwardness and lack of prosperity and delineates a physical and political barrier between Israeli authorities and the Bedouin community, who rear camels for meat, milk and tourism".[10]

This contribution sketches out the geopolitical ecology of camels in Israel. The following section introduces animal protection in Israeli society; the religious and moral considerations for animal protection that can be found in Judaism are discussed. These foundations have inspired the legislation on animals in Israel. However, while the basis for animal protection and care is strong in Jewish tradition and progress has been made in some areas, this arena of unregulated and unofficial camel husbandry is a point of contention that entails political, economic, cultural and religious complexities. The study draws on secondary data, such as the legislature, news items, images, websites and academic articles. Primary data draw from an interview with a prominent figure in the Israeli Camel Breeders Association (ICBA) and a zoo technologist (participant A).

IMAGE 7.1 Dromedary camel (Atkins, 2021a).

Wildlife Protection and Laws in ISRAEL

Policymakers of Israel have united to increase the importance of the issue of cruelty to animals and animal suffering as a topic at the Knesset and have been promoting animal welfare and animal rights in an unprecedented way in recent years, irrespective of their political affiliation.[11] For example, a subcommittee for cruelty towards animals has been created, and Animals Rights Day is marked with vegan dishes to be served to the Members of Parliament.[12] Apart from Egypt, who, in 2014 added into its Constitution the principle of humane treatment of animals in 2014, Israel is the only country in the Middle East to enact anti-animal cruelty legislation and to regulate their welfare.[13]

In October 2010, Israel joined other parties to the Convention on Biological Diversity in adopting an updated strategic plan for biodiversity for 2011–2020. Aimed at guiding international and national efforts to save biodiversity, the plan consists of 20 specific targets, called the Aichi Biodiversity Targets. Five strategic goals were identified as crucial to achieve these targets. Actions have been taken by both governmental and non-governmental bodies in Israel in an effort to do so.[14]

Religious and Moral Fundaments of Animal Protection in Judaism

The most fundamental connection between human beings and animals is found in Genesis. Adam named all non-human and human animals who are thought to have been speaking the same language before the 'original sin'. Despite the belief that the animal kingdom was to be under the dominion of man who was given permission to employ animals in useful services, the Torah states that the original intention of the scripts depicts Adam and Eve as vegetarians, with meat-eating not permitted.[15] Additionally, Genesis emphasises the link between humanity – adam – and the earth – adamah.[16]

Following on in the history of the Old Testament is the story of Noah's ark, symbolising a fundamental turning-point regarding the relationship between human and non-human animals. Only after punishing man's behaviours, did God decide to allow humans to eat animals within the Seven Laws – known as the Noahide laws[17] – due to man's supposed intrinsic weakness? As a consequence, only after the flood, has man been given the limited 'right' to kill animals for food?

The principle of *tsaar ba'alei chayim, Tza'ar* is an (ancient) Hebrew word for 'suffering', prohibiting unnecessary pain to animals, was laid down by the Torah more than 3,000 years ago. There is consequently a biblical limit to man's cruelty and use of animals for human need (Lercier, 2017). Israeli rabbi Asa Kesiar has argued that the slaughter of animals in contemporary times violates tza'ar ba'alei chayim and should not be considered kosher.[18] Additionally, Israeli rabbi Simchah Roth has argued that contemporary slaughter 'constitutes cruelty to animals which is forbidden by the Torah'.[19]

From the Rabbinic Interpretation

One of the most famous Jewish scholars of the 12th century Orthodox movement, Maimonides, considered animals to exist for their own sake, and independently of man because they were created by God's will. He further considered there was no difference between the pain of Man and this of other living creatures. An interesting perspective in his teaching of the restriction of killing the offspring in the sight of its mother, based on the feelings of love and tenderness that both human and non-human animals share towards their young: such a scene would convey extreme pain and has led to the Jewish prohibition of killing a mother and its offspring on the same day.[20]

Another very interesting perspective regards the extinction of species. From a Jewish point of view, it is not permitted to bring an entire species to extinction, according to Nachmanides, based on the idea that nothing is deemed to have been created in vain, according to the Talmud. Reform Judaism, for its part, considers that dominion over animals comes with an obligation to protect all God's creatures, as they all have an intrinsic value, also supported by the views of Maimonides. Notably, the concept of *tikkun olam*, meaning healing the world, calls for supporting the protection of endangered species and their habitats. Moreover, it considers the duty of care to domestic animals to be a moral obligation, while hunting is considered by the three movements as being a violation of Jewish ethical codes, such as the principles of tsaar ba'alei chayim and bal tashchit, as well as a cruel and wasteful sport.[21]

Overview of the Legislation on Animals in Israel: Cruelty, Companions, Experiments and Wildlife

The two main Israeli authorities heading the statutory protection of animals in Israel are the Ministry for the Environment and the Ministry of Agriculture. The Ministry of Agriculture is charged with enacting regulations concerning the keeping of animals, the conditions of transporting animals, the means of killing animals (except for the slaughter for food), training animals and animal exhibitions.[22]

Anti-cruelty Legislation and General Animal Protection Framework

The Animal Protection Act on Cruelty to Animals 5754-1994 is the main Israeli legislation regulating the treatment of animals listing the punishment for acts of cruelty towards animals.[23]

The law on cruelty to animals while seemingly 'a broad yet efficient text aimed at regulating a wide range of human behaviours towards all animals' suffers major flaws. Twenty-five years after its institution, the Ministry of Agriculture is beholden to farmers, with 'livestock' animals, the most vulnerable of creatures are those who suffer.[24] It is important to note that camels, although bred for their meat and milk, are not mentioned. The religious slaughter of animals for the purposes of food is not covered by this legislation, as the legislator does not want to interfere with either Jewish or Muslim ritual slaughter.[25] Because camels are not eaten by the Jewish community in Israel and the husbandry of camels is not regulated, there is a risk of unregulated abuse.

> (1) Participant A: "there are also Bedouins that keep camels in terrible conditions look I'm trying to be politically correct there is a link let me think a bit third world countries do not place emphasis on animal welfare for example in India that is third world there are the best laws in the world in the area of camels but they aren't put in practice and there is no regulation and accountability"

Pertinent for camels as we shall see in a later discussion, particularly during the COVID-19 epidemic, is the regulation relating to the slaughter of animals concerned with specific regulations of the Rabies and Animal Diseases ordinances of 1934 and 198530. This is excluded for the general interest of the State to prevent and eradicate zoonoses.

The law on cruelty to animals protects animals used for work, aiming to ensure the respect of natural limitations imposed upon animals, resulting in care for their physical condition, and must be accounted for when prohibiting unfit animals to work. Working any animal to exhaustion is equally forbidden under Section 3 of the law. This provision derives from Jewish laws. For example, it requires that animals rest on Shabbat. Significantly, the Knesset amended the law in 2015 to establish the duty of care of the animal's guardian, as well as a provision for the basic needs of an animal as a question of welfare, ensuring that abandonment can result in sanction when perpetrated by non-owners also: the law is to be applied both to the owner and to the holder of the animal, regardless of ownership. In addition to this, another new and major provision was introduced by the 2015 amendment, singling out the responsibility of senior executives of corporations that handle animals, such as slaughterhouses, obliging them to prevent abuse against animals and emphasising their responsibility of supervising animal welfare from the top down.[26]

Wild Animal Protection and Biodiversity Conservation

The Wildlife Protection Law (1955)[27] serves as Israel's implementation tool for the Convention on International Trade in Endangered Species of Wild Fauna and Flora.[28]

In the same order of ideas, the National Parks, Nature Reserves, National Sites and Memorial Sites Law 575248 (1998)[29] instituted national parks, defined as an area serving the preservation of nature among others, and nature reserves defined as 'an area in which animals, vegetation, abiotic objects, soil, caves, water or landscape, which are of scientific or educational interest, are preserved from undesirable changes in their appearance, their biological composition or their development process' to be declared by the Ministry of the Interior, and established the protection of natural assets regarding their worth or danger of extinction.

Camel Ecology in Israel and Conservation Status

Climate and Topography of Israel

Within the small land area of Israel, two opposing climatic ecologies are found: Mediterranean in the north and desert in the south. The central part of the country is a transition area between these two climatic regions where desert biota is gradually replaced by Mediterranean biota.[30] Since human settlements are relatively few in desert regions, such as in the Negev, and while the desert ecosystems are under legal conservation protection, threats to the desert biodiversity indicated by the Change in Abundance of Selected Species Index suggest that in 2000, the Negev supported only 60–80% of their biodiversity abundance. In addition, by 2050, these desert regions may lose up to 60% more of their biodiversity.[31] In fact, we need not wait until 2050, as there is increasing evidence suggesting that the process of desertification in the Negev has already begun and may accelerate in the future. In the light of this, an efficient long-term strategy for the Negev's development is essential. This plan requires minimising adverse environmental impacts on one hand and pursuing economic feasibility on the other.[32]

The Dromedary Camel Ecology in Israel

Geographic Distribution and Habitat

The camel belongs to the camelidae family of mammals among the order of Artiodactyls and to the suborder of tylopoda (animals with padded feet). Differentiating this from ruminants, camelidae family is comprised of two main species of three genera: Camelus, Lama and Vicugna (see Figure 7.1).[33] There are three main species of camels: the Bactrian camel, *Camelus bactrianus*, characteristic for their two humps is found primarily in colder climates in Central Asia. The second species, the Dromedary or Arabian camel, *Camelus dromedarius*, sports one hump and is found in the Middle East, Africa and South Asia.[34]

While the Dromedary and Bactrian camels are both domesticated species, the third, the Wild Bactrian camel, *Camelus ferus*, is wild and very shy, living in remote areas of northwest China and Mongolia, the only truly wild camel in the world.[35] The Wild Bactrian camels are critically endangered and number approximately 1,400, inhabiting the Gobi and Taklamakan Deserts in China and Mongolia.[36] The Dromedary and Bactrian species are present in almost all the arid lands of the old world (except Southern Africa), in over 35 million km^2.[37]

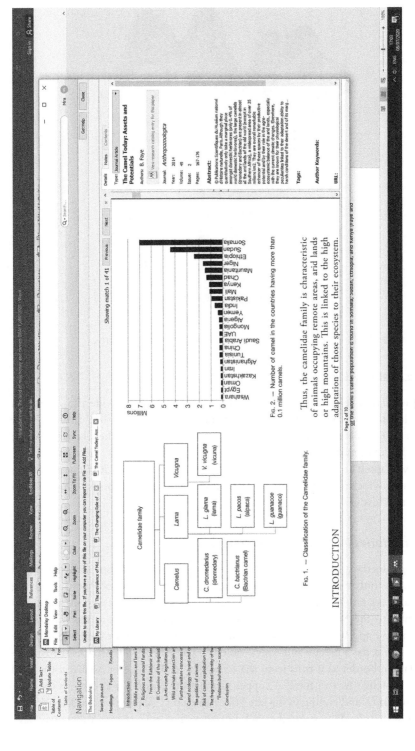

FIGURE 7.1 Zoological classification of the Camelidae family.[38]

IMAGE 7.2   Wild Bactrian Camel, Camelus Ferus[39] (Atkins, 2021b).

Specialist Physiology and Ecology

Camels have a split upper lip and can open their mouth very wide allowing them to select the soft parts of thorny desert plants. In a sandstorm, they can close their nostrils. Camels can survive up to six months on the fat in their humps. While in other mammals the fat is distributed throughout the body, the camel is perfectly adapted to life in an arid, harsh environment because its fat accumulates in a single location, the hump(s). This allows the camel to dissipate heat with a minimal loss of water.[40]

Dromedaries in the Israeli Landscape

The dromedary camel, Camelus dromedarius, in comparison with sheep and dogs, was only recently domesticated, with early inhabitants of Palestine relying on donkeys rather than camels.[41] The introduction of camels as pack and travel animals to the Southern Levant, contrary to popular belief, as recently as between 930 and 900 B.C., was at a crucial economic point in the history of the region of today's Negev and Arava Valley.[42] The Arava Valley marks the Israeli–Jordanian border as it runs from the Dead Sea to the Gulf of Aqaba in the Red Sea. This area was a centre of copper production beginning as early as the 14th century B.C. and ending in the late 9th century B.C. Sapir-Hen and Ben-Yosef[43] suggest that the domesticated camels buried at sites in the Arava Valley may have been among the first creatures to leave Arabia and enter Israel. Today, the Arava region produces more than half of Israel's agricultural exports, despite its harsh environment.

Today, there are approximately 4,000 camels in the Negev,[44] about two camels per 100 Bedouin, whereas, from 1955 to 1961, there were between 56 and 61 camels per 100 Bedouin. The large difference in this ratio is due to changes in the Bedouin lifestyle.[45] However, it is difficult to precisely estimate the number of camels in Israel primarily due to the nature of the Bedouin nomadic and pastoralist lifestyle, moving frequently. As a result, many Bedouin settlements are not officially recognised by Israeli authorities. Consequently, camels are not vaccinated and registered, contributing to a growing tension between Jewish populations, Israeli authorities and the Bedouin communities.[46]

The Politics of Camels

The Bedouin Community in Israel

The nomadic lifestyle of the Bedouin has been continuously threatened with the introduction of cars, economic and land development factors, slowly closing in on open and wild desert spaces.[47] Traditionally, Negev Bedouin depended on semi-nomadic pastoralism for their livelihood and has a long history of camel husbandry where they were used as pack animals, for transportation and for ploughing.[48] In Bedouin of the Negev (1967 in Degen, El-Meccawi and Kam, 2019), Marx states that '[t]he Arabic term badawi, from which Bedouin is derived, denotes a nomadic inhabitant of the desert (bādiah) who depends for his livelihood on herds of camels and sheep'. However, with the changing economy, landscape and increased urbanisation, camel rearing is decreasing.

Camels were a source of pride and a symbol of richness for Bedouin.[49] They were used for riding, racing and display on special occasions such as weddings and often used for the traditional bride price, the mohar (mahr – مَهْر) (El-Aref, 1944 in Degen, El-Meccawi and Kam, 2019). In 2009, the Bedouin citizens of the Negev constituted 15.6% of the total Arab population of Arab citizens Israel (1,239,230 not including the 296,370 Arab residents of East Jerusalem).[50] It is mainly nomadic and semi-nomadic Muslim herders who raise camels in arid and semi-arid landscapes.[51]

Camel Tagging and Chipping

Dromedary camels represent a highly politicised arena in Israel. The nature of the ICBA evidences the politically charged nature of this. The ICBA is chaired by an Israeli of Jewish European descent, which may be suggestive that Bedouin, who are the main population of camel owners, are so marginalised that the chairman acts as a mediator between the community and authority figures.

(2) "There was a need for someone to represent them in front of the governmental bodies that is the ministry of agriculture the veterinary services, the Knesset and the like there were also laws that were coming out that we wanted to be involved with" (Participant A).

When asked why camel husbandry is not an officially recognised agricultural practice and whether the camel breeders' association face government backlash, the political tension is evident in the following interaction:

(3) Participant A: of course of course yes the basic thing is that the Ministry of Agriculture does not officially recognise camel husbandry like sheep for example
Interviewer: why
Participant A: do you really want to get into that
Interviewer: I'm trying to understand
Participant A: due to a lot of reasons political reasons, reasons of control from a lot of reasons you have to understand that most of the camels in Israel are owned by the Bedouin population

Since camel husbandry is not a recognised agricultural practice, they are not allotted grazing grounds and are not allowed to forage freely. However, some Bedouin allow their camels to roam. As a result, there have been a number of road accidents involving camels; 15 people have been killed and 350 injured since 2008 due to straying camels, and in cases where their owners were traced, they were held responsible for these accidents.[52] Road signs have been erected in the Negev warning drivers to beware of camels near the road. Resolution of wildlife–human conflicts in Israel falls under the jurisdiction of the Israel Nature and Parks Authority (INPA), the single government agency responsible for all aspects of wildlife and nature protection, including hunting. The INPA is connected with the Ministry of Environment, not the Ministry of Agriculture. Nevertheless, the INPA emphasises the importance of cooperation with farmers for the successful resolution of wildlife–agriculture conflicts, which leads to the better overall conservation of wildlife.[53]

In the case of roaming camels, the Ministry claims that the Bedouin's lack of responsiveness and cooperation has been a major obstruction in solving the road collisions: 'Cooperation is very problematic'.[54] The Ministry of Agriculture notes that the legal responsibility for capturing camels that endanger the road users is under the authority of the police, while the veterinary services' statutory role in the Ministry of Agriculture is to protect public health and animals from animal diseases. As such, the Ministry holds that they

assist the authorities through special search and seizure operations. Such operations are carried out by the Central Enforcement and Investigation

Unit of the Ministry in cooperation with the local authority, the Israel Police and the Green Patrol office's veterinary services.

Thus, camels are symbolic intermediaries in the political arena of the Israeli government and the Bedouin. For example, participant A cites the camel tagging law as an accomplishment of the ICBA, as both another incremental step towards rendering camel breeding official and as a sign of partial recognition and collaboration with authorities. However, it remains unclear how the Bedouin perceive the new tagging law. Tagging is an accounting practice that entails the exercise of power and control on the part of the government, as well as accountability on the part of the owner. Tagging is reminiscent of the Nazi practice of tattooing inmates with number identification in concentration camps. Funnell[55] argues that accounting numbers substituted the humanity of prisoners, denying their humanity and individuality. In a similar manner, marking animals with numbers renders them a mere commodity, devoid of individuality and sentience. Additionally, similarly to the Nazi accounting operations, the process of accounting for camels through tagging enhances government control over both camels as commodities as well as Bedouin because it renders the camel owners visible: 'making certain aspects of reality "visible" it creates the possibility of controlling these elements. It is this partiality in representation and its control potential which constitutes its real social influence as well as its social danger'.[56]

While tagging can be seen as a cruel practice, evidence in the field suggests that there is a need for subcutaneous tagging, particularly in the event where camels were maimed and deformed when owners ripped their tagged ears off.

(2) Interviewer: and who accounts for camel welfare on the farms?
Participant A: theoretically the veterinary services it's very theoretical there is a department that deals with animal welfare but they are rarely out in the field. In extreme cases with Brucella [Brucellosis – ML) even a few people died from camel milk so if a vet arrives to take blood for Brucella and if they see that the camels are in a catastrophic state what most vets will not be able to detect as they do not have the indicators but if that happens then camels can be confiscated but that does not happen often the veterinary services do not have inspectors out in the field that go and check if someone complains then they will come.

The government has long held a long-term plan to phase out the Bedouin's nomadic lifestyle and incorporate the community into the dominant urban, wage-earning way of life.[57] It could be said that the tagging of camels inserts Bedouin and camels into a bureaucratic system, which is a form of surveillance aimed at forcing a cultural and lifestyle alteration. Surveillance inscribed at the level of society is not merely a tool for resolving security dilemmas.[58] In sorting the population, surveillance techniques facilitate the subjection of the Palestinians to Israeli power, 'rendering them susceptible to all manner of state intervention, from quotidian monitoring to military onslaught' (Anderson, 2011: 213). Israel's legal code allows for everyone from tax authorities to the military police to instigate surveillance of individuals, which, in this context is done through camels.

In the early 1960s, the Israeli government initiated a policy of planned sedentarisation of the Negev Bedouin.[59] The Bedouin speak bitterly about the lack of grazing lands, expensive feed and the recent tax laws on camels. They are convinced that the government's intention is to rid the Negev of camels. Nonetheless, there is an obvious affection and special feeling for camels among Bedouin.[60]

However, even in urban settings, Bedouin continue to raise livestock for which the main motivation is economic. Some Bedouin have large flocks and/or

TABLE 7.1 Average of animal cost in a market NIS = New Israeli Shekel 1 NIS = 0.23 GBP

Animal	Type	Cost (in NIS)
Sheep	Lambs of raising	400–500
	Rams of slaughter (40–60 kg)	1,300–1,700
	Ewes of breeding	900–1,100
	Rams of breeding	2,000–3,000
Goat	Kids of raising	300–450
	Bucks of slaughter (40–60 kg)	900–1,400
	Does of breeding	800–1,200
	Bucks of breeding	1,800–2,200
Camel	Calves of slaughter	1,500–2,500
	Cows of breeding	5,000–8,000
Cattle	Male beef calves of slaughter (450 kg)	5,600–5,900
	Male dairy calves of slaughter (450 kg)	4,600–5,400
Rabbit	Sub-audit	15–20
	Adult female	30–40
	Adult male	30–40
Bedouin chicken	Male	40–50
	Female	30–40
Pigeon	Local (*baladi*)	15–20 pairs
	Fancy	50–500 pairs
Turkey	Adult female	50–60
	Adult male	50–60
Duck	Adult female	40–45
	Adult male	40–45
Geese	Adult female	55–70
	Adult male	55–70

Degen and El-Meccawi "Livestock Production among Urban Negev Bedouin," 331.

herds and livestock are their prime source of income, and keeping livestock allows them to maintain their traditional lifestyle. Incomes of urban Bedouin families are among the lowest in the country and unemployment is high. Retention of some livestock, which provides families with milk and other dairy products, as well as with meat and eggs, may be a rational choice as a supplement for those Bedouin who are financially stressed. Keeping animals acts as a hedge against the risk of unemployment and, if sheep, goat and camel production does become more profitable, owning some animals makes it easier to start.[61]

In one particular Bedouin community, Tel Sheva, one of the seven established urban Bedouin communities founded in 1967 and which received local council status in 1984, animals were raised by 68% of the households.[62] Conversely, only about 17% of Bedouin urban entrepreneurs residing in Rahat cited livestock trade, large-scale irrigated farming and greenhouse farming as their 'type of business'. Nonetheless, livestock production and trading still play an important role in Bedouin lifestyles.

There is much less need for camels today, as many of their traditional uses are not required. Camels are not used for transport, as pickup trucks have taken over, and are not used to plough the land, as tractors have replaced them. Negev Bedouin do not generally slaughter camels, although the meat can be eaten according to Moslem dietary laws. In the past, some camels and male calves were sold to traders from the administered territories where they were slaughtered for meat. However, this option is practically non-existent today due to security reasons. Females are milked, as Bedouin believe that milk is very healthy.

Camels are also used in ecotourism in Israel. Eight tourist sites in the Negev offer camel rides. These sites are generally staffed by Bedouin and offer Bedouin meals, accommodations (in tents and luxurious quarters) and workshops on Bedouin activities, such as weaving and pita making. They can host large events such as weddings and bar/bat mitzvahs and can serve kosher food. However, it is important to note that except for the Negev Camel Ranch and Succat Ha-Midbar, all sites earned less income from camel rides than from other activities.[63]

Health Risks Arising from Camel Exploitation

While marking the camels may enforce accountability on owners to some extent, the health risk arising from breeding and keeping camels will not be solved by penning them in, or tagging them, as brutally demonstrated by COVID-19.

Emerging and re-emerging viral diseases are of great public health concern. The recent emergence of severe acute respiratory syndrome (SARS)-related coronavirus (SARS-CoV-2) in December 2019 in China, which causes COVID-19 disease in humans, and its current spread around the world, leading to the first pandemic in history to be caused by a coronavirus, highlights the significance of zoonotic viral diseases.[64]

The crisis borne out of the COVID-19 pandemic has highlighted the problems inherent in animal agriculture, the destruction of the ecosystem and the interrelation, the fragile web of all living beings depending on each other's survival. The zoonotic aspect of the COVID-19 virus points to several problematic human–animal intersections: the human consumption of potentially infected wild animals, the illegal wildlife trade and the crowded conditions in which humans and animals interact within live animal markets, on the one hand, and industrialised animal agriculture on the other.

Atkins et al.[65] highlight that there is growing evidence of links between biodiversity loss, species extinction and COVID-19. The pandemic may expose even further the risk of biodiversity loss and alert investors to the need to protect species.

As Paulin[66] notes 'industrial farming and intense animal density in small and restricted spaces, the destruction of habitats and of ecosystems, [and] a general increase in the consumption of meat in many industrialised countries since the 19th century' all shape relationships between humans, animals and disease. Importantly, COVID-19 and other zoonoses are not limited to wild animals, even

> your average chicken or pig farm is perfectly capable of starting a deadly outbreak. While the wet markets in China might be particularly risky due to the wide variety of animals in close contact with each other, any situation in which a large number of animals are kept in cramped quarters with frequent human contact poses a threat.[67]

With the outbreak of COVID-19, the Ministry of Agriculture and Development issued a protocol for caring for camels.[68] However, many Bedouin are reluctant to raise camels because of recent tax laws. Camel herding is not recognised by the Israeli Ministry of Agriculture as a branch of animal production and, consequently, camel owners cannot acquire permits to graze their herds on government lands, as can some sheepherders.

The Koran sanctions consumption of camel meat if the camel is slaughtered according to halal traditions. From 1961 to 2009, camel meat production worldwide increased at a rate of about 2.8% per year, mainly due to consumption in predominantly Muslim countries.[69] In the Negev, Bedouin usually sell excess young male and culled camels to traders from the administered territories. It is compulsory for camels in Israel to be vaccinated against rabies and brucellosis and some Bedouin also vaccinate against tetanus and inject their animals against internal and external parasites.[70]

When vaccinated, each camel receives an individually numbered ear tag and is registered with the government and tax authorities. Most Bedouin are reluctant to register their camels and, consequently, many camels are not vaccinated. This has led to outbreaks of brucellosis, a serious illness that mostly affects sheep but also camels and other mammals.[71] The infection was traced to unpasteurised camel milk or camel milk products.[72] Brucellosis is a common zoonotic infection around the world, affecting humans and several domestic animals including sheep, goats, cows and camels. The main source of infection is food-borne through the ingestion of unpasteurised, contaminated dairy products.[73] Shimol et al.[74] report a local brucellosis outbreak in 15 extended Bedouin family members following the ingestion of infected camel milk and emphasise that the Bedouin population of southern Israel is at increased risk for acquiring brucellosis due to frequent contact with domestic animals and ingestion of unpasteurised animal milk.

There are two farms in the Negev that produce camel milk commercially. The one at Tarabin village, 'Bereshit', was established in 2005 and is owned in partnership by a Bedouin from the Tarabin el-Sana tribe and a Jewish Israeli. Brucellosis was detected in three camels in 2017 and the Ministry of Health closed down all milking.[75]

COVID-19 has given us a window into a whole slew of infectious diseases associated with camel husbandry. For example, another health risk involving camel husbandry in Israel is hepatitis E virus (HEV), an emerging cause of viral hepatitis worldwide with human HEV infection associated with the consumption of meat products, especially pork.[76] Recently, HEV-7 has been shown to infect camels and humans. Bassal et al. examine HEV seroprevalence in dromedary camels and among Bedouin, Arabs (Muslims, non-Bedouin) and Jews.[77] The high seropositivity in camels and in over 40-year-old Bedouin and non-Bedouin Arabs suggests that HEV is endemic in Israel. The low HEV seroprevalence in Jews could be attributed to a higher socioeconomic status.

An additional health risk involving camels in Israel is borne by an outbreak of trypanosomiasis caused by Trypanosoma evansi involving horses, camels and donkeys.[78] Animal trypanosomiasis is a wasting disease affecting mainly equids, camels and cattle. It is characterised by 'chronic weight loss, icterus, subcutaneous edema, anaemia and neurological abnormalities, transmitted by blood-sucking flies'.

Finally, the Middle East respiratory syndrome coronavirus, MERS-CoV, a member of the Betacoronavirus was first identified in Saudi Arabia in 2012.[79] Dromedary camels are one potential source of human MERS-CoV infection. As of July 2020, there were 2,494 laboratory-confirmed human MERS-CoV cases reported to WHO, including at least 858 MERS-CoV-related deaths.[80]

Camels, Identity and Indexicality

Camels in the Jewish–Israeli Community

It was a picture of a camel that started the Taglit project, or as it is known in America, The Birthright Project ('ancestral right' or 'birthright'), allowing every Jew to enter Israel following the Law of Return at 18 to 32 years of age for a ten-day educational journey. This project was hatched by Yossi Beilin, an Israeli politician identifying with a Zionist-left wing, who came across a photo that was printed in the early 1990s on the front page of the Atlanta Herald, the Chairman of the Jewish Federations of North America riding a camel on the occasion of Israel's Independence Day. Yossi Beilin is quoted commenting that

> It annoyed me, because we were introduced as a country with camels, 'Yossi Beilin recalled, and the anger echoed in his words as if it had happened yesterday.' How many Israelis have ever seen camels in their lives? I told myself, Halas.[81,82]

Following this utterance, camels could be said to negatively index the identity that Israel would like to create for itself. Additionally, the use of Israelis here denotes Jewish–Israelis, suggesting that Jewish–Israelis, as opposed to Arab–Israelis, strive for a separate identity. Indeed, in recent years, there has been criticism that the Birthright programme is 'right wing' and does not include dialogue with Palestinians.[83]

Camels have accompanied many Jewish migrants to Israel and have featured as a link connecting them to their old country. Such is the story of Heftisba Babayof who immigrated to Israel on a convoy of camels from Bukhara to Jerusalem at the end of the 19th century, fighting against poverty and supporting her family single-handedly by starting a laundrette.[84]

Camels were not only symbolic of the richness left behind by immigrants from Arabic countries, but were also token of local richness, not only economic but of a magical childhood, adventures in a land not yet spoilt by modernity as captured by the reminiscence of Lea Naor Mikovsky:

> When we saw in the distance the small camel convoy, two camels approaching the wadi, and Dad riding the first camel. Dad would make strange noises only the camel understood. The camel listened to the voices and slowly folded its front legs, and Dad was leaning over us. Then the camel was a little snorty, gently folding and carefully folding his two hind legs as well, looking at us with huge, brown, good eyes. Dad would come down from the camel, pat it on his long neck and the camel would roll his two broad lips, he looked like he was smiling, but his eyes remained sad. Dad would talk to the camel in a strange voice that sounded like a grunt to us. Only the camel understood. This is how we entered our yard accompanied by jealous looks of all the neighborhood children, we felt like princesses [...].[85]

These are the memories of Lea Naor (Mikovsky) a grandmother to Yuval, both participating in a heritage project. Lea, reminiscent of her childhood adventures in the wadi, was collecting mushrooms, playing in the mud and waiting for her camel-riding father to emerge from work, like a sultan. For Yuval who commented on the story was told by his grandmother, it seemed to him far-fetched that a Jewish, Ashkenazi family had camels. Yuval's perception of camels highlights the negative indexicality carried by camels and the Israeli–Jewish national collective desire (and bureaucratic plan) to rid itself of this association, as well as the physical 'reminder' of the Bedouin and their 'backward' lifestyle. Essentially, it could be said that phasing out the nomadic lifestyle of Bedouin is a form of localised camel extinction through sociocultural and political extinction of the species. The loss of knowledge through the Bedouin generation is a major contributor to this loss.

However, the young generation of Bedouin lament their ever-growing distance from tradition and loss of passed-down knowledge and skills from elders:

(1) Participant A: look in the years in the last 15 years there are young Bedouins that wish to return to the tradition not be nomadic they do cruise around with their Jeep and mobile phone but they have a certain need what that is interesting there is no transmission of knowledge from the adults to the young so they have many problems in breeding.

Much like Lea, 'Bedouin, especially the elders, recall the past and their relation with camels, the long treks and the open spaces, and the many uses of camels'.[86] Degen and El-Meccawi[87] reveal that only 33% of all Bedouin interviewed thought that they were most identified with camels, 53% with sheep/goats (shoats) and 13% with horses. Importantly, all respondents said that it was important to maintain camels to preserve their traditional lifestyle, as 'Bedouin need camels, sheep and goats, they need to respect their animals – but in cities, this is impossible, in cities there is no room, there is only a mess [balagan]'.[88] The perceived orderliness of bureaucracy and accounting for camels living in urban settings are all described and experienced by Bedouin as a 'mess'. The confines of a city juxtapose sharply with the 'mess' of unrecognised settlements, as perceived by authorities.

The lack of official status for camel husbandry presents a two-pronged risk. The health and welfare of camels are virtually unaccounted, unregulated and uncontrolled. This in turn threatens human health through zoonoses and outbreaks of HEV, MERS, and COVID-19, Trypanosoma, as discussed above. Similar to the camel tagging issue, addressing camel breeding health risks results in the same political tension. The possible remedy in the form of registration and bureaucracy reduces the identity of the nomadic lifestyle of Bedouin, but at the same time may promote the status of the organisation and the breeders' access to agricultural economic benefits such as access to agricultural water that is markedly cheaper than regular drinking water, pastures and access to veterinary services. However, as can be seen in other areas of animal agriculture,[89] official status, as well as means of regulation do not ensure the welfare of the animals. How can camels be emancipated and Bedouin lifestyle and identity supported?

And the Camels Roam Free: An Imaginary Emancipatory Account for Israeli Camels

While the Dromedary camels are not native to Israel, having been domesticated, used and bred since 930 and 900 B.C.[90] and despite the government's wish to eliminate Israel from being associated with camels indexing backwardness, they remain important for Bedouin culture and have had a strong bond with earlier settlers in Israel. However, taking into account the complex issues surrounding camels in Israel, there is a need for a new story, a new solution and a better future for camels and people.

There is a case to be made for a rewilding of the dromedaries, setting them free from enslavement. In accounting terms, the chapter sheds light on two concepts. Firstly, those wild camels are not equal to captive camels. In other words, when we think about extinction and accounting for species facing or undergoing extinction, we think in absolute numbers. The balance sheet is conjured, and we tally up the individuals. However, the case of camels reveals that although there are 'physical' camels in captivity, and in this way, they are not extinct, their wild selves are essentially a different species. Secondly, rendering camels more accounted for by formalising camel husbandry expedites their cultural extinction (Maroun, W. (2021), personal communication, 5 February.).

Bedouin are in a unique position, with their expertise and knowledge to be stewards of these wonderful beings and develop a safari – a unique desert wildlife safari park, the kind that does not exist in Israel yet. The camels can join other native-desert already free-living wild animals. A safari programme can help Bedouin, especially women who are already in charge of taking care of the livestock and retrain, while still maintaining their roles and contact with the open spaces of the desert. Currently, Israel does not have a true conservation safari area, and the Negev is continuously threatened with urbanisation and 'development'.[91]

This programme will also eliminate the health risks involved with breeding camels for milk and meat, as discussed in an earlier section, as well as help develop a new sector of tourism that emphasises the natural beauty and freedom of dromedary camels.

The rewilding project may go beyond the borders of Israel and cross into neighbouring countries, much like the Serengeti (Maroun, W. (2021), personal communication, 5 February.). Can rewilding camels and other species protect them from extinction broker peace in the Middle East? Given the ongoing 6th mass extinction, governments have a duty to protect biodiversity (Jones and Solomon, 2013). Despite the implementation of global sustainable development goals (SDGs) and other intergovernmental initiatives to address the biodiversity crisis, governments have been slow to respond, and many have not been able to achieve their SDG 14, 15 and the Aichi targets (Convention on Biological Diversity, 2019).

Rewilding of previously domesticated animals has been documented in several projects. For example, the Tauros Project has been working towards rewilding several species of domesticated bovines.[92] The aim of the project is to enable the bovines to become fully self-sufficient, wild-living cattle species.

Rewilded camels can join the unique Israeli desert wildlife, alongside the red-necked ostrich, the majestic feline caracal, the sweet sand cat and the sneaky rock hyrax. Israeli camels are highly adapted to the food available to them: they can eat over 98% of all the flora in the Negev.

> (3) Participant A: camels are a very resilient very tough animals [...] camels in Israel can eat 98% of plants in the Negev that means that the range of the vitamins and minerals is very large in an intensive breeding like we do here we have to supply those needs.

The quote above can be said to demonstrate that the artificial confinement of camels in breeding farms results in a difficult balancing act of supplying, artificially through vitamin capsules and food supplements, attempting to mimic the natural and healthy food that is available to them were they free-living wildly.

Camel captivity and breeding also result in other cruel behaviours towards them. For example, camel training involves highly cruel and violent methods

> (4) Participant A: Also on the subject of camel training we invest a lot of time for example the traditional Bedouin the training method is very aggressive we are teaching over the years to do it differently without force and violence the method that we developed here in Israel I also teach in Australia and India.

However, the adoption of kinder methods that do not seemingly involve violence and cruelty have a financial motivation, as noted regarding his different training methods with Indian camel breeders for tourism:

> (5) Participant A: slowly it is more and more accepted it's not easy because our method requires more work more time but the people can see the difference and slowly it is accepted but it is not in a fast pace in India I said if you want to work with European tourism it is impossible that you work in this way that the camels have blood spurting out of their noses and the beatings and then before I came to do the course when was this I can't remember 9 years ago more than 200 signed up but the minute the Indians understood this has to do with their livelihood the course was very attractive.

While the interviewee suggests that their training method is not violent at all and has no violent components, it could be argued that subduing an animal to follow the orders of a human is a form of violence as 'animal training sits towards the uncomfortably overt end of human dominance'.[93] Indeed, participant A admits that the 'kinder' methods are anthropocentric in value:

(6) Participant A: we developed this method for our own needs.

In other words, the primary motivation for the adoption of non-violent training methods according to participant A was to be able to control the camels in front of 'European tourists' who would gall and be upset by violence inflicted on camels and blood spurting out of their nose due to the pulling ring fitted as a means of control.

To conclude, this contribution is aimed to paint the current context for camels and humans in Israel. Given Israeli society activism and involvement in denouncing animal abuse and religious roots for veganism and respect for animal equity, I believe that we can hope for a vegan future as Israel is already home to the highest number of vegans per capita and to promising research to provide alternatives to intensive farming and the breeding and killing of animals.

Acknowledgements

I would like to thank Professor Warren Maroun for his extensive feedback and comments on an earlier draft of this chapter.

Appendix

Camel timelines (Adapted from Irwin, 2010).

Camel Mile(stones) (1)

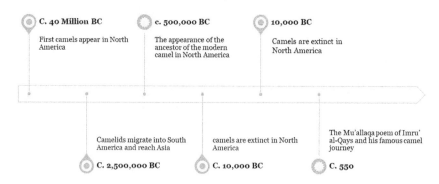

FIGURE 7A.1 Camels in history.

Camel Mile(stones) (2)

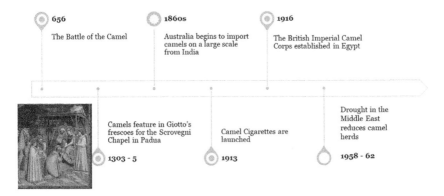

656
The Battle of the Camel

1860s
Australia begins to import camels on a large scale from India

1916
The British Imperial Camel Corps established in Egypt

Camels feature in Giotto's frescoes for the Scrovegni Chapel in Padua
1303 - 5

Camel Cigarettes are launched
1913

Drought in the Middle East reduces camel herds
1958 - 62

FIGURE 7A.2   Camels in history.

Camel Mile(stones) (3)

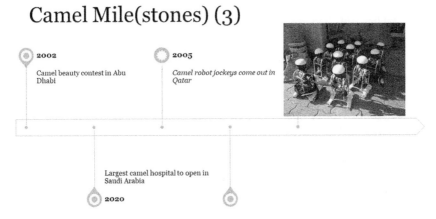

2002
Camel beauty contest in Abu Dhabi

2005
Camel robot jockeys come out in Qatar

Largest camel hospital to open in Saudi Arabia
2020

FIGURE 7A.3   Camels in history.

Notes

1 Simon C. Nemtzov, "Management of Wildlife-Human Conflicts in Israel: A Wide Variety of Vertebrate Pest Problems in a Difficult and Compact Environment," *Proceedings of the Vertebrate Pest Conference* 20, no. 20 (2002): 348–353, https://doi.org/10.5070/v420110190.

2 Israel Ministry of Foreign Affairs, "Topographical Map of Israel," MFA, 2013, https://mfa.gov.il/MFA/AboutIsrael/Maps/Pages/Topographical-map-of-Israel.aspx.

3 R. Bassal et al., "Seroprevalence of Hepatitis E Virus in Dromedary Camels, Bedouins, Muslim Arabs and Jews in Israel, 2009–2017," *Epidemiology and Infection* 147, no. e92 (2019): 1–5, https://doi.org/10.1017/S0950268819000062; Central Bureau of Statistics, "הייסולכוא[Population by Religion and Population Group]," Central Bureau of Statistics, 2019, https://www.cbs.gov.il/he/subjects/Pages/הייסולכוא-תד-יפל-תצובקו-הייסולכוא.aspx.

4 Robert Irwin, *Camel* (London: Reaktion Books, Limited, 2010).

5 B. Faye and G. Konuspayeva, "The Sustainability Challenge to the Dairy Sector - The Growing Importance of Non-Cattle Milk Production Worldwide," *International Dairy Journal* 24, no. 2 (2012): 50–56, https://doi.org/10.1016/j.idairyj.2011.12.011.

6 Bernard Faye, "The Camel Today: Assets and Potentials," *Anthropozoologica* 49, no. 2 (2014): 167–176, https://doi.org/10.5252/az2014n2a01.

7 Martin Heide, "The Domestication of the Camel: Biological, Archaeological and Inscriptional Evidence from Mesopotamia, Egypt, Israel and Arabia, and Literary Evidence from the Hebrew Bible," *Ugarit-Forschungen* 42 (2011): 331–381.

8 Bassal et al., "Seroprevalence of Hepatitis E Virus in Dromedary Camels, Bedouins, Muslim Arabs and Jews in Israel, 2009–2017"; Shalom Ben Shimol et al., "Human Brucellosis Outbreak Acquired through Camel Milk Ingestion in Southern Israel," *Israel Medical Association Journal* 14, no. 8 (2012): 475–478.

9 Hepatitis E (HEV) infection is mostly silent but manifests as liver inflammation, mostly through faecal-oral transmission. HEV is thought to be a zoonosis, with animals, mostly domestic, as a reservoir.

10 Irwin, *Camel*.

11 Zeev Klein, "Ban on Live Animal Shipments Passes Key Hurdle in Knesset," *Israel Hayom [Online]*, November 15, 2018, https://www.israelhayom.com/2018/11/15/ban-on-live-animal-shipments-passes-key-hurdle-in-knesset/.

12 Marine Lercier, "The Legal Protection of Animals in Israel," *Derecho Animal* 8, no. 4 (2017): 1–29, http://revistes.uab.cat/da/article/view/v8-n4-lercier; The Knesset, "Subcommittee on Cruelty towards Animals," *The Knesset*, 2020, https://knesset.gov.il/committees/eng/committee_eng.asp?c_id=577; Sue Surkes, "Lawmakers Go Vegan for the Day to Support Animal Rights," *Israel Hayom [Online]*, February 6, 2018, https://www.timesofisrael.com/lawmakers-go-vegan-for-the-day-to-support-animal-rights/.

13 The Arab Republic of Egypt, "Art. 45: Humane Treatment of Animals" (2014), https://www.globalanimallaw.org/database/national/egypt/.

14 Israel Ministry of Environmental Protection, "Aichi Biodiversity Targets," Israel Ministry of Environmental Protection, 2016, https://www.sviva.gov.il/English/env_topics/biodiversity/AichiTargets/Pages/default.aspx.

15 Lercier, "The Legal Protection of Animals in Israel."

16 Lercier.

17 The Noahide Code discusses the concern for suffering caused to animals found in Judaism's Seven Laws of Noah, which apply to all humankind. One of the seven laws, *ever min ha chai*, prohibits eating the flesh of live animals. This law is derived from Genesis 9:4 HE, as interpreted in the Talmud Chabad, "The 7 Noahide Laws: Universal Morality," Chabad, accessed July 3, 2020, https://www.chabad.org/library/article_cdo/aid/62221/jewish/The-7-Noahide-Laws-Universal-Morality.htm.

18 Asa Keisar, "Veganism and Kashrut," *Asa Keisar Blog*, 2020, https://asakeisar.com/en/veganism-and-kashrut/.

19 Simuchah Roth, "And You Shall Be Holy People unto Me [Exodus 22:30]: Why an Observant Jew Should Follow a Plant-Based (Vegan) Diet," *BMV*, 2010, http://www.bmv.org.il/v/vegan.html.

20 Lercier, "The Legal Protection of Animals in Israel."

21 Lercier.

22 Lercier.

23 The Knesset, "Cruelty to Animals Law (Animal Protection 5754-1994," Pub. L. No. 5754, 5754 1 (1994), https://www.animallaw.info/sites/default/files/stisreal_animal_protection.pdf.

24 Zafrir Rinat, "Israel's Animal Protection Law Is a Failure, Says Report," *Haaretz [Online]*, February 10, 2020, https://www.haaretz.com/israel-news/.premium-israel-s-animal-protection-law-is-a-failure-says-report-1.8510037.

25 Lercier, "The Legal Protection of Animals in Israel."

26 Lercier.
27 Ministry of Environmnetal Protection, "Wildlife Protection Law 1955," Ministry of Environmental Protection, 2019, https://www.gov.il/en/departments/legalInfo/wildlife_protection_law_1955.
28 Israel Ministry of Environmental Protection, "Nature, Biodiversity, & Open Spaces," *Ministry of Environmental Protection*, 2012, http://www.environment.gov.il/English/Legislation/Pages/NatureBiodiversityOpenSpaces.aspx.
29 Nature and National Parks Protection Authority, "National Parks, Nature Reserves, National Sites and Memorial Sites Law 5758 (1998)," Pub. L. No. Law (No. 2) 5762-2002, 1 (1998), https://www.sviva.gov.il/English/Legislation/Documents/National Parks, Nature Reserves, National Sites, Memorial Sites Laws and Regulations/NatioalParksNatureReservesNationalSitesAndMemorialSitesLaw1998.pdf.
30 Israel Ministry of Environmental Protection, "Biodiversity of Our Ecosystems," *Israel Ministry of Environmental Protection*, 2016, https://www.sviva.gov.il/English/env_topics/biodiversity/ecosystems/Pages/default.aspx.
31 Israel Ministry of Environmental Protection.
32 Israel Ministry of Environmental Protection.
33 Faye, "The Camel Today: Assets and Potentials"; Bernard Faye, "Role, Distribution and Perspective of Camel Breeding in the Third Millennium Economies," *Emirates Journal of Food and Agriculture* 27, no. 4 (2015): 318–327, https://doi.org/10.9755/ejfa.v27i4.19906; Irwin, *Camel*.
34 J. Hare, "Bactrian Camel: Camelus Ferus," *IUCN Red List of Threatened Species*, 2008, https://www.iucnredlist.org/species/63543/12689285; Heide, "The Domestication of the Camel: Biological, Archaeological and Inscriptional Evidence from Mesopotamia, Egypt, Israel and Arabia, and Literary Evidence from the Hebrew Bible."
35 Irwin, *Camel*; National Geographic, "Bactrian Camel," National Geographic, accessed July 3, 2020, https://www.nationalgeographic.com/animals/mammals/b/bactrian-camel/.
36 Heide, "The Domestication of the Camel: Biological, Archaeological and Inscriptional Evidence from Mesopotamia, Egypt, Israel and Arabia, and Literary Evidence from the Hebrew Bible."
37 Faye, "The Camel Today: Assets and Potentials."
38 Adapted from Faye, 2014: 168.
39 John Hill, "Wild Bactrian Camel," 2011, https://commons.wikimedia.org/wiki/User:John_Hill.
40 Heide, "The Domestication of the Camel: Biological, Archaeological and Inscriptional Evidence from Mesopotamia, Egypt, Israel and Arabia, and Literary Evidence from the Hebrew Bible"; Irwin, *Camel*.
41 Irwin, *Camel*; Lidar Sapir-Hen and Erez Ben-Yosef, "The Introduction of Domestic Camels to the Southern Levant: Evidence from the Aravah Valley," *Tel Aviv* 40, no. 2 (2013): 277–285, https://doi.org/10.1179/033443513X13753505864089.
42 Sapir-Hen and Ben-Yosef, "The Introduction of Domestic Camels to the Southern Levant: Evidence from the Aravah Valley."
43 Sapir-Hen and Ben-Yosef.
44 The Negev (south or dry land in Hebrew), part of the Sahara- Arabian desert belt, is a triangular-shaped area of 12,500 km^2. It is in the Mediterranean climate zone bordered by the Mediterranean Sea and the Sinai desert in the west and the Judean desert and Aravah Rift Valley in the east. The Negev can be divided into two main climatic regions: a northwestern semi-arid region characterized by flat plains with deep loess soils where rainfall decreases from 400 mm in the north to 200 mm in the south (at Beer Sheva) and an arid southeastern region comprising hilly desert steppe where rainfall decreases from 200 mm in the north to 25 mm in the south (at Eilat) A. Allan Degen, Shaher El-Meccawi, and Michael Kam, "The Changing Role of Camels among the Bedouin of the Negev," *Human Ecology* 47 (2019): 193–204, https://doi.org/10.1007/s10745-019-0062-y.

45 Degen, El-Meccawi, and Kam.
46 Almog Ben Zahari, "הנדימה אל תדמוע ומיס ןומז הגילמס שלה - והס ממכישיס לגרוס תאונות טנינלוית [The Country Does Not Comply with Its Camel Marking Regulations and They Continue to Cause Fatal Accidents]," *Haaretz [Online]*, October 6, 2019, https://www.haaretz.co.il/news/education/.premium-1.7948723; Faye, "The Camel Today: Assets and Potentials."
47 Allan A. Degen and Shaher El-Meccawi, "Livestock Production among Urban Negev Bedouin," *Outlook on Agriculture* 38, no. 4 (2009): 327–335, https://doi.org/10.5367/000000009790422106.
48 Degen, El-Meccawi, and Kam, "The Changing Role of Camels among the Bedouin of the Negev."
49 Degen, El-Meccawi, and Kam.
50 Arik Rudnitzky and Thabet Abu Ras, *The Bedouin Population in the Negev* (The Abraham Fund Initiatives, 2012), https://www.europarl.europa.eu/meetdocs/2009_2014/documents/droi/dv/138_abrahamfundstudy_/138_abrahamfundstudy_en.pdf.
51 Faye (2014) "The Camel Today: Assets and Potentials." *Anthropozoologica* 49, no. 2 (2014): 167–176.
52 Ilana Curiel, "Boy Killed, 8 Injured in Car-Camel Accident in Negev," *Ynet [Online]*, January 16, 2018, https://www.ynetnews.com/articles/0,7340,L-5072018,00.html.
53 Nemtzov, "Management of Wildlife-Human Conflicts in Israel: A Wide Variety of Vertebrate Pest Problems in a Difficult and Compact Environment."
54 Ben Zahari, "טנינלוית תאונות לגרוס ממכישיס והס - שלה הגילמס ומז ןומיס תדמוע אל הנדימה [The Country Does Not Comply with Its Camel Marking Regulations and They Continue to Cause Fatal Accidents]."
55 W Funnell, "Accounting in the Service of the Holocaust," *Critical Perspectives on Accounting* 8 (1998): 435–464, https://doi.org/10.1006/cpac.1997.0164.
56 Jane. Broadbent, "The Values of Accounting and Education: Some Implications of the Creation of Visibilities and Invisibilities in Schools," in *Advances in Public Interest Accounting - Volume 6*, ed. Cheryl L. Lehman et al. (Greenwich, CT: JAI Press Ltd., 1995), 69–98.
57 Degen, El-Meccawi, and Kam, "The Changing Role of Camels among the Bedouin of the Negev."
58 Charles Anderson, "Surveillance and Control in Israel/Palestine: Population, Territory, and Power," 2011.
59 Degen, El-Meccawi, and Kam, "The Changing Role of Camels among the Bedouin of the Negev."
60 Degen, El-Meccawi, and Kam.
61 Degen and El-Meccawi, "Livestock Production among Urban Negev Bedouin."
62 Degen and El-Meccawi.
63 Degen, El-Meccawi and Kam, "The Changing Role of Camels among the Bedouin of the Negev," 201.
64 Ravendra P. Chauhan et al., "Systematic Review of Important Viral Diseases in Africa in Light of the 'One Health' Concept," *Pathogens* 9, no. 301 (2020): 1–83, https://doi.org/10.3390/pathogens9040301.
65 Jill Atkins et al., "Revealing Plato's 'Shadow Kingdom': Rendering Pandemic Risk Explicit in Integrated Extinction Accounting and Engagement," 2020, 1–35.
66 "A Reflection on Human-Animal Relations in Light of COVID-19," *Niche Canada*, 2020, https://niche-canada.org/2020/04/30/a-reflection-on-human-animal-relations-in-light-of-covid-19/.
67 Owen Rogers, "Public Opinion On 'Wet Markets': Perspectives From Asia," *Faunalytics*, 2020, https://faunalytics.org/public-opinion-on-wet-markets-perspectives-from-asia/.
68 Zvia Mildenberg, "[Dealing with Camels during the Corona Epidemic Crisis] התנהלות עם גמלים בעת משבר מגפת הקורונה" (Beit Dagan, 2020), https://www.moag.gov.il/vet/Yechidot/briut_gamal_pinot_hay/Documents/hozer_gmailm_25.3.2020.pdf.

69 Faye, "Role, Distribution and Perspective of Camel Breeding in the Third Millennium Economies."

70 Degen, El-Meccawi, and Kam, "The Changing Role of Camels among the Bedouin of the Negev."

71 Ministry of Agriculture and Development, "מושירא(RIA) : השדח היצלוגר תניחב חוד, סילמג יוהיזו ומיס[Report on New Regulation: Camel Registration, Marking and Identification]."

72 Shimol et al., "Human Brucellosis Outbreak Acquired through Camel Milk Ingestion in Southern Israel."

73 Shimol et al.

74 Shimol et al.

75 Degen, El-Meccawi, and Kam, "The Changing Role of Camels among the Bedouin of the Negev."

76 Bassal et al., "Seroprevalence of Hepatitis E Virus in Dromedary Camels, Bedouins, Muslim Arabs and Jews in Israel, 2009–2017."

77 Bassal et al.

78 Dalia Berlin et al., "Longitudinal Study of an Outbreak of Trypanosoma Evansi Infection in Equids and Dromedary Camels in Israel," *Veterinary Parasitology* 174 (2010): 317–322, https://doi.org/10.1016/j.vetpar.2010.09.002.

79 Jennifer L. Harcourt et al., "The Prevalence of Middle East Respiratory Syndrome Coronavirus (MERS-CoV) Antibodies in Dromedary Camels in Israel," *Zoonoses and Public Health* 65, no. 6 (2018): 749–754, https://doi.org/10.1111/zph.12482.

80 WHO, "Middle East Respiratory Syndrome Coronavirus (MERS-CoV)," World Health Organisation, 2020, https://www.who.int/emergencies/mers-cov/en/.

81 Halas, a slang word in Hebrew meaning 'enough', 'stop it'. It is a borrowed word from Arabic meaning 'that's it', 'it's done.'

82 Tzvika Klein, "לארשיל םלועה ידוהי תא הרביחש תינכותה :םירהונ םיריעצה[The Young People Are Flocking: The Program That Connected the Jews [of the World to Israel," *Makor Rishon*, June 8, 2020, https://www.makorrishon.co.il/magazine/235415/.

83 Klein.

84 Israeli Museum Jerusalem, "תרבחמו הלמש םישנ יתש [Two Women a Dress and a Notebook]," *Israeli Museum Jerusalem*, 2020, https://www.imj.org.il/he/exhibitions/תרבחמו-הלמש-םישנ-יתש.

85 Leah Naor Mikovsky, "[We Had Camels] היו ונל גמליס," *Hakesher Harav Dori*, 2017, http://www.ravdori.co.il/stories/סילמג-ונל-ויה/.

86 Degen, El-Meccawi, and Kam, "The Changing Role of Camels among the Bedouin of the Negev."

87 Degen and El-Meccawi, "Livestock Production among Urban Negev Bedouin," 334.

88 Degen and El-Meccawi, 334.

89 Liz Specht and Jan Dutkiewicz, "Let's Rebuild the Broken Meat Industry—Without Animals: Covid-19 Has Laid Bare Many Flaws of Industrialized Animal Agriculture. Plant- and Cell-Based Alternatives Offer a More Resilient Solution," *Wired*, 2020, https://www.wired.com/story/opinion-lets-rebuild-the-broken-meat-industry-without-animals/amp?fbclid=IwAR0KqkO4yHYvczNMdxkU8A7CWCLmbC6lw8EDJKc_IdDXmlPiIhTao4nolAI; Sarat Colling, "Animal Agency, Resistance, and Escape," in *Critical Animal Studies: Towards Trans-Species Social Justice*, ed. A. Matsuoka and J. Sorenson (London: Rowman & Littlefield International Ltd, 2018), 21–44; A. Matsuoka and J. Sorenson, *Critical Animal Studies: Towards Trans-Species Social Justice*, ed. A. Matsuoka and J. Sorenson (London: Rowman & Littlefield International Ltd, 2018).

90 Sapir-Hen and Ben-Yosef, "The Introduction of Domestic Camels to the Southern Levant: Evidence from the Aravah Valley."

91 Reut Spiegelman, "תומרה לכב בגנה חותיפ דשמהל םיביוחמ ונא :ליכ ל"כנמ מ"מ["Acting CEO of ICL: We Are Committed to the Continued Development of the Negev at

All Levels," *Calcalist [Online]*, 2017, https://www.calcalist.co.il/conference/articles/0,7340,L-3727308,00.html.

92 Rewilding Europe, "Born to Be Wild: The Aurochs – Europe's Defining Animal," *Rewilding Europe*, 2020, https://rewildingeurope.com/rewilding-in-action/wildlife-comeback/tauros/.

93 Tony Milligan, "The Ethics of Animal Training," in *Pets and People: The Ethics of Companion Animals [e-Book]*, ed. Christine Overall (Oxford Scholarship Online, 2017).

References

Anderson, Charles. "Surveillance and Control in Israel/Palestine: Population, Territory, and Power," 2011.

Atkins, Jill, Federica Doni, Abeer Hassan, and Warren Maroun. "Revealing Plato's 'Shadow Kingdom': Rendering Pandemic Risk Explicit in Integrated Extinction Accounting and Engagement," in Extinction Governance, Finance, and Accounting Implementing a Species Protection Action Plan for the Financial Markets, edited by Atkins, Jill and Macpherson, Martina, 2020.

Bassal, R., M. Wax, R. Shirazi, T. Shohat, D. Cohen, D. David, S. Abu-Mouch, et al. "Seroprevalence of Hepatitis E Virus in Dromedary Camels, Bedouins, Muslim Arabs and Jews in Israel, 2009–2017." *Epidemiology and Infection* 147, no. e92 (2019): 1–5. https://doi.org/10.1017/S0950268819000062.

Berlin, Dalia, Abedelmajeed Nasereddin, Kifaya Azmi, Suheir Ereqat, Ziad Abdeen, and Gad Baneth. "Longitudinal Study of an Outbreak of Trypanosoma Evansi Infection in Equids and Dromedary Camels in Israel." *Veterinary Parasitology* 174 (2010): 317–322. https://doi.org/10.1016/j.vetpar.2010.09.002.

Broadbent, Jane. "The Values of Accounting and Education: Some Implications of the Creation of Visibilities and Invisibilities in Schools." In *Advances in Public Interest Accounting - Volume 6*, edited by Cheryl L. Lehman, Marilyn Neimark, Barbara Merino, and Tony Tinker, 69–98. Greenwich, CT: JAI Press Ltd., 1995.

Central Bureau of Statistics. "הייסולכוא[הייסולכוא תצובקו תד יפל הייסולכוא[Population by Religion and Population Group]." Central Bureau of Statistics, 2019. https://www.cbs.gov.il/he/subjects/Pages/הייסולכוא-יפל-תד-תצובקו-הייסולכוא.aspx.

Chabad (no date) "The 7 Noahide Laws: Universal Morality." *Chabad*. Accessed July 3, 2020. https://www.chabad.org/library/article_cdo/aid/62221/jewish/The-7-Noahide-Laws-Universal-Morality.htm.

Chauhan, Ravendra P., Zelalem G. Dessie, Ayman Noreddin, and Mohamed E. El Zowalaty. "Systematic Review of Important Viral Diseases in Africa in Light of the 'One Health' Concept." *Pathogens* 9, no. 301 (2020): 1–83. https://doi.org/10.3390/pathogens9040301.

Colling, Sarat. "Animal Agency, Resistance, and Escape." In *Critical Animal Studies: Towards Trans-Species Social Justice*, edited by A. Matsuoka and J. Sorenson, 21–44. London: Rowman & Littlefield International Ltd, 2018.

Curiel, Ilana. "Boy Killed, 8 Injured in Car-Camel Accident in Negev." *Ynet [Online]*, January 16, 2018. https://www.ynetnews.com/articles/0,7340,L-5072018,00.html.

Degen, Allan A., and Shaher El-Meccawi. "Livestock Production among Urban Negev Bedouin." *Outlook on Agriculture* 38, no. 4 (2009): 327–335. https://doi.org/10.5367/000000009790422106.

Degen, Allan A., Shaher El-Meccawi, and Michael Kam. "The Changing Role of Camels among the Bedouin of the Negev." *Human Ecology* 47 (2019): 193–204. https://doi.org/10.1007/s10745-019-0062-y.

Dey, Colin, and Shona Russell. "Who Speaks for the River? Exploring Biodiversity Accoutning Using an Arena Approach." In *Accounting for Biodiversity*, edited by Michael John Jones and Jill Solomon, 263–284. New York: Routledge, 2014.

Faye, Bernard. "Role, Distribution and Perspective of Camel Breeding in the Third Millennium Economies." *Emirates Journal of Food and Agriculture* 27, no. 4 (2015): 318–327. https://doi.org/10.9755/ejfa.v27i4.19906.

———. "The Camel Today: Assets and Potentials." *Anthropozoologica* 49, no. 2 (2014): 167–176. https://doi.org/10.5252/az2014n2a01.

Faye, B., and G. Konuspayeva. "The Sustainability Challenge to the Dairy Sector - The Growing Importance of Non-Cattle Milk Production Worldwide." *International Dairy Journal* 24, no. 2 (2012): 50–56. https://doi.org/10.1016/j.idairyj.2011.12.011.

Funnell, W. "Accounting in the Service of the Holocaust." *Critical Perspectives on Accounting* 8 (1998): 435–464. https://doi.org/10.1006/cpac.1997.0164.

Harcourt, Jennifer L., Nir Rudoler, Azaibi Tamin, Eyal Leshem, Michal Rasis, Michael Giladi, and Lia M. Haynes. "The Prevalence of Middle East Respiratory Syndrome Coronavirus (MERS-CoV) Antibodies in Dromedary Camels in Israel." *Zoonoses and Public Health* 65, no. 6 (2018): 749–754. https://doi.org/10.1111/zph.12482.

Hare, J. "Bactrian Camel: Camelus Ferus." *IUCN Red List of Threatened Species*, 2008. https://www.iucnredlist.org/species/63543/12689285.

Heide, Martin. "The Domestication of the Camel: Biological, Archaeological and Inscriptional Evidence from Mesopotamia, Egypt, Israel and Arabia, and Literary Evidence from the Hebrew Bible." *Ugarit-Forschungen* 42 (2011): 331–381.

Hill, John. "Wild Bactrian Camel," 2011. https://commons.wikimedia.org/wiki/User:John_Hill.

Irwin, Robert. *Camel*. London: Reaktion Books, Limited, 2010.

Israel Ministry of Environmental Protection. "Aichi Biodiversity Targets." Israel Ministry of Environmental Protection, 2016. https://www.sviva.gov.il/English/env_topics/biodiversity/AichiTargets/Pages/default.aspx.

———. "Biodiversity of Our Ecosystems." Israel Ministry of Environmental Protection, 2016. https://www.sviva.gov.il/English/env_topics/biodiversity/ecosystems/Pages/default.aspx.

———. "Nature, Biodiversity, & Open Spaces." Ministry of Environmental Protection, 2012. http://www.environment.gov.il/English/Legislation/Pages/NatureBiodiversityOpenSpaces.aspx.

Israel Ministry of Foreign Affairs. "Topographical Map of Israel." *MFA*, 2013. https://mfa.gov.il/MFA/AboutIsrael/Maps/Pages/Topographical-map-of-Israel.aspx.

Israeli Museum Jerusalem. "תרבחמו הלמש םיש יתש [Two Women a Dress and a Notebook]." *Israeli Museum Jerusalem*, 2020. https://www.imj.org.il/he/exhibitions/תש-יתש-הלמש-םיש-הלמה-ומחברת.

Keisar, Asa. "Veganism and Kashrut." *Asa Keisar Blog*, 2020. https://asakeisar.com/en/veganism-and-kashrut/.

Klein, Tzvika. "לארשיל םלועה ידוהי תא הריחש תינכותה :םירהונ םיריעצה[The Young People Are Flocking: The Program That Connected the Jews [of the World to Israel." *Makor Rishon*. June 8, 2020. https://www.makorrishon.co.il/magazine/235415/.

Klein, Zeev. "Ban on Live Animal Shipments Passes Key Hurdle in Knesset." *Israel Hayom [Online]*, November 15, 2018. https://www.israelhayom.com/2018/11/15/ban-on-live-animal-shipments-passes-key-hurdle-in-knesset/.

Lercier, Marine. "The Legal Protection of Animals in Israel." *Derecho Animal* 8, no. 4 (2017): 1–29. http://revistes.uab.cat/da/article/view/v8-n4-lercier.

Matsuoka, A., and J. Sorenson. *Critical Animal Studies: Towards Trans-Species Social Justice.* Edited by A. Matsuoka and J. Sorenson. London: Rowman & Littlefield International Ltd, 2018.

Mildenberg, Zvia. "[Dealing with Camels during the Corona Epidemic Crisis] תולהנתה עם גמילס בעת משבר מגפת הקורונה." Beit Dagan, 2020. https://www.moag.gov.il/vet/Yechidot/briut_gamal_pinot_hay/Documents/hozer_gmailm_25.3.2020.pdf.

Milligan, Tony. "The Ethics of Animal Training." In *Pets and People: The Ethics of Companion Animals [e-Book]*, edited by Christine Overall. Oxford Scholarship Online, 2017.

Ministry of Agriculture and Development. "השדח היצלוגר תניחב חוד : (RIA)רושיר, זומיס [Report on New Regulation: Camel Registration, Marking and Identification] גמילס[זוהיי," 2018. http://regulation.gov.il/uploads/reports/7/רושיר זומיס יוהיזו גמלים.pdf.

Ministry of Environmnetal Protection. "Wildlife Protection Law 1955." Ministry of Environmental Protection, 2019. https://www.gov.il/en/departments/legalInfo/wildlife_protection_law_1955.

Naor Mikovsky, Leah. "[We Had Camels] גמילס ונל ויה.ם." Hakesher Harav Dori, 2017. http://www.ravdori.co.il/stories/גמילס-ונל-ויה/.

National Geographic. "Bactrian Camel." *National Geographic.* Accessed July 3, 2020. https://www.nationalgeographic.com/animals/mammals/b/bactrian-camel/.

Nature and National Parks Protection Authority. National Parks, Nature Reserves, National Sites and Memorial Sites Law 5758 (1998), Pub. L. No. Law (No. 2) 5762-2002, 1 (1998). https://www.sviva.gov.il/English/Legislation/Documents/National Parks, Nature Reserves, National Sites, Memorial Sites Laws and Regulations/National ParksNatureReservesNationalSitesAndMemorialSitesLaw1998.pdf.

Nemtzov, Simon C. "Management of Wildlife-Human Conflicts in Israel: A Wide Variety of Vertebrate Pest Problems in a Difficult and Compact Environment." *Proceedings of the Vertebrate Pest Conference* 20, no. 20 (2002): 348–353. https://doi.org/10.5070/v420110190.

Paulin, Catherine. "A Reflection on Human-Animal Relations in Light of COVID-19." *Niche Canada*, 2020. https://niche-canada.org/2020/04/30/a-reflection-on-human-animal-relations-in-light-of-covid-19/.

Rewilding Europe. "Born to Be Wild: The Aurochs – Europe's Defining Animal." *Rewilding Europe*, 2020. https://rewildingeurope.com/rewilding-in-action/wildlife-comeback/tauros/.

Rinat, Zafrir. "Israel's Animal Protection Law Is a Failure, Says Report." *Haaretz [Online]*, February 10, 2020. https://www.haaretz.com/israel-news/.premium-israel-s-animal-protection-law-is-a-failure-says-report-1.8510037.

Rogers, Owen. "Public Opinion On 'Wet Markets': Perspectives From Asia." *Faunalytics*, 2020. https://faunalytics.org/public-opinion-on-wet-markets-perspectives-from-asia/.

Roth, Simuchah. "And You Shall Be Holy People unto Me [Exodus 22:30]: Why an Observant Jew Should Follow a Plant-Based (Vegan) Diet." *BMV*, 2010. http://www.bmv.org.il/v/vegan.html.

Rudnitzky, Arik., and Thabet. Abu Ras. *The Bedouin Population in the Negev.* The Abraham Fund Initiatives, 2012. https://www.europarl.europa.eu/meetdocs/2009_2014/documents/droi/dv/138_abrahamfundstudy_/138_abrahamfundstudy_en.pdf.

Sapir-Hen, Lidar, and Erez Ben-Yosef. "The Introduction of Domestic Camels to the Southern Levant: Evidence from the Aravah Valley." *Tel Aviv* 40, no. 2 (2013): 277–285. https://doi.org/10.1179/033443513X13753505864089.

Shimol, Shalom Ben, Larissa Dukhan, Ilana Belmaker, Svetlana Bardenstein, David Sibirsky, Chiya Barrett, and David Greenberg. "Human Brucellosis Outbreak Acquired through Camel Milk Ingestion in Southern Israel." *Israel Medical Association Journal* 14, no. 8 (2012): 475–478.

Specht, Liz, and Jan Dutkiewicz. "Let's Rebuild the Broken Meat Industry—Without Animals: Covid-19 Has Laid Bare Many Flaws of Industrialized Animal Agriculture. Plant- and Cell-Based Alternatives Offer a More Resilient Solution." *Wired*, 2020. https://www.wired.com/story/opinion-lets-rebuild-the-broken-meat-industry-without-animals/amp?fbclid=IwAR0KqkO4yHYvczNMdxkU8A7CWCLmbC6lw 8EDJKc_IdDXmlPiIhTao4nolAI.

Spiegelman, Reut. "[מ"מ] מנכ"ל ICL: אנו מחויבים להמשך פיתוח הנגב בכל רמה'[Acting CEO of ICL: We Are Committed to the Continued Development of the Negev at All Levels." *Calcalist [Online]*, 2017. https://www.calcalist.co.il/conference/articles/0,7340, L-3727308,00.html.

Surkes, Sue. "Lawmakers Go Vegan for the Day to Support Animal Rights." *Israel Hayom [Online]*, February 6, 2018. https://www.timesofisrael.com/lawmakers-go-vegan-for-the-day-to-support-animal-rights/.

The Arab Republic of Egypt. Art. 45: Humane treatment of animals (2014). https://www.globalanimallaw.org/database/national/egypt/.

The Knesset. Cruelty to Animals Law (Animal Protection 5754-1994, Pub. L. No. 5754, 5754 1 (1994). https://www.animallaw.info/sites/default/files/stisreal_animal_protection.pdf.

———. "Subcommittee on Cruelty Towards Animals." *The Knesset*, 2020. https://knesset.gov.il/committees/eng/committee_eng.asp?c_id=577.

WHO. "Middle East Respiratory Syndrome Coronavirus (MERS-CoV)." World Health Organisation, 2020. https://www.who.int/emergencies/mers-cov/en/.

Zahari, Almog Ben. "המדינה לא עומדת בתקנות סימון וגמלים שלה - והם ממשיכים לגרום לתאונות קטלניות [The Country Does Not Comply with Its Camel Marking Regulations and They Continue to Cause Fatal Accidents]." *Haaretz [Online]*, October 6, 2019. https://www.haaretz.co.il/news/education/.premium-1.7948723.

8

MIDDLE EASTERN EXTINCTIONS

Building a Religious Motivation for Species Protection

*Tariq Almontaser, Jill Atkins, Ali Elfadli,
Abdullah Eskandrany, Abeer Hassan, Omar Mowafi,
Simon Norton and Mohamed Saeudy*

IMAGE 8.1 A young fawn fallow deer native to the Middle East (*Artwork by Isobel Edgley*).

The extinction and biodiversity accounting literature focused initially on developed economies including the UK and Europe, spreading recently to research on Africa, especially South Africa, China and other countries in the Far East. The Middle East, however, has not received attention in the academic literature.

DOI: 10.4324/9781003045557-11

Further, there seems to be less information readily available on species extinctions and biodiversity degradation in Middle Eastern countries. In this chapter, we address species extinctions in Saudi Arabia, Jordan and Libya to provide insights into the situation in these countries, problems and issues arising, as well as potential solutions. The authors present the causes of species extinctions in the Middle East as well as provide information on some of the initiatives underway to prevent extinctions. Whilst most of this book focuses on motivations for species protection grounded in financial materiality, accountability, legitimacy and ethics, this chapter builds a religious rationale, indeed imperative, for species protection and biodiversity conservation. Part I of this chapter discusses the status of threatened species in Saudi Arabia, providing an understanding of the importance of religion as a rationale for species protection. In Part II, the status of threatened species in Jordan is discussed. Part III provides detailed interview evidence on the deterioration of biodiversity in Libya and the need for enhanced species protection.

Part I

Species Extinction in Saudi Arabia: Wildlife in Saudi Arabia

ABDULLAH ESKANDRANY

The Saudi Wildlife Authority (SWA) was created with the issuance of a royal decree on 20/05/1986 in Riyadh and is known as the National Commission for Wildlife conservation and development (NCW, 2021). It aims to plan and develop protection that can reduce the threat to wildlife in different areas (both inland and at sea), rehabilitate species that face the risk of extinction and restore the environmental balance regarding biodiversity. The goals are to mandate, restore and manage the Kingdom's indigenous plants and animals. In 1991, the kingdom began to receive support from the IUCN. As we can see, the SWA was established many years ago, but only recently have they been taking steps to join the international trend to preserve biodiversity. The size of some protected areas has been expanded and new zones have been developed. Previously, there were 15 traditional conservation areas, representing 4% of the country's total area. These included 12 wild reserves and three marine areas. In June 2018, these four nature reserves were expanded and two more were added to cover 10% of the country's total area. Also, SWA passed on some of its managed protected areas to a new authority called the Royal Reserves. In a news article, Karasik (2018) suggested that, after the government introduced these new protected areas, the next step was to enhance employees' skills by offering extensive training and starting a social campaign to raise public awareness about protected areas. The importance of public awareness has also been mentioned in other academic journal articles (Zafar-ul Islam et al., 2018; Al-Tokhais and Thapa, 2019).

A Recent Development Plan for Protecting Endangered Species in Saudi Arabia

It remains difficult to define some endangered and threatened plant species in Saudi Arabia according to the IUCN categories due to a lack of information about the size of their population, their distribution or their exact location (Al-Khulaidi et al., 2018). Moreover, some of these types might not be included on the IUCN Red List. For example, Hall et al. (2010) suggested that Douepea arabica (known as Hedge and Kit Tan) in Saudi Arabia is endangered because of agriculture and road construction, and so needs to be added to the IUCN Red List. This is one illustration demonstrating the need for Saudi Arabia to develop more effective extinction accounting and governance frameworks. At present, there is no complete list of endangered animals and plant species for the country. This may be due to the vast geographical area involved and the difficulties and the cost of assessing species populations.

Accountability for extinction is important at the present time, which may explain the government's tendency to support and increase protected areas to create future economic benefits. The Saudi vision 2030 economic reform targets improvements in biodiversity and the environment. According to Zafar-ul Islam et al. (2018), Arabian leopards in Saudi Arabia are now almost extinct, with only a very small number of them left. However, the Saudi Government has launched a new strategic plan called Saudi Leopard Conservation to protect them from extinction. Moreover, recently, the Saudi government signed an agreement with the big-cat conservation group, Panthera, with funding of 20 million to support the conservation of leopards globally (Cannon, 2019). Another important aspect here is that, by doing so, the government thought that it would enhance local tourism. Therefore, it seems that taking measures to prevent extinction can be used as a tool nowadays by governments who seek to reap future economic benefits and improve the biodiversity in the country. This can also be seen in the transfer of the leopards' conservation area to *Al-Ula* city, where many tourism projects take place (Skirka, 2019).

Islam et al. (2011) stated that poaching remains an issue in Saudi Arabia, where strict legislation and a national awareness program to inform Saudi citizens about the importance of protecting biological species from extinction are required. The demand for public awareness and involvement of the citizens through establishing protected areas have also been noted (Al-Johany, 2007). Zafar-ul Islam et al. (2020) reveal that poaching affects the survival of endangered animals, such as the Arabian leopard, even by eliminating their prey. Therefore, the Saudi government has taken steps to stem animal and plant extinction (see below photos related to illegal poaching activity).[1,2] At the end of 2020, a list of fines was created for 93 types of animal, starting from 1,000 SAR up to 1,500.000 SAR for Panthera pardus nimr (the Arabian leopard) and Geronticus eremita (see MEWA, 2020). Also, they banned tree logging (i.e. cutting down trees for the purpose of logging) as well as imposed fines for doing so.

IMAGE 8.2 Evidence of illegal poaching activity in Saudi Arabia.

IMAGE 8.3 Evidence of illegal poaching activity in Saudi Arabia.

IMAGE 8.4 Evidence of illegal poaching activity in Saudi Arabia.

IMAGE 8.5 Evidence of illegal poaching activity in Saudi Arabia.

In light of the steps taken by the government, companies' measures to protect endangered animals and the environment are lacking. Magbool (2009) found that the top management of Saudi's private corporations did not tend to support environmental management and protection. In a PhD thesis that presented a case study of one of the largest companies in Saudi Arabia (Sabic), Al Shahrani (2018) recommended that industrial corporations should pay attention to environmental security rather than focusing only on profit maximisation. Corporations play an important role in extinction accountability, as highlighted in published frameworks (Atkins and Maroun, 2018). This shows the absence of Saudi companies from protecting the environment and endangered species. Culture and religion might be an important channel for motivating both individuals and corporations to take steps to promote the protection of the environment and endangered species, as will be discussed below.

A Research Centre and Its Relationship with the Islamic Religion

There are two wildlife research centres in Saudi Arabia, one in the west and one in the central region. The former is the Prince Saud Al-Faisal Wildlife Research

Centre (P.S.F.W.R.C) and hosts a total of 700 houbara bustard, 191 Arabian oryx, 17 Scarface jaguars, 4 striped hyenas, 16 Arabian leopards (males 12 and females 4), 4 caracal, and 10 gazelles.[3] Nevertheless, the leopards' conservation moved to alula, as stated above.

In the instructions panel located next to the main entrance to the centre, a verse from the Quran is displayed, sura Alanáam Aya 38 (see Figure 8.1 below), which highlights how creatures are part of the community. In other words, animals are creatures, just like human beings. Just like humans, the Islamic faith states that animals are completely accountable for all good and bad deeds that they engage in towards each other. This is a straightforward example of how Islamic principles are applied to the wildlife research centre.

The Importance of Religion in Motivating Various Institutions to Display Awareness

Ecological biodiversity activists should understand the role of religion in motivating people through enhancing their awareness of the environment. Al-Tokhais and Thapa (2019) stated that biodiversity conservation in Saudi Arabia should be supported through cooperation between the public and private sectors and NGOs, as well as through significant input from other interest groups. According to Mohamed (2016), all of these organisations share common goals, which are to build awareness, practice and understanding of Islamic eco-ethics and aim to make the world a better place for all creatures, which they fulfil with varying degrees of success. Thus, activists can use religion to motivate more people around the world to embrace biodiversity awareness.

Different Religions' Perspectives on Animals

There appears to be some degree of commonality between different religions regarding attitudes towards animals. Judaism, Christianity and Islam originated in the Middle East, such that the animals mentioned in their respective holy

FIGURE 8.1 Information panel at the main entrance of P.S.F.W.R.C.
Source: the author.

books might belong to similar species since they originated in the same area. All of the aforementioned religions believe that animals are part of God's creation. Also, some faiths even impose restrictions when it comes to eating certain animals; e.g. kosher in Judaism and halal in Islam. Moreover, other religions, such as Buddhism, believe that it is important not to hurt any living person or animal. These different religions can provide tremendous motivation when it comes to protect animals.

The Islamic Religion, Background, Perspectives and Motivation Regarding Animals

It is vital to provide an overview of Islam, as it is the religion followed in the Kingdom of Saudi Arabia and plays a role in every part of people's life. The Islamic belief has two sources of legislation: the Quran and the Sunnah of Prophet Muhammad (Hadith). The Hadith, in Arabic, means 'news' or 'a story' that records traditions or sayings of the Prophet Muhammad, collected reports and narrations of the Prophet's Sunnah; it is simply a literature of Islam (Cragg, 2020). Allah, in the Quran, commands every Muslim to obey the Prophet Muhammad unconditionally. The Quran always deals with matters in a more general, broader sense, while more details are provided in the Sunnah of Prophet Muhammad. The Quran views animals as part of the community. All creatures are accountable for their good and bad deeds towards each other. Prophet Muhammad shows how to act mercifully towards all creatures, and the hunting of certain animals is prohibited. Moreover, Islam prohibits hunting in specific places (e.g. Makkah) and at specific times (e.g. during hajj) (see Rashid, 2012).

The Quran tells many different stories about species. For example, "the Quran states that the human should meditate on the beauty of Creation", as they are such fascinating creatures. For example, how do camels function/walk long distances/ store water in their hump? The Quran also prohibits the eating of certain animals, as mentioned above (e.g. pigs). Moreover, it mentions animal species that are pleasant and beautiful and the beauty of riding. There are 114 chapters or sections (suras) in the Quran, six of which are named after animals' names (the cow, ants, the spider, bees, elephants and the Anaam). The cow chapter is the longest (sura) in the Quran. One of the examples of how the Quran recognises and appreciates the existence of animals can be observed within the sura of 'Anaam'. The word Anaam can be thought of as a component of animals (i.e. camels, cattle, sheep and goats), including both males and females. The Quran states that some creatures were created to help humans (to serve and benefit them through providing, e.g. transport, and medicine, like honey). Furthermore, it mentions how both humans and animals share water resources and plants. The Quran refers to 27 types of animals which are essential in the Arab setting (Ektebsa, 2020) (see Table 8.1).

There are many stories in the Sunnah that command Muslims to be merciful towards animal species. People who are merciful to those on earth will receive forgiveness from God (Allah).[4] There is a story of a thirsty dog who was given

TABLE 8.1 The animals mentioned in the Quran

Mules	Cows	Mosquitoes	Camels	Snakes	Zebras	Beddings
Locusts	Pigs	Monkeys	Lice	Goats	Birds	Crows
Bees	Hoopoes	Frogs	Flies	Donkies	Ants	Spiders
Whales	Elephants	Lions	Dogs	Sheep	Horses	Wolves

water by a man; God thanked him for his (good) deed and forgave him.[5] There is a reward for those who help any animal. If a person spends money on horses for the sake of Allah, it is akin to his giving money to charity.[6] Another well-known story among Muslims is that of a tortured cat. The cat was locked up by a woman who did not feed it and did not leave it to eat from the vermin of the earth. This woman went to Hell because of this cat, as related by the Prophet.[7] Therefore, many stories show how to treat animals as well as the environment. The stories mentioned above are well-known among Muslims as illustrating how Islam motivates Muslims to deal with all creatures. Combining them all to show Muslims how the Islamic religion supports biodiversity could enhance ecological environment awareness. The ways in which the Islamic faith motivates Muslims to treat animals may be summarised as follows:

- Animals are part of our community, and they share with humans all of the resources needed to live, so, they have…rights.
- When people show mercy to animals, they receive mercy back from God.
- Treating animals kindly brings rewards for good deeds.
- Everything that God created is for a reason.
- Torturing animals is prohibited.
- Animals have feelings that humans must be aware of to some extent and understand.

Summary

There are many stories in the Islamic religion that can be cited to promote people's awareness, especially Muslims. Developing an awareness of the risk of the extinction of animals and plants is essential in light of the great efforts that have been made by the Saudi government to combat this. Since most people in Saudi Arabia are Muslim and Islam is the major influence on the culture there, people must be encouraged by using religious concepts. Also, it is important to encourage companies to play their role by using these approaches and also through corporate social responsibility (CSR). CSR should include the protection of the environment and endangered animals and plants should be added to its agenda. By doing so, this would be one of the mechanisms for raising awareness among people and saving endangered animals and plants. Lastly, extinction accounting and governance are one of the areas which needs to be developed in

IMAGE 8.6 A houbara bustard, commonly found in Saudi Arabia but the population has steadily declined by 25% since 2004 (*Artwork by Isobel Edgley*).

order to manage the risk and communicate the reports about endangered animals and plants. This would unify the efforts of the IUCN, the Saudi government and companies through the reports and management.

Part II

Biodiversity and Species Extinction in Jordan

Omar Mowalfi

This section provides salient information regarding Jordanian biodiversity and ecosystems and then highlights the main issues and phenomena in order to pave the way for extinction accounting to be applied in a Jordanian context and its importance in future academic research in Jordan. Biodiversity accounting and extinction accounting remain essentially unexplored in the literature in the Middle East region, especially in Jordan. Although there is a growing literature in science and ecology, there is no consideration of these issues in the management, finance or accounting literature.

The research discussed here has been extracted from Jordanian government reports mainly from the Royal Society for the Conservation of Nature (RSCN) and corporate social responsibility reports from some largest corporations listed on the Amman Stock Exchange (ASE) regarding biodiversity and ecosystem to understand their perceptions towards extinction accounting. The discussion falls into several sections, as follows: (1) introduction and opening story of biodiversity and ecosystem in Jordan including the climate of the Middle East and list of the species diversity and the protected areas (reserves) in Jordan; (2) the main reasons for species extinctions in Jordan; (3) social issues regarding biodiversity and ecosystem and extinction accounting in Jordan; and (4) justifications for developing research into extinction accounting in Jordan from natural and governance perspectives.

The purpose of this chapter is to open the door to explore extinction accounting in the Jordanian context and try to highlight this theory as this work considers the first one to this theory in Jordan. Jordan is one of the Middle Eastern countries, as these countries are located in the centre of the world. In addition, many species in these countries are subject to extinction for many institutional reasons highlighted in this work.

Section (1): Introduction of Biodiversity and Ecosystem in Jordan

The story started with the RSCN Founded in 1966 its website www.rscn.org.jo. This organisation is an independent and voluntary organisation that is devoted to the conservation of Jordan's natural resources and protects wildlife; it was established in 1966 with the late King Hussein as Honorary President. RSCN (2020) listed the following recorded species in the biodiversity system in Jordan: Flora: 2,500 plants species, birds: 434 bird species, mammals: 82 species belong to 24 families and reptiles: 98 species belong to 18 families. Below are some photos of the endangered species in Jordan (Figure 8.2).

The vulnerable species which subject to extinction are protected in ten protected areas (natural reserves). Below are their list and the map to show their distribution in Jordan:

The protected areas (RSCN, 2020):

1. Shaumari Wildlife Reserve,
2. Azraq Wetland Reserve,
3. Mujib Biosphere Reserve,
4. Ajloun Forest Reserve,
5. Dana Biosphere Reserve,
6. Dibeen Forest Reserve,
7. Yarmouk Forest Reserve,
8. Fifa Nature Reserve,

Roe deer

Nazareth Iris
(Irisbismarckiana)

Syrain Serin

Black Iris

Arabian Oryx

https://www.rscn.org.jo/ar

FIGURE 8.2   Examples of endangered species in Jordan.

9. Wadi Rum Protected Area, and
10. Qatar Reserve.

In addition, there are six **proposed** projects to open new protected areas (RSCN, 2020):

1. Rajel,
2. Abu Rukbah,
3. Byer,
4. Aqaba Mountains,
5. Shoubak, and
6. Burqu.

The Figure 8.3 below presents the existing and planned/proposed protected areas (natural reserves) in Jordan according to RSCN (2020).

Jordan and the Middle East are in the heart of the world and they are subject to different climates that are arid zones (deserts) and the mild Mediterranean (Mild winter, hot and dry summer). In addition, the majority of immigrant species are passing the Middle East in their immigration seeking warm weather or food (reference). This increases the biodiversity in this area of the

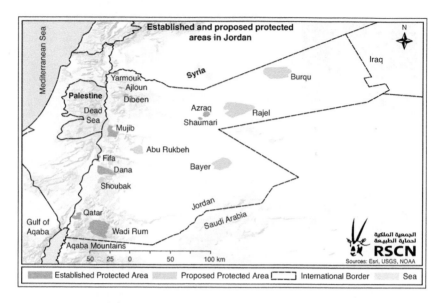

FIGURE 8.3 Map of the existing and planned/proposed protected areas (natural reserves) in Jordan.

Source: (RSCN, 2020), distribution of reserves in Jordan.

world and highlights the importance of studying this area from an extinction perspective.

Section (2) The Main Reasons and Their Impacts on Species Extinction in Jordan

The main reasons for the extinction of some species in Jordan are listed on the management plan Dana Reserve (2020). These six reasons are grazing, woodcutting, hunting, living in the protected areas, tourism and agriculture. Table 8.2 below explains the main consequences for each one of the extinction of species in Jordan:

The reasons listed in the table above are generated from the human actions with natural reserves and vulnerable species. The following section explains some social issues related to extinction accounting.

Section (3) Social Issues regarding Biodiversity, Ecosystem and Extinction Accounting in Jordan

This section highlights three social issues that are relevant to Jordanian biodiversity and ecosystem and affect the risk of extinction of some animals and plants. These issues are mentioned clearly in the governmental reports (RSCN, 2020; Dana Reserve Management Report, 2020). These reports raised a red flag for

TABLE 8.2 Causes of Species Extinction in Jordan

Reasons of Extinction	The consequences
1 Grazing	1. Decrease or disappearance of many palatable plant species for livestock, and may lead to an increase in unpalatable species, which negatively affects the balance between plant species within one habitat. Examples include the increase in the level of desertification. 2. Reducing the successful growth rate of many young seedlings in general. 3. It may lead to soil erosion, especially in the sloping areas. 4. Decreasing the seed stocks in the soil of some species, which reduces the ability of these species to germinate when the dry periods or the overgrazing are gone, which negatively affects the recovery of the habitat.
2 Woodcutting	Woodcutting in some areas of the reserves resulted in the cutting of many trees by more than 50% of the particular trees and despite the few infringements that are taking place in the protected areas, that unfair woodcutting, especially those who are not residents in the protected areas and whose encroachment is the most dangerous for the reserves. Moreover, it is expected to increase the attempts to carry out the woodcutting operations in the reserve for heating purposes because of the sharp rise in fuel prices, which will constitute additional pressure on the tree's wealth in the reserve (RSCN, 2020).
3 Hunting	The hunting operations in the reserve resulted in a very large decrease in the numbers of vulnerable animals and with other factors led to the disappearance of completely some types of the reserve animals and their surroundings, such as: Al-Ghazal Al-Afari (depending on the fauna log, the Dana Reserve Research Centre, 2020). The problem is that this hunting is used for entertainment purposes.
4 Housing in the reserves	Housing in the reserves itself is not considered to have a clear impact on them because of the small areas inhabited in general. However, housing is a very important reason that leads to other reasons of extinction, such as woodcutting and grazing.
5 Tourism	RSCN adopted the definition of ecotourism in the protected areas and their surroundings. However, there are several negative impacts of tourism on wildlife that are: 1 The effect is based on direct interaction with nature, such as the effect on vegetation present in tourist facilities while walking. 2 Noise effect: It is the result of the noise produced by visitors during their walking and their presence in protected areas, which leads to some birds leaving their nests and leaving some wild animals to the areas adjacent to the visitors' presence. 3 Littering

(Continued)

Reasons of Extinction	*The consequences*
6 Agriculture	As a high priority, administration of the reserves prevented the agriculture inside them, absolutely, except for the agriculture that existed before the establishment of the reserve due to the negative impact of the agriculture process. When the agriculture process takes place in any of the protected areas, the natural system is changed very significantly. The process leads to the loss of natural system in the reserve, and therefore this leads to the disappearance of the original and natural plants and a change in the soil in the cultivation area, which leads to the abandonment of animals, birds and other organisms to the region, which leads to the destruction of the region naturally and a major change in vital processes in the region.

From the Dana Reserve Managerial Report (2020).

extinction threats to 121 types of species which match with the IUCN (2019) red list of species subject to extinction in Jordan.

The first social issue is the need for more awareness in the different institutions in Jordan to deal with extinction. This issue is highlighted in the following points:

- The CSR reports in the listed corporation in ASE focus on human rights (women and youth) more than animals' rights and ecosystems in general due to the press from the society as a consequence of the Arab Spring.
- The main environmental CSR disclosures in the majority of listed corporations in Jordan are for renewable energy and reducing pollution but ignoring extinction as there are a limited number of projects to deal with extinction risk.
- One of the good indicators to enhance the awareness in Jordan regarding the ecosystem and extinction is establishing few numbers of non-governmental organisations (Ministry of Social Development, 2020) and only one political party (Ministry of Political and Parliamentary Affairs, 2016) as they work as activists against extinction to protect the Jordanian ecosystem. However, their role in Jordanian society is still limited.
- There are laws and regulations to control and save species in Jordan; however, there is a weak application of them in real-life (RSCN, 2020).
- The focus on supporting the Jordanian national reserves is to make them tourism destinations (economic/investment perspective) and ignore the extinction risk resulting from tourism.
- Social media's role in enhancing Jordanian society's awareness regarding extinction is still limited.
- Miscoordination between the environmental research centres and applications of them in the real-life (Dana Management Report, 2020).

The following section explains the role of the research centres and their main studies' aims based on the RSCN (2020) report for future research.

Section (4) Lists and Discusses the Justifications of Developing Research towards Extinction Accounting in Jordan from Natural and Governance Perspectives

Understanding the discussion above opens the door of future research regarding extinction and helps the researcher to build up the accounting framework of extinction (Atkins and Maroun, 2018) in Jordan. There is a lack of studies in Jordan and other Middle Eastern courtiers for extinction. To pave the way for extinction research in Jordan, the RSCN (2020) reports provide a framework for potential extinction accounting research focused on two dimensions. The first one is the research regarding natural reserves and ecosystem in depth. The second one is the research regarding the plans for the governance system in Jordan to fight extinction.

* **Potential research regarding natural reserves, biodiversity and ecosystem:**
- The lack of coverage of the intermediate areas of the reserves in most of these studies. For example, large parts of the Iranian geographic region in Dana Reserve are still not explored due to the lack of accessibility.
- The lack of establishing some monitoring programs to evaluate the initial studies for the extinction of some species in Jordan, and consequently there is an inability to evaluate the results and indicators of these studies (Dana Reserve Management Report, 2020).
- The presence of significant research weaknesses for the biodiversity of the natural reserves that did not take place or that they lost a large part of their value by obsolescence. For example, the need for new botanical studies in the reserves and the need to conduct a study of natural pasture in the reserve and to determine pastoral loads (Dana Reserve Management Report, 2020).
- One of the most important aspects of this potential research is studying the Syrian and Gaza vulnerable animals and plants which are transferred to Jordan because of the instability in these areas. There is an absence of any monitoring programs to protect them in the natural reserves in Jordan.
- Another important research aspect which is still unexplored is the Syrian refugees' impact on the biodiversity and ecosystem in Jordan. Jordan has around 673,000 Syrian refugees based on United Nations (UNHCR, 2022) but there is an absence of research to evaluate their impact on the ecosystem in Jordan.
- The need for research to set practical plans to conserve important species, taking into account the potential impacts of climate change (Jamaliah and Powell, 2018) and tourism consequences (Weir, 2018)

★ **Potential research regarding governance systems to fight extinction in Jordan according to RSCN (2020) reports:**

– The need to study the administrative plans and internal systems of natural reserves.
– The need to develop a plan for environmental monitoring and link it to detailed studies that contribute to improving the management of each natural reserve and providing the databases for each.
– Working to involve the local community and stakeholders in the decision-making processes of the protected programs based on a new governance system that promotes the principle of participatory and integrates local communities in the management of protected areas.
– Studies to involve school and university courses to learn students in the schools and universities in Jordan about national reserves.
– Developing administrative, organizational and financial structures for each reserve ensuring the sustainability of its work and managing its activities. This is supported by Atkins and Maroun (2018).

Summary

This work presented the road map for extinction accounting in the Middle East region, Jordan as a focus. It presented the natural reserves in Jordan. Then it explained the reasons for extinction in Jordan from human practices and a social context. Finally, it highlighted the main future research recommended in extinction in Jordan from two perspectives. The first one is research for the

IMAGE 8.7 Extinction of some animals in Jordan (*Artwork by Isobel Edgley*).

ecosystem itself and the second research is for the comprehensive governance system to fight extinction in Jordan.

Part III

The Current Status of Biological Diversity and Species Extinctions in Libya

TARIQ ALMONSTASER AND ALI ELFADLI

This section discusses the recent status of biological diversity in Libya. It considers the recent situation for animals and plants and discusses the reasons for species being threatened by extinction. We then discuss the effects of some commercial and industrial activities on biological diversity in Libya, especially the threat to marine biodiversity in Libya. Lastly, we discuss the importance of religion in protecting the environment in Libyan culture.

There are no accurate surveys of biological diversity in Libya. The last report issued by the General Authority for the Environment, a governmental institution, was in 2010 under the name of the fourth national report on the implementation of the Convention on Biological Diversity (CBD). The report addresses the following topics: the status of biodiversity, its trends and threats; the current state of the strategies and the conservation of national work related to biodiversity; and incorporating biodiversity considerations into sectors and among sectors. Since then, there have been significant changes in Libya that have had implications for biological diversity. Consequently, this report is no longer reliable and there is an urgent need to update reports to provide a clearer picture and of the current reality regarding biodiversity in Libya. To gather updated information, we conducted interviews with interested parties and environmental workers. Our interviewees are presented in Table 8.3.

Salih Bourziqa, Director General and Founder of Al-Hayat Organization for the Protection of Land and Marine Organisms that was approved by IUCN in 2018 as a non-governmental member in Libya, stated:

> There are no accurate statistics in Libya, the last report issued by the Environment Agency was in 2010. There are important events that occurred after this date and many changes have happened. The revolution has had disastrous results for the environment in general in Libya. For example according to a study conducted by Omar Al-Mukhtar University in 2007, there were 300,000 hectares of forest and later in 2016 another study conducted found that the vegetation is equivalent to 100,000 hectares meaning that we lost 200,000 hectares of forests as a result of attacks and fires.

In relation to the statistical problems faced in Libya, Mr. Ibrahim Al-Kahwaji, Advisor at the International Union for Conservation of Nature and founding

TABLE 8.3 General information about the interviewees

No	date		Name	Position
1	28-05-2020	Facebook messenger	Ibrahim Al-Kahwaji	Adviser Consultant at the International Union for Conservation of Nature, founding member of the Libyan Wildlife Conservation Society Trust
2	02-06-2020	Skype	Elmaky Elagil	Director of Nature Conservation Dep. Environment General Authority(EGA)-Libya RAC/SPA National Focal Point
3	02-06-2020	Skype	Mohamed Sharif	The head of the Biosafety Department and a member of the Biodiversity Team in the Nature Conservancy Department
4	31-05-2020	Facebook messenger	Salih Bourziqa	Director General and Founder of Organisation of Life to Protect Wildlife and Marine Alhaya Organization for the Protection of Wildlife and Marine Organisms
5	06-06-2020	Questions sent and answers received by email	Mohamed Maklouf	Member of the Faculty in the Department of Botany, Faculty of Science, University of Tripoli

member of the Libyan Organization for the Protection of Wildlife and the civil activist in the environmental field, commented:

> Unfortunately, there are no accurate surveys organized for the species of animals under threat of extinction in Libya and the concerned authorities do not play their role effectively as there is no coordination between these bodies. For example, the General Authority for the Environment has a supervisory advisory function but in fact, it carries out executive activities and this results in reliance on people who are not specialized in carrying out surveys. Also, animals are not present inside the sanctuaries only, there are many outside these sanctuaries and we do not have any information about them or their movements. There have been successful attempts to introduce some species to Libya, but they were lost due to lack of surveys. In addition, I would like to point out the absence of the interactive role by all parties, including society. In short, the absence of surveys in Libya contributed to an increase in the exposure of possibly many species to extinction, due to the lack of information on these species and the failure to monitor them.

In relation to plant diversity, Dr. Mohamed Makhlouf, a faculty member at the Botany Department at the University of Tripoli and a founding member of the Commission on Human and Biosphere Reserves commented that:

> The last report on biological diversity in Libya was issued by the Environment Public Authority 2010, after which no report was issued, and the report did not address threatened plant species with extinction, and there are as yet no accurate figures, published studies, or evidence based on plant species threatened with extinction.

Regarding the difficulties with issuing reports, Mr. Elmaky Elagil, Director of the Nature Conservation and Natural Resources Department of the General Authority for the Environment, said:

> We are facing financial difficulties to issue reports that need a work team. They need money and rewards. Also, the political division, which in turn led to the division of institutions, including the General Authority for the Environment, negatively affected and contributed significantly to obstructing the issuance of reports. We are currently working on issuing the fifth report, which we hope will be ready soon, if conditions stabilize.

The fourth report provides the most important species of wild animals that are vulnerable to extinction and indicates that there are 455 vertebrate species and 3,958 invertebrate species as shown in Table 8.4 below.

The report also indicates that mammals are one of the most sensitive groups in Libya and that this group has suffered many extinctions. Table 8.5 shows the types of mammals recorded that are threatened at a global level. It is believed that some are extinct from Libya.

TABLE 8.4 Status of species in Libya according to group

	Total	Number of endemic species	Number of threatened species
Protista	?	?	?
Mollusks	139	?	?
Spiders	170	?	?
Insects	3763	?	?
Amphibia	2	?	?
Fish	98	1	1
Reptilia	113	1	4
Aves	356	?	41
Mammalia	76	4	12

The fourth national report on the implementation of the Convention on Biological Diversity- Libya, p. 39.

TABLE 8.5 Threatened Libyan mammals

	The scientific name	The international status
1	Felis margarita	Near threatened
2	Rhinonphous mehelyi	Vulnerable
3	Acinonyx jubatus	Vulnerable
4	Gazella dorcas	Vulnerable
5	Ammortagus lervia	Vulnerable
6	Gazella leptoceros	Endangered
7	Allactaga tetradactyla	Endangered
8	Monachus monachus	Critically endangered
9	Gazella dama	Critically endangered
10	Addax nasomaculatus	Critically endangered
11	Gerbillus grobbeni	Critically endangered
12	Gerbillus syrticus	Critically endangered
13	Oryx dammah	Extinct in the wild

TABLE 8.6 Threatened reptiles in Libya

	The scientific name	Faction	Rank	The international status
1	Acanthodactylus pardlis	Lacertidae	Squamata	Acanthodactylus pardails
2	Chalcides ocellatus	Scincidae	Squamata	Chalcides ocellatus
3	Testudo kleinmanni	Testudinidae	Testudines	Testudo kleinmanni
4	Testudo graeca	Testudinidae	Testudines	Testudo graeca

Regarding reptiles, the report indicates 113 species of reptiles, including 4 threatened with extinction, as illustrated in Table 8.6.

In terms of birds, the report indicated the registration of 356 species, of which 41 are threatened, whether at the local or global level. The following Table 8.7 shows the birds threatened with extinction in Libya.

The interviewees emphasised that most animals are vulnerable to the threat of extinction. For example, Mr. Saleh, when asked about the most important species exposed to extinction, answers:

> In my opinion, all animals in Libya are at risk of extinction, I can give you some examples: Tricis deer no longer appears, there are only a few numbers of them, a chivalric animal or what is known locally as night hunting, the African golden wolf, a squid bird which is considered extinct at present. The desert rabbit is no longer seen, there are only few of them around.

Mr. Saleh also indicated that other species threatened with extinction were not included in the report. There are factors that changed after 2011 such as an increase in poaching. All kinds of species including migratory birds that were passing through Libya in the monsoon periods became extinct as the migration

TABLE 8.7 Threatened birds in Libya

	The scientific name	*The national status*	*The international status*
1	Aegypius monachus	Near-threatened	Near-threatened
2	Aenigmatolimnas marginalis	Rare/accidental	Least concerned
3	Aquila clanga	Vulnerable	Vulnerable
4	Aquila heliaca	Vulnerable	Vulnerable
5	Aythya nyroca	Near-threatened	Near-threatened
6	Caprimulgus ruficollis	Rare/accidental	Least concerned
7	Chersophilus duponti	Rare/accidental	Near-threatened
8	Chlamydotis undulata	Vulnerable	Vulnerable
9	Cinclus cinclus	Rare/accidental	Least concerned
10	Circus macrourus	Near-threatened	Near-threatened
11	Columba palumbus	Rare/accidental	Least concerned
12	Coracias abyssinicus	Rare/accidental	?
13	Coracias garrulus	Near-threatened	Near-threatened
14	Corvus albus	Rare/accidental	Least concerned
15	Crex crex	Near-threatened	Near-threatened
16	Endangered	Rare/accidental	Falco cherrug
17	Falco concolor	Near-threatened	Near-threatened
18	Falco naumanni	Vulnerable	Vulnerable
19	Falco subbuteo	Extirpated	Least concerned
20	Falco vespertinus	Near-threatened	Near-threatened
21	Gallinago media	Near-threatened	Near-threatened
22	Glareola nordmanni	Near-threatened	Near-threatened
23	Larus audouinii	Near-threatened	Near-threatened
24	Limosa limosa	Near-threatened	Near-threatened
25	Luscinia luscinia	Rare/accidental	Least concerned
26	Marmaronetta angustirostris	Vulnerable	Vulnerable
27	Mergus serrator	Rare/accidental	Least concerned
28	Milvus milvus	Near-threatened	Near-threatened
29	Neophron percnopterus	Endangered	Endangered
30	Numenius arquata	Near-threatened	Near-threatened
31	Numenius tenuirostris	Critically endangered	Critically endangered
32	Oenanthe finschii	Least concerned	Rare/accidental
33	Oenanthe xanthoprymna	Rare/accidental	Least concerned
34	Oxyura leucocephala	Endangered	Endangered
35	Phylloscopus orientalis	Rare/accidental	?
36	Pluvianus aegyptius	Rare/accidental	Least concerned
37	Puffinus mauretanicus	Critically endangered	Critically endangered
38	Stercorarius pomarinus	Rare/accidental	Least concerned
39	Struthio camelus	Extirpated	Least concerned
40	Sylvia undata	Near-threatened	Near-threatened
41	Tetrax tetrax	Near-threatened	Near-threatened

The fourth national report on the implementation of the Convention on Biological Diversity-Libya, p. 41.

paths changed. The valleys (ram ram), the human deer that used to be present in the coastal border strip, have become officially extinct, even worldwide. Mr. Ibrahim Al-Kahwaji also confirms that most animals are threatened with extinction in Libya, where he says:

> I can confirm that most animals in Libya are under threat of extinction, unfortunately, perhaps except for rodents and some types of foxes and small rabbits, despite being subjected to poaching, their status is still fine. But if we look at animals such as valleys Barbary sheep these species are subject to abnormal extermination. One of the most important species exposed to extinction are the 'valleys', and there are only some hundreds of them. There are two types, one of which lives in the north and the other in the south. Both are under threat of extinction. Another species called the 'Quorks deer' is under threat of extinction due to poaching. There is a kind of Egyptian turtle reptile that no longer exists except in Libya. In my view its number reaches tens of thousands and these are a precedent and a very rare case. This species is distinct and differs from that in Palestine and Egypt. There are tens of thousands of this type escaping to Egypt. This is a personal viewpoint from my experience and may conflict with the opinions of others in the absence of accurate statistics and surveys.

Regarding the vegetation cover, Dr. Mohamed Makhlouf refers to the most important types of endangered species, based on his personal studies, which are represented in the following Table 8.8.

TABLE 8.8 Endangered plant species

	Family	Name	Notes
1	Alliaceae	*Allium ampeloprasum*	
2	Alliaceae	*Allium longanum*	
3	Alliaceae	*Allium schubertii*	
4	Amaryllidaceae	*Narcissus tazetta*	
5	Apiaceae	*Bupleurum gerardi*	
6	Apiaceae	*Foeniculum vulgar*	
7	Asteraceae	*Artemisia vulgaris*	
8	Asteraceae	*Ptilostemon gnaphaloides*	
9	Capparaceae	*Capparis spinosa* L. Ssp.*orientalis*	
10	Caprifoliaceae	*Lonicera nummulariifolia*	
11	Crassulaceae	*Sedum ebracteatum*	
12	Crassulaceae	*Sedum rubens*	
13	Ephedraceae	*Ephedra alata*	
14	Ericaceae	*Arbutus pavarii*	
15	Fabaceae	*Anagyris foetida*	
16	Fumariaceae	*Fumaria capreolata*	

	Family	Name	Notes
17	Globulariaceae	*Globularia alypum*	
18	Lamiaceae	*Salvia fruticosa*	
19	Lamiaceae	*Teucrium apollinis*	
20	Lamiaceae	*Thymus capitatus*	
21	Lauraceae	*Laurus azorica*	
22	Lauraceae	*Laurus nobilis*	
23	Leonticaceae	*Bongardia chrysogonum*	
24	Liliaceae	*Smilax aspera*	
25	Myrtaceae	*Myrtus communis*	
26	Poaceae	*Lebiella cyrenaica*	Extinct
27	Polygalaceae	*Polygala aschersoniana*	
28	Primulaceae	*Cyclamen tohlfesianum*	
29	Rosaceae	*Crataegus pallasii*	
30	Rosaceae	*Rubus sanctus*	
31	Rubiaceae	*Putoria calabrica*	
32	Saxifragaceae	*Saxifraga tridactylites*	
33	Scrophulariaceae	*Veronica anagallis–aquatica*	
34	Tiliaceae	*Corchorus depressus*	
35	Typhaceae	*Typha domingensis*	
36	Typhaceae	*Typha elephantina*	
37	Vahliaceae	*Vahlia dichotoma*	
38	Valerianaceae	*Valerianella muricata*	
39	Verbenaceae	*Phyla nodiflora*	Extinct?
40	Rosaceae	*Potentilla reptans*	
41	Scrophulariaceae	*Veronica anagalloides*	

Reasons Why Species Are Threatened with Extinction in Libya

Thousands of years ago, Libya was covered in green savannah, but over the last 5,000 years or so, the country has been invaded by waves of desertification and drought, such that today we find that most forms of life are concentrated in the coastal strip and desert oases, with increasing depletion of marine resources. The following Table 8.9 shows the most important dangers and threats facing biodiversity in Libya.

All our interviewees confirmed that the situation since 2011 has resulted in disaster for biodiversity in Libya. For example, Ibrahim Al-Qahwaji indicated that cutting forests increased rapidly after the revolution in 2011, especially in the Jabal Al-Akhdar region, as well as in Tripoli, the Wadi Al-Rabi` area and Ain Zara. Smuggling animals abroad is another reason for extinction threats for some species, with Ibrahim Al-Kahwaji commenting that:

> ...for the turtle, smuggling abroad is one of the most significant causes of extinction threat.

TABLE 8.9 Threats to forests

The threat	Reasons
1 Fires	– Natural fires due to drought and high temperatures.
	– Fires accidentally made by visitors to the forest.
	– Fires created by criminals to convert forests into private farms.
2 Cutting forest trees	– In order to produce coal.
	– To convert forests into private farms.
	– For the purpose of construction.
	– To build roads
3 Poaching	– Caring for large numbers of animals to the extent that the ability of forests to regenerate is no longer tolerated.
	– Caring for unsuitable animals that damage forests.
4 Pollution	– Factories' smoke.
	– Ineffective treatment of solid waste.
	– Pouring wastewater into the forest without treatment.
5 Drought	– Increased temperatures with lower rates of rain.
	– Misuse of plants.
6 Misuse of plants	– Excessive use of medicinal plants

See the fourth report on the implementation of the Convention on Biological Diversity (Libyan General Authority for the Environment, 2010, p. 53).

Poaching increased dramatically after 2011 in Libya, with, Saleh Bourziqa stating that:

> In my view, the two most important reasons are poaching and lack of awareness. An example of poaching is the threat of extinction facing the famous bird which is called (Alshahin), he is the fastest bird in the world, he lays its eggs in April, so the hunters take these chicks and the big birds die. Their numbers have decreased greatly, in 2012 there were only two birds. This led us to think of an event to release the bird. The response from hunters was very good, as they released 36 birds in the Zintan region alone, and they started competing to release the birds, as a result, their numbers increased.

The unstable political situation and the lack of law enforcement were the two important issues that led to an increase in the threats that affect Libyan biodiversity, and Mohamed Sharif indicated that:

> We, at the Environmental Public Authority, have issued draft laws on environmental protection and biosafety with respect to genetically modified organisms, but up to this point these drafts have not been approved as a result of poor government performance and political interactions. The absence of the law's effectiveness increased the attacks by violators. Laws were not effective until before 2011 but increased twice after 2011.

Elmaky Elagil added that:

> before 2011, the previous regime in Libya has not been working to improve the environmental situation effectively and did not take sustainable measures such as awareness and projects with a specialization of protection
>   After the revolution people began taking advantage of the absence of the law and usurping land and claiming ownership.

This was consistent with Mohamed Maklouf's view and he stated:

> In addition to the factors discussed in the fourth report issued by the General Authority for the Protection of the Environment in 2010, these factors still exist; however, the aggression against natural plants has increased steadily and deforestation by cutting or artificial fires for the purpose of converting them into private lands for residential or commercial purposes, which led to the deterioration of large areas of forests and cover The natural plant frighteningly, which led to the disappearance of many plant species as well as Fauna animal organisms that depend on this vegetation, which causes an environmental imbalance in those areas, which may show negative effects in the future.

It can be concluded that the main reasons for species being threatened with extinction are fires, cutting forest trees and poaching. After the revolution in 2011 in Libya and the consequences of instability, these factors have increased and other factors have raised such as the lack of law enforcement and usurping land as a result and smuggling animals like turtles.

Impacts of Some Commercial and Industrial Activities on Biological Diversity in Libya

There are some commercial, industrial and service activities that have a negative impact on the environment and biological diversity. Despite Law No. 15 on protecting and improving the environment set conditions for these activities to protect the environment, there are many activities that did not adhere to the law and still engage in activities that are remarkable to the environment and biological diversity. Saleh Bourziqa gives examples of these activities, such as the Derna cement factory that was built among the forests and another for carpets that releases sewage in the valleys that have rain water on which birds feed, which causes disease to these birds, as well as the infection transmitted by birds when they collapse from other valleys.

The tourism sector has activities that have negative impacts on the environment and biological diversity. In this regard, Mr. Ibrahim Al-Kahwaji says:

> The tourism sector, in particular the summer resorts, carry out activities such as throwing waste at sea and on the beaches which have a negative

impact, he resorts that are created along the coast in May each year, which is the period of sea turtle breeding, noise and lighting negatively affects the breeding of these turtles. Also, tourism projects have negative effects, such as building hotels in forest areas. The tourism sector must be controlled in line with the conservation of the environment and biological diversity.

Dr. Mohamed Makhlouf also points to the risks to the vegetation due to the activities of some factories. He says:

> There are a lot of commercial and industrial companies that have unfortunately harmed the environment, and they were created without an environmental impact assessment study, such companies are the cement factory in Alkomes city near the sea and the city and the vegetation and what it causes from pollution to these nearby environments which are noticed clearly, also the Abu Kamash complex and its impact on vegetation in that region.

The Impact of Civil and Governmental Organizations on Factories and Polluting Companies

Many governmental and civil institutions take over the management and protection of biological diversity:

- Environment Public Authority
- General Authority for Agriculture
- Agriculture Research Center
- Marine Biology Research Center
- Animal Wealth Research and Studies Center
- National Authority for Scientific Research
- Universities and Higher Institutes
- Private Associations.

(Source: Fourth National Report on Implementation of the Convention on Biological Diversity in Libya 2010)

After the political changes that occurred in Libya in the year 2011, the number of civil organisations in Libya has increased, especially those who are specialised in the field of environmental protection and biological diversity, and they have done many activities and projects; some of them are voluntary and some are receiving support from the International Union for the Conservation of Nature and the Partnership Fund for Critical Environmental Systems.

These organisations are supposed to play an important role in pressuring commercial, industrial and service companies to play their role in terms of environmental protection, an important part of the social responsibility of these companies. Several studies in Libya have pointed to the apparent shortcomings of companies operating in various sectors by playing their part in the social contribution in general and contributing to protecting the environment in particular; Ibrahim Al-Kahwaji says

> Usually, we invite these institutions to the activities that we do, such as conferences and workshops, but unfortunately only a few of them respond. In addition, we do not find cooperation from these institutions with regard to our financial procedures and banks, for example, they do not facilitate our procedures, which negatively affects the activities that we do.

When one of the interviewees asks if they give attention to the financial reports, he answers:

> No, we are not familiar with the financial reports, but we were in contact with the committee working on sustainable development reports, one of whose goals is how to protect the environment in which companies with polluting activities operate.

He added

> I believe that including information about the environmental contributions of companies will be very useful information for us, and through this information we can define our strategies.

and when he asked have you ever requested that the financial reports include information about the company's environmental contributions? he answered:

> Actually not, but I think it is very useful if we get that information. It is a good idea and we will in the future claim this information and include it in the financial reports.

All interviewees believe that these companies should play their role in helping organisations, for example Ibrahim Al-Kahwaji says:

> Neighboring countries, such as Tunisia and Algeria, provide a good example in this context. Civil society organizations have virtually dispensed with the support of international organisations, because they are satisfied with the support provided by the private sector. In Libya, there are some institutions that provide support to civil organisations that you trust in their work. There are also some companies that provide some support to civil organizations, such as the Italian company ENI Gas. Printing companies also believe that they provide good support to organizations working in the field of the environment, through the discounts granted to them on logos and brochures related to the environment.

As says Elmaky Elagil:

> In my view, any organisation that has activities that affect the environment must play its role in protecting the environment. The oil sector, for example, is supposed to play its role in supporting environmental organisations and activities. Currently we are receiving support from the Nature Conservancy that supports small organisations working in the field of nature I believe that the oil company should play a fundamental role, as it is one of the most polluting institutions in the environment. Likewise in the private sector, it must play its role, as Law 15 stipulates that the project must be evaluated if it has environmental impacts.

Civil organisations do not have the power to influence and constitute real pressure on companies and Saleh Bourziqa says

> I see civil organizations are still weak and cannot put up any pressure.

Governmental institutions have a greater role, due to governmental and legal support. In this context, Elmaky Elagil when asked about the extent of the pressures that their institution exerts answers:

> We have meetings with the National Oil Corporation, there are some activities such as changing the oils to plastic, so we stopped this project because it was damaging to the environment. The cement factory in Ain Al-Fazala in Tobruk we stopped because the factory was near the reserve. We stopped the tourist villages. We have stopped plans for the Lake Juliana project because it has bird species nesting in that lake in which it is included in the red list, so we have provided them with strategies and plans. We can say overall that we are exerting pressure, but at the same time we take into account the current conditions and the lack of capabilities.

Threats to Marine Biodiversity in Libya

Libya is considered one of the well-recognised eco-diversity contexts where foraging grounds are available for many marine species (Stokes et al., 2015). While this country witnessed the record of the highest ever temperature in the globe, it snows almost every year in many coastal cities on the eastern side. Sahara covers more than half of its area and, accordingly, the country is known to experience 'absolute scarcity' in terms of sustainable water resources (United Nations Development Programme, 2011). However, it is one of the 50 most peaceful countries worldwide in terms of eco-crises (United Nations, 2016).

The biodiversity-related legislation of the country consists a set of laws, regulations and agreements. Internationally, Libya has signed two agreements: firstly, Barcelona Convention for the Protection of the Marine Environment and the Coastal Region of the Mediterranean in 2004 and in 2000, the agreement of wetlands protection (Ramsar). Domestic biodiversity-related laws and regulations involve only the onshore context. For instance, Law No. 15 in 1989 about the protection of Animals and Trees; Law No. 5 in 1982 about protection Rangeland and Forests (amended by Law No. 14 in 1992) and prime ministry Decree No. 631 in 1992 about Natural Reserves and Parks.

This section focuses on the reasons for the extinction of marine species, especially bluefin tuna. This section shall be presented using the current literature and available data related to extinction and biodiversity in the Libyan context. We aim to help interested researchers and concerning firms, which are likely to be affected and influenced by the threats of this phenomenon. Giving early warning of the significance and of corporate reporting is essential as it has the potential to contribute to the efforts against such threats (Atkins and Maroun, 2018). Another motivation to study this phenomenon in Libya is the political change (Arab Spring) in the region. It imposed – by more vociferous stakeholders (Almontaser, 2019) – the priority of considering effective strategies to tackle the threats of extinction and boosting the biodiversity against so-called polluters.

Hamza, Raïs and Grissac (2011) argue that 'overfishing' is a major problem for the Mediterranean countries in general and Libya in particular. As production of fishing bluefin tuna is still new compared to neighbours, Libyan production peaked in the 2000s (via national fisheries, but also due to illegal fishing in Libyan waters by other nations). Hamza et al. (2011) state that overfishing in the Libyan marine region was the reason for replacing many types of *extinct* fish in the local market by other invasive species.

In contrary to Hamza et al.'s (2011) argument, the analysis of FOA data[8] about the capture production of marine water may be interpreted as that the threats of extinction of some kind of fish in Libya are not an overfishing issue. The data reveal that some Mediterranean countries – they all have similar marine biodiversity attributes and climate conditions – have captured production of marine water ten times larger than Libya in 2018 regarding *the length of coastline*. For example, one KM of the Spanish coastline has produced averagely 185 tons, while Libya is just 18 tons. Other European Mediterranean countries have production volume (tons per KM) in 2018 lower than Spain and greater than Libya. All these countries comply with the United Nations Convention on Biodiversity and Agenda 21. Furthermore, EU and Libya signed a Fisheries Partnership Agreement (*European Parliament resolution on a fisheries partnership agreement*, 2019). However, this agreement does not involve any biodiversity issue. Accordingly, the fishery production of other neighbours is incomparable with Libya, and Libyan fisheries' efforts are yet immature. By all means, the current volume of Libyan fishery production cannot be entitled 'overfishing'.

We argue that the reasons for this type of inshore extinction (or immigration) could be, firstly, the negative impact of the constant toxic waste into the coastal region and, secondly, the consequences of offshore oil operations (in both upstream and midstream levels).

According to Ocean Health Index[9] 'Biodiversity – Species', France marine region has scored 49 (the worst region is 239) in 2019, while Spain, Italy and Greece have scored 62, 133 and 134 respectively. Libyan marine region reveals the disastrous status of threatened biodiversity by scoring 205 (see Figure 8.4). This could be the first cause of the reduction of the average size of bluefin tuna hunted on the coast of Libya. It dropped from averagely 124 kg in 2001 to only 65 kg in 2009 (WWF, 2010). This may be a painful introduction to extinction of this type of tuna.

Offshore oil operations are managed and achieved mainly by MNCs (Martinez, 2014). Nevertheless, the response of MNCs to the global crisis/issues is less important than local matters of host countries (Kolk and Lenfant, 2010). For instance, the oil spill of the Gulf of Mexico at the beginning of 2010 did not motivate MNCs who are operating the upstream activities to disclose a single word about that crisis, especially BP. According to its website, this company disclosed that environmental crisis – three years later, in 2013 – just twice. That crisis has immediately risen the worries of many Mediterranean countries about offshore MNCs' operations in Libya (Almontaser, 2019). However, BP offshore operations in Libya were not as important as the Gulf of Mexico (Macalister, 2012). Nevertheless, the uncertainties of Mediterranean countries did not motivate BP to increase the concerning disclosure on its website. This apathetic-like response could be explained as either an approach of avoiding disclosing bad information (Deegan and Rankin, 1996) or a strategy of crisis marginalisation by avoiding being an exaggerative anti-pollution publisher (Sethi, 1978).

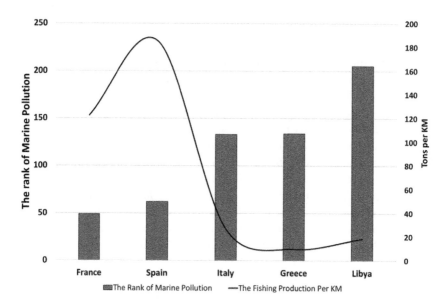

FIGURE 8.4 The threats against marine biodiversity in Libya in 2018.
Source: Websites of Ocean Health Index and FAO.

Most of the oil midstream companies are Libyan national firms and, of them, Azawiya oil refinery is the most popular (Mansur et al., 2014). The location of refinery operations of this company is surrounded by urban area and it is 50 KM far from Capital city. The political change in 2011 was in favour of people living close to the operational location of the company and they became more vociferous for their rights in relation to the impact of refinery operations, especially water pollution (Kailani and Saleh, 2012). Despite stakeholders' pressure on this company shutdown temporally its operations many times since 2011 (Kailani and Saleh, 2012), the company disclosed once (and very brief) on the website[10] about the proactive consideration of any water pollution incident. Such toxic incidents are most likely the reason for the loss of biodiversity – according to Ocean Health Index – and increase the number of extinct marine species (Hamza et al., 2011).

The Influence of the Religious Factor on Environmental Awareness

Religion plays an important role especially within the Middle East. Libya can be one country in the Middle East where religion can be one institutional factor that has an important role in shaping the behaviour of originations (Elfadli, 2019). Most of the interviewees emphasised the importance of religion in increasing environmental awareness and its positive impact that can be used as an aid to organisations working in environmental activities to achieve their goals, as well as helping commercial, industrial and service institutions to play their part in protecting the environment. Most of the interviewees see that the principles of the Islamic religion are closely compatible with the principles of protecting and preserving nature. For example, Elmaky Elagil cites any of the Holy Quran as evidence of the compatibility of the Islamic religion with the protection and preservation of nature. He says:

> There is no doubt that religion is very important, so Quran says
> ظَهَرَ الْفَسَادُ فِي الْبَرِّ وَالْبَحْرِ بِمَا كَسَبَتْ أَيْدِي النَّاسِ لِيُذِيقَهُم بَعْضَ الَّذِي عَمِلُوا لَعَلَّهُمْ يَرْجِعُونَ
> Corruption has appeared throughout the land and sea by [reason of] what the hands of people have earned so He may let them taste part of [the consequence of] what they have done that perhaps they will return
> So the human being is the basis of corruption and he is the one who pollutes the environment.

The influence of religion in Libya can play a stronger role than the laws established by governments, and Ibrahim Alghwagy says:

> Laws dealing with environmental protection exist from a long time ago, but their impact did not reach the influence of the religion. In my view, civil society organisations can use religious discourse to help them communicate the environmental messages that they were created for

There are many examples of the influence of religion, Ibrahim Al-Kahwaji says

> In 2012, and as a result of the instability situation during that period, Poaching increased, so we, as civil society organizations, went to the Dar Al efta and explained to them the situation and issued a fatwa prohibiting poaching that was circulated to mosques and published in social media.
>
> We also communicated directly with the mosques in some events. For example, when attacking the famous Maslahat reserve that contains rare plants, we went to the front of the mosque in that area and asked him to educate people about the danger of this. So the sermons of the mosque in that mosque turned into awareness lectures on the environment. There have been some other events in which we went to the mosques to raise awareness, when the outbreak of leishmaniasis, for example, they gave us the opportunity to speak after the end of the Friday sermon, to educate people about this disease. I see the effect was positive, as laws dealing with environmental protection have existed from a long time ago, but their impact did not reach the influence of religion, which I see in my view as being stronger in our Arab societies. In my view, civil society organizations can employ religious discourse to help them deliver the environmental messages that they were created for.

Summary

This section has discussed the recent status of biological diversity in Libya, and it considers the recent report issued by the environment authority in Libya in 2010. To gather updated information, five interviews were conducted with founders of environmental organisations and managers in Libyan government environment institutions. The fourth environment report provides information about the threat species of animals and plant face. As mentioned by all the interviewees, all animals are under threat of extinction and these threats have increased dramatically since 2011 as the instability situation for the country because of the revolution and its negative side effect for all aspects in Libya including the environment and biodiversity. The report indicated the most important reasons behind the threats which are fires, cutting trees, poaching, pollution, drought and misuse of plants. In addition, interviewees added that, after 2011, these reasons of threats have increased and other factors are appeared, such as the lack of law enforcement and usurping land and smuggling animals like turtles. The chapter discusses the effects of some commercial and industrial activities on biological diversity in Libya, and the fourth report mentioned a smock raise from factories, the solid waste and ineffective treatment of solid waste and pouring wastewater into the forest without treatment. In addition, interviewees indicated tourist activities such as summer camps created by tourist companies and how these activities affect turtles and polluted beaches, and they indicated bullet hotels and factories in areas near natural reserves. The interviewee indicated that the oil sector is one of the most affected sectors in the environment. They also mentioned some small businesses whose activities polluted the environment such as carpet factories drawing wastewater in the forest. Most interviewees had no idea about the term CSR social accounting responsibility, and their organisations do not put significant pressure on companies to take their responsibility towards the environment. They thought integrating information about the environment and biodiversity in annual reports of these companies would be very helpful and can improve their projects to protect the environment. We also found that the marine biodiversity of the Libyan coastal line is affected by the degree of pollution. It could be the main reason for the extinction (or immigration) of bluefin tuna. Local and MNCs operating in the offshore oil sector in Libya share a part of the dilemma. Finally, the chapter discusses religion as one of the important factors that play an important role in Libyan society and not considered in the environment report, interviewees confirm that the religious factor with the principles of protecting and preserving nature and the influence of religion in Libya can play a stronger role than the laws established by governments.

The implication of the findings seems to be that civilian organisations, government institutions and society as a whole need to play a further role to protect biodiversity in Libya. Diffuse awareness of CSR needs to be considered in these organisations and institutions to put more pressure on companies to protect the environment. Religion can be one important tool to help raise awareness in society.

Further research on biodiversity in different aspects in Libya is needed. Regarding accounting research, most research in Libya discussed CSR in general. More focused research about biodiversity is needed, for example, the role-plays by companies to protect biodiversity in Libya.

Conclusion

This chapter has explored the current status of species of flora and fauna threatened with extinction in the Middle East, focusing on Saudi Arabia, Jordan and Libya. Distinctly different countries from a political and economic perspective, they all have species extinctions in common as a serious and growing issue. It is clear to see that all three countries share common causes of species extinctions and biodiversity loss, many deriving from industrial activity but also from other human interventions such as poaching and tree felling. The analyses in this chapter provide a strong mandate for a Middle Eastern Extinction Governance, Extinction Finance and Extinction Accounting built on a need to preserve species for reasons of financial materiality arising from the implications of species loss, as highlighted throughout this book. However, in a Middle Eastern context, this chapter also emphasises the importance of a religious imperative for preventing species extinction and protecting and enhancing biodiversity. Furthermore, this chapter demonstrates the appalling impact of war and political upheaval on flora and fauna and the need to find solutions to preserve the natural world around us even more urgently in situations of struggle and strife. More than anything this chapter provides a springboard for researchers to explore and develop extinction accounting frameworks that can be applied across Middle Eastern organisations as well as governmental level in order to bring together science, ecology and business, thereby saving and protecting species from extinction.

Notes

1 Images 1-3 from www.swa.gov.sa on [26/02/2020].
2 Image 4 from https://rb.gy/f1vegm on [23/02/2021].
3 These statistics were collected by the author from (P.S.F.W.R.C) in July 2019.
4 Jami` at-Tirmidhi 1924; In-book reference: Book 27, Hadith 30; English translation: Vol. 4, Book 1, Hadith 1924; at https://sunnah.com.
5 USC-MSA web; (English) reference: Book 49, Hadith 23; Arabic reference: Book 49, Hadith 1696; at https://sunnah.com.
6 Sunan Abi Dawud 4089; In-book reference: Book 34, Hadith 70; English translation: Book 33, Hadith 4078; at https://sunnah.com.
7 Sahih Muslim 2242 d; In-book reference: Book 45, Hadith 172; USC-MSA web (English) reference: Book 32, Hadith 6345; at https://sunnah.com.
8 Available online at: http://www.fao.org/fishery/rfb/en, Accessed in 1 June 2020.
9 http://data.oceanhealthindex.org/comparisons, Accessed in 15 June 2020.
10 I have checked the website (https://arc.com.ly) from 2008 to 2015 using Archive.org.

References for Part I

Al-Johany, A. M. H. (2007) 'Distribution and Conservation of the Arabian Leopard Pan-thera Pardus Nimr in Saudi Arabia'. *Journal of Arid Environments*, 68, 20–30.

Al-Khulaidi, A., Al-Sagheer, N. A., Al-Turki, T. & Filimban, F. (2018) 'Inventory of Most Rare and Endangered Plant Species in Albaha Region Saudi Arabia'. *IJBPAS*, 7, 443–460.

Al-Tokhais, A. & Thapa, B. (2019) 'Stakeholder Perspectives Towards National Parks and Protected Areas in Saudi Arabia'. *Sustainability*, 11, 2323.

Al Shahrani, A. a. A. (2018). *Assessing the Efforts of Major Industrial Companies in Maintaining Environment Security in the Kingdom of Saudi Arabia - Applied Study on Saudi Basic Industries Corporation (Sabic).* Doctoral, Naif Arab University for Security Sciences.

Atkins, J. & Maroun, W. (2018) 'Integrated Extinction Accounting and Accountability: Building an Ark'. *Accounting, Auditing & Accountability Journal*, 31, 750–786.

Cannon, J. C. (2019) *Leopards Get a $20m Boost from Panthera Pact with Saudi Prince.* Online: Mongabay. Available: https://news.mongabay.com/2019/06/leopards-get-a-20m-boost-from-pact-with-saudi-prince/ [15/02/2021].

Cragg, A. K. (2020) *Hadith | Islam.* Online: @britannica. Available: https://www.britannica.com/topic/Hadith.

Ektebsa. (2020) *Animals Whose Names Are Mentioned in the Quran.* Online. Available: https://www.ektebsa7.com.

Hall, M., Miller, A. G., Llewellyn, O., Abbasi, T. M., Al-Harbi, R. J., Al-Wetaid, A. H. & Al-Shammari, K. F. (2010) 'A Conservation Assessment of Douepea Arabica (Brassicaceae): A Critically Endangered Plant Species from Saudi Arabia'. *Oryx*, 44, 547–550.

Islam, M. Z.-U., Ismail, K. & Boug, A. (2011) 'Restoration of the Endangered Arabian Oryx Oryx Leucoryx, Pallas 1766 in Saudi Arabia Lessons Learnt from the Twenty Years of Re-Introduction in Arid Fenced and Unfenced Protected Areas'. *Zoology in the Middle East*, 54, 125–140.

Karasik, T. (2018). 'Saudi Arabia's Lasting Natural Treasure Is Its Ecosystems, Not Its Oil'. *Arab_News*, 2018-06-06.

Magbool, S. S. (2009). *Corporate Environmental Management of Private Businesses in Saudi Arabia.* Doctoral, University of Huddersfield.

Mewa. (2020) *The Executive Regulations for Hunting a Wild Animal.* Online: Ministry of Environment Water & Agriculture. Available: https://istitlaa.ncc.gov.sa/ar/Civil/Mewa/Pages/default.aspx [23/02/ 2021].

Mohamed, N. (2016) 'Revitalising the Ecological Ethics of Islam by Way of Islamic Education | مركز دراسات التشريع والأخلاق الإسلامي'. *Research Center for Islamic Legislation & Ethics (CILE).*

Ncw. (2021) *About.* Online: National Center Wildlife. Available: https://www.ncw.gov.sa/Ar/AboutUs/Pages/default.aspx [15/02 2021].

Rashid, H. (2012) *Quranic Verse – Hajj- Prohibition of Hunting Game in Ihram; Exceptions; Expiation/Penalty for Hunting.* Online. Available: https://tsmufortruth.wordpress.com/2012/10/07/quranic-verse-hajj-prohibition-of-hunting-game-in-ihram-exceptions-expiationpenalty-for-hunting/ [25/02/ 2021].

Skirka, H. (2019) *Al Ula Conservation Project Can Help Arabian Leopards Come Roaring Back.* Online: The national news. Available: https://www.thenationalnews.com/lifestyle/travel/al-ula-conservation-project-can-help-arabian-leopards-come-roaring-back-1.861529 [15/02/ 2021].

Zafar-Ul Islam, M., Boug, A., Judas, J. & As-Shehri, A. (2018) 'Conservation Challenges for the Arabian Leopard (Panthera Pardus Nimr) in the Western Highlands of Arabia'. *Biodiversity*, 19, 188–197.

Zafar-Ul Islam, M., Volmer, R., Al Boug, A., Shehri, A. A. & Gavashelishvili, A. (2020) 'Modelling the Effect of Competition for Prey and Poaching on the Population of the Arabian Leopard, Panthera Pardus Nimr, in Saudi Arabia (Mammalia: Felidae)'. *Zoology in the Middle East*, 66, 95–106.

References for Part II

Almontaser, T. (2019). *The Impact of Management Reconstruction on Corporate Social Responsibility Online Reporting by Libyan Oil Companies in the Wake of the Arab Spring.* University of Reading (Accessable from 16th October 2022). Retrieved from http://centaur.reading.ac.uk/87869/

Atkins, J., and Maroun, W. (2018). Integrated extinction accounting and accountability: Building an ark. *Accounting, Auditing and Accountability Journal*, 31(3), 750–786.

Deegan, C., and Rankin, M. (1996). Do Australian companies report environmental news objectively? An analysis of environmental protection authority". *Accounting, Auditing & Accountability Journal*, 9(2), 50–67.

Dana Reserve management Report. 2020. Royal Society for the Conversation of Nature. [Online]. Available at: http://www.abctaxa.be/jordan/biodiversity/protected-areas/dana-biosphere-reserve/dana-management-plan-2016-2020/download/en/1/Dana%20Managment%20Plan%202016-2020.pdf?action=view

Elfadli, A. (2019). *Corporate Governance of Banks in Libya* (Vol. 1). Walter de Gruyter GmbH & Co KG.

European Parliament resolution on a fisheries partnership agreement, Pub. L. No. 143 (2019). European Parliament.

Hamza, A., Raïs, C., and Grissac, A. J. de. (2011). *Towards a Representative Network of Marine Protected Areas in Libya.* Retrieved from http://data.iucn.org/dbtw-wpd/edocs/2011-037.pdf

IUCN. 2019. International Union for Conservation of Nature Red List of endangered species in Jordan. [Online]. Available at: https://www.iucnredlist.org/search/list?query=Jordan&searchType=species

Kailani, E. El, and Saleh, Z. (2012). *Extractive Industry and Conflict Risk in Libya*. Brussels. Retrieved from http://eplo.org/activities/ongoing-projects/civil-society-dialogue-network/csdn-outputs-2010-2013/

Kolk, A., and Lenfant, F. (2010). MNC Reporting on CSR and Conflict in Central Africa. *Journal of Business Ethics*, 93(Suppl. 2), 241–255.

Libyan General Authority for the Environment. (2010). *The Fourth National Report on the Implementation of the Convention on Biological Diversity*. Available at: https://www.cbd.int/doc/world/ly/ly-nr-04-ar.pdf [Last Accessed 09 Jan 2022].

Macalister, T. (2012). Why Libya's "sweet" crude oil is not enough to tempt BP or Shell | Business | The Guardian.

Mansur, A. A., Adetutu, E. M., Kadali, K. K., Morrison, P. D., Nurulita, Y., and Ball, A. S. (2014). Assessing the hydrocarbon degrading potential of indigenous bacteria isolated from crude oil tank bottom sludge and hydrocarbon-contaminated soil of Azzawiya oil refinery, Libya. *Environmental Science and Pollution Research*, 21(18), 10725–10735.

Martinez, L. (2014). Oil, violence and international actors: The case of Libya. *Canadian Journal of African Studies*, 48(2), 243–256.

Ministry of Political and Parliamentary Affairs. 2016. List of political parties. [Online]. Available at: https://www.moppa.gov.jo/AR/ListDetails/%d8%a7%d9%84%d8%a7%d8%ad%d8%b2%d8%a7%d8%a8_/1033/15

Ministry of Social Development. (2020). List of Associations. [Online]. Available at: http://societies.gov.jo/ar/pages/%D8%B3%D8%AC%D9%84_%D8%A7%D9%84%D8%AC%D9%85%D8%B9%D9%8A%D8%A7%D8%AA

Sethi, S. P. (1978). Advocacy Advertising--The American Experience. *California Management Review*, 21(1), 55–67.

Stokes, K. L., Broderick, A. C., Canbolat, A. F., Candan, O., Fuller, W. J., Glen, F., ... Godley, B. J. (2015). Migratory corridors and foraging hotspots: Critical habitats identified for Mediterranean green turtles. *Diversity and Distributions*, 21(6), 665–674.

United Nations. (2016). *World Risk Report*. World Risk Report. https://doi.org/9783946785026

United Nations Development Programme. (2011). *Arab Development Challenges Report 2011*. Available at: https://www.undp.org/publications/arab-development-challenges-report-2011 [Last Accessed 09 Jan 2022].

UNHCR. 2022. Syria Regional Refugee Response – Jordan. [Online]. Available at: https://data2.unhcr.org/en/situations/syria/location/36

WWF. (2010). *Living Planet Report: Biodiversity, biocapacity and Development*. https://doi.org/10.1113/jphysiol.1976.sp011294

References for Part III

Atkins, J. and Atkins, B., 2016. *The Business of Bees: An Integrated Approach to Bee Decline and Corporate Responsibility*. Abingdon: Greenleaf Publishing Limited.

Atkins, J. and Atkins, B., 2019. *Around the World in 80 Species: Exploring the Business of Extinction*. London and New York: Routledge.

Atkins, J. and Maroun, W., 2018. Integrated extinction accounting and accountability: building an ark. *Accounting, Auditing and Accountability Journal*, 31(3), pp. 750–786.

Jamaliah, M.M. and Powell, R.B., 2018. Ecotourism resilience to climate change in Dana Biosphere Reserve, Jordan. *Journal of Sustainable Tourism*, 26(4), 519–536.

Weir, K., 2018. The purposes, promises and compromises of extinction accounting in the UK public sector. *Accounting, Auditing & Accountability Journal*, 31(3), pp. 875–899.

9

THE NEED FOR GOOD GOVERNANCE IN SECURING ENVIRONMENTAL JUSTICE

Steve Trent

Introduction

There are numerous definitions of environmental justice and its variant ecological justice. In the USA, environmental justice is used by the Environmental Protection Agency (EPA) in the context of environmental laws and policies[1] and has historically been concerned only with justice among people. 'Environmental justice' became popular in the 1980s as a response to the discrimination that resulted in toxic dumping, landfill and other land-use decisions that disproportionately impacted communities of colour. In effect, environmental policies were used as an attack on civil rights. Ecological justice is most often defined as justice that encompasses civil rights, but also includes the natural world outside of humans.[2]

However, the purpose of this book is not to delve into semantics; rather, we are focused on real-world solutions. For the basis of this chapter, we will define environmental justice as incorporating such aspects as ensuring environmental policies are fair for all, regardless of race, national origin, gender, religious belief, income or other such personal factors. But it must also encompass ecological justice, whereby species have an intrinsic right to survive and flourish and humanity exists alongside thriving ecosystems. Our use of natural resources must be sustainable in all senses, in that it can replenish itself, but also in that it is still capable of supporting healthy ecosystems regardless of any benefit provided to humans.

We see environmental justice as a global issue, recognising our shared obligation to ensure that the poorest, most vulnerable, disenfranchised and marginalised communities have equal access to the benefits of a secure environment and that, in turn, the natural world can thrive alongside humanity. While we would be wise to recall that, ultimately, we all depend on the natural environment but for our very survival, we contend that the world beyond humankind – the natural world – has fundamental value and intrinsic rights.

DOI: 10.4324/9781003045557-12

It is in this context that we argue that our broader iteration of environmental justice is vital to the understanding of, and resolution to, fundamental concerns of social and economic justice.

Environmental justice in this sense has never been more important. Humanity is facing a planetary crisis of a scale and severity that is unprecedented for our species and which will impact all areas of our lives, curtailing basic freedoms and rights and degrading our ability to house, feed, clothe and educate ourselves. How we approach this central issue of environmental justice will either prevent or cause wars and conflict; it will either lead to greater equality or cause even sharper divisions; it will determine our future, not just as communities or nation states, but as a species.

The Twin Crises: Climate and Biodiversity

The climate crisis is here. Every day brings new damning stories from every corner of the world. In the Pacific, sea-level rise is threatening the very existence of small island nations – Tuvalu, Kiribati and the Marshall Islands[3] are seeing sea-level rise slowly gaining on their land, salinising once-fertile agricultural fields and contaminating sources of drinking water. In Africa, Cape Town very nearly ran out of water[4] in 2018, suffering from a drought[5] that spread across all southern countries in the continent. The resultant grain shortages, collapsing fish stocks as rivers dried up, and loss of cattle as herders were forced to cull their animals left 11 million people facing food shortages.[6] In the Arctic, temperatures have risen almost twice as much as the global average[7] during the last decade. The Sami, who have been reindeer herders in Northern Europe since before records began, are watching their animals die, losing not only livelihoods but also an entire culture.[8]

These human stories are unfolding against a backdrop of stark facts. The average temperatures over the last decade, 2010–2019, were the highest on record.[9] The second hottest year on record was 2019, exceeded only by 2016[10] and tied with 2020.[11] The current atmospheric concentrations of greenhouse gases are unprecedented in the last 800,000 years.[12]

'Maria', 'Idai', 'Irma', 'Harvey', 'Katrina', 'Kenneth': A litany of names of increasingly destructive hurricanes and cyclones that are causing the death or displacement of millions. And it is fitting that they are given human names – this crisis is ours to claim. The science is clear and compelling that it is our anthropogenic emissions that are driving runaway global heating.

Running in parallel to this emergency, and inextricably linked to it, is the global biodiversity crisis. The world is facing its sixth mass extinction,[13] with the global rate of species extinction already at least tens to hundreds of times higher than it has averaged over the past 10 million years. Unlike the past five, this one is human-driven. Human activities 'threaten more species now than ever before' as around one in four species of plants and animals are threatened, suggesting that around 1 million species already face extinction, many within decades, said the UN Global Assessment Report in 2019.[14] This was reiterated again in 2020, when the UN Convention on Biological Diversity reported[15] that we had missed all 20 targets set to bring biodiversity to a halt.

The latest tragedy to emerge from our exploitation of the natural world is the COVID-19 pandemic. As rampant ecological degradation accelerates, stressed wild animals that would not mix closely in the wild are brought into close contact with other species – and with humans. The conditions are perfect for the emergence of new viruses.[16]

We are finally beginning to understand that our current relationship with the natural world is not just a danger to the ecological security of the planet but to human health – to ourselves. Ebola, bird flu, swine flu, Middle East respiratory syndrome, Rift Valley fever, SARS, West Nile virus and Zika virus: all these made the jump from animals to humans, almost always as a result of human behaviour.[17]

To prevent further potentially more infectious harmful outbreaks it requires us to reassess our connection to nature. In order to prevent pandemics, we need to halt the destruction of ecosystems and the climate crisis that is driving wildlife from their natural home ranges and into contact with humans.[18]

Weaving through these crises and tragedies is the fact that the world's poorest and most vulnerable communities pay the highest price are most badly affected by environmental injustice.

Global heating has led to a 25% increase in inequality[19] between countries over the past half-century, as hotter, poorer countries tend to suffer the most from the actions of cooler, richer ones. The World Bank estimates[20] that the COVID-19 pandemic will push some 49 million of the world's most vulnerable people into extreme poverty in 2020. Equity and fairness are scarce in a world where the fundamental concepts of environmental justice are ignored, denied and circumvented.

Good governance and a rules-based order are fundamental to putting us on track to an equitable, sustainable future. This chapter focuses on two of our most crucial planetary life support systems, climate and oceans, to examine the issues and lay out some solutions.

Climate Crisis

The climate crisis has long been associated with environmental injustice, and for good reason. Ninety-nine percentage of all deaths from weather-related disasters occur in the world's 50 least developed countries – countries that have contributed less than 1% of global carbon emissions.[21] While emissions underpin economic growth and prosperity for some, other nations are suffering as a result of profound climate injustice. Put simply, some have got rich at the expense of others.

All nations, but developed countries especially, need to step up their actions to reduce emissions and achieve greater equity. The full ambition of the Paris

Agreement must be realised to achieve the near-term, wholesale transformation to a zero-carbon economy. A global shift to renewable energy would see economic, social and environmental benefits for all countries.[22] A green recovery can support jobs and prosperity that would far outweigh what the petrochemical industry could provide.

Renewable energy sources could also deliver energy independence – and with its vast associated benefits – to the world's poor, transforming lives for the better.[23] Furthermore, by combatting this injustice, the developed world will also be serving its own interests, preventing the catastrophic impacts of runaway global heating and delivering a green dividend of immense economic and social value.

Guiding Governance

Governments can use regulation to safeguard the life support systems that our planet provides, or use it to unravel them. Uniquely, governments control fiscal and monetary policy, and these are the best tools and the most obvious route to drive change.

One simple example is the progress that could be made in tackling the climate crisis through the use of far more progressive, aggressive carbon emission taxes, phasing these in to increase over a short span of years until goals are met. These would include 'carbon border pricing', where a tax is levied on imports from outside the country or bloc from countries with less stringent climate policies. This idea is currently under consultation in the EU[24] for a range of sectors from cement to textiles. It avoids the risk of the injustice of 'carbon leakage',[25] where EU companies and individuals simply shift the emissions resulting from commodity production to an area outside the EU.

Such fiscal incentives would drive both large-scale, low-carbon infrastructure development and new technological innovation, along with the switch to zero-carbon goods and services.

These taxes should be revenue-neutral to avoid debate about the size and reach of government, and the full range of benefits should be included in their analysis; for example, less burning of fossil fuels in and around current pollution hot spots like London[26] will reduce the burden on health services of treating respiratory illnesses.

Carbon taxes should also be weighted such that they are applied fairly, not applying a disproportionate burden on the less wealthy. In some proposals, these carbon taxes could be directly returned to citizens through equal rebates so that 'the majority of American families, including the most vulnerable, will benefit financially by receiving more in "carbon dividends" than they pay in increased energy prices'.[27]

By supporting microgeneration, governments can also drive energy independence, bringing huge benefits to poorer sections of society and reducing costs in core sectors such as health care and education. Such taxes would help to correct the market failures driving the climate crisis[28] and steer all economic actors towards a low-carbon future.

It is important to note that introducing taxes over regions such as at the EU or US federal levels requires unanimity. The most useful additional tool is legislation, such as banning imports of agricultural commodities grown on recently deforested land, or mandatory due diligence on environmental damage for companies importing to the EU. These legislative approaches should be introduced immediately to start the progress which an effective carbon tax will continue.

Monetary policy, the sister to fiscal policy, can and should be used to drive the transition to zero carbon. The establishment of 'green banks and green finance' directly supported by central banks to drive research and development; provide green finance for national infrastructure; drive corporate interest and green entrepreneurs could, if ambitious enough, rapidly drive the shift towards zero-carbon economies.

This example has centred on carbon emissions, but other 'externalities' – factors that are not valued by our markets – need to be factored in, such as the impacts on ecosystems and the support they provide to humanity. Conserving a forest will provide flood prevention, air purification and carbon storage, for instance, but such value is almost never taken into account.[29] Creating simple instruments, such as taxes, regulations and investment incentives, to account for these vital services, can help us thrive as part of a healthy planet.

Climate Refugees

We must recognise that the climate crisis is upon us, and many are already suffering. Since 2008, weather-related hazards have displaced more than 24 million people each year,[30] equivalent to 65,753 people every day, 46 people every minute. These events, from hurricanes and typhoons to floods and fires, are increasing in their frequency and severity.

Millions of people are forced to flee their homes when such storms make landfall or where wildfires spread uncontrollably. Many more are forced to leave their homes because of 'slow-onset' events caused by our warming atmosphere, prolonged droughts or sea-level rise that destroy the basic needs for survival, the ability to grow food, create safe shelter or even access drinking water. And as the basic necessities of life become precious commodities, migration or even the risk of conflict surges wildly.[31]

One stark example is Bangladesh, where one in every seven people will be displaced by climate change by 2050, estimates say.[32] Bangladesh does not have the capacity to absorb such mass displacement – most poorer nations do not – so refugees will be forced across national boundaries into neighbouring countries or even beyond. India has clearly foreseen this eventuality: its border fence traps some of the most vulnerable Bangladeshi coastal districts.[33] In the event of a disaster such as a cyclone or a flood, Bangladesh is sealed on three sides by India, and some may be left with nowhere to go.

Global heating demands global cooperation and good governance, and, above all perhaps, by strong incisive political leadership to tackle what ultimately amounts to an existential threat to humankind. International agreements are a blunt tool for what is often a complex and multifaceted situation on the ground, but the speed of the climate crisis means that such coordinated global action is urgently needed.

> We had hundreds of date palm trees, we made sweets with those. We had coconut, jackfruit and mango trees. Our ponds were full of fishes. But the river took away everything.

These are the words of Renu Bibi, who lost her home to flooding in Bangladesh and was forced to travel to Dhaka's slums, where Environmental Justice Foundation staff interviewed her. Just a few years ago, the term 'climate refugee' was unconventional and controversial. Many, even among those who recognised the threat of climate change, argued there was no need for it, and others questioned the use of terminology that had no legal basis. That missed the point.

While it is true they are not refugees in the original, legally accepted sense – because they are not fleeing persecution, war or violence[34] – they are fleeing an equally devastating threat to their lives through the destruction of their homes and livelihoods, the very basis of their survival.

Climate refugees need legal recognition: their plight must be clearly defined. Once this clear legal definition is in place, we can begin to create a much-needed international agreement to secure their rights and protection.

The UN Global Compact on Migration,[35] ratified in December 2018, aims to improve the governance of migration and the welfare of migrants. It recognised 'the adverse effects of climate change' as a distinct driver of forced migration. That is a step in the right direction, but no more than a step.[36]

The Global Compact is a soft-power tool that does not place any binding obligations on states. Yet despite the light touch of this agreement, several countries have withdrawn, including the USA, Australia, Austria, Chile, the Czech Republic, Hungary and Poland.

In 2015, Ioane Teitiota, a resident of the Republic of Kiribati, applied for asylum in New Zealand – the first time a person had identified themselves as a climate refugee. Teitiota cited overcrowding, failing crops, contaminated water supplies, social tensions and violence as among the reasons he needed to leave his island home, which – with a highest point of less than ten feet above sea level – is critically threatened by impending sea-level rise.

Despite the risk to his island nation, Teitiota's application was rejected because the Supreme Court of New Zealand ruled his life was not in immediate danger. The 10–15 years before Kiribati will be underwater, the court found, would be enough time for other arrangements to come to light.

Teitiota brought his case to the UN Human Rights Committee. While the committee accepted New Zealand's original judgement, it also stated that in future, countries may be acting unlawfully[37] if they return someone to their country of origin when that person's right to life is threatened by the climate crisis.

Essentially, this sets the stage to provide climate refugees a similar legal status to people fleeing war or persecution. It is significant, but it raises more questions. We do not know how immediate the danger would have to be for someone to be able to claim asylum because of the climate crisis, or how an individual might be required to prove their level of vulnerability. We do know that individuals can still be returned to their home country if there is any safe location within that country's borders.

This is important because in the near term, few countries will lack any safe place for people to be returned to. Forcing refugees from larger nations to stay in, or return to, their home countries will create that same overcrowding, tensions and competition for resources that Teitiota feared – situations we've already seen in Syria and other places. And the communities they're resettled into may not remain safe much longer.

The Agreement

There is an urgent need for an unambiguous, legally binding agreement to protect vulnerable people who have been forced from their homes as a result of the climate crisis. This must be an independent agreement, entirely outside of the scope of the 1951 Geneva Convention Relating to the Status of Refugees. All countries that have contributed to the climate crisis must take responsibility for their actions and ensure the protection of those suffering its worst impacts.

There are outstanding questions: What makes someone a climate refugee; how immediate does the danger need to be before they qualify; and what obligations exist for the nations that have contributed to and benefitted the most from carbon emissions? The answers must form the fundamental building blocks of an international agreement on the forced migration that will take place under the climate crisis.

Climate breakdown often acts to magnify and multiply conflicts and resource shortages.[38] An international agreement on climate refugees must recognise the complex and multifaceted nature of the climate crisis and its related societal threats. It must fully engage with the role of global heating as a 'threat multiplier'.

A new agreement must also resist the temptation to buy a small amount of time by sending people to areas that are only temporarily safer than the ones they left, simply to defer cost or long-term solutions. It must seek durable answers that are robust across political transitions and the economic turbulence that characterises most economies. Any agreement will need to engage and secure notions of sovereignty and cultural identity alongside the economic, social and environmental needs of forced migrants.

The EU is well-placed to take a leading role in building this agreement and, we argue, has a moral obligation that complements the fact that it is in its own enlightened self-interest to do so.

As a political and economic union, the EU has the capacity and structures in place to bring countries together and create an agreement that works and, crucially, provides united, strong leadership for change. As a region that has emitted 22% of the CO_2 now heating our planet,[39] failure or success in this will define the Union's standing and relationship with this most critical issue of environmental justice.

If there is one thing that the climate crisis is showing us, it is that issues and experts need to come out of their 'silos' if they are to be successful in addressing crosscutting impacts on not just the global environment, but on human rights and developmental needs. A high-profile, fully resourced, interagency task force is therefore needed to coordinate the work of the multiple bodies in the European Commission, including Environment, Climate Action, Migration and Humanitarian Affairs, International Cooperation and Development as well as the High Representative of the Union for Foreign Affairs and Security Policy. The climate crisis is here and is developing at speed. An international agreement is not a simple thing. But it is the right thing.

Justice at sea

Environmental justice, in the sense we are defining it here, comes at the intersection of safeguarding the environment and securing human rights. A poignant case is the exploitation of the oceans that has led to the exploitation of people.

Since industrial fishing began in the early 1950s, 90% of the world's large ocean fish – such as sharks, cod and swordfish – have been lost.[40] Over 90% of the planet's fish stocks are now either fully exploited or overfished,[41] according to the latest 2020 report from the UN Food and Agriculture Organisation.

Illegal, unreported and unregulated fishing accounts for up to 40% of catches in some regions and costs between US$10 and US$23.5 billion annually, according to the best estimates to date.[42]

Vulnerable coastal communities that rely on healthy fish stocks for food security and income suffer as a consequence of the illegal depletion of fish stocks and the increasing competition for those that remain. In West Africa, a region with high levels of illegal fishing – including by foreign fleets – 6.7 million people depend directly on fisheries for food and livelihoods.

Rampant overfishing and illegal fishing are not just bad for the natural environment: they have substantially increased the risks of serious human rights abuses. As ocean ecosystems are degraded and fish stocks fall, so does income from the vessels.[43] To make a profit, unscrupulous companies exploit workers, often engaging in violent human rights abuses and employing forced, bonded and slave labour.[44]

Fishers, by the nature of their work, operate in an isolated environment, far from law enforcement, and may literally be trapped aboard ship at sea for months or even years.[45] This makes them more vulnerable and in need of better protections. Investigations by the Environmental Justice Foundation have uncovered cases of slavery, debt bondage, insufficient food and water, filthy living conditions, physical and sexual assault and even murder aboard fishing vessels from 13 countries operating across three oceans.

Labour costs can account for up to 60% of total vessel expenses,[46] and fishing operators therefore seek to take advantage of large labour pools from poorer countries in an attempt to drive down costs. With lower salaries, less social protection and weaker labour rights compared to their domestic counterparts, migrant workers are extremely vulnerable to traffickers, exploitative brokers, and abusive captains or crew.[47]

Those who engage in slavery and human trafficking in fisheries capitalise on capacity gaps in monitoring, surveillance and enforcement. Weak governance has allowed these two issues to become embedded in many national seafood supply chains. Practices such as trans-shipment at sea – where fish is transferred from one vessel to another – and the use of flags of convenience further exacerbate these risks, making it more difficult to identify and track possible cases of illegal fishing and human rights abuses and less likely that governments can take enforcement action, sanction and deter wrongdoing.[48]

Just as there is a direct causal link between illegal, unsustainable fishing and human rights abuses at sea, the approach to stopping them must also be aligned with both issues.

Transparency

The first and most effective line of defence against these twin tragedies is surprisingly simple: transparency.

Many regulators and seafood buyers in the developed and developing world are well aware of the devastating impacts of illegal fishing, but their efforts to remove illegally caught fish from their markets and supply chains are frustrated by a lack of transparency in the global seafood industry.

This lack of transparency allows illegal operators to create as much confusion as possible around their identities[49]; escaping detection by changing vessel names; concealing ownership; flying different flags to avoid detection; or removing ships from fishing registries, effectively making them disappear beyond the purview of any enforcement operations. Vessel identification systems – which allow the boats to be tracked – are tampered with, switched off or missing altogether; 'front' companies are set up so that the true beneficiaries of illegal practices can evade prosecution.[50]

All this makes it difficult or impossible to identify the 'actors' involved, including not only the fishing vessels but also the states that are ostensibly responsible for overseeing their activities. The route of the products through supply chains to markets and retailers is also mired in doubt. The challenges in uncovering a vessel's illegal activities, both current and past, mean that illegal operators are at low risk of capture and sanction by the authorities.[51]

There are a number of simple, low-cost measures that would shine a light into this murky world. They include measures such as giving all vessels a unique number, making vessel tracking data public, and publishing lists of fishing licences and punishments handed out for fisheries crimes (see box). Many of these measures are available now – both technically feasible and financially affordable. Indeed, the costs of not implementing them are one our oceans and the millions of people dependent upon them cannot afford to bear.

Along with a few other measures, this vital information would shed light on vessel identities, activities and ownership and make a fundamental difference in

---

BOX 9.1 TRANSPARENCY IN FISHERIES

Give all vessels a unique number: Like cars' number plates, but these would stay with vessels from shipyard to scrapyard, regardless of name or flag changes, and should be kept in a global record of fishing vessels.

Make vessel tracking data public: This will mean neighbouring countries, non-governmental organisations and others can all help with surveillance.

Publish lists of fishing licences and authorisations: Who is allowed to fish where, when, what for and how? Combined with vessel tracking data, this means anyone can monitor and raise the alarm about illegal fishing.

Publish punishments handed out for fisheries crimes: The arrests and sanctions imposed for illegal fishing or human rights abuse on fishing vessels should be public, so offenders can be identified.

Ban transferring fish between boats at sea – unless carefully monitored: This practice enables unscrupulous companies to keep workers at sea, unpaid, for months or years. It also makes the source of the fish, once landed, very difficult to trace.

Set up a digital database of vessel information: Storing information on fishing vessel registration, licences, catch and crew is vital and could eventually enable catches to be certified as fished legally and ethically.

Stop the use of flags of convenience: Some countries let any vessel fly their flags for a fee – but don't properly monitor them, allowing the owners of illegally fishing vessels to remain unaccountable.

Publish details of the true owners of each vessel: False front companies are often used so that the true beneficiaries of illegal fishing are safe from prosecution.

Punish anyone involved in illegal, unreported and unregulated fishing: Countries must ensure that none of their citizens support, engage in or profit from illegal fishing, no matter where they are or which flag they are flying.

Adopt international standards for fishing vessels and the trade in fisheries products: These include the Port State Measures Agreement, the Work in Fishing Convention and the Cape Town Agreement.

the fight to win legal, sustainable and ethical fisheries. In the hands of governments, seafood processors and retailers, NGOs and others, this information could be used to identify and eradicate the damaging practices that are driving illegal, unsustainable exploitation of the oceans and human rights abuses at sea.

Conclusion

Environmental justice is complex. The solutions that we have presented in this chapter are not groundbreaking or especially ingenious, nor do they resolve every problem of environmental justice. However, they are simple and economically advantageous – to both wealthy and poorer nations – requiring no unrealistic outlay of investment, even in the early stages. What they do require is long-term political will, together with sound, methodical governance delivered through a rules-based order; an understanding of evolving science; and a willingness to collaborate internationally.

Humanity can be its own worst enemy, consuming without restriction in a tragic story that starts with exploitation that is as rapid and as extensive as possible and ends in the destruction of the natural systems that underwrite our survival. Currently, the distribution of the world's wealth is based almost entirely on which countries have led the field in the exploitation of people and the world's natural resources. As a species, we have evolved to become a 'super-predator' with virtually no checks on our ability to consume. But as a species, we also have it within us to organise, analyse and look to the future. We are capable of building international frameworks and systems that are workable, just and sustainable.

The climate crisis is building as we write this, with breaking news almost every day of unprecedented wildfires, floods, storms, ice melts and other climate-driven calamities. The Living Planet Report 2020 found that wildlife populations are in free fall,[52] with an average of 68% decline of monitored populations of mammals, birds, fish, amphibians and reptiles. These are increasingly urgent signs that we must act, and now.

Environmental justice may be complex in its application, but it is simple in principle. We must keep a few basic, essential guiding principles to the fore and above all that the services and goods provided by ecosystems and the environment must be fairly distributed, and that those ecosystems must be given space to thrive for their own sake, understanding that their well-being will ultimately determine our own. Collectively, humanity must acknowledge and accommodate that our economies are, singly and together, wholly owned subsidiaries of the natural environment. If we can use these principles to steer our decisions, we will be taking the road, one step at a time, to a sustainable, just and survivable world.

Notes

1 US Environmental Protection Agency, *Factsheet on the EPA's Office of Environmental Justice.* Available from https://www.epa.gov/environmentaljustice/factsheet-epas-office-environmental-justice.

2 Baxter, B., *A Theory of Ecological Justice*, 2004, London, Routledge.

3 Salem, S., *Climate Change and the Sinking Island States in the Pacific*, 2020, E-International Relations. Available from https://www.e-ir.info/2020/01/09/climate-change-and-the-sinking-island-states-in-the-pacific/.

4 Voiland, A., *Cape Town's Water is Running Out*, 2018, Earth Observatory Nasa. Available from https://earthobservatory.nasa.gov/images/91649/cape-towns-water-is-running-out.

5 Carlowicz, M., *Drought Threatens Millions in Southern Africa*, 2019, Earth Observatory Nasa. Available from https://earthobservatory.nasa.gov/images/146015/drought-threatens-millions-in-southern-africa.

6 Carlowicz, M., *Drought Threatens Millions in Southern Africa*, 2019, Earth Observatory Nasa. Available from https://earthobservatory.nasa.gov/images/146015/drought-threatens-millions-in-southern-africa.

7 Screen, J. and Simmonds, I. *The Central Role of Diminishing Sea Ice in Recent Arctic Temperature Amplification*. Nature, 2010, **464**, p. 1334–1337.

8 Environmental Justice Foundation, *Rights at Risk: Arctic Climate Change and the Threat to Sami Culture*, 2019. Available from https://ejfoundation.org/reports/rights-at-risk-arctic-climate-change-and-the-threat-to-sami-culture.

9 United Nations Environment Programme, *Facts about the Climate Emergency*, 2019. Available from https://www.unep.org/explore-topics/climate-action/facts-about-climate-emergency.

10 Blunden, J., *Reporting on the State of the Climate in 2019*, NOAA Climate.gov, 2020. Available from https://www.climate.gov/news-features/understanding-climate/reporting-state-climate-2019.

11 Bateman, J., *2020 Was Earth's 2nd-Hottest Year, Just Behind 2016*, NOAA, 2021. Available from https://www.noaa.gov/news/2020-was-earth-s-2nd-hottest-year-just-behind-2016.

12 US Environmental Protection Agency, *Climate Change Indicators: Atmospheric Concentrations of Greenhouse Gases*, 2019. Available from https://www.epa.gov/climate-indicators/climate-change-indicators-atmospheric-concentrations-greenhouse-gases.

13 Ceballos, G., Ehrlich, P. R., Dirzo, R., *Biological Annihilation via the Ongoing Sixth Mass Extinction Signaled by Vertebrate Population Losses and Declines*, Proceedings of the National Academy of Sciences 2017, **114**(30), E6089-E6096.

14 S. Díaz, J. Settele, E. S. Brondízio E.S., H. T. Ngo, M. Guèze, J. Agard, A. Arneth, P. Balvanera, K. A. Brauman, S. H. M. Butchart, K. M. A. Chan, L. A. Garibaldi, K. Ichii, J. Liu, S. M. Subramanian, G. F. Midgley, P. Miloslavich, Z. Molnár, D. Obura, A. Pfaff, S. Polasky, A. Purvis, J. Razzaque, B. Reyers, R. Roy Chowdhury, Y. J. Shin, I. J. Visseren-Hamakers, K. J. Willis, and C. N. Zayas (eds.), *Summary for Policymakers of the Global Assessment Report on Biodiversity and Ecosystem Services of the Intergovernmental Science-Policy Platform on Biodiversity and Ecosystem Services*, 2019, IPBES secretariat, Bonn, Germany.

15 Secretariat of the Convention on Biological Diversity, *Global Biodiversity Outlook 5 – Summary for Policy Makers*, 2020. Montréal. Available from https://www.unep.org/resources/report/global-biodiversity-outlook-5-gbo-5.

16 Environmental Justice Foundation, *Viral Diseases from Wildlife in China: Could SARS Happen Again*, 2013. Available from https://ejfoundation.org/reports/viral-diseases-from-wildlife-in-china-could-sars-happen-again.

17 Carrington, D. *Coronavirus: 'Nature Is Sending Us a Message', Says UN Environment Chief*, The Guardian, 2020. Available from https://www.theguardian.com/world/2020/mar/25/coronavirus-nature-is-sending-us-a-message-says-un-environment-chief.

18 Pongsiri, M. J., et al., *Biodiversity Loss Affects Global Disease Ecology*, BioScience, 2009, **59**(11), p. 945–954.

19 Diffenbaugh, N.S., and Burke, M., *Global Warming Has Increased Global Economic Inequality*, PNAS, 2019, **116**(20) p. 9808–9813.

20 Sánchez-Páramo, C., *COVID-19 Will Hit the Poor Hardest. Here's What We Can Do About It*, World Bank Blogs, 2020. Available from https://blogs.worldbank.org/voices/covid-19-will-hit-poor-hardest-heres-what-we-can-do-about-it.

21 Global Humanitarian Forum, *The Anatomy of a Silent Crisis*, 2009. Available from http://www.ghf-ge.org/human-impact-report.pdf.

22 IRENA, *Renewable Energy Benefits: Measuring the Economics*. IRENA, 2016, Abu Dhabi. Available from https://www.irena.org/-/media/Files/IRENA/Agency/Publication/2016/IRENA_Measuring-the-Economics_2016.pdf.

23 Diffenbaugh, N.S., and Burke, M., *Global Warming Has Increased Global Economic Inequality*, PNAS, 2019, **116**(20) p. 9808–9813.

24 European Commission, *Commission Launches Public Consultations on Energy Taxation and a Carbon Border Adjustment Mechanism*, 2020. Available from https://ec.europa.eu/taxation_customs/news/commission-launches-public-consultations-energy-taxation-and-carbon-border-adjustment_en.

25 Guarascio, F., and Ekblomhttps, J., *Explainer: What an EU Carbon Border Tax Might Look Like and Who Would Be Hit*, Reuters, 2019. Available from https://www.reuters.com/article/us-climate-change-eu-carbontax-explainer/explainer-what-an-eu-carbon-border-tax-might-look-like-and-who-would-be-hit-idUSKBN1YE1C4.

26 Greater London Authority, *London Atmospheric Emissions (LAEI) 2016*, 2021. Available from https://data.london.gov.uk/dataset/london-atmospheric-emissions-inventory--laei--2016.

27 Climate Leadership Council, *Economists' Statement on Carbon Dividends*, 2019. Available from https://www.econstatement.org/.

28 Bowen, A., *The Case for Carbon Pricing*, Grantham Research Institute in Climate Change and the Environment, The Centre for Climate Change Economics and Policy, 2011. Available from https://www.lse.ac.uk/GranthamInstitute/wp-content/uploads/2014/02/PB_case-carbon-pricing_Bowen.pdf.

29 Science for Environment Policy, *Ecosystem Services and the Environment. In-depth Report 11*, 2015 European Commission, Science Communication Unit, UWE, Bristol. Available from https://ec.europa.eu/environment/integration/research/newsalert/pdf/ecosystem_services_biodiversity_IR11_en.pdf.

30 Internal Displacement Monitoring Centre, *Global Internal Displacement Database*, 2020. Available from https://www.internal-displacement.org/database/displacement-data.

31 Environmental Justice Foundation, *Beyond Borders: Our Changing Climate and Its Role in Conflict and Displacement*, 2017. Available from https://ejfoundation.org/reports/beyond-borders.

32 Displacement Solutions, *The Bangladesh HLP Initiative*, 2019. Available from https://displacementsolutions.org/ds-initiatives/climate-change-and-displacement-initiative/bangladesh-climate-displacement/.

33 Environmental Justice Foundation, *On the Frontlines: Climate Change in Bangladesh*, 2018. Available from https://ejfoundation.org/reports/on-the-frontlines-climate-change-in-bangladesh.

34 UNHCR, *What Is a Refugee?* 2020. Available from https://www.unrefugees.org/refugee-facts/what-is-a-refugee/.

35 UN, Global compact for safe, orderly and regular migration, 2018. Available from https://refugeesmigrants.un.org/sites/default/files/180713_agreed_outcome_global_compact_for_migration.pdf.

36 Environmental Justice Foundation, *EJF View on the Global Compact on Migration*, 2018. Available from https://ejfoundation.org/reports/ejf-view-on-the-global-compact-on-migration.

37 Human Rights Committee, *Views adopted by the Committee under article 5 (4) of the Optional Protocol, Concerning Communication No. 2728/2016*, **, ****, 2019. Available

from https://tbinternet.ohchr.org/_layouts/15/treatybodyexternal/Download.aspx-?symbolno=CCPR%2fC%2f127%2fD%2f2728%2f2016&Lang=en.

38 Environmental Justice Foundation, *Beyond Borders: Our Changing Climate and Its Role in Conflict and Displacement*, 2017. Available from https://ejfoundation.org/reports/beyond-borders.

39 Ritchie, H., *Who Has Contributed Most to Global CO2 Emissions?* Our World in Data, 2019. Available from https://ourworldindata.org/contributed-most-global-co2.

40 Myers, R., Worm, B., *Rapid Worldwide Depletion of Predatory Fish Communities.* Nature, 2003, **423**, p. 280–283.

41 FAO, *The State of World Fisheries and Aquaculture 2020. Sustainability in Action.* 2020, Rome. Available from http://www.fao.org/3/ca9229en/CA9229EN.pdf.

42 Agnew D.J., et al. *Estimating the Worldwide Extent of Illegal Fishing.* PLOS ONE 2009, **4**(2): e4570. Available from https://journals.plos.org/plosone/article?id=10.1371/journal.pone.0004570.

43 Environmental Justice Foundation, *Out of the Shadows: Improving Transparency in Global Fisheries to Stop Illegal, Unreported and Unregulated Fishing*, 2018. Available from https://ejfoundation.org/resources/downloads/Transparency-report-final.pdf.

44 Environmental Justice Foundation, *Human Rights Abuse in the Global Seafood Industry*, 2019. Available from https://ejfoundation.org/reports/blood-and-water-human-rights-abuse-in-the-global-seafood-industry.

45 Environmental Justice Foundation, *Human Rights Abuse in the Global Seafood Industry*, 2019. Available from https://ejfoundation.org/reports/blood-and-water-human-rights-abuse-in-the-global-seafood-industry.

46 https://books.google.co.th/books?id=_6-k-XebM7IC&printsec=frontcover&#v=onepage&q&f=false.

47 Environmental Justice Foundation, *Human Rights Abuse in the Global Seafood Industry*, 2019. Available from https://ejfoundation.org/reports/blood-and-water-human-rights-abuse-in-the-global-seafood-industry.

48 Environmental Justice Foundation, *Out of the Shadows: Improving Transparency in Global Fisheries to Stop Illegal, Unreported and Unregulated Fishing*, 2018. Available from https://ejfoundation.org/resources/downloads/Transparency-report-final.pdf.

49 Stop Illegal Fishing, *Illegal Fishing? Evidence and Analysis*, 2017, Gaborone, Botswana. Available from https://stopillegalfishing.com/wp-content/uploads/2017/03/Illegal-Fishing-Evidence-and-Analysis-WEB.pdf.

50 Environmental Justice Foundation, *China's Hidden Fleet in West Africa: A Spotlight on Illegal Practices within Ghana's Industrial Trawl Sector*, 2018. Available from https://ejfoundation.org/reports/briefing-chinas-hidden-fleet-in-west-africa-a-spotlight-on-illegal-practices-within-ghanas-industrial-trawl-sector-1.

51 Environmental Justice Foundation, *Out of the Shadows: Improving Transparency in Global Fisheries to Stop Illegal, Unreported and Unregulated Fishing*, 2018. Available from https://ejfoundation.org/resources/downloads/Transparency-report-final.pdff.

52 WWF, *Living Planet Report 2020 - Bending the Curve of Biodiversity Loss.* Almond, R.E.A., Grooten M. and Petersen, T. (Eds). 2020, WWF, Gland, Switzerland. Available from https://www.wwf.org.uk/sites/default/files/2020-09/LPR20_Full_report.pdf.

10

A REGENERATIVE APPROACH TO BIODIVERSITY AND SPECIES EXTINCTION ACCOUNTING

Peta Milan

Biodiversity and extinction accounting have been receiving greater attention as areas for research and debate in the past ten years, expounded by the emergence of COVID-19. Emerging arguments for the link between business-related biodiversity losses and increasing health risks[1] lead to global economic risks and losses. In our attempt to formalize a comprehensive framework for accounting for biodiversity and species extinction, we have found that recognizing biodiversity and species extinction, in their current form, has not slowed the rate of biodiversity losses or extinction rates nor has the compliance of organizations to various ESG indices. Why? Why, with all of the good work many of us are undertaking, have our methodologies not yet resulted in a slowing down of erosion of our natural ecosystems? This chapter introduces a framework from which we can rethink biodiversity and species extinction accounting, in addition to ESG metrics, that will shift our lens from "doing less bad" towards a "value-adding" assessment. Implementing a regenerative framework demands that we ground ourselves in a place.

Our place is the here and now, so let us start with the here and now. Where is here? Here is where we, as a global business and investment community, face unprecedented risk, uncertainty and change. The threats posed by climate change are at an unparalleled high, whereby, according to the UNDRR Report – produced with Belgium's Centre for Research on the Epidemiology of Disasters at UCLouvain[2] – there were 7,348 recorded disaster events worldwide, during the last two decades. The statistics are startling with approximately 1.23 million people having died – approximately 60,000 per year – with more than four billion affected in total, many of those affected more than once. These two decades of disaster have caused $2.97 trillion in losses to the global economy, with data also indicating that poorer nations experienced death rates more than four times higher than richer nations. By comparison, the previous 20-year period

DOI: 10.4324/9781003045557-13

(1980–1999) saw 4,212 reported disasters from natural hazards, with 1.19 million deaths, more than three billion people affected and economic losses totalling $ 1.63 trillion. We have close to double the impact numbers and costs since the previous two decades, and predictive climate science says more is to come. Likewise, a recent UN Report[3] urges us current global response insufficient saying that transformative change is needed to restore and protect nature; and opposition from vested interests can be overcome for public good. This UN Report was the most comprehensive assessment of its kind identifying that 1,000,000 species are threatened with extinction.

Likewise, the Intergovernmental Panel on Climate Change urges us to strive towards a global warming target of 1.5 degrees increase, yet we are hurtling towards 3.2 degrees, which will result in the loss of much of our oceanic ecosystems, which provides 50–80% of the world's oxygen. Already, the ocean has absorbed about 30% of the anthropogenic carbon dioxide, resulting in ocean acidification and changes to carbonate chemistry that are unprecedented for at least the last 65 million years, resulting in the loss of many species.[4] Now, despite the science, there are still many climate deniers out there who say the changes are not due to the hand of humans and change would have happened anyway, and to a degree, they are right, change really is the only constant.

However, what scientists refer to as the Great Acceleration[5] is undeniable given the evidence. Since 1945, the advent of globalization in its current form and post-war international industrial collaboration have seen unprecedented increases in carbon emissions, decline in land quality, acceleration of species extinction and oceanic warming and expansion in social inequalities. Perhaps now, one may finally question the economic models which worked well for us pre-globalization but have not worked so much in our favour with respect to ecosystem impact. The accelerated impacts have led us to this point of crisis which leaves us all now scratching our heads and wondering what to do to fix it?

What has been our response to all of the urgency, warnings and evidence of devastation thus far? Primarily, it has been to adapt and ready our business as usual to better prepare for impending threats and risk, which is akin to battening down the hatches when a storm approaches, planning to ride it out. We hear the word resilience a lot. We work to create indices, measures and accounting frameworks for our impact on the losses we cause to biodiverse environments, societies and species and strive to bring an "impact consciousness" to our governance. This is a small step in the right direction. The problem we face is that net-zero targets cannot be achieved by business as usual and the rate of loss of biodiverse regions and species is too accelerated to take a "do less bad" approach and expect any kind of transformative result. This paradigm of thinking is in line with Western Cartesian view of breaking wholes down into existent parts, so we can control, manage and mitigate. This is the same mechanistic thinking that got us into trouble in the first place. Within the mechanistic view, there is a disconnect between the natural living systems principles[6] within which the environment naturally operates and oversimplified and reductionistic views we often take to solving problems and accounting for value. The results are purely transactional, which leads to some of the challenges faced by current models of biodiversity and species extinction accounting.

The pragmatic commitment to "making nature count"[7] or "do less bad" can limit the framework within which we view the problem, focusing attention on the increasingly technical process of measuring and valuing ecosystem services, thereby removing attention from more fundamental questions about the causes of biodiversity loss and the imbalanced political and economic contexts in which natural capital, and therefore biodiversity accounting, is being developed.[8] Secondly, there is the tendency to underestimate the power of understanding the nature of complexity to transform how nature is viewed, valued and organized. Well-meaning attempts that tackle these accounting challenges, such as the current Environmental Profit & Loss (EP&L) designed by Kering, still underestimate the impacts of agricultural management on biodiversity and ecosystem services by two to five times.[9] The fundamental flaw in our thinking is the current world view requires reducing nature to a series of ecosystem services (serving humans), which in turn can be compared and possibly exchanged with one another, such as the carbon storage capacity of one forest compared to that of another. This process of oversimplification and abstraction fundamentally changes the way nature is viewed, valued and managed and disconnects us from the natural order, namely that biodiversity and natural ecosystems are network of reciprocal relationships of mutual benefit for the participants, keeping the whole in balance. The human-centricity of our perception is embodied in our very definitions that underpin our frameworks as demonstrated by the widely accepted definition of ecosystem services as defined by MEA 2005.

> Ecosystem services are the benefits people obtain from ecosystems. These include provisioning services such as food, water, timber, and fiber; regulating services that affect climate, floods, disease, wastes, and water quality; cultural services that provide recreational, aesthetic, and spiritual benefits; and supporting services such as soil formation, photosynthesis, and nutrient cycling.[10]

When we ask how we go about "making nature count", we beg the question of count for whom? For local communities, national policymakers, international financial institutions, corporations? This is not just a question of semantics. When we assess value on its human-centric benefits, we remove ourselves from genuine and assessable impact. Natural living systems do not revolve around the needs and benefits of humans. COVID-19 has been a glaring slap in the face awaking us to this reality. What is ignored in many accounts of natural capital, biodiversity and species extinction accounting is the fact that nature, and the stakeholders impacted by human action, must be radically transformed in order to fit the economic and financial logics of "decision-makers", namely governments, businesses and investors.[11] Companies more often than not ask themselves how they can maintain their status quo and account for impact, whereby if there were an authentic assessment of impact undertaken across all of the stakeholders, non-human included, it would prove the status quo untenable.

The human-centricity, and lack of reciprocity, is echoed in biodiversity accounting through the SEEA-EEA which provides the "methodology to help understand the contribution of biodiversity (ecosystem and species diversity) to human well-being and the economy by explicitly considering its role as a determinant of ecosystem condition essential for the generation of ecosystem service flows".[12]

An EU Report on the obstacles facing effective mapping and assessment of ecosystem services stated:

> The importance of systemic thinking and multi-functionality is not a side issue when it comes to considering the links between biodiversity and ecosystem services. In fact, the true significance of biodiversity may only be revealed when the whole system, across the full spectrum of ecosystem services, including different locations and across many years, is considered.[13]

The problem is that while reports such as the UN's are keen to acknowledge the limitations of ecosystem service valuation, they are less clear on how such limitations, which ultimately relate to the complexity and continuously evolving nature of ecosystems, can or should be overcome within an approach that is fundamentally about simplification. With the challenges we face, driven both by our propensity towards linear and reductionist thinking and by the pressing time-based urgency looming upon us to act in a way that will bring our social and environmental ecosystems back into balance, I propose a new way to think – a kind of "thinking technology", which will enable us to shift the lens towards a regenerative design, development and action paradigm. This is a way of modelling our businesses, which will not require us to "Kill the Business to Save the Business" as I have heard some speaker's tout. The only thing we have to kill is our desire for comfort in linearity and simplification. We are humans, our very make-up is complex, and we are participants in a complex web of interactions with our non-human environment, so let us start by considering that complexity is a natural and honest starting point. Let us explore how we can work with complexity to innovate business, investment models and our accounting frameworks that connect to the essence of how things really work.

The word "regenerative" is now bandied about as the new and improved "sustainability". Be careful! The term is being used in industry by those who do not understand its meaning. I have seen "regenerative funds" come to the market, which are still funding monoculture practices, which are inherently not regenerative. Regenerative thinking and practice represent a practical framework based on living systems processes and are specifically designed to enable people to think about the underlying dynamics and energies, taking a co-evolutionary approach to design. These frameworks can be used diagnostically, to understand existing phenomena, or creatively, to enable systems to shift towards a manifestation of potential.[14] They enable us to manage flux and change as natural aspects of the world, without the need to create silos of thought or oversimplify. When challenges are viewed through the lens of a regenerative framework, we access a profound insight into potential that is present but not yet born. Bringing this potential into the world is a defining characteristic of regenerative work. You may be asking what this has to do with biodiversity and species extinction accounting? Business is not linear, and nor is much else in life if we are honest about the complex nature of living systems. Some of the impacts are referenced in the beforementioned EU 2015 Report, whereby "negative trends in nature will continue to 2050 and beyond in all of the policy scenarios explored in the Report, except those that include transformative change – due to the projected impacts of increasing land-use change, exploitation of organisms and climate change, although with significant differences between regions".[15] The Report finds that around 1 million animal and plant species are now threatened with extinction, many within decades, more than ever before in human history.

Our resistance towards being genuinely inclusive about impact and accountable for measuring our actions in terms of reciprocal benefit and cost results in a myopic view of the world, which despite our good intentions only serves to increase inequality and negative impacts across the broader ecosystem.

In contrast to our linear biases, however, businesses are also actually living systems made up of complex pressures and demands, communities of people, and different interest groups, human and non-human. When the regenerative approach is implemented in business, then the concept of "stakeholder" expands, and we start to explore the reciprocal nature of relationships and assess value in terms of evolutionary co-creation. We can better understand how our actions can result in a loss of mutual benefit for the participants and what leads to decline in biodiversity and increased extinction rates. As regenerative practice anchors us in our inherent potential, we have the capability to innovate mutually beneficial opportunities that enhance both business and human interest as well as the broader ecosystem.

We can place extinction and biodiversity accounting practices as they currently stand on the scale between degenerating and regenerating. We can see that green and sustainability practices sit on the degenerating scale due to the "do less bad" context from which they operate. Doing less bad on the green and sustainable position in the scale is still good but is not enough to be transformative at this time of crisis. Restorative and regenerative practices, however, are focused on value-adding (Figure 10.1).

Value-adding is different to what many of us know as Michael Porter's "value-added".

Porter in his work on value chain described the following:

The value that's created and captured by a company is the profit margin:

Value Created and Captured − Cost of Creating that Value = Margin.[16]

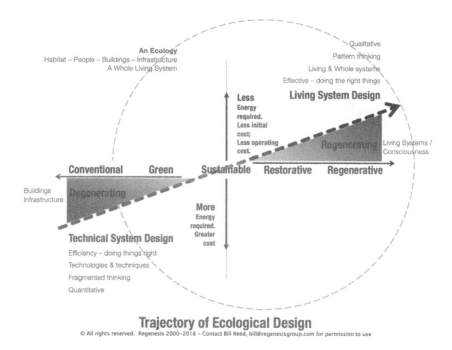

Trajectory of Ecological Design

FIGURE 10.1   Trajectory of ecological design.
Source: Used with permission from Bill Reed of Regenesis.

Porter's transactional view assesses value created in a fixed moment in time or for a fixed unit of production. The value itself is of a finite nature, whereas the "value-adding" of a regenerative model exists in a relational context and is continuous in nature, viewing the participants in enterprise, or the organization or the ecosystems as co-evolving, continuously identifying potential in the risks, and seeing threats and restraints as opportunities to create. There is an opportunity to expand biodiversity and extinction frameworks to include value-adding measurement, but this will also take a commitment from businesses and regulators alike to support value-adding methodologies and measurement. This is nothing short of a required deep cultural change given the *modus operandi* of most business is value extraction, as opposed to value-adding and a desire for simplification as a means to manage data as opposed to accounting for complexity or reciprocity.

Thankfully, we are witnessing the emergence of new businesses and expertise specializing in regenerative practices, due to the pressing need to think beyond the degenerative spectrum, the "do less bad" or the accounting for losses mindset. These organizations specializing in restorative and regenerative technologies are guiding companies to recognize their own potential. Jade Eli Technologies (JET)[17] are specialists in regenerative innovation consulting and work with some of the largest brands in Europe and Africa to help them find competitive advantage via a living systems approach, rather than a problem-solving approach. They have coined the phrase *digital evolution* whereby digital strategies or technologies *enable* innovation rather than confusing the technology *as* the innovation. JET understands that innovation is a mindset, and if the contextual lens is regenerative through which we view innovation, then innovation and digitalization become evolutionary in nature, as does the ability to engage your entire ecosystem in co-creation. Competitive advantage becomes a natural expression of the essence or potential inherent in unique ecosystems, rather than something that has to be devised. The result is business models become fundamentally value-adding to the ecosystem within which they participate, and financial performance is a natural example of that. The value impact measurement tools developed in JET's process allow business to account in value-adding and reciprocal terms.

As case study example of how regenerative value-adding approaches become financially rewarding, I draw from the work of US-based Regenesis. When approached to work on the Lions Gate Secondary Wastewater Treatment Plant,[18] Metro Vancouver faced tight timelines and a requirement to meet ambitious environmental and sustainability goals. The project was complex as it involved 20 different organizations which made up the project team, plus opposition from community and lobbyists who were rallying against the developers and the prospect of increased utility prices and an environment that was in biodiversity decline. The project had identified 320 distinct deliverables to be achieved in 18 months prior to Regenesis stepping in. Despite the urgency to act in order to meet the timelines, the Regenesis facilitators decided to rally the stakeholders together and slow the process down, spending four of their precious 18 months to do a deep exploration of the project's potential. The team identified nine core themes. Without the scope or space to document the entire process in this chapter, it is important to note the results from a seemingly counter-intuitive move by Regenesis to slow things down. They managed to significantly reduce the expected deliverables, by about 50%. They reduced community conflict significantly such that building and community approvals were achieved 18 months ahead of schedule but not only that it was an extremely rare unanimous approval in community support. The public was willing to pay the higher rates as they "valued the values", there was a 98% reduction in change requests and the phase completion came in under time and under budget. According to Ben Haggard, Regenesis founder and Carol Sanford, "A regenerative economy is a developmental economy. It grows, thrives, and evolves to the extent that all of its participants are becoming increasingly intelligent about how to work within and contribute to the well-being of living systems".[19] The case of Lions Gate demonstrates that the approach pays in dividends and that in taking a regenerative approach we can account for biodiversity regeneration over time as a direct result of the project.

Lastly, we are seeing new and innovative ventures, such as Transcendent Media Capital,[20] a venture studio, which designs businesses for investors, from the ground up, deeply framed in regenerative design. They specialize in designing alternative, yet profitable business models tackling leverage points[21] across whole systems social and environmental challenges, providing new solutions to traditional notions of scaling that are degenerative. Inherent in their business modelling is design for accounting for value-adding impact and value capture opportunities. The companies mentioned here, and others equally as innovative, often sit outside of mainstream ideas and thought, yet they are paving the way for a shift towards a regenerative mindset, where communities, businesses, investors and entrepreneurs alike can evolve towards a value-adding paradigm. They serve to bring the agility needed to safely navigate the risks and uncertainties of the future and design value-adding methodologies for biodiversity and extinction accounting, whereby hopefully one day, if as a collective we become value-adding or regenerative, the need for extinction accounting will be moot.

The next big challenge for the biodiversity and extinction accounting practice is to explore how to move beyond the confines and comfort of checkboxes and measures based on an oversimplified and human-centric notion of ecosystems services and natural capital. The next stage of evolution is to expand our thinking beyond how less bad our companies are impacting their communities and planet. Can we shift towards an open discovery and discourse about how we can assess how value-adding organizations are becoming and can we develop a more evolved accounting framework utilizing the great work from pioneers such as Atkins,[22] to account for impact to reciprocal relationships between species? First, this will require that see our work and relationships as nested, or interdependent. The first and most important work is that which we do with ourselves.[23] Can we be rigorous and intelligent enough to ask ourselves the tough questions such as "what are my biases and how are my experiences shaping my world view?" "What other perspectives can I take and who can I bring into my decision-making circle that will help me to see things differently?" "If I feel something is risky, why? What is the perceived risk and how else might I see the issue?" The work we do with ourselves requires us to be honest, rigorous and persistent and the growing capability of self-awareness is always nested within growing the capabilities of our team and communities. These capabilities are in turn nested within improving the health and the value of the system within which we function. If we are able to see ourselves, our choices and our work as part of this deeply interconnected network, which reflects living systems, we can in turn design methodologies by which we can assess whether organizations are value-adding and whether the investments we are making are moving us into restorative or regenerative processes. If we have rigour and commitment enough to shift our lens and design according to living systems frameworks, we will start to participate in the restoration of our biodiversity, have an impact powerful enough, that as a collective we may be able to move towards not just net-zero, but negative emissions, and in turn, we reharmonize our place in nature. We then stand a much better chance that in 10 to 20 years' time our businesses will still exist, and our investment still delivers returns.

Notes

1 Hassan, A. (2020). Does loss of biodiversity by businesses CAUSE Covid-19. Retrieved from https://www.eauc.org.uk/does_loss_of_biodiversity_by_businesses_cause_c.

2 Anon, An overview of the last 20 years. *The Human Cost of Disasters An overview of the last 20 years 2000-2019.* Available at https://www.undrr.org/sites/default/files/inline-files/Human%20Cost%20of%20Disasters%202000-2019%20FINAL.pdf.

3 United Nations. (2019). UN report: NATURE'S Dangerous DECLINE 'Unprecedented'; species extinction Rates 'Accelerating' – United Nations sustainable development. Retrieved from https://www.un.org/sustainabledevelopment/blog/2019/05/nature-decline-unprecedented-report/.

4 Anon (2018). SPECIAL REPORTGlobal Warming of 1.5°C. *Intergovernmental Panel on Climate Change.* Available at https://www.ipcc.ch/sr15/chapter/chapter-3/.

5 Steffen, W., Crutzen, P.J., & McNeill, J.R. (2007). The Anthropocene: Are Humans Now Overwhelming the Great Forces of Nature. *AMBIO: A Journal of the Human Environment,* 36(8), pp. 614–621.

6 Miller J.G. (1985) General Living Systems Theory. In: Pichot, P., Berner, P., Wolf, R., Thau, K. (eds) *Biological Psychiatry, Higher Nervous Activity.* Springer, Boston, MA. https://doi.org/10.1007/978-1-4684-8329-1_100

7 Bresnihan, P. (2018, August 19). Valuing *Nature*: Perspectives and *Issues.* Retrieved from https://www.nesc.ie/publications/valuing-nature/.

8 Alkemade, R., van Oorschot, M., Miles, L., Nellemann, C., Bakkenes, M., & ten Brink, B. (2009). GLOBIO3: A framework to investigate options for reducing global terrestrial biodiversity loss. *Ecosystems,* 12(3), 374–390. https://link.springer.com/article/10.1007/s10021-009-9229-5.

9 Chaplin-Kramer, B., & Green, J. (2020). Biodiversity and ecosystem services in environmental profit and loss accounts. Retrieved from https://www.cisl.cam.ac.uk/resources/publication-pdfs/BESinEPLWorkingPaper.pdf.

10 Dooley, E. E. (2005). EHPnet: Millennium Ecosystem Assessment. *Environmental Health Perspectives,* 113(9). doi:10.1289/ehp.113-a591

11 Bresnihan, P. (2018, August 19). Valuing Nature: Perspectives and Issues. Retrieved from https://www.nesc.ie/publications/valuing-nature/.

12 King, S., & Wilson, L. (2015). Experimental Biodiversity Accounting as a Component of the System of Environmental Economic Accounting Experimental Ecosystem Accounting (SEEA-EEA). Retrieved from https://www.unep-wcmc.org/system/dataset_file_fields/files/000/000/343/original/ANCA_Technical_guidance_Experimental_Biodiversity_Accounting_final_.pdf?1450350840.

13 European Commission. (2015). Ecosystem Services and Biodiversity. Retrieved from https://ec.europa.eu/environment/integration/research/newsalert/pdf/ecosystem_services_biodiversity_IR11_en.pdf.

14 Sanford, C., & Haggard, B., 2020. The Regenerative Economic Shaper: A Framework for Architecting the Next Economy. *Regenesis Group.* Available at https://regenesisgroup.com/resources/.

15 European Commission. (2015). Ecosystem Services and Biodiversity. Retrieved from https://ec.europa.eu/environment/integration/research/newsalert/pdf/ecosystem_services_biodiversity_IR11_en.pdf.

16 Porter, M.E., 1985. *The Competitive Advantage: Creating and Sustaining Superior Performance.* New York City: New York Free Press.

17 https://jade-eli.com/.

18 Mang, P., Haggard, B., & Regenesis, 2016. *Regenerative Development and Design: A Framework for Evolving Sustainability,* New Jersey: Wiley and Sons.

19 Sanford, C., & Haggard, B., 2020 et al.

20 https://www.transcendent-media.com.

21 Meadows, D. (2012, April 05). Leverage points: Places to intervene in a system. Retrieved from http://donellameadows.org/archives/leverage-points-places-to-intervene-in-a-system/.
22 Atkins, J.F. orcid.org/0000-0001-8727-0019 and Maroun, W. (2018) Integrated extinction accounting and accountability: Building an Ark. Accounting, Auditing & Accountability Journal, 31 (3). pp. 750-786. ISSN 0951-3574.
23 Mang, P., Haggard, B., & Regenesis, 2016 et al.

PART III

Extinction Finance

How Financial Market Mechanisms Can Save Species

11

'EXTINCTION BONDS' ADDRESSING BIODIVERSITY ISSUES THROUGH SUSTAINABLE FINANCE

Martina Macpherson and Christoph Biehl

Introduction

The extinction accounting framework is setting a new standard in terms of emancipatory accounting in the middle of the current mass extinction crisis.[1]

In this chapter, we explore the role that financial markets participants can play in providing meaningful and long-term nature-linked mitigation and adaptation strategies for financial markets. Can financial instruments, namely Sustainability-Linked Bonds (SLBs), be a part of the solution?

We apply the 'Extinction Accounting Framework' (EAF) to the concept of KPI-focussed, sustainability-linked bonds to create the 'Extinction Bond Framework'. By doing so, we provide a framework for financial products to address biodiversity and species extinction issues, providing a financial market tool to support the 'Ecological Transition'.[2]

Our 'Extinction Bond Framework' ties in with the current materiality discussion related to environmental, social and corporate governance (ESG) issues, links to widely used sustainability reporting standards and guidelines, and follows well-established management accounting concepts and classification systems.

To note, in December 2020, the International Capital Markets Association (ICMA) and the French Ministry of Finance for the Ecological and Inclusive Transition also confirmed and highlighted the role of sustainable bond markets in promoting biodiversity.[3] This development is supported by a dedicated ICMA guidance document on 'Impact Reporting for Biodiversity Projects' that we are highlighting, among other leading disclosure and reporting frameworks, in this chapter.

DOI: 10.4324/9781003045557-15

Context

Investor engagement activities related to species extinction became an established practice in the last decade. One of the key engagement initiatives started in 2016 with Hermes EOS (now Federated Hermes) co-organising a dedicated species extinction engagement programme, supported by an event for asset owners, in London (see Hermes EOS, 2016[4]). The event called for better disclosure on species loss in corporate reports, with a focus on the chemical sector in the German market context, inter alia synthesised in our previous book 'The Business of Bees'[5,6] (2016).

A few years later, the engagement debate on biodiversity and species extinction had evolved to the next level, in academia and industry, as indicated by the increasing appetite for collaboration. One collaboration was the 'Species Extinction Engagement Event', at Investec Group in London in May 2019,[7] another one was the multi-stakeholder engagement webinar,[8] where calls from groups across the investment and capital markets chain were made for the integration of species extinction governance and accounting criteria into investment decision-making.[9]

Over the last 18 months, biodiversity and species protection have finally become key areas of focus in the world of sustainable finance. This trend was fuelled by initiatives like the publication of the UK's 'Dasgupta Review'[10] on the 'Economics of Biodiversity' (Report, 02/2021), increased attention in the run-up to the long-expected 'Convention on Biological Diversity' (CBD) COP 15 Summit ('Kunming Summit'), 17–30 May 2021,[11] and contextually by the ongoing biodiversity- and zoonotic-linked COVID-19 crisis.

Multiple reports, frameworks and statements have been issued, connecting the world of natural and financial capital, across academia, investment, and banking, mapping nature losses versus financial risks[12] – some of which are also highlighted in this book.

Meanwhile, the Nature Conservancy and Environmental Finance, among others, recently highlighted in a survey (11/2019)[13] that many private investors may still be deterred from investing in projects that enhance natural capital (and biodiversity) due to a lack of suitable data to measure the impact of their investments.

These findings and the collaboration initiatives around natural capital, biodiversity and species extinction are very timely as we have been losing ecosystem services at an unprecedented rate. In our planet's long history, we are now living in a new geological age, the 'Anthropocene'. In this 'age of humans', we are, for the first time, the most extinction-defining factor for our planet.

Pervasive human-driven pollution, climate change, an ever-increasing use of land and over-consumption are just some of the determining factors contributing to this dangerous loss of biodiversity, natural habitat and species, which in turn results in the overall loss of ecosystem services:

- According to the IPBES Report (05/2019[14]), approximately 75% of the land-based environment and 66% of the marine environment have been significantly altered by human activity.

- The same Report highlights that natural ecosystems have declined by 47%, while the global biomass of wild mammals has fallen by 82%, and global wildlife populations have declined by 60% over the last 40 years.

Other, recent studies[15] derive similar conclusions assessing the impact of agriculture since the introduction of agricultural practices 11,000 years ago. They highlight that Earth has lost an estimated 50% of its terrestrial plants and roughly 20% of its animal biodiversity. They confirm that 1 million of our Earth's 7 million to 10 million plant and animal species could face extinction in the near future.[16]

These outcomes are truly devastating as more than half of the world's total gross domestic product, or US$ 44 trillion dollars, is either highly or moderately dependent on nature's ecosystem services, with biodiversity loss and ecosystem loss classified as one of the top five threats to humanity in the coming decade, by the World Economic Forum (see, e.g., WEF Report, 01/2020[17]).

Looking at the Intergovernmental Science-Policy Platform on Biodiversity and Ecosystem Services Report (05/2019[18]), we see one of many 'truly horrifying pronouncements of late' with extinction rates is currently hundreds of times higher than the historic rate, with 1 million species at threat of extinction, as highlighted earlier.

Loss in biodiversity and the resulting reduction in ecosystem services will have far-reaching consequences for the global economy, the world of finance and society at large – with fewer insects to pollinate plants, fewer plants to provide clean air, water and soil, and fewer forests to safeguard human settlements from floods and other natural disasters. We are quite literally 'biting the hand that feeds us', or as one would say in German: 'we are sawing through the very same branch that we are sitting on'.

With the world of finance and global corporations awakening to the impacts of climate change, experts expect that climate action could deliver at least US$26 trillion in economic benefits through 2030.[19] Meanwhile, there is a real sense of a 'climate urgency', as the Global ('Green' and 'Just') Transition cannot be achieved without addressing interconnected environmental (and social) issues, and without focussing on defined biodiversity and species extinction targets to support the 'Ecological Transition'.

Fortunately, the recognition of sustainability responsibilities for policy, finance, business and civil society is becoming increasingly clear:

- On the policy and regulatory side, the new EU Taxonomy (07/2020[20]), supported by 'Guidelines on Non-Financial Reporting'[21] and 'Guidelines on Non-Financial Reporting: Supplement on Reporting Climate-Related Information',[22] tries to turn environmental issues and urgency, into a framework for policy and industry best practices and actions. The EU Taxonomy includes six environmental categories and includes a dedicated category on 'Protection and Restoration of Ecosystems and Biodiversity'[23] and applies to products issued by actors in the financial and insurance industry. The EU

Taxonomy applies to corporate disclosure EU NFRD (EU 2014/95),[24] and to the ESG disclosure of products issued by actors in the financial and insurance industry: with the help of the financial products regulation EU SFDR (EU 2019/2088),[25] which will come into effect on 10 March 2021, European financial product providers will need to comply, or explain, if and how they address 'Sustainability Risks', at entity and product level, in pre-contractual and periodic reporting. These risks will also include biodiversity risks.

- For corporate dialogue on biodiversity, alongside the work on the EU Taxonomy and the work of non-governmental organisations (NGOs), the EU Commission launched a dedicated workstream for multi-stakeholder engagement: the 'EU Business @ Biodiversity Platform'.[26] At EU level, it provides a unique forum for dialogue to explore the links between business, and biodiversity and natural capital and works towards fulfilling the objectives of the 'EU Biodiversity Strategy to 2030'.

- Further, on the NGO-led and multilateral side of collaborative and collective action, we have seen multiple commitments towards biodiversity, natural habitat and species protection. By protecting 'Life Below Water' (= UN SDG Goal 14) and 'Life on Land' (= UN SDG Goal 15), the United Nations' 'Agenda 2030' (2015[27]) is highlighting and interconnecting the issues linked to biodiversity and conservation of species across the investment value chain. The United Nations also hosts an annual 'United Nations Convention on Biological Diversity'[28] which brings together political, financial and business leaders, and other leading nature-linked coalitions and task forces such as the 'Capitals Coalition' (formerly Natural Capital Coalition),[29] the newly established 'Task Force on Nature-related Financial Disclosures' (TNFD, to launch in May 2021[30]) and the 'Business for Nature's Call for Action' (launched in 2020[31]).

  - Building on the terminology established in the climate change discourse (see Task Force on Climate-related Financial Disclosures – TCFD[32]), the TNFD provides a promising new framework which distinguishes between two types of nature-related risks for investors:

    - Physical risks: The risk resulting directly from reduced ecosystem services such as the lack of pollination for the agricultural industry or reduced flood control for the real estate market. Certain industries are more exposed to physical risk from biodiversity loss than others, for instance, tourism, agriculture, fishery or forestry.

    - Transitional risks: The risk resulting from societal and political pressure, including reputational, regulatory scrutiny and litigation risks. As societies will face an increasing loss in ecosystem services over the coming years, pressure on societies is expected to grow, and transitional risk will steadily increase. Industries that will be especially affected include agriculture, forestry, oil and gas, mining and construction.

  - In addition, financial market participants need to carefully consider liability risks and implications for litigation considering new (EU) regulation, as highlighted in a framework in the latest 'Handbook for Nature-related Financial Risks' by the Cambridge Institute for Sustainability Leadership.[33]

- We are referring to the work of TNFD, and of other important coalitions in more detail in other parts of this book.

For the investment, banking and insurance sectors, the decline of biodiversity and species has emerged as a material strategic risk that can impact decision-making, financial performance as well as extra-financial outcomes and impacts.

Biodiversity as a strategic ESG issue is rooted in academic research spanning analysis that dates back almost 30 years: according to the World Resource Institute, IUCN and the UN Environment Programme (Report, 1992[34]), the destruction of the natural world can result in defaults, lower returns and increasing insurance liabilities.

More recently, the issues have become better understood in the business and financial community: for example, the 'Organisation for Economic Cooperation and Development' (OECD, Report, 05/2019[35]) outlined that businesses, banks and investors may also face higher costs of capital, and a loss and or additional costs related to investment, lending and underwriting activities.

However, in financial services, biodiversity has only become an area of focus more recently, and hence, the full financial cost of biodiversity and species loss is not yet well-understood and remains difficult to calculate.

In one of the first studies of its kind, the Dutch Central Bank ('De Nederlandsche Bank NV') outlined (Report, 06/2020[36]) that the country's financial intuitions held EUR 510 billion (US$ 604 billion) of investments that were highly or very highly dependent on one or more ecosystem services. The Central Bank, in alignment with the 'Network for Greening the Financial System – Central Banks Network',[37] has been focussing its efforts to measure the interconnected issues and impacts related to climate and nature risks.

Although biodiversity loss poses great challenges, and potentially significant economic and financial risks to all actors, it also provides new investment opportunities, in active and passive investment, and across capital markets. Sustainable finance has a vital role to play to support and finance ecosystem governance, protection and global climate and nature-related 'Ecological Transition' efforts.

In the following section, we hence aim to identify and evaluate the usability of financial instruments, in detail sustainable bonds, for biodiversity and species extinction mitigation and adaptation purposes.

The Role of Sustainable Finance Debt Instruments

Sustainable finance strategies, these are so-called green, blue, social, sustainable and more recently sustainability (KPI)-linked bonds, have achieved a strong momentum over the last decade. According to Moody's Investors Service, global issuances for 2021 are expected to reach a total of US$ 650 billion in 2021, for the first time.[38]

Definitions and Principles

When defining sustainable versus sustainability-linked debt instruments (see more details in the Appendix), we differentiate between so-called project-based and target-based structures:

- <u>Sustainable Bonds</u> are use-of-proceeds (or labelled), project-based bonds, where the proceeds are exclusively applied to eligible environmental and/or social projects. The Green Bond Principles (GBP), the Social Bond Principles (SBP) and the Sustainability Bond Guidelines (SBG), referred to as the 'Principles', have become the leading framework for Sustainable Bond issuances. The International Capital Market Association (ICMA) serves as the Secretariat, assuming 'administrative duties, and providing guidance for the governance of the "Principles"'. As the 'Principles' are designed for industry-wide use, bond issuers and investors as well as banks are invited to participate.[39]
- <u>Sustainability-Linked Bonds</u> (SLBs, often also referred to as KPI-linked bonds) are so-called non-labelled or target-based bonds. SLBs are tied to bespoke ESG metrics at the core of the company, rather than to specific projects and use of proceeds for these projects. ICMA has published principles for sustainability-linked bonds in June 2020, offering guidance for issuers that want to raise environmentally friendly debt with financial terms – e.g. a variable coupon rate – tied to the achievement of specific ESG goals.[40]
- <u>Sustainability-Linked Loans</u> (SLLs) are any types of target-linked loan instruments and/or contingent facilities, such as bonding lines, guarantee lines or letters of credit, which can incentivise the borrower's achievement of ambitious, predetermined sustainability performance objectives. The interest rate is flexible and depends on the level of achievement of the predetermined sustainability targets.[41] The Loan Markets Association (LMA) issued guidance, definitions and a dedicated framework for SLLs in 2020 (Table 11.1).[42]

Momentum, Growth and Innovation in Sustainable Finance

The momentum for Sustainable Bonds and Sustainability-Linked Bonds continues to grow: global issuance reached US$ 491 billion in 2020; and for 2021, it is estimated to reach US$ 650 billion, representing a year-over-year growth of 32%, according to Moody's (Report, 02/2021).[43]

   Key drivers for sustainable finance momentum and growth over the course of 2021 include:

- The European Central Bank (ECB)'s announcement in Q3 2020 that it would begin accepting sustainability-linked bonds as collateral, signalling the likelihood of substantial growth of these instruments.[44]

TABLE 11.1 Project-based vs target-based structures for sustainable bonds

Classification	Project-based structures			Target-based structures
Type	Green bonds	Social bonds	Sustainability and SDGs bonds	KPI-linked bonds
Short description	• Funds dedicated to green projects • Follow the ICMA GBPs framework	• Funds dedicated to social projects • Follow the ICMA SBPs framework	• Funds dedicated to both green and social projects • Follow the ICMA SBPs and GBPs framework	• No requirements for use-of-proceeds framework • The issuer is committed to meet sustainability targets; otherwise, the coupon/return will increase • ICMA SLB Principles
Subject to a framework?	Yes	Yes	Yes	ICMA SLB
Project-based?	Yes	Yes	Yes	No
Funds committed?	Yes	Yes	Yes	No
Issuer returns flexibility?	Yes	Yes	Yes	Yes
Direct impact if KPI not met?	No	No	No	Yes
Included in green indices?	Yes	No	No	No
Will attract dedicated green investors?	Yes	No	No	Yes
Impact reporting?	Yes	Yes	Yes	Through KPIs

Based on Alliance Bernstein's ESG Bond Structures Framework (31/08/2020).
Alliance Bernstein, "Making Sense of ESG Bond Structures," 2020, https://www.alliance bernstein.com/library/Making-Sense-of-ESG-Bond-Structures.htm.

• Strong government support for the sustainable bond market, as governments look to finance their sustainable development initiatives, from green infrastructure to COVID-19 recovery, and particularly as the new Biden administration in the USA pursues new policies linking economic and environmental objectives with financial expectations.

- Increasing emerging markets issuances from sovereigns and corporate entities.
- The development of transition finance, as heightened focus by governments and investors on climate change draws issuer attention towards financing their carbon transition plans and outlining their strategies.[45]

Growth in sustainable finance, across the labelled and non-labelled segments, is driven by innovative labels and structures, and by governments and the financial sector increasing their focus on climate, nature and social issues and actions.

This development will accelerate further given the market attention on Paris-aligned pathways, a global demand for KPI-linked financing in line with the UN Sustainable Development Agenda ('Agenda 2030') and the EU's commitments centring on the 'Just (Energy) Transition'.[46]

Sustainability-Linked Bonds (SLBs) and Sustainability-Linked Loans (SLLs) have the potential to take market growth to a new scale, while maintaining clarity around the issuer's key ESG performance indicators (KPIs) and metrics: the recently launched ICMA 'Sustainability-Linked Bond Principles' state that 'KPIs must be relevant, core and material to the issuer's overall business, and of high strategic significance to the issuer's operations, they must be measurable or quantifiable on a consistent methodological basis, externally verifiable and able to be benchmarked'.[47]

Herein, we see the clear potential for defining, measuring and reporting on biodiversity and species extinction/protection KPIs.

Sustainable Bonds Principles, Frameworks and External Reviews

ICMA launched the first 'Green Bond Principles' (GBP) in 2014,[48] followed by the consecutive launches of the 'Social' (2016/2020)[49] and 'Sustainability' (2018)[50] 'Bond Guidelines'.

Following ICMA's 'GBP Principles' (2014–2020), other market participants, such as ESG research and rating firms, and the Climate Bonds Initiative, developed ESG Bond external review frameworks, so-called Second-Party Opinions (SPOs) or Green Bond Verification Statements.

Climate Bonds Initiative was one of the first SPO providers that also developed a 'Standard for (labelled) Green Bonds',[51] focussing and addressing a range of climate and environmental issues including agriculture, forestry and inter alia biodiversity and natural habitat.

Investors, standard setters[52] and public sector issuers (especially in the Nordics[53]) have been calling for (impact) reporting and external reviews over a Sustainable Bond's life cycle to avoid and address 'green and impact washing'[54]:

- Traditional, use-of-proceeds (labelled) Green Bonds often include an external review, provided either at the pre-issuance or sometimes also at the post-issuance stage.
- Climate Bonds Initiative provides a public database for labelled Green Bond and external reviews that are publicly available.[55]

For a detailed overview on the type of reviews and reviewers, such as Second-Party Opinion (SPO) providers, assurance firms and the Climate Bonds Standard and Certification, please see the Appendix.

Other jurisdictions, in particular in Asia, also started to introduce their own Green Bond taxonomies: China took an early lead and collaborated with market participants on the development of the first 'Green Bond Endorsed Project Catalogue' (2015)[56] which outlines the eligibility of projects financed with green bonds in China.

Since mid-2019, multiple standardisation efforts for Green and Sustainable Bonds have followed:

- The 'EU Green Bond Standard' (EU GBS) proposed by the European Commission's Technical Expert Group on Sustainable Finance (TEG) in March 2020[57] explicitly requires that EU Green Bonds are allocated to economic activities that meet the requirements of the EU Taxonomy.
- China's 'Green Bond Endorsed Project Catalogue' was updated in May 2020, when Chinese regulators removed controversially debated project categories, such as clean coal.[58] This development broadly signals a greater internationalisation of the Chinese green bond market over time.
- In 2020, ICMA and the Loan Markets Association (LMA) issued a series of new 'Principles' and guidance documents for debt instruments, to support the market's demand beyond labelled, use-of-proceeds Sustainable Bonds, including ICMA's 'Sustainability-Linked Bond Principles',[59] LMA's 'Green Loan Principles'[60] and ICMA's 'Guidance on Transition Bonds'.[61]

Sustainability-Linked Bond (SLB) Stakeholders, Documentation and External Reviews

A Sustainability-Linked Bond (SLB) issuance involves three main parties: issuers, investors and underwriters. The issuance is often supported by a credit rating for the issuer and involves key issuance documents and an array of placement agents ('arrangers').

As per ICMA's 'SLB Principles' (2020), SLB issuances must include financial documentation such as the 'Prospectus', and an SPO, provided by an independent verifier, often an ESG research and rating firm (Figure 11.1 and Table 11.2).

Sustainability-linked Bond Issuance – Stakeholders and Documentation

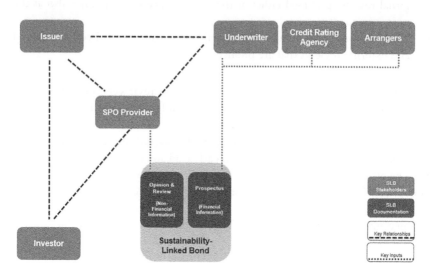

FIGURE 11.1 Outline of the stages, stakeholder and documentation value chain for sustainability linked bonds – SLBs.

Source: Martina Macpherson, Dr Christoph Biehl, SLB Framework, 2020.

TABLE 11.2 Sustainability-linked bonds principles – components and features (ICMA's 'SLB Principles')

Five core components[a]	*Key features*
1. Selection of key performance indicators (KPIs)	**KPIs should be:** • relevant, core and material to the issuer's overall business, and of high strategic significance to the issuer's operations • measurable or quantifiable on a consistent methodological basis • externally verifiable • to be benchmarked
2. Calibration of sustainability performance targets (SPTs)	• The SPTs should be ambitious • The target setting exercise should be based on a combination of benchmarking approaches • Disclosures on target setting should make clear reference timelines, baselines, etc.
3. Bond characteristics	The SLBs' financial and/or structural characteristics can vary depending on whether the selected KPIs reach the predefined SPTs. The potential variation of the coupon is the most common example, but it is also possible to consider the variation of other SLBs' financial and/or structural characteristics.

Five core components[a]	Key features
4. Reporting	**Issuers of SLBs should publish, and keep readily available and easily accessible:** • Up-to-date information on the performance of the selected KPIs, including baselines where relevant • A verification assurance report relative to the SPT outlining the performance against the SPTs and the related impact, and timing of such impact, on the bond's financial and/or structural characteristics • Any information enabling investors to monitor the level of ambition of the SPTs Reporting should be published regularly and at least on an annual basis.
5. Verification	Issuers should seek independent and external verification of their performance level against each SPT for each KPI by a qualified external reviewer with relevant expertise, by an SPO or assurance provider at least once a year.

Source: ICMA, 'SLB Principles', 2020.

Notes

a ICMA has defined five core SLB components and a range of key features which need to be defined and communicated by the bond issuer to assess the issuer's environmental and/or social credentials and benefits.
International Capital Markets Association, "Sustainability-Linked Bond Principles."

The Suitability of Sustainability-Linked Bonds (SLBs) and Sustainability-Linked Loans (SLLs)

As outlined, Sustainability Linked Bonds (SLBs) and Sustainability Linked Loans (SLLs) can provide flexibility, adaptability and additionality for an alignment with sustainability and impact KPIs, such as biodiversity and species extinction/protection criteria addressing key issues linked to the 'Ecological Transition'.

From a financial benefits standpoint, SLBs and SLLs can provide an attractive instrument for issuers that want to demonstrate their commitment to sustainable finance but do not have sufficient green or social projects to underpin the issuance of a green, social or sustainability 'use of proceeds' bond.

To note in relation to non-financial and sustainability-linked benefits:

• There is no exhaustive list of KPIs that can be used; issuers have relatively free rein to use KPIs that fit their specific sustainability and business strategy. Hence, they are well-placed to cover smaller, e.g. wildlife conservation and preservation projects using pre-defined impact criteria that are fundamental and reflective of an ecological transition.
• The Technical Expert Group on Sustainable Finance at the EU Commission has suggested that KPIs could be linked to an improvement of the share

of EU Taxonomy-aligned activities,[62] a potentially attractive proposition for issuers looking to demonstrate their commitment to sustainable finance within a regulated framework.

• The role of the independent verifiers, e.g. SPO providers, is crucial for the issuer and for investors, as highlighted in the 'Five Core Components' of ICMA's 'SLB Principles Framework': for the assessment of materiality, ambition and accountability of the issuer in relation to the pre-defined KPIs as well as for the ongoing monitoring and reporting on the issuer's ESG strategy. Similar rules and requirements apply for SLLs.

• Following debates around the 'sustainability credentials' and 'green washing' efforts of some of the early SLB issuers and issuances, such as Enel's SLB (2019),[63] it is also important to note that issuers, investors and SPO providers need to work closely together to define, monitor and report on the non-financial benefits, sustainability KPIs and target setting, over the life cycle of the debt instrument.

When assessing the market opportunity for biodiversity SLBs and SLLs, and the links to the food and beverage, agriculture, and forestry sectors, as well as to global conservation efforts or UN SDG ambitions, we observe that a range of biodiversity impact debt vehicles have already been developed over the last two to three years.

As discussed, in this book, 'Wildlife Conservation - Rhino Bonds' (RIB) have become a key instrument to meet financial and extra-financial goals when and where Nature and Biodiversity Impact efforts are concerned: in 2019, ZSL launched a US$ 50 million RIB with a five-year term.[64] It is aimed at increasing the number of African black rhinos across five sites in Kenya and South Africa to prevent extinction. It covers a total of 700 black rhinos that form about 12% of the world's entire black rhino population. The 'Rhino Impact Bond' (RIB) is 'the world's first financial instrument for species conservation, transferring the risk of funding conservation from donors to impact investors by linking conservation performance to financial performance', according to Conservation Capital, the company who arranged the bond offer.

Over the last 18 months, biodiversity-linked and UN SDG-linked (impact) loans have also become more popular. Here are three examples:

• In 2019, Rabobank launched a 'Planet Impact Loan' scheme that stems from a collaborative public–private partnership project to create a 'Biodiversity Monitor', and promotes a harmonious, sustainable relationship between dairy farming and the environment.[65] The 'Monitor' team developed practical, science-based key performance indicators (KPIs) that are associated with biodiversity, focussing on areas including greenhouse gases, land use and soil use. The 'Monitor' equips farmers with new means to demonstrate their progress on biodiversity, and Rabobank is then better able to reward them with lower interest rates. Following the success of this instrument in the Netherlands, Rabobank is developing a sustainability scoring model that will be applied in other countries where farmers are Rabobank clients.

- In June 2020, Agrial finalised a EUR 900 million syndicated loan with 15 French and international banking partners, with Natixis acting as sustainability agent.[66] The interest rate on the syndicated loan will be indexed to numerous social and environmental indicators, which will be reviewed by an independent auditor on a yearly basis. Agrial opted for indicators that align with its sustainable development commitments and goals out to 2025, particularly with a focus on safety at work, reducing energy use, increasing sales of crop protection products that offer alternatives to synthetic chemicals, developing the animal feed business without antibiotics or GMO, as well as developing organic products.

- Meanwhile, in April 2020, BNP Paribas acted as sustainability coordinator for the first biodiversity-linked loan by the Finnish forest bio-industry company UPM's EUR 750 million revolving credit facility (RCF).[67] This financial instrument aims to achieve a net positive biodiversity impact and a 65% reduction in CO_2 emissions from fuels and purchased electricity.

When assessing all these KPI- and impact-linked debt vehicles, we note that they lack specific species extinction/protection accounting targets. Hence, in the following, we aim to outline the opportunity for the development of an 'Extinction Bond Framework' based on the SLB Principles.

Extinction Bonds: The Next Generation of KPI-Linked Impact Instruments

The key challenge of addressing the extinction crisis through financial instruments is the gap between intention and impact. To bridge this gap, Atkins and Maroun[68] have developed a 'Species Extinction Accounting Framework'.

This Framework goes beyond the existing biodiversity accounting approaches, which essentially just 'account for fossils'. It is without a doubt important to keep a track and to check, and audit, on what type of species are going extinct; however, this type of accounting for fossils will not have a positive impact per se or change the very fact that species are going extinct.

The emancipatory aspect of Atkins and Maroun's Framework is that it promotes action in the fight against extinction and that it aims to define and measure impact.

> Extinction accounting frameworks contain potentially emancipatory elements in that extinction accounting "should" lead to extinction prevention.
> *(Atkins & Maroun, 2020, p. 1840)*

The Framework created by Atkins and Maroun addresses company[69] and consolidated macro accounts,[70] which include the work of stakeholders in addition to the company's efforts.

FIGURE 11.2 The five stages of the 'Extinction Bond Framework', based on Atkins and Maroun (2018, 2020).[71]

The combination of those approaches can provide an ideal framework for 'Extinction Bonds' using a KPI-linked SLB Framework and applying 'Biodiversity' and 'Species Extinction' criteria (Figure 11.2).

We Outline a '5-Step' Approach for an SLB-based 'Extinction Bond' Framework

Step 1 – Context of Extinction Threat at Entity

In the first step of the process, the 'Species Extinction Framework' requires the establishment of the (i) context and an analysis of the (ii) 'Extinction Threat'. The outcome of this analysis determines the basis for the following steps.

The context and the analysis of the threat shall include an identification and an assessment of the ecosystem within which the company, i.e. the issuer, operates. It shall determine the value of this ecosystem in economic or financial as well as in biological or extra-financial terms. This step is highly issuer-specific and depends on the geographical context of issuer's operations and its supply chain.

This initial step is essential to define the 'bond characteristics' of the Sustainability-Linked (SLB) 'Extinction Bond':

- The identification of the relevant ecosystems in biological terms builds the foundation for the identification of the Bond's 'sustainability performance targets' (SPTs). Key performance indicators (KPIs) are then determined as measures to determine the progress made towards the SPTs – more on this in the following steps of this framework.

- The process of identifying and contextualising an extinction threat/s shall be based on the information contained within the IUCN's '(Species) Red List'.[72] This annual list published by IUCN can provide key reference points for this first stage of the contextual analysis.

Step 2 – Materiality Assessment

The second step of the framework shall provide a key link between the definitions in economic or financial and in sustainability or extra-financial terms for a sector-specific, species extinction-focussed materiality assessment.

The starting point for Step 2 is the definition of 'Materiality'. There are many different standards and frameworks available, inter alia, the concepts of 'financial', and 'double/dual' materiality implicitly referred to by Atkins and Maroun[73] and explicitly included in the EU non-financial disclosure directive, EU NFRD -2014/95,[74] as well as the newly emerging concept of 'dynamic materiality'.[75]

For this materiality assessment, we shall define four dimensions of 'Extinction Impact', centring around a set of core questions:

1. does the issuer increase the extinction threat,
2. does the issuer mitigate the extinction threat,
3. does the extinction threat pose a risk to the issuer and
4. does the extinction threat pose an opportunity to the issuer.

The outcome of the materiality assessment shall provide a list of key risks and opportunities in economic or financial and in sustainability or non-financial terms.

Atkins and Maroun[76] suggest a ranking by (i) 'impact', (ii) 'likelihood' and (iii) 'time frame', which is necessary to determine a suitable course of action and suitable 'outcome pathways'.

The materiality assessment is an essential step for the sustainability-linked 'Extinction Bond', as it shall establish the link between the issuer in question and the sustainability performance targets in scope, which are designed to create a positive impact versus the underlying extinction threat.

Unlike the sustainable performance targets (SPTs), which are an outcome of the first and second stages, the KPIs are purely the outcome of the materiality assessment and determine how 'material' progress towards the SPTs can be measured.

The KPIs shall be designed in a 'financial', 'double/dual' or 'dynamic materiality' context. This aspect can differ significantly depending on the 'Materiality Concept' applied in the analysis,[77] i.e. to highlight which financial and extra-financial aspects are to be material.

Step 3 – Reporting and Dialogue

Once steps 1 and 2 have been completed, and SPTs and KPIs have been designed and implemented, the issuer is required to report against the pre-defined species extinction and conservation targets.

The reporting shall be determined by the outcome of the first two stages and is, therefore, not limited to traditional one-directional issuer reporting. Instead, it shall be a dialogical, multi-stakeholder process.

Atkins and Maroun[78] suggest the process can and should involve key stakeholders relevant to the issuer and to the extinction threat in question. The list of relevant stakeholders ranges from on-the-ground reporting, e.g. by local conservational groups, to stewardship activities by multinational institutional investors. The latter have as active owners the chance (some would classify this as fiduciary duty) to engage in the reporting through engagement meetings. The achievement of SPTs can form part of an engagement plan between the issuer and the investor.

There are an increasing number of disclosure and reporting frameworks, principles and guidelines that can be used to guide the reporting activities; see Appendix for details.

While it is important to note that there are fundamental differences in approach and methodology between these disclosure and reporting standards, guidelines and frameworks, if used already by the issuer, can all serve as a starting point in the creation of SPTs, KPIs and the reporting framework. However, as none of the existing frameworks provides a suitable guidance for all steps of the 'Extinction Bond Framework', a 'mix and match' approach is required.

Step 4 – Impact Assessment

The fourth step entails the evaluation of the issuer's actual performance in relation to the SPTs using the species extinction and conservation KPIs.

In this process, the parties from Step 3 shall be included to jointly analyse the impact, to reflect on the nature of the impact and to assess, using the KPIs, whether it is in line with the pre-defined sustainable performance targets.

This impact assessment forms the first element of the verification process as it shall provide the information necessary to evaluate 'if, where, how and when' the SPTs have been achieved.

To meet ICMA's SLB Principles 'Core Component #5', as outlined above, this step shall also require an assessment of all SPTs and KPIs, by a 'qualified external reviewer with relevant expertise' (see above, ICMA's 'SLB Principles').[79]

Meanwhile, other standards that shall underpin the assessment may include fundamental ESG standards, such as ISO 14001 ff., 26001 ff. and 45001 ff., for an issuer's environmental and social performance assessment.

For an overview of ESG, Green and Sustainable Bond standards, frameworks and principles, please refer to the next section.

Step 5 – Refine and Implement

'Refine and Implement' forms the final step, Step 5, of the overall process and shall constitute the second part of the verification process. Given the iterative nature of the 'Extinction Bond' (SLB) framework, it is at the same time the basis for the first stage of the next iteration, i.e. the last step of 'reporting period/cycle one' leading over to 'reporting period/cycle two'.

This stage is the key to the emancipatory character of the 'Framework' as it shall allow for impact reporting to lead towards long-term change.

So far, the extinction threat has been defined, targets have been established, and achievements have been reported and assessed.

Crucially, in Step 5, a consolidated review is being created that shall identify the discrepancies between the pre-defined species extinction and conservation targets, i.e. to avoid the extinction of the species under threat, versus the achievement/outcomes by the issuer over the last reporting period.

Those potential deficiencies form the basis for the next iteration of the 'Framework': addressing the discrepancies through stages 1 to 4 during the next reporting period.

Mapping of Existing ESG Disclosure and Reporting Principles, Frameworks and Standards

The aim of the mapping of ESG disclosure and reporting frameworks, principles and guidance documents is to not create yet another theoretical disclosure framework, with little uptake from reporting issuers.

Through the mapping of existing Principles, Standards and Frameworks, we aim to ensure that the 'Extinction Bond' (SLB) Framework shall build on ongoing and ever-evolving standardisation efforts of reporting and accounting frameworks, and on existing sustainability and extra-financial achievements and assessments undertaken by issuing companies, investors, SPO providers and standard setters, such as ICMA (Table 11.3).

Conclusions

The 'Convention on Biological Diversity' defines biodiversity as 'the diversity of species, variation of genes and different ecosystems'.[80] Biodiversity and species diversity are key factors for resilience. Acting against biodiversity loss and species extinction means preventing the collapse of nature's sub-systems.

Having outlined the importance of biodiversity protection frameworks on the one side and the opportunities linked to sustainable finance instruments on the other, we define three key takeaways:

1. The Ecosystem and Species Extinction Crisis requires urgent and consolidated action from all market participants.

TABLE 11.3 Mapping of the 'Extinction Accounting' Framework (Atkins and Maroun 2020, 2018), and ICMA's 'SLB Principles' versus existing ESG disclosure and reporting frameworks, principles and guidance that, in turn, shall be used in the 'Extinction Bond Framework'.

Extinction bond framework	Extinction accounting framework	Sustainability-linked bonds	Frameworks, principles and guidance
Step I Contextualisation of the extinction threat	**Ecosystems** **Extinction accounting context** • Explanation of ecosystems • Value in economic and biological terms • List of species IUCN Red List	• **Bond characteristics**	• Equator Principles • EU SFDR • GRI • IUCN Red List • IFC Performance Standards • KBA – Key Biodiversity Areas • Natura 2000 Network • TNFD • UN SDGs
Step II Materiality assessment	**Risk and impact assessment** • Risk to species and ecosystem • Economic terms • Environmental terms • Ranked by impact, likelihood and time frame	**SPTs: Sustainability performance targets** • **KPIs: Key performance indicators**	• Equator Principles • EU SFDR • EU Taxonomy • Greenfin • GRI • IFC Operating Principles for Impact • IFC Performance Standards • ISO TC 322, 323, 331, 26000 • ICMA SLB Principles • Natural Capital Protocol • OECD Guidelines • SASB • TNFD • UN SDGs/UN SDG Impact Standards • Value Balancing Alliance

Extinction bond framework	Extinction accounting framework	Sustainability-linked bonds	Frameworks, principles and guidance
Step III Reporting and dialogue	**Action reporting** • Conservation groups • Government (different levels) **Partnerships** • Research groups • Academics • Joint private sector initiatives **Private sector efforts** • Companies creating positive impact • Companies reducing negative impact	• **Reporting**	• IFC Performance Standards • Natura 2000 Network • SASB • TNFD • UN Global Compact • UN SDG Impact Standards (Bonds) • WEF Stakeholder Capital Metrics • BSI 42020 • CDP • Equator Principles • EU SFDR • EU Taxonomy • Greenfin • GRI • ICMA Harmonised Framework for Impact Reporting • ICMA SLB Principles • IFRS • ISO TC 322, 26000 • IUCN Red List • IFC Operating Principles for Impact
Step IV Impact assessment	• Analysis • Reflection • Assessment	**Verification**	• EU SFDR • Equator Principles • GRI • ICMA SLP Principles • IFC Operating Principles
Step V Refine and implement	**Consolidated review and identification of deficiencies**		• IFC Performance Standards • UN Global Compact • UN SDG Impact Standards (Bonds) • WEF Stakeholder Capital Metrics

Please see Appendix B for additional Frameworks, Principles and Guidance, detailed references and links to sources.

The destruction of biodiversity and natural capital to the point of extinction has led to an increasing number of threats, the latest being the COVID-19 zoonotic pandemic which is having a devastating impact on our society and on the global economy. In this situation, the '(Sustainability-Linked) Extinction Bond Framework' can provide new opportunities leveraging sustainable financial products for ecological, transformational change. A dedicated 'Species Extinction Accounting Framework' as outlined in this book provides a set of pathways to address extinction threats, preserving biodiversity and building resilient sustainable financial markets.

2. There is a clear market opportunity for Sustainable Finance Debt Instruments and a New Generation of Sustainability-Linked Extinction Bonds.

Over the last few years, a series of sustainable finance debt instruments have been launched, some of them in line with dedicated biodiversity, agricultural oversight management and forestry preservation KPIs. In addition, some equity and debt impact instruments, e.g. for rhino preservation efforts, have come to market. We observe that there are currently no specific issuances of species extinction-linked SLBs. The same gap is prevalent in SLLs. Our approach for the 'Extinction Bond Framework' may be able to address this void enabling sustainable finance product innovation and growth. Central banks, accepting SLBs as collateral, issuers and investors have a key role to play in scaling the SLB market. Meanwhile, regulators and ESG research providers need to establish a level playing field when and where availability of clear, consistent and comparable ESG data for biodiversity and species extinction is concerned.

3. To avoid confusion between New Financial Instruments and Existing Sustainable Bond Frameworks and Metrics for Biodiversity alignment and digitalisation are key.

Over the last decade, the sheer pluralism of sustainable bond frameworks, standards and taxonomies has led to an ever-increasing confusion, from investors to issuers, in relation to the green and social credentials, and to multiple 'green and impact washing debates' as briefly outlined in this chapter. When aligning the 'Species Extinction Framework' with ICMA's 'Sustainability Linked Bond Principles' and mapping the 'Framework' against commonly used materiality, disclosure and reporting frameworks, we conclude that additionality of species extinction metrics does not require a new layer of additional standards, frameworks or a new approach for external reviews. On the contrary, our proposed approach for an 'Extinction Bond' also highlights the opportunity set for more alignment in the sustainable finance arena. This in turn aligns well with other ambitions such as ICMA's Sustainable Bond Principles (-2014–2020) work, and the European Commission's Green Bond Standard (2019 ff.) efforts.

Outlook

The capacity for transformational change of and by the financial market cannot be understated. Innovation and momentum achieved by sustainable finance innovation are showing the way.

We identify three trends for financial market participants, reflecting on the impact of the COVID-19 pandemic, which could lead in turn to 'transformational energy' in the context of identifying and addressing biodiversity and species extinction/protection challenges and opportunities:

1. Stronger Biodiversity Commitments from governments and corporate actors:
   Governments have to acknowledge the current mass extinction crisis and have to commit to solutions, urgently, to avoid another 'Tragedy on the Horizon'. A positive development – the European Commission has highlighted the need for a 'Green Taxonomy' and a 'Green Deal' to be tied to post-COVID-19 recovery measures. The European Green Deal provides a road map to boost efficiency of resources by moving to a clean, circular economy, which in turn can restore biodiversity and regenerate ecosystem services.

   In response to multi-stakeholder engagement efforts, with corporates and sovereigns, and in the context of the COVID-19 pandemic, we are observing, as highlighted at the beginning of this chapter, an ever-increasing amount of new biodiversity and natural capital pledges and commitments from corporate actors and NGO – and most recently, also from investors.[81]

   These pledges also go hand in hand with the better operational environmental and social oversight management of corporations and their supply chains[82] and will shape things in the months and years ahead. However, for meaningful corporate change and action towards natural capital, biodiversity and species protection and preservation to occur, and for regenerative systems to develop, global, corporate governance challenges have also to be addressed.

2. **Assurance of ESG Data and Sustainability Information:** Sustainability-Linked Extinction Bonds stand and fall with the quality of the underlying ESG data. Availability of high-quality reliable data is essential to create the KPIs and measure progress against the SPTs. However, investors lack biodiversity and extinction data and there are prevalent challenges in applying existing data to address biodiversity and extinction risks in a meaningful way. The focus here needs to be data quality and data availability – neither must be prioritised of the other. Assurance of data and technological advances for screening of big data sets are important ways to better address inherent biases linked to self-reported, annualised ESG information.

   Digitalisation efforts supported by 'tagging' of financial and extra-financial information, e.g. as launched by SASB, PwC and XBRL in 2020,[83] can assist in providing better means for reporting and assurance as well as for climate- and nature-based adaptation.[84] They are supported by the EU's 'Digital Strategy'[85] and newly emerging green FinTech efforts and digital alliances[86] such as 'Vision2030' (01/2020).[87] This World Economic Forum (WEF) ESG FinTech initiative aims to apply advanced technologies to achieve the SDGs, including the biodiversity goals UN SDG 14, 15.

To achieve scale for reporting and assurance, digitalisation, e.g. 'tagging' efforts of financial and extra-financial information, can assist in providing new means for climate adaptation.[88] They are supported by the EU's 'Digital Strategy'[89] and newly emerging green FinTech efforts and digital alliances.

3. **Engagement across the investment value chain and capital markets:** The introduction of stewardship codes around the world brings home one key point: Societies are demanding investors to take up an active role in the management of ESG risks to companies and the society as a whole. Essential steps in the extinction bond framework contain loopholes and grey areas. Active ownership based on a dedicated engagement plan can close the loopholes and fence off the grey areas. The risks linked to biodiversity loss and extinction have prompted calls for a task force on nature-related financial disclosures (TNFD). COVID-19 has highlighted the sheer size of biodiversity risk, which is currently not being considered in decision-making.

Appendix A

Definitions and Developments for Sustainable Debt Instruments introduced in this chapter:
Throughout this chapter, we refer to a variety of sustainable debt instruments. These include 'use of proceeds', 'green bonds', 'social bonds' and 'sustainability bonds' (together, 'sustainable bonds'), whose proceeds are typically earmarked to finance specific eligible environmental and social projects; and sustainability-linked instruments, whose proceeds can typically be used for general corporate purposes, but whose interest rates are tied to the achievement of various sustainability targets.[90] These instruments include:

- **Green bonds:** Bonds where the proceeds will be exclusively applied to finance or refinance new and/or existing eligible green projects, such as renewable energy, energy efficiency, clean transportation, sustainable water management and green buildings. Typically issued in accordance with the Green Bond Principles.
- **Social bonds:** Bonds where the proceeds will be exclusively applied to finance or refinance new and/or existing eligible social projects, such as affordable basic infrastructure, access to essential services, affordable housing and food security. Typically issued in accordance with the Social Bond Principles.

- **Sustainability bonds:** Bonds where the proceeds will be exclusively applied to finance or refinance a combination of new and/ or existing eligible green and social projects. Typically issued in accordance with the Sustainability Bond Guidelines.
- **Sustainability-linked bonds** are any type of bond instrument for which the financial and/or structural characteristics can vary depending on whether the issuer achieves pre-defined sustainability or ESG objectives.
- **Sustainability-linked loans:** Loan instruments and/or contingent facilities that incentivise the borrower's achievement of predetermined sustainability performance objectives. Typically issued in accordance with the Sustainability-Linked Loan Principles.
- **Green loans** (*out of scope for this chapter*): Any type of loan instrument made available exclusively to finance or refinance new and/or existing eligible green projects. Typically issued in accordance with the Green Loan Principles.

Sustainable bond labels are emerging continuously: in 2020, ICMA issued new guidance for issuers on 'Climate Transition Bond Instruments'[91] where the proceeds are typically used to help carbon-intensive companies to enter on the transition journey. Verifications, at entity and project level, for some of the latest issuances already coexist. More alignment between normative and regulatory Sustainable Bond frameworks is also to be expected, with ICMA currently launching a new SFDR-centred working group to explore the impact of regulation on Secondary Sustainable Bond Markets and financial products.[92]

TABLE A.1 External reviews at pre-issuance stage for use-of-proceeds bonds

Type of review	What? (details)	Who? (providers)
Third-party Assurance	Assurance reports state whether the green issuance is aligned with a reputable international framework, such as the Green Bond Principles (GBP) or Green Loan Principles (GLP)	Accounting/audit firms
Second-Party Opinion (SPO)	SPOs provide an assessment of the issuer's green bond framework, analysing the 'green' or 'social' credentials of eligible projects/assets. Some also provide a sustainability 'rating', giving a qualitative indication of aspects of the issuer's framework and planned allocation of proceeds.	Environmental Social Governance (ESG) service providers such as Deutsche Börse – ISS ESG/ oekom Research, Morningstar/Sustainalytics, Moody's/Vigeo Eiris, DNV GL and scientific experts such as CICERO, CECEP Consulting.

(Continued)

Type of review	What? (details)	Who? (providers)
Green Bond Rating	Some (credit) rating agencies assess the bond's alignment with the Green/Social/Sustainability Bond Principles and the integrity of its 'green' and 'social' credentials.	Rating agencies such as S&P Global Ratings, JCRA, R&I, RAM Holding (formerly also Moody's).
Climate/Green Bond Certification (e.g. in accordance with the Climate Bonds Standard)	The Climate Bonds Standard is the only Paris Agreement-aligned standard available in the market. Independent verification confirms that the use of proceeds adheres to the Climate Bonds Standard and sector-specific criteria.	Verifiers approved by the Climate Bonds Standard and Certification Scheme which include SPO providers highlighted above.

TABLE A.2 External reviews at post-issuance stage for use-of-proceeds bonds

Type of review	What? (details)	Who? (providers)
Second-Party Opinion or Third-Party Assurance Report	Assurance of allocation of proceeds to eligible green projects.	Auditing firms such as KPMG, Deloitte et al., SPO providers as highlighted above.
Impact Reporting	Reporting that seeks to quantify the climate or environmental impact of a project/asset numerically.	Issuer, audit firms, SPO providers as highlighted above, and scientific experts.
Climate/Green Bonds Certification Report (e.g. in accordance with the Climate Bonds Standard)	Assurance against the Climate Bonds Standard, including the allocation of proceeds to eligible green projects and types of green projects.	Verifiers approved by the Climate Bonds Standard and Certification Scheme which include SPO providers highlighted above.

Based on Climate Bonds Initiative, External Reviews at Pre-Issuance and Post-Issuance Stage, 2016.[93]

Appendix B

TABLE A.3 Overview of the frameworks, principles and guidance documents used in this chapter.

Framework/guideline/standard	Introduction	Latest update
AMF Decree 29	2019	2021
(update on mandatory biodiversity reporting pending)		
Audubon Core[94]	2013	2018
BSI 42020[95]	2013	2018
CBD – Aichi Biodiversity Targets[96]	2010	2018
CBD – Convention on Biological Diversity (BIP-CBD)[97]	1993	2018
CDP (Climate Change)[98]	2002	2021
CDP (Forests)[99]	2011	2021
CDP (Water Security)[100]	2009	2021
Darwin Core (metadata standard)[101]	2009	
ENCORE[102]	2018	
Equator Principles[103]	2010	2020
EU Directive Non-Financial Disclosure Regulation[104]	2014	2021
EU Sustainable Finance Disclosure Regulation[105]	2019	
EU Taxonomy[106]	2020	2021
Forum Nachhaltige Geldanlagen – FNG (Label EU/D)[107]	2015	
Global Footprint Network[108]	2003	2017
Global Reporting Initiative – GRI 204, 301, 304, 307, 308	2000	2016
Global Reporting Initiative – GRI 303	2000	2018
Greenfin (Label EU/F)[109]	2019	
ICMA Harmonised Framework for Impact Reporting[110]	2019	2020
ICMA SLB Principles[111]	2020	
IFC Operating Principles for Impact[112]	2019	
IFC Performance Standards[113]	2012	
IFRS/SSB and Framework Development[114]	2021	
International Union for Conservation of Nature (IUCN) Red List[115]	1964	2012
IPBES List of Core Indicators[116]	2012	2020
ISO 26000[117]	2010	2017
ISO TC 322[118]	2018	
ISO TC 323[119]	2018	
ISO TC 331[120]	2020	
Key Biodiversity Areas (KBA)[121]	2017	
Natura 2000 Network[122]	2008	
Natural Capital Protocol 2016[123]	2016	
Natural Capital Protocol Toolkit[124]	2016	
Natural Collections Description (NCD)[125]	2008	
OECD Guidelines for Multinational Enterprises[126]	1976	2011
SHIFT[127]	2017	2021
Sustainability Accounting Standards Board – SASB (Conceptual Framework)[128]	2017	
Sustainability Accounting Standards Board – SASB		

(Continued)

Framework/guideline/standard	Introduction	Latest update
(Materiality Map)[129]	2018	
Task Force on Nature-related Financial Disclosures (TNFD)[130]	2021	
TDWG Access Protocol for Information Retrieval (TAPIR)[131]	2010	
TDWG Vocabulary Maintenance Standard (VMS)[132]	2017	
Towards Sustainability (Label EU / BE)[133]	2019	
Trase Finance[134]	2020	
UNESCO World Heritage Site[135]	1972	2020
United Nations Global Compact (UNGC)[136]	2000	2004
UN SDGs – United Nations Sustainable Development Goals[137]	2015	
UN SDGs Impact Standard Bonds[138]	2021	
Value Balancing Alliance[139]	2021	
World Economic Forum (WEF) Stakeholder Capital Metrics[140]	2020	

Please find below the extended match of the frameworks, principles and guidance documents used in this chapter in the context of the **'Extinction Bond Framework' (EBF)**.

When using the information provided, please note the following:

- In the original frameworks, some of the EBF stages, especially stage one, can be implicitly included. For example, in order to report on metrics, one has to first establish the context and define the metrics.
- Several frameworks, principles and guidance documents cover extinction as a part of biodiversity and biodiversity as part of environmental questions. Therefore, neither extinction nor biodiversity is explicitly mentioned. The general information is still relevant and useful when KPIs and SPTs are defined with respect to the extinction threat.
- The following list does not discriminate between frameworks, principles and guidance. This does not mean that some are not more suitable than others. A detailed analysis is unfortunately beyond the scope of this chapter.
- Several frameworks, principles and guidance documents included are only available as drafts or are work in process. The information is up-to-date as of February 2021.
- For any further questions, please contact the authors Martina Macpherson and Christoph Biehl.

Step 1 – Contextualisation of the Extinction Threat

Comments:

This step defines what you later base your targets, strategy, policy and reporting on. Questions include, but are not limited to: Where do you operate? What is the situation on the ground? Supply chain mapping is essential in this step.

TABLE A.4 An overview of frameworks, principles or guidance that can be useful to address Step 1

Frameworks, principles, or guidance	Details
Aichi Biodiversity Targets[141]	Strategic Goal A and targets
Audubon Core[142]	Technical standard covering inter alia vocabulary around collections on biodiversity.
BSI 42020[143]	Pre-application
CBD BIP[144]	Article 2
CBD BIP[145]	Biodiversity Indicator Partnership
CDP[146]	CDP Forests: F0.6
CDP[149]	CDP Forests: F9.3
CDP[149]	CDP Forests: F10.1
CDP[149]	CDP Forests: F12
CDP[149]	CDP Forests: F14.1a
CDP[149]	CDP Forests: F14
CDP[149]	CDP Forests: F14.6
Darwin Core[147]	The standard includes a glossary to organise and standardise sharing of biodiversity and extinction information.
ENCORE[148]	NCFA ENCORE tool
Equator Principles[149]	Principle 4: Environmental and Social Management System and Equator Principles Action Plan
EU NFRD[150]	3.1 Disclosure on Business Model
EU NFRD[151]	4.6 (a) Thematic aspects: KPIs
EU NFRD[153]	4.6. (e) Thematic aspects: Supply Chain
EU SFDR[152]	JC 2021 03: Article 32 j
EU SFDR[154]	JC 2021 03: Article 45 j
EU SFDR[154]	JC 2021 03: Article 55
FNG[153]	Minimum criteria
Global Footprint Network[154]	Global Footprint Network
Greenfin Label[155]	Criterion 2.1
GRI[156]	GRI 204: Procurement Practices
GRI[157]	GRI 301: Materials
GRI[158]	GRI 303: Water and Effluents
IPBES[159]	Mapping of indicators and frameworks
ICMA SLB Principles[160]	Calibration of SPTs
ICMA SLB Principles[161]	Bond characteristics
IFC Operating Principles for Impact[161]	Principle 1: Define strategic impact objective(s), consistent with the investment strategy.
IFC Operating Principles for Impact[162]	Principle 4: Assess the expected impact of each investment, based on a systematic approach.
IFC Performance Standards[162]	1: Risk Management
IFC Performance Standards[163]	3: Resource Efficiency and Pollution Prevention
IFC Performance Standards[163]	6.4–6.8: E&S risks and impacts identification process
IFC Performance Standards[163]	6.16: Critical Habitat
IFC Performance Standards[163]	6.20: Legally Protected and Internationally Recognised Areas

(Continued)

Frameworks, principles, or guidance	*Details*
ISO 26000[163]	Clause 3
ISO 26000[164]	Clause 4
IUCN[164]	A global standard for the identification of Key Biodiversity Areas
IUCN[165]	A global standard for the identification of Key Biodiversity Areas
KBA Key Biodiversity Area[165]	KBA Key Biodiversity Area
Natura 2000 Network[166]	Natura 2000 Network
Natural Capital Protocol 2016[167]	Frame Stage: Step 1
Natural Capital Protocol 2016[168]	Scope Stage: Step 2
Natural Capital Protocol 2016[168]	Annex A
Natural Collections Description[168]	Data standard to describe a collection of biodiversity or extinction information.
SASB[169]	(xx-xx-)160a.2
TDWG TAPIR[170]	Computer protocol to enable search of biodiversity data.
TNFD[171]	TNFD
Trase Finance[172]	Trase Finance
UN Global Compact[173]	7: Businesses should support a precautionary approach to environmental challenges.
UN SDGs[174]	14.a
UN SDGs[177]	14.4 Overfishing (target)
UN SDGs[177]	14.5 Habitat (target)
UN SDGs[177]	SDG 15 targets
UNESCO World Heritage Site[175]	Natural site
UNESCO World Heritage Site[178]	Mixed site
UNESCO World Heritage Site[178]	Natural site in danger
UNESCO World Heritage Site[178]	Mixed site in danger
Value Balancing Alliance[176]	Scoping 2.5
Value Balancing Alliance[177]	Land use 2.5
Vocabulary Maintenance Standard[178]	Vocabulary standard reflecting the flexibility of biodiversity and extinction information.
WEF Stakeholder Capital Metrics[179]	Pillar Planet: 5.2

Step 2 – Materiality Assessment

Comments:

The materiality assessment should include four dimensions of materiality: positive effect on the firm, negative effect on the firm, positive effect on the species and negative effect on the species.

TABLE A.5 An overview of frameworks, principles or guidance that can be useful to address Step 2

Frameworks, principles, or guidance	Details
Aichi Biodiversity Targets[180]	Strategic Goal B and targets
Aichi Biodiversity Targets[183]	Strategic Goal C and targets
Aichi Biodiversity Targets[183]	Strategic Goal D and targets
BSI 42020[181]	Pre-application
BSI 42020[184]	Validation and registration
BSI 42020[184]	Decision-making
CBD BIP[182]	Biodiversity Indicator Partnership
CDP[183]	CDP Climate Change: Sector Introduction
CDP[184]	CDP Forests: Sector Introduction
CDP[187]	CDP Forests: F11.6a
CDP[187]	CDP Forests: F9.5
CDP[187]	CDP Forests: F9.5a
CDP[187]	CDP Forests: F10.2
CDP[187]	CDP Forests: F10.2a/b
CDP[187]	CDP Forests: F11.2 and 11.3
CDP[187]	CDP Forests: F13
CDP[187]	CDP Forests: F14.1a
Equator Principles[185]	Principle 1: Review and Categorisation
Equator Principles[188]	Principle 2: Environmental and Social Assessment
Equator Principles[188]	Principle 3: Applicable Environmental and Social Standards
Equator Principles[188]	Principle 4: Environmental and Social Management System and Equator Principles Action Plan
EU NFRD[186]	2.2 Materiality
EU NFRD[189]	2.3 Climate-related risks, dependencies and opportunities
EU NFRD[189]	2.3 (2) Physical risks
EU NFRD[189]	4.6 (a) Thematic aspects: KPIs
EU NFRD[189]	4.6. (e) Thematic aspects: Supply Chain
EU SFDR[187]	Adverse sustainability impact
EU SFDR[190]	JC 2021 03: Article 13 3d
EU SFDR[190]	JC 2021 03: Article 16 1b
EU SFDR[190]	JC 2021 03: Article 3d
EU SFDR[190]	JC 2021 03: Article 23 1c
EU SFDR[190]	JC 2021 03: Article 24
EU SFDR[190]	JC 2021 03: Article 30 b
EU SFDR[190]	JC 2021 03: Article 30 c

(Continued)

Frameworks, principles, or guidance	*Details*
EU SFDR[190]	JC 2021 03: Article 32 b
EU SFDR[190]	JC 2021 03: Article 32 g
EU SFDR[190]	JC 2021 03: Article 32 h
EU SFDR[190]	JC 2021 03: Article 32 i
EU SFDR[190]	JC 2021 03: Article 34 2
EU SFDR[190]	JC 2021 03: Article 39
EU SFDR[190]	JC 2021 03: Article 40
EU SFDR[190]	JC 2021 03: Article 41
EU SFDR[190]	JC 2021 03: Article 45 b
EU SFDR[190]	JC 2021 03: Article 45 g
EU SFDR[190]	JC 2021 03: Article 45 h
EU SFDR[190]	JC 2021 03: Article 45 i
EU SFDR[190]	JC 2021 03: Article 47
EU SFDR[190]	JC 2021 03: Article 52
EU SFDR[190]	JC 2021 03: Article 53
EU SFDR[190]	JC 2021 03: Article 54
EU SFDR[190]	Principle Adverse Impact 14
EU Taxonomy[188]	Climate change mitigation
EU Taxonomy[191]	Climate change adaptation
EU Taxonomy[191]	The sustainable use and protection of water and marine resources
EU Taxonomy[191]	Pollution prevention and control
EU Taxonomy[191]	The protection and restoration of biodiversity and ecosystems
Greenfin Label[189]	Criterion 1.2
Greenfin Label[192]	Criterion 1.3
Greenfin Label[192]	Criterion 3.1
Greenfin Label[192]	Criterion 3.2
GRI[190]	GRI 304: Biodiversity
GRI[191]	GRI 308: Supplier Environmental Assessment
Harmonised Framework for Impact Reporting[192]	#1 Preserving terrestrial natural habitats
Harmonised Framework for Impact Reporting[195]	#2 Preserving marine natural habitats
Harmonised Framework for Impact Reporting[195]	#2 Preserving marine natural habitats
IPBES[193]	Mapping of indicators and frameworks
ICMA SLB Principles[194]	Selection of KPIs
ICMA SLB Principles[197]	Calibration of SPTs
IFC Operating Principles for Impact[195]	Principle 1: Define strategic impact objective(s), consistent with the investment strategy.
IFC Operating Principles for Impact[198]	Principle 2: Manage strategic impact on a portfolio basis.
IFC Operating Principles for Impact[198]	Principle 4: Assess the expected impact of each investment, based on a systematic approach.
IFC Operating Principles for Impact[198]	Principle 5: Assess, address, monitor and manage potential negative impacts of each investment.

Frameworks, principles, or guidance	*Details*
IFC Performance Standards[196]	6.9 and 6.10: Protection and Conservation of Biodiversity
IFC Performance Standards[199]	6.17-6.19: Critical Habitat
IFC Performance Standards[199]	6.20: Legally Protected and Internationally Recognised Areas
IFRS Development[197]	Part 5: Scope 44–51
ISO 26000[198]	6.5.6: Protection of the environment, biodiversity and restoration of natural habitats
ISO TC 322[199]	ISO regarding sustainable finance, focus on impact and economic activity.
ISO TC 323[200]	ISO covering circular economy, which can be one tool to remove stress from habitats.
ISO TC 331[201]	ISO in preparation covering biodiversity. It sets out to standardise inter alia definitions, impact assessment and reporting.
ISO TC 331[204]	The standard is supposed to link directly to the SDGs.
IUCN[202]	A global standard for the identification of Key Biodiversity Areas
IUCN[205]	IUCN RED LIST CATEGORIES AND CRITERIA
KBA Key Biodiversity Area[203]	KBA Key Biodiversity Area
Natura 2000 Network[204]	Natura 2000 Network
Natural Capital Protocol 2016[205]	Scope Stage: Step 3
Natural Capital Protocol 2016[208]	Scope Stage: Step 4
OECD Guidelines[206]	IV. Environment 6c
OECD Guidelines[209]	IV. Environment 6d
SASB[207]	(xx-xx-)160a.1
SASB[210]	(xx-xx-)160a.2
SASB[210]	(xx-xx-)160a.3
SHIFT[208]	Shift Natural Capital Toolkit
TNFD[209]	TNFD
UN Global Compact[210]	7: Businesses should support a precautionary approach to environmental challenges.
UN Global Compact[211]	8: Businesses should undertake initiatives to promote greater environmental responsibility.
UN SDG Impact Standard Bonds[212]	Standard 1: Strategy
UN SDG Impact Standard Bonds[215]	Standard 2: Management Approach
UN SDG Impact Standard Bonds[215]	Standard 1.1
UN SDG Impact Standard Bonds[215]	Standard 1.2

(*Continued*)

Frameworks, principles, or guidance	*Details*
UN SDG Impact Standard Bonds[215]	Standard 2.1
UN SDG Impact Standard Bonds[215]	Standard 2.4
UN SDGs[213]	14.4.1 Indicator
UN SDGs[216]	14.5.5 Indicator
UN SDGs[216]	SDG 15 indicators
WEF Stakeholder Capital Metrics[214]	Dynamic Materiality 2.1

Step 3 – Reporting and Dialogue

<u>Comments:</u>

The reporting and dialogue should be based on the materiality assessment and be part of a multi-stakeholder dialogue.

TABLE A.6 An overview of frameworks, principles or guidance that can be useful to address Step 3

Frameworks, principles or guidance	*Details*
Audubon Core[215]	Technical standard covering inter alia vocabulary around collections on biodiversity. Improves clarity in reporting.
BSI 42020[216]	Validation and registration
BSI 42020[219]	Decision-making
CBD BIP[217]	Biodiversity Indicator Partnership
CDP[218]	CDP Climate Change
CDP[221]	CDP Climate Change: C4.4
CDP[221]	CDP Climate Change: C12.2a
CDP[219]	CDP Forests: F9.3a
CDP[222]	CDP Forests: F9.6
CDP[222]	CDP Forests: F10.1a
CDP[222]	CDP Forests: F10.2c
CDP[222]	CDP Forests: F11.1a
CDP[222]	CDP Forests: F15
CDP[222]	CDP Forests: F16
Darwin Core[220]	The standard includes a glossary to organise and standardise sharing of biodiversity and extinction information. Improves clarity in reporting.
Equator Principles[221]	Principles 5: Stakeholder Engagement
Equator Principles[224]	Principle 9: Independent Monitoring and Reporting
EU NFRD[222]	3.5 Key Performance Indicators
EU NFRD[225]	4.6 Thematic aspects: Environmental Matters
EU SFDR[223]	Sustainability risk policy
EU SFDR[226]	JC 2021 03: Article 13 3a
EU SFDR[226]	JC 2021 03: Article 16 1b

Frameworks, principles or guidance	Details
EU SFDR [226]	JC 2021 03: Article 19 a
EU SFDR [226]	JC 2021 03: Article 20 3a
EU SFDR [226]	JC 2021 03: Article 22a
EU SFDR [226]	JC 2021 03: Article 23 1c
EU SFDR [226]	JC 2021 03: Article 23 3
EU SFDR [226]	JC 2021 03: Article 30 a
EU SFDR [226]	JC 2021 03: Article 32 c
EU SFDR [226]	JC 2021 03: Article 32 h
EU SFDR [226]	JC 2021 03: Article 32 i
EU SFDR [226]	JC 2021 03: Article 32 k
EU SFDR [226]	JC 2021 03: Article 35
EU SFDR [226]	JC 2021 03: Article 40
EU SFDR [226]	JC 2021 03: Article 41
EU SFDR [226]	JC 2021 03: Article 43
EU SFDR [226]	JC 2021 03: Article 45 c
EU SFDR [226]	JC 2021 03: Article 45 h
EU SFDR [226]	JC 2021 03: Article 45 i
EU SFDR [226]	JC 2021 03: Article 45 k
EU SFDR [226]	JC 2021 03: Article 48
EU SFDR [226]	JC 2021 03: Article 53
EU SFDR [226]	JC 2021 03: Article 54
EU SFDR [226]	JC 2021 03: Article 56
EU SFDR [226]	JC 2021 03: Article 58a
EU SFDR [226]	JC 2021 03: Article 58d
EU SFDR [226]	JC 2021 03: Article 59
EU SFDR [226]	JC 2021 03: Article 62
EU SFDR [226]	JC 2021 03: Article 64a
EU SFDR [226]	JC 2021 03: Article 64d
EU SFDR [226]	JC 2021 03: Article 65
EU SFDR [226]	JC 2021 03: Article 68
EU Taxonomy[224]	Climate change mitigation
EU Taxonomy[227]	Climate change adaptation
EU Taxonomy[227]	The sustainable use and protection of water and marine resources
EU Taxonomy[227]	Pollution prevention and control
EU Taxonomy[227]	The protection and restoration of biodiversity and ecosystems
Greenfin Label[225]	Criterion 1.1
Greenfin Label[228]	Criterion 3.1
Greenfin Label[228]	Criterion 3.2
GRI[226]	GRI 304: Biodiversity
GRI[227]	GRI 303: Water and Effluents
GRI[228]	GRI 307: Environmental Compliance
Harmonised Framework for Impact Reporting[229]	#1 Preserving terrestrial natural habitats
ICMA SLB Principles[230]	Reporting

(Continued)

Frameworks, principles or guidance	*Details*
IFC Operating Principles for Impact[231]	Principle 3: Establish the Manager's contribution to the achievement of impact.
IFC Operating Principles for Impact[234]	Principle 9: Publicly disclose alignment with the Principles and provide regular independent verification13 of the alignment.
IFC Performance Standards[232]	6.20: Legally Protected and Internationally Recognised Areas
ISO 26000[233]	Clause 5
ISO 26000[236]	6.5.6: Protection of the environment, biodiversity and restoration of natural habitats
ISO TC 322[234]	'Standardised metrics to allow the measurement and improved transparency of sustainable finance flows and the ESG performance of sustainable finance activities, financial institutions and markets'.
IUCN[235]	A global standard for the identification of Key Biodiversity Areas
IUCN[238]	IUCN RED LIST CATEGORIES AND CRITERIA
KBA Key Biodiversity Area[236]	KBA Key Biodiversity Area
Natura 2000 Network[237]	Natura 2000 Network
Natural Collections Description[238]	Data standard to describe a collection of biodiversity or extinction information.
SASB[239]	(xx-xx-)160a.3
SASB[242]	(xx-xx-)160a.2
TDWG TAPIR[240]	'TAPIR is a computer protocol designed for discovery, search and retrieval of distributed data over the Internet'.
TNFD[241]	TNFD
Towards Sustainability[242]	3.1 Implementing Guidelines
UN Global Compact[243]	7: Businesses should support a precautionary approach to environmental challenges.
UN Global Compact[244]	8: Businesses should undertake initiatives to promote greater environmental responsibility.
UN Global Compact[245]	9: Businesses should encourage the development and diffusion of environmentally friendly technologies
UN SDG Impact Standard Bonds[246]	Standard 3: Transparency
UN SDG Impact Standard Bonds[249]	Standard 2.2
UN SDG Impact Standard Bonds[249]	Standard 2.3
UN SDG Impact Standard Bonds[249]	Standard 3
Vocabulary Maintenance Standard[247]	Vocabulary standard reflecting the flexibility of biodiversity and extinction information. Improves clarity in reporting and communication between stakeholders.
WEF Stakeholder Capital Metrics[248]	Planet: Nature Loss

Step 4 – Impact Assessment

Comments:

The impact assessment aims to capture the status quo: What have you achieved between bond issuance and reporting date? Here, it is essential to include parties identified in **Step 3** in order to arrive at a meaningful impact assessment. The framework of comparison is set up by the strategy, policy, SPTs and KPIs. Third-party data providers can be used to support this process.

TABLE A.7 An overview offrameworks, principles or guidance that can be useful to address Step 4

Frameworks, principles or guidance	Details
Aichi Biodiversity Targets[249]	Strategic Call E and indicators
Audubon Core[250]	Technical standard covering inter alia vocabulary around collections on biodiversity. Improves clarity in reporting.
BSI 42020[251]	Determination
BSI 42020[254]	Implementation/construction
CBD BIP[252]	Biodiversity Indicator Partnership
CDP[253]	CDP Climate Change: C13.1a
CDP [256]	CDP Climate Change: C13.2a
CDP[254]	CDP Forests: Sector Introduction
CDP[257]	CDP Forests: F0.7
CDP[257]	CDP Forests: F11.6a
CDP[257]	CDP Forests: F9.5a
CDP[257]	CDP Forests: F9.6a
CDP[257]	CDP Forests: F10.3
CDP[257]	CDP Forests: F16
Darwin Core[255]	The standard includes a glossary to organise and standardise sharing of biodiversity and extinction information. Improves clarity in reporting.
Equator Principles[256]	Principle 4: Environmental and Social Management System and Equator Principles Action Plan
Equator Principles[259]	Principle 7: Independent Review
EU SFDR[257]	JC 2021 03: Article 32 f
EU SFDR[260]	JC 2021 03: Article 32 k
EU SFDR[260]	JC 2021 03: Article 38
EU SFDR[260]	JC 2021 03: Article 43
EU SFDR[260]	JC 2021 03: Article 45 f
EU SFDR[260]	JC 2021 03: Article 45 k
EU SFDR[260]	JC 2021 03: Article 51
EU SFDR[260]	JC 2021 03: Article 56
EU SFDR[260]	JC 2021 03: Article 58a
EU SFDR[260]	JC 2021 03: Article 58d
EU SFDR[260]	JC 2021 03: Article 59
EU SFDR[260]	JC 2021 03: Article 62
EU SFDR[260]	JC 2021 03: Article 64a

(Continued)

Frameworks, principles or guidance	*Details*
EU SFDR[260]	JC 2021 03: Article 64d
EU SFDR[260]	JC 2021 03: Article 65
EU SFDR[260]	JC 2021 03: Article 68
GRI[258]	GRI 304: Biodiversity
GRI[259]	GRI 307: Environmental Compliance
ICMA SLB Principles[260]	Verification
IFC Operating Principles for Impact[261]	Principle 5: Assess, address, monitor and manage potential negative impacts of each investment.
IFC Operating Principles for Impact[264]	Principle 6: Monitor the progress of each investment in achieving impact against expectations and respond appropriately.
IFC Performance Standards[262]	6.24: Management of Ecosystem Services
ISO TC 322[263]	'In addition, the standards can help identify gaps, normalise metrics and improve comparability, focussing on material aspects of sector relevant performance'.
Natural Capital Protocol 2016[264]	Measure and Value Stage: Steps 5–7
Natural Capital Protocol 2016[267]	Annex B
Natural Collections Description[265]	Data standard to describe a collection of biodiversity or extinction information.
TDWG TAPIR[266]	Computer protocol to enable search of biodiversity data.
UN Global Compact[267]	8: Businesses should undertake initiatives to promote greater environmental responsibility.
UN SDG Impact Standard Bonds[268]	Standard 1.3
UN SDG Impact Standard Bonds[271]	Standard 2.5
Value Balancing Alliance[269]	Impact pathway 2.5.2
Value Balancing Alliance[272]	Quantification and monetary valuation
Vocabulary Maintenance Standard[270]	This vocabulary standard simplifies communication between different stakeholders in the biodiversity space.
WEF Stakeholder Capital Metrics[271]	Pillar Planet: 5.2

Step 5 – Refine and Implement

Comments:

This step is a key aspect of Atkins and Maroun's extinction accounting framework as it encompasses the emancipatory aspect of the framework. Accountability is achieved through implementing improvements based on the **Step 4** impact assessment. This can form part of coordinated active ownership activities, e.g. through an engagement plan between investors and issuers. The outcome is a continuously improving positive impact on species threatened by extinction.

TABLE A.8 An overview of frameworks, principles or guidance that can be useful to address Step 5

Frameworks, principles or guidance	Details
BSI 42020[272]	Implementation/construction
CDP[273]	CDP Forests: F9.5a
Equator Principles[274]	Principle 4: Environmental and Social Management System and Equator Principles Action Plan
Equator Principles[277]	Principle 7: Independent Review
EU SFDR[275]	JC 2021 03: Article 32 1
EU SFDR[278]	JC 2021 03: Article 45 1
EU SFDR[278]	JC 2021 03: Article 57
EU SFDR[278]	JC 2021 03: Article 58a
EU SFDR[278]	JC 2021 03: Article 58d
EU SFDR[278]	JC 2021 03: Article 59
EU SFDR[278]	JC 2021 03: Article 62
EU SFDR[278]	JC 2021 03: Article 64a
EU SFDR[278]	JC 2021 03: Article 64d
EU SFDR[278]	JC 2021 03: Article 65
EU SFDR[278]	JC 2021 03: Article 68
ICMA SLB Principles[276]	Verification
IFC Operating Principles for Impact[277]	Principle 5: Assess, address, monitor and manage potential negative impacts of each investment.
IFC Operating Principles for Impact[280]	Principle 6: Monitor the progress of each investment in achieving impact against expectations and respond appropriately.
IFC Operating Principles for Impact[280]	Principle 8: Review, document and improve decisions and processes based on the achievement of impact and lessons learned.
Natural Capital Protocol 2016[278]	Apply Stage: Step 8
Natural Capital Protocol 2016[281]	Apply Stage: Step 9
UN SDG Impact Standard Bonds[279]	Standard 4: Governance
UN SDG Impact Standard Bonds[282]	Standard 1.3
UN SDG Impact Standard Bonds[282]	Standard 2.5
UN SDG Impact Standard Bonds[282]	Standard 4

Notes

1 Jill Atkins and Warren Maroun, "The Naturalist's Journals of Gilbert White: Exploring the Roots of Accounting for Biodiversity and Extinction Accounting," Accounting, Auditing and Accountability Journal 33, no. 8 (2020): 1835–1870, https://doi.org/10.1108/AAAJ-03-2016-2450; Jill Atkins and Warren Maroun, "Integrated Extinction Accounting and Accountability: Building an Ark," Accounting, Auditing

and Accountability Journal 31, no. 3 (2018): 750–786, https://doi.org/10.1108/AAAJ-06-2017-2957; Mervyn King and Jill Atkins, The Chief Value Officer: Accountants Can Save the Planet (Greenleaf Publishing, 2016); Jill Atkins and Barry Atkins, The Business of Bees: An Integrated Approach to Bee Decline and Corporate Responsibility, ed. Jill F. Atkins and Barry Atkins (Sheffield: Routeledge, 2016), https://doi.org/10.4324/9781351283922.

2 John W. Bennett, The Ecological Transition, The Ecological Transition, 1976, https://doi.org/10.1016/c2013-0-05659-9.

3 ICMA, "The Role of the Sustainable Bond Markets in Promoting Biodiversity," 2020, https://icma.podbean.com/e/the-role-of-the-sustainable-bond-markets-in-promoting-biodiversity/.

4 Hermes EOS, "Public Engagement Report," 2016.

5 Atkins and Atkins, The Business of Bees: An Integrated Approach to Bee Decline and Corporate Responsibility, 2016.

6 Christoph F. Biehl and Martina N. Macpherson, "Bees and Accountability in Germany: A Multi-Stakeholder Approach," in The Business of Bees, ed. Jill F Atkins and Barry Atkins (Sheffield: Routledge, 2016).

7 Investec Bank, "Natural Capital, Species Extinction & Sustainable Financial Markets - Capitals Coalition," 2019, https://capitalscoalition.org/events/natural-capital-species-extinction-sustainable-financial-markets/.

8 BrightTALK, "Natural Capital, Species Extinction & Sustainable Finance - The Impact of SDGs," ESG Channel, 2019, https://www.brighttalk.com/webinar/preserving-natural-capital-and-species-sdg-15/.

9 Jill F. Atkins and Martina Macpherson, "Developing a Species Protection Action Plan – An Integrated Approach for Taxonomies, Reporting and Engagement for the Financial Services Sector," SSRN Electronic Journal, June 26, 2019, https://doi.org/10.2139/ssrn.3398308.

10 Sir Partha Dasgupta, "The Economics of Biodiversity: The Dasgupta Review" (HM Treasury, 2021), https://www.gov.uk/government/publications/final-report-the-economics-of-biodiversity-the-dasgupta-review.

11 For more information, see inter alia Convention on Biological Diversity, COP15, 17-30 May 2021, Link: https://www.cbd.int/meetings/COP-15.

12 Cambridge Institute for Sustainability Leadership, "Handbook for Nature-Related Financial Risks: Key Concepts and a Framework for Identification," 2021, https://www.cisl.cam.ac.uk/resources/sustainable-finance-publications/handbook-nature-related-financial-risks.

13 Environmental Finance, "Investing in Nature: Private Finance for Nature-Based Resilience," 2019, https://www.environmental-finance.com/content/research/-investing-in-nature-private-finance-for-nature-based-resilience.html.

14 IPBES, "Global Assessment Report on Biodiversity and Ecosystem Services of the Intergovernmental Science-Policy Platform on Biodiversity and Ecosystem Services" (Bonn, Germany, 2019), https://www.ipbes.net/global-assessment.

15 See also for further references: Unexpectedly large impact of forest management and grazing on global vegetation biomass, in National Library of Medicine (2018), Link: https://pubmed.ncbi.nlm.nih.gov/29258288/; National Library of Medicine, Pervasive human-driven decline of life on Earth points to the need for transformative change (2019), Link: https://pubmed.ncbi.nlm.nih.gov/31831642/.

16 Corey J. A. Bradshaw et al., "Underestimating the Challenges of Avoiding a Ghastly Future," Frontiers in Conservation Science 1 (January 13, 2021): 615419, https://doi.org/10.3389/fcosc.2020.615419.

17 World Economic Forum, "The Global Risks Report" 15 (2020): 1–114, http://wef.ch/risks2019.

18 IPBES, "Global Assessment Report on Biodiversity and Ecosystem Services of the Intergovernmental Science-Policy Platform on Biodiversity and Ecosystem Services."

19 Helan Mountford et al., "Unlocking the Inclusive Growth Story of the 21st Century," The New Climate Economy, 2018.
20 On Thursday, June 2020, the European Parliament formally adopted the EU Taxonomy Regulation, and it has now been published in the Official Journal of the European Union. The Taxonomy creates a classification system for sustainable economic activities that will help guide investments towards more sustainable technologies and business. European Commission, "EU Taxonomy for Sustainable Activities," accessed March 4, 2021, https://ec.europa.eu/info/business-economy-euro/banking-and-finance/sustainable-finance/eu-taxonomy-sustainable-activities_en.
21 European Commission, "Guidelines on Non-Financial Reporting," Official Journal of the European Union 215, no. 1 (2019): 1–20.
22 European Commission, "Guidelines on Non-Financial Reporting: Supplement on Reporting Climate-Related Information," Official Journal of the European Union (2019): 30.
23 European Parliament and the Council, "Regulation (EU) 2020/852 of the European Parliament and of the Council of 18 June 2020 on the Establishment of a Framework to Facilitate Sustainable Investment, and Amending Regulation (EU) 2019/2088," Official Journal of the European Union, no. L198 (2020): 1–31.
24 European Parliament and the Council, "DIRECTIVE 2014/95/EU OF THE EUROPEAN PARLIAMENT AND OF THE COUNCIL of 22 October 2014 Amending Directive 2013/34/EU as Regards Disclosure of Non-Financial and Diversity Information by Certain Large Undertakings and Groups," Official Journal of the European Union L330 (2014). – EU NFRD amends the accounting directive 2013/34/EU, companies are required to include non-financial statements in their annual reports from 2018 onwards. EU NFRD is currently under review, the 2nd edition in process following a public consultation process in 2020.
25 European Parliament and the Council, "Regulation (2019/2088) on Sustainability-Related Disclosures in the Financial Services Sector," Official Journal of the European Union L317 (2019): 1–16.
26 European Commission, "The EU Business @ Biodiversity Platform," 2020, https://ec.europa.eu/environment/biodiversity/business/index_en.htm.
27 UN Department of Economic and Social Affairs, "Transforming Our World: The 2030 Agenda for Sustainable Development," accessed March 4, 2021, https://sdgs.un.org/2030agenda.
28 Executive Secretary of the Convention on Biological Diversity, "Sustainable Development: Convention on Biological Diversity Report of the Executive Secretary of the Convention on Biological Diversity," UN Biodiversity Conference 21, no. 1 (2020): 1–9.
29 The Capitals Coalition, "The Capitals Coalition," 2021, https://capitalscoalition.org/.
30 "TNFD - Taskforce on Nature-Related Financial Disclosures," Timeline, accessed March 4, 2021, https://tnfd.info/.
31 "Call to Action — Business For Nature," accessed March 4, 2021, https://www.businessfornature.org/call-to-action.
32 "Task Force on Climate-Related Financial Disclosures," accessed December 4, 2020, https://www.fsb-tcfd.org/.
33 Cambridge Institute for Sustainability Leadership, "Handbook for Nature-Related Financial Risks: Key Concepts and a Framework for Identification," 2021.
34 World Conservation Monitoring Centre, "Global Biodiversity: Status of the Earth's Living Resources," Biological Conservation, 1992, https://doi.org/10.1016/0006-3207(93)90147-s.
35 OECD, "Biodiversity: Finance and the Economic and Business Case for Action, Report Prepared for the G7 Environment Ministers' Meeting, 5–6 May 2019," 2019, https://doi.org/10.1787/a3147942-en.

36 Dutch Central Bank, "Indebted to Nature," no. June (2020).
37 Network for Greening the Financial System, "Guide for Supervisors: Integrating Climate-Related and Environmental Risks into Prudential Supervision," no. May (2020): 1–62, https://www.ngfs.net/sites/default/files/medias/documents/ngfs_guide_for_supervisors.pdf.
38 "Sustainable Finance Outlook: Moody's Sees Sustainable Bond Issuance Soaring to $650B in 2021 - ESG Today," accessed March 4, 2021, https://www.esgtoday.com/sustainable-finance-outlook-moodys-sees-sustainable-bond-issuance-soaring-to-650b-in-2021/?fbclid=IwAR0HWFAxswGiPDhylKoPpXUA3NAwiU54H_tADS-9iX5BVgZEch92DCgHqjM.
39 ICMA, "Green, Social and Sustainability Bonds," accessed March 4, 2021, https://www.icmagroup.org/sustainable-finance/#:~:text=Green%2C Social and Sustainability Bonds are any type of bond,environmental and%2For social projects.&text=As the principles are designed,banks are invited to participate.
40 International Capital Markets Association, "Sustainability-Linked Bond Principles," no. June (2020), https://www.icmagroup.org/assets/documents/Regulatory/Green-Bonds/June-2020/Sustainability-Linked-Bond-PrinciplesJune-2020-100620.pdf.
41 Loan Market Association, "Sustainability Linked Loan Principles," Loan Market Association, 2019, https://www.lma.eu.com/application/files/8015/5307/4231/LMA_Sustainability_Linked_Loan_Principles.pdf.
42 Loan Market Association.
43 Moody's, "Sustainable Bond Issuance to Hit a Record $650 Billion in 2021," 2021, https://www.moodys.com/research/Moodys-Sustainable-bond-issuance-to-hit-a-record-650-billion--PBC_1263479?cid=YJZ7YNGSROZ5414.
44 European Central Bank, "ECB to Accept Sustainability-Linked Bonds as Collateral," 2020, https://www.ecb.europa.eu/press/pr/date/2020/html/ecb.pr200922~482e4a5a90.en.html.
45 Moody's, "Sustainable Bond Issuance to Hit a Record $650 Billion in 2021."
46 European Commission, "The Just Transition Mechanism: Making Sure No One Is Left Behind," accessed March 4, 2021, https://ec.europa.eu/info/strategy/priorities-2019-2024/european-green-deal/actions-being-taken-eu/just-transition-mechanism_en.
Def.: The Just Transition Mechanism (JTM) is a key tool to ensure that the transition towards a climate-neutral economy happens in a fair way, leaving no one behind. It provides targeted support to help mobilise at least €150 billion over the period 2021–2027 in the most affected regions, to alleviate the socio-economic impact of the transition.
47 Loan Market Association, "Sustainability Linked Loan Principles."
48 ICMA, "Green Bond Principles - Voluntary Process Guidelines for Issuing Green Bonds," 2018.
49 ICMA, "Social Bond Principles," The Social Bond Principles, 2020.
50 ICMA, "Sustainability Bond Guidelines," 2018.
51 Climate Bonds Initiative, "Certification under the Climate Bonds Standard," accessed March 4, 2021, https://www.climatebonds.net/certification.
52 For an overview on post-issuance verification of labelled Green Bonds, see, e.g., Climate Bonds Initiative, "Post-Issuance Reporting in the Green Bond Market," 2019.
53 Nordic Public Issuers Sector, "Position Paper on Green Bonds Impact Reporting," 2020.
54 The debate made it into the consultations and guidance documents related to the new 'European Green Bond Standard' (EU GBS).
55 Climate Bonds Initiative, "Labelled Green Bonds Data: Latest 3 Months," accessed March 4, 2021, https://www.climatebonds.net/cbi/pub/data/bonds.

56 GFC, "China Green Bond Endorsed Project Catalogue (2015 Edition)," October 22, 2015, http://www.greenfinance.org.cn/displaynews.php?cid=79&id=468.

57 EU TEG on Sustainable Finance, "USABILITY GUIDE Context and Background Information," no. March (2020).

58 Green Finance Platform, "People's Bank of China Green Bond Endorsed Project Catalogue (2020 Edition)," 2020, https://www.greenfinanceplatform.org/financial-measures-database/peoples-bank-china-green-bond-endorsed-project-catalogue-2020-edition.

59 ICMA, "Sustainability-Linked Bond Principles," 2020.

60 Loan Market Association, "Green Loan Principles," 2018, https://www.lma.eu.com/application/files/9115/4452/5458/741_LM_Green_Loan_Principles_Booklet_V8.pdf.

61 ICMA, "Climate Transition Finance Handbook Guidance for Issuers," 2020.

62 EU TEG on Sustainable Finance, "USABILITY GUIDE Context and Background Information."

63 Enel Group, "Sustainability-Linked Bonds," accessed March 4, 2021, https://www.enel.com/investors/investing/sustainable-finance/sustainable-finance/sustainability-linked-bonds.
Details: On 10 October 2019, Enel, the National Electrical Energy Agency in Italy, launched a multi-tranche SLB for institutional investors totalling EUR 2.5 billion. The bond issue was structured in three tranches. The goal setting of each tranche was linked to one of the United Nations Sustainable Development Goals (U.N. SDGs). It was scrutinized by investors. Reuters, "Enel Ditches Green Bonds for Controversial New Format | Reuters," October 4, 2019, https://www.reuters.com/article/enel-ditches-green-bonds-for-controversi-idUSL5N26O0403.

64 SymInvest, "New 'Rhino Bonds' to Allow Investors to Help with Wildlife Conservation | SymInvest - Microfinance Investment Intelligence," July 18, 2019, https://www.syminvest.com/news/new-rhino-bonds-to-allow-investors-to-help-with-wildlife-conservation/2019/7/18/8372.

65 Finance for the Future, "Rabobank: Building Biodiversity with Impact Loans," accessed March 4, 2021, www.financeforthefuture.org.

66 Natixis, "Agrial and Natixis Sign the First Sustainability-Linked Credit Facility for a French Agricultural Cooperative," 2019, https://pressroom-en.natixis.com/news/-agrial-and-natixis-sign-the-first-sustainability-linked-credit-facility-for-a-french-agricultural-cooperative-7615-8e037.html.

67 BNP Paribas, "UPM Links EUR 750m Loan to Forest Biodiversity and CO2 Targets," April 22, 2020, https://cib.bnpparibas.com/sustain/upm-links-eur-750m-loan-to-forest-biodiversity-and-co2-targets_a-3-3484.html.

68 Atkins and Maroun, "The Naturalist's Journals of Gilbert White: Exploring the Roots of Accounting for Biodiversity and Extinction Accounting"; Atkins and Maroun, "Integrated Extinction Accounting and Accountability: Building an Ark."

69 Atkins and Maroun, "Integrated Extinction Accounting and Accountability: Building an Ark."

70 Atkins and Maroun, "The Naturalist's Journals of Gilbert White: Exploring the Roots of Accounting for Biodiversity and Extinction Accounting."

71 The aim of the 'extinction bond framework' is not to create a new framework from scratch, but to combine the existing extinction accounting framework, the ICMA sustainability-linked bond framework and existing standards and frameworks. This approach allows for a staggered transition into the extinction bond framework, based on good work that already exists within companies.
Atkins and Maroun, "The Naturalist's Journals of Gilbert White: Exploring the Roots of Accounting for Biodiversity and Extinction Accounting"; Atkins and Maroun, "Integrated Extinction Accounting and Accountability: Building an Ark"; International Capital Markets Association, "Sustainability-Linked Bond Principles."

72 IUCN, "The IUCN Red List of Threatened Species," 2020, https://www.iucnre-dlist.org/.

73 Atkins and Maroun, "The Naturalist's Journals of Gilbert White: Exploring the Roots of Accounting for Biodiversity and Extinction Accounting."

74 European Parliament and the Council, "DIRECTIVE 2014/95/EU OF THE EUROPEAN PARLIAMENT AND OF THE COUNCIL of 22 October 2014 Amending Directive 2013/34/EU as Regards Disclosure of Non-Financial and Diversity Information by Certain Large Undertakings and Groups."

75 Christoph Frederic Biehl, Ian Hume Thomson, and Madeleine Travers, "Rethinking Materiality: The Missing Link | Special Report | IPE," IPE International Publishers Ltd., 2020, https://www.ipe.com/reports/leading-viewpoint-rethinking-materiality-the-missing-link/10048668.article.

76 Atkins and Maroun, "The Naturalist's Journals of Gilbert White: Exploring the Roots of Accounting for Biodiversity and Extinction Accounting."

77 Christoph Frederic Biehl, Ian Hume Thomson, and Madeleine Travers, "Rethinking Materiality: The Missing Link | Special Report | IPE."

78 Atkins and Maroun, "The Naturalist's Journals of Gilbert White: Exploring the Roots of Accounting for Biodiversity and Extinction Accounting."

79 International Capital Markets Association, "Sustainability-Linked Bond Principles."

80 UNEP, "Convention on Biological Diversity" (2006), https://www.cbd.int/convention/articles/?a=cbd-02.

81 Finance for Biodiversity Pledge, "Finance for Biodiversity Pledge," accessed March 4, 2021, https://www.financeforbiodiversity.org/.

82 AVPN, "Impact Investing in a Post-COVID World: ESG Trends, Measurement & Analysis Across Asia-Pacific," 2020, https://avpn.asia/event/avpn–webinar-impact-investing-in-a-post-covid-world-esg-trends-measurement-analysis-across-asia-pacific/.

83 Madhu Mathew. "As Markets Move Toward Structured Non-Financial Reporting, SASB Engages PwC's XBRL Practice to Support Build of XBRL Taxonomy – SASB," October 1, 2020, accessed March 6, 2021, https://www.sasb.org/blog/-as-markets-move-toward-structured-non-financial-reporting-sasb-engages-pwcs-xbrl-practice-to-support-build-of-xbrl-taxonomy/.

84 eit Climate-KIC, "Integrating Nature with Technology to Strengthen Climate Adaptation," 2021, https://www.climate-kic.org/news/integrating-nature-with-technology-to-strengthen-climate-adaptation/.

85 European Commission, "The European Digital Strategy: Shaping Europe's Digital Future," 2020, https://ec.europa.eu/digital-single-market/en/content/european-digital-strategy.

86 Macpherson, Martina, Andrea Gasperini, and Matteo Bosco. "Artificial Intelligence and FinTech Technologies for ESG Data and Analysis." SSRN Electronic Journal, February 15, 2021. https://doi.org/10.2139/ssrn.3790774.

87 World Economic Forum, "Vision 2030," January 2020, accessed March 6, 2021, https://www.weforum.org/projects/frontier-2030.

88 eit Climate-KIC, "Integrating Nature with Technology to Strengthen Climate Adaptation," 2021, https://www.climate-kic.org/news/integrating-nature-with-technology-to-strengthen-climate-adaptation/.

89 European Commission, "The European Digital Strategy: Shaping Europe's Digital Future," 2020, https://ec.europa.eu/digital-single-market/en/content/european-digital-strategy.

90 For definitions and classifications, see ICMA, "Green Bond Principles - Voluntary Process Guidelines for Issuing Green Bonds," 2018.
Moody's, "Sustainable Bond Issuance to Hit a Record $650 Billion in 2021," 2021, https://www.moodys.com/research/Moodys-Sustainable-bond-issuance-to-hit-a-record-650-billion--PBC_1263479?cid=YJZ7YNGSROZ5414.

91 ICMA, "Climate Transition Finance Handbook Guidance for Issuers," 2020. Martina Macpherson contributed to the ICMA transition bond working group and guidelines.

92 Martina Macpherson is a co-founder of this ICMA initiative, launching on 10 March 2021.

93 Climate Bonds Initiative, External Reviews, 2016, Link: https://www.climate bonds.net/market/second-opinion.

94 Biodiversity Information Standards - TDWG, "Audubon Core," accessed March 4, 2021, https://www.tdwg.org/standards/ac/.

95 BSI 42020, "Smart Guide to Biodiversity in Planning and Development Integrating Biodiversity into All Stages of the Planning Process," 2013.

96 UNEP. Aichi Targets - Convention on Biological Diversity (2010).

97 Angela Cropper, "Convention on Biological Diversity," Environmental Conservation 20, no. 4 (1993): 364, https://doi.org/10.1017/s0376892900023614.

98 CDP, "CDP Climate Change 2021 Questionnaire" (2021), https://guidance.cdp.net/en/guidance?cid=18&ctype=theme&idtype=ThemeID&incchild=1&microsite=0&otype=Questionnaire&tags=TAG-13071%2CTAG-605%2CTAG-599.

99 CDP, "CDP Forests 2021 Questionnaire," 2021, https://guidance.cdp.net/en/tags?cid=19&ctype=theme&gettags=0&idtype=ThemeID&incchild=1&microsite=0&otype=Questionnaire&page=1&tgprompt=TG-124%2CTG-127%2CTG-125.

100 CDP, "CDP Water Security 2021 Questionnaire," 2021, https://guidance.cdp.net/en/tags?cid=20&ctype=theme&gettags=0&idtype=ThemeID&incchild=1&microsite=0&otype=Questionnaire&page=1&tgprompt=TG-124%2CTG-127%2CTG-125

101 Biodiversity Information Standards - TDWG, "Darwin Core," 2009, https://www.tdwg.org/standards/dwc/.

102 Natural Capital Finance Alliance, "ENCORE," accessed March 5, 2021, https://encore.naturalcapital.finance/en.

103 Equator Principles IV, "The Equator Principles," 2020.

104 European Commission, "Guidelines on Non-Financial Reporting: Supplement on Reporting Climate-Related Information," Official Journal of the European Union, 2019, C 209/1-30.

105 European Supervisory Authorities, "Final Report on Draft Regulatory Technical Standards," 2021.

106 European Commission, "EU Taxonomy for Sustainable Activities," accessed March 4, 2021, https://ec.europa.eu/info/business-economy-euro/banking-and-finance/sustainable-finance/eu-taxonomy-sustainable-activities_en.

107 Forum Nachhaltige Geldanlage, "FNG-Siegel Für Nachhaltige Investmentfonds," 2020.

108 Global Footprint Network, "Measure What You Treasure," 2017, accessed March 5, 2021, https://www.footprintnetwork.org/.

109 French Ministry for Ecology and Inclusive Transition, "Greenfin Label Criteria Guidelines April 2019," 2019.

110 ICMA, "Handbook Harmonized Framework for Impact Reporting," no. June (2019): 1–39, https://www.icmagroup.org/assets/documents/Regulatory/Green-Bonds/June-2019/Handbook-Harmonized-Framework-for-Impact-Reporting-WEB-100619.pdf.

111 ICMA, "Sustainability-Linked Bond Principles," 2020.

112 IFC, "Investing for Impact: Operating Principles for Impact Management," International Finance Corporation, 2019.

113 IFC, "Performance Standards on Environmental and Social Sustainability," 2012.

114 IFRS, "Consultation Paper on Sustainability Reporting" 46, no. September (2020): 4–6, https://cdn.ifrs.org/-/media/project/sustainability-reporting/consultation-paper-on-sustainability-reporting.pdf.

115 IUCN, "The IUCN Red List of Threatened Species," 2020, https://www.iucnred list.org/.

116 IPBES. "IPBES Core Indicators," 2018. https://ipbes.net/core-indicators.

117 ISO, "ISO 26000: Guidance on Social Responsibility," 2018, https://doi.org/ 10.1007/978-3-642-28036-8_251.

118 Executive Summary, "STRATEGIC BUSINESS PLAN ISO / TC 322 Sustainable FInance," no. April (2020).

119 ISO Technical Committees, "ISO/TC 323 - Circular Economy," accessed March 5, 2021, https://www.iso.org/committee/7203984.html.

120 ISO, "Biodiversity High on Standards Agenda," August 4, 2020, https://www.iso. org/news/ref2539.html.

121 Key Biodiversity Areas, "Key Biodiversity Areas," accessed March 5, 2021, http:// www.keybiodiversityareas.org/.

122 European Commission, "Natura 2000," 2008, https://ec.europa.eu/environment/ nature/natura2000/index_en.htm.

123 Natural Capital Coalition, "Natural Capital Protocol," 2016.

124 Natural Capital Protocol Toolkit, 2016, https://www.wbcsd.org/Programs/ Redefining-Value/Business-Decision-Making/Assess-and-Manage-Performance/ Natural-Capital-Protocol-Toolkit.

125 Biodiversity Information Standards - TDWG, "Natural Collections Descriptions (NCD)," accessed March 5, 2021, https://www.tdwg.org/standards/ncd/.

126 OECD, "OECD Guidelines for Multinational Enterprises 2011 Edition," 2011.

127 SHIFT, "Natural Capital Toolkit," accessed March 5, 2021, https://shift.tools/ contributors/551.

128 SASB, "SASB Conceptual Framework," accessed March 5, 2021, https://www.sasb. org/standards/conceptual-framework/.

129 SASB, "SASB Materiality Map," accessed March 5, 2021, http://materiality.sasb. org/.

130 "TNFD - Taskforce on Nature-Related Financial Disclosures," initiative to launch May 2021, accessed March 4, 2021, https://tnfd.info/.

131 Biodiversity Information Standards - TDWG, "TDWG Access Protocol for Infor- mation Retrieval (TAPIR)," accessed March 5, 2021, https://www.tdwg.org/ standards/tapir/.

132 Biodiversity Information Standards - TDWG, "Vocabulary Maintenance Standard (VMS)," accessed March 5, 2021, https://www.tdwg.org/standards/vms/.

133 Belgian Financial Sector Federation, "A Quality Standard For Sustaina- ble A and Socially Responsible Financial Products," 2019, https://ec.europa.eu/info/ publications/180524-proposal-sustainable-finance_en.

134 Trase Finance, "Intelligence for Deforestation-Free Finance," 2020, accessed March 5, 2021, https://trase.finance/.

135 UNESCO World Heritage Centre, "World Heritage List," accessed March 5, 2021, https://whc.unesco.org/en/list/.

136 UN Global Compact, "UN Global Compact: Principles," accessed March 5, 2021, https://www.unglobalcompact.org/what-is-gc/mission/principles.

137 United Nations, "Global Indicator Framework for the Sustainable Development Goals and Targets of the 2030 Agenda for Sustainable Development Goals and Tar- gets of the 2030 Agenda for Sustainable Development."

138 UN Development Programme, "SDG IMPACT STANDARDS Bonds (2nd Draft)," 2020.

139 Value Balancing Alliance, "Methodology Impact Statement General Paper: Version 0.1," 2021.

140 World Economic Forum, "Measuring Stakeholder Capitalism: World's Largest Companies Support Developing Core Set of Universal ESG Disclosures," Janu- ary 22, 2020, https://www.weforum.org/press/2020/01/measuring-stakeholder-

capitalism-world-s-largest-companies-support-developing-core-set-of-universal-esg-disclosures.

141 UNEP. Aichi Targets - Convention on Biological Diversity (2010).

142 Biodiversity Information Standards - TDWG, "Audubon Core," accessed March 4, 2021, https://www.tdwg.org/standards/ac/.

143 BSI 42020, "Smart Guide to Biodiversity in Planning and Development Integrating Biodiversity into All Stages of the Planning Process," 2013.

144 Angela Cropper, "Convention on Biological Diversity," Environmental Conservation 20, no. 4 (1993): 364, https://doi.org/10.1017/s0376892900023614.

145 Biodiversity Indicators Partnership, "Global Indicators under the BIP," 2006 / 2015, accessed March 4, 2021, https://www.bipindicators.net/.

146 CDP, "CDP Forests 2021 Questionnaire," 2021, https://guidance.cdp.net/en/tags?cid=19&ctype=theme&gettags=0&idtype=ThemeID&incchild=1&microsite=0&otype=Questionnaire&page=1&tgprompt=TG-124%2CTG-127%2CTG-125.

147 Biodiversity Information Standards - TDWG, "Darwin Core," 2009, https://www.tdwg.org/standards/dwc/.

148 Natural Capital Finance Alliance, "ENCORE," accessed March 5, 2021, https://encore.naturalcapital.finance/en.

149 Equator Principles IV, "The Equator Principles," 2020.

150 European Commission, "Guidelines on Non-Financial Reporting: Supplement on Reporting Climate-Related Information," Official Journal of the European Union, 2019, C 209/1-30.

151 European Commission, "Guidelines on Non-Financial Reporting: Methodology for Reporting Non-Financial Information," Official Journal of the European Union 215, no. 1 (2019): 1–20.

152 European Supervisory Authorities, "Final Report on Draft Regulatory Technical Standards," 2021.

153 Forum Nachhaltige Geldanlage, "FNG-Siegel Für Nachhaltige Investmentfonds," 2020.

154 Global Footprint Network, "Measure What You Treasure," 2017, accessed March 5, 2021, https://www.footprintnetwork.org/.

155 French Ministry for Ecology and Inclusive Transition, "Greenfin Label Criteria Guidelines April 2019," 2019.

156 GRI 204, 2016.

157 GRI 301, 2016.

158 GRI 303, 2018.

159 IPBES. "IPBES Core Indicators," 2018. https://ipbes.net/core-indicators.

160 ICMA, "Sustainability-Linked Bond Principles," 2020.

161 IFC, "Investing for Impact: Operating Principles for Impact Management," International Finance Corporation, 2019.

162 IFC, "Performance Standards on Environmental and Social Sustainability," 2012.

163 ISO, "ISO 26000: Guidance on Social Responsibility," 2018, https://doi.org/10.1007/978-3-642-28036-8_251.

164 IUCN, "The IUCN Red List of Threatened Species," 2020, https://www.iucnredlist.org/.

165 Key Biodiversity Areas, "Key Biodiversity Areas," accessed March 5, 2021, http://www.keybiodiversityareas.org/.

166 European Commission, "Natura 2000," 2008, https://ec.europa.eu/environment/nature/natura2000/index_en.htm.

167 Natural Capital Coalition, "Natural Capital Protocol," 2016.

168 Biodiversity Information Standards - TDWG, "Natural Collections Descriptions (NCD)," accessed March 5, 2021, https://www.tdwg.org/standards/ncd/.

169 The definition differs between the industry standards. However, in general, it is covered under 160a.2 SASB, "SASB Materiality Map," accessed March 5, 2021, http://materiality.sasb.org/.

170 Biodiversity Information Standards - TDWG, "TDWG Access Protocol for Information Retrieval (TAPIR)," accessed March 5, 2021, https://www.tdwg.org/standards/tapir/.

171 "TNFD - Taskforce on Nature-Related Financial Disclosures," initiative to launch May 2021, accessed March 4, 2021, https://tnfd.info/.

172 Trase Finance, "Intelligence for Deforestation-Free Finance," 2020, accessed March 5, 2021, https://trase.finance/.

173 UN Global Compact, "UN Global Compact: Principle 7," accessed March 5, 2021, https://www.unglobalcompact.org/what-is-gc/mission/principles/principle-7.

174 United Nations, "Global Indicator Framework for the Sustainable Development Goals and Targets of the 2030 Agenda for Sustainable Development Goals and Targets of the 2030 Agenda for Sustainable Development," 2020.

175 UNESCO World Heritage Centre, "World Heritage List," accessed March 5, 2021, https://whc.unesco.org/en/list/.

176 Value Balancing Alliance, "Methodology Impact Statement General Paper: Version 0.1," 2021.

177 Value Balancing Alliance, "Methodology Impact Statement Focus: Environment: Version 0.1," 2021.

178 Biodiversity Information Standards - TDWG, "Vocabulary Maintenance Standard (VMS)," accessed March 5, 2021, https://www.tdwg.org/standards/vms/.

179 World Economic Forum, "Measuring Stakeholder Capitalism: World's Largest Companies Support Developing Core Set of Universal ESG Disclosures," January 22, 2020, https://www.weforum.org/press/2020/01/measuring-stakeholder-capitalism-world-s-largest-companies-support-developing-core-set-of-universal-esg-disclosures.

180 UNEP. Aichi Targets - Convention on Biological Diversity.

181 BSI 42020, "Smart Guide to Biodiversity in Planning and Development Integrating Biodiversity into All Stages of the Planning Process."

182 Biodiversity Indicators Partnership, "Global Indicators under the BIP."

183 CDP, "CDP Climate Change 2021 Questionnaire" (2021), https://guidance.cdp.net/en/guidance?cid=18&ctype=theme&idtype=ThemeID&incchild=1&microsite=0&otype=Questionnaire&tags=TAG-13071%2CTAG-605%2CTAG-599.

184 CDP, "CDP Forests 2021 Questionnaire."

185 Equator Principles, "The Equator Principles."

186 European Commission, "Guidelines on Non-Financial Reporting: Supplement on Reporting Climate-Related Information," Official Journal of the European Union, 2019, 30.

187 European Supervisory Authorities, "Final Report on Draft Regulatory Technical Standards."

188 European Commission, "EU Taxonomy for Sustainable Activities," accessed March 4, 2021, https://ec.europa.eu/info/business-economy-euro/banking-and-finance/sustainable-finance/eu-taxonomy-sustainable-activities_en.

189 French Ministry for Ecology and Inclusive Transition, "Greenfin Label Criteria Guidelines April 2019."

190 GRI 304, 2016.

191 GRI 308, 2016.

192 ICMA, "Handbook Harmonized Framework for Impact Reporting," no. June (2019): 1–39, https://www.icmagroup.org/assets/documents/Regulatory/Green-Bonds/June-2019/Handbook-Harmonized-Framework-for-Impact-Reporting-WEB-100619.pdf.

193 IPBES. "IPBES Core Indicators."

194 ICMA, "Sustainability-Linked Bond Principles."
195 IFC, "Investing for Impact: Operating Principles for Impact Management."
196 IFC, "Performance Standards on Environmental and Social Sustainability."
197 IFRS, "Consultation Paper on Sustainability Reporting" 46, no. September (2020): 4–6, https://cdn.ifrs.org/-/media/project/sustainability-reporting/consultation-paper-on-sustainability-reporting.pdf.
198 ISO, "ISO 26000: Guidance on Social Responsibility."
199 Executive Summary, "STRATEGIC BUSINESS PLAN ISO / TC 322 Sustainable FInance," no. April (2020).
200 ISO Technical Committees, "ISO/TC 323 - Circular Economy," accessed March 5, 2021, https://www.iso.org/committee/7203984.html.
201 ISO, "Biodiversity High on Standards Agenda," August 4, 2020, https://www.iso.org/news/ref2539.html.
202 IUCN, "The IUCN Red List of Threatened Species."
203 Key Biodiversity Areas, "Key Biodiversity Areas."
204 European Commission, "Natura 2000."
205 Natural Capital Coalition, "Natural Capital Protocol."
206 OECD, "OECD Guidelines for Multinational Enterprises 2011 Edition," 2011.
207 SASB, "SASB Materiality Map."
208 SHIFT, "Natural Capital Toolkit," accessed March 5, 2021, https://shift.tools/contributors/551.
209 "TNFD - Taskforce on Nature-Related Financial Disclosures."
210 UN Global Compact, "UN Global Compact: Principle 7."
211 UN Global Compact, "UN Global Compact: Principle 8," accessed March 5, 2021, https://www.unglobalcompact.org/what-is-gc/mission/principles/principle-8.
212 UN Development Programme, "SDG IMPACT STANDARDS Bonds (2nd Draft)," 2020.
213 United Nations, "Global Indicator Framework for the Sustainable Development Goals and Targets of the 2030 Agenda for Sustainable Development Goals and Targets of the 2030 Agenda for Sustainable Development."
214 World Economic Forum, "Measuring Stakeholder Capitalism: World's Largest Companies Support Developing Core Set of Universal ESG Disclosures."
215 BSI 42020, "Smart Guide to Biodiversity in Planning and Development Integrating Biodiversity into All Stages of the Planning Process."
216 BSI 42020, "Smart Guide to Biodiversity in Planning and Development Integrating Biodiversity into All Stages of the Planning Process," n.d.
217 Biodiversity Indicators Partnership, "Global Indicators under the BIP."
218 CDP, CDP Climate Change 2021 Questionnaire.
219 CDP, "CDP Forests 2021 Questionnaire."
220 Biodiversity Information Standards - TDWG, "Darwin Core."
221 Equator Principles, "The Equator Principles."
222 European Parliament and the Council, "DIRECTIVE 2014/95/EU OF THE EUROPEAN PARLIAMENT AND OF THE COUNCIL of 22 October 2014 Amending Directive 2013/34/EU as Regards Disclosure of Non-Financial and Diversity Information by Certain Large Undertakings and Groups," Official Journal of the European Union L330 (2014).
223 European Supervisory Authorities, "Final Report on Draft Regulatory Technical Standards."
224 European Commission, "EU Taxonomy for Sustainable Activities."
225 French Ministry for Ecology and Inclusive Transition, "Greenfin Label Criteria Guidelines April 2019."
226 GRI 304, 2016.
227 GRI 303, 2018.
228 GRI 307, 2016.

229 ICMA, "Handbook Harmonized Framework for Impact Reporting."

230 ICMA, "Sustainability-Linked Bond Principles."

231 IFC, "Investing for Impact: Operating Principles for Impact Management."

232 IFC, "Performance Standards on Environmental and Social Sustainability."

233 ISO, "ISO 26000: Guidance on Social Responsibility."

234 Summary, "STRATEGIC BUSINESS PLAN ISO / TC 322 Sustainable FInance."

235 IUCN, "The IUCN Red List of Threatened Species."

236 Key Biodiversity Areas, "Key Biodiversity Areas."

237 European Commission, "Natura 2000."

238 Biodiversity Information Standards - TDWG, "Natural Collections Descriptions (NCD)."

239 SASB, "SASB Materiality Map."

240 Biodiversity Information Standards - TDWG, TDWG Access Protocol for Information Retrieval (TAPIR).

241 "TNFD - Taskforce on Nature-Related Financial Disclosures."

242 Belgian Financial Sector Federation, "A Quality Standard For Sustainable Aand Socially Responsible Financial Products," 2019, https://ec.europa.eu/info/publications/180524-proposal-sustainable-finance_en.

243 UN Global Compact, "UN Global Compact: Principle 7."

244 UN Global Compact, "UN Global Compact: Principle 8."

245 UN Global Compact, "UN Global Compact: Principle 9," accessed March 5, 2021, https://www.unglobalcompact.org/what-is-gc/mission/principles/principle-9.

246 UN Development Programme, "SDG IMPACT STANDARDS Bonds (2nd Draft)."

247 Biodiversity Information Standards - TDWG, Vocabulary Maintenance Standard (VMS).

248 World Economic Forum, "Measuring Stakeholder Capitalism: World's Largest Companies Support Developing Core Set of Universal ESG Disclosures."

249 UNEP. Aichi Targets - Convention on Biological Diversity.

250 Biodiversity Information Standards - TDWG, "Audubon Core."

251 BSI 42020, "Smart Guide to Biodiversity in Planning and Development Integrating Biodiversity into All Stages of the Planning Process."

252 Biodiversity Indicators Partnership, "Global Indicators under the BIP."

253 CDP, CDP Climate Change 2021 Questionnaire.

254 CDP, "CDP Forests 2021 Questionnaire."

255 Biodiversity Information Standards - TDWG, "Darwin Core."

256 Equator Principles, "The Equator Principles."

257 European Supervisory Authorities, "Final Report on Draft Regulatory Technical Standards."

258 GRI 304, 2016.

259 GRI 307, 2016.

260 ICMA, "Sustainability-Linked Bond Principles."

261 IFC, "Investing for Impact: Operating Principles for Impact Management."

262 IFC, "Performance Standards on Environmental and Social Sustainability."

263 Summary, "STRATEGIC BUSINESS PLAN ISO / TC 322 Sustainable FInance."

264 Natural Capital Coalition, "Natural Capital Protocol."

265 Biodiversity Information Standards - TDWG, "Natural Collections Descriptions (NCD)."

266 Biodiversity Information Standards - TDWG, TDWG Access Protocol for Information Retrieval (TAPIR).

267 UN Global Compact, "UN Global Compact: Principle 8."

268 UN Development Programme, "SDG IMPACT STANDARDS Bonds (2nd Draft)."

269 Value Balancing Alliance, "Methodology Impact Statement Focus: Environment: Version 0.1."

270 Biodiversity Information Standards - TDWG, Vocabulary Maintenance Standard (VMS).
271 World Economic Forum, "Measuring Stakeholder Capitalism: World's Largest Companies Support Developing Core Set of Universal ESG Disclosures."
272 BSI 42020, "Smart Guide to Biodiversity in Planning and Development Integrating Biodiversity into All Stages of the Planning Process."
273 CDP, "CDP Forests 2021 Questionnaire."
274 Equator Principles, "The Equator Principles."
275 European Supervisory Authorities, "Final Report on Draft Regulatory Technical Standards."
276 ICMA, "Sustainability-Linked Bond Principles."
277 IFC, "Investing for Impact: Operating Principles for Impact Management."
278 Natural Capital Coalition, "Natural Capital Protocol."
279 UN Development Programme, "SDG IMPACT STANDARDS Bonds (2nd Draft)."

References

Alliance Bernstein. "Making Sense of ESG Bond Structures," 2020. https://www.alliancebernstein.com/library/Making-Sense-of-ESG-Bond-Structures.htm.

Atkins, Jill F., and Barry Atkins. *The Business of Bees: An Integrated Approach to Bee Decline and Corporate Responsibility.* Edited by Jill F. Atkins and Barry Atkins. Sheffield: Routeledge, 2016. https://doi.org/10.4324/9781351283922.

Atkins, Jill F., and Martina Macpherson. "Developing a Species Protection Action Plan – An Integrated Approach for Taxonomies, Reporting and Engagement for the Financial Services Sector." *SSRN Electronic Journal*, June 26, 2019. https://doi.org/10.2139/ssrn.3398308.

Atkins, Jill F., and Warren Maroun. "Integrated Extinction Accounting and Accountability: Building an Ark." *Accounting, Auditing and Accountability Journal* 31, no. 3 (2018): 750–786. https://doi.org/10.1108/AAAJ-06-2017-2957.

———. "The Naturalist's Journals of Gilbert White: Exploring the Roots of Accounting for Biodiversity and Extinction Accounting." *Accounting, Auditing and Accountability Journal* 33, no. 8 (2020): 1835–1870. https://doi.org/10.1108/AAAJ-03-2016-2450.

AVPN. "Impact Investing in a Post-COVID World: ESG Trends, Measurement & Analysis Across Asia-Pacific," 2020. https://avpn.asia/event/avpn-webinar-impact-investing-in-a-post-covid-world-esg-trends-measurement-analysis-across-asia-pacific/.

Bennett, John W. *The Ecological Transition. The Ecological Transition*, 1976. https://doi.org/10.1016/c2013-0-05659-9.

Biehl, Christoph F., Ian Hume Thomson, and Madeleine Travers. "Rethinking Materiality: The Missing Link | Special Report | IPE." IPE International Publishers Ltd., 2020. https://www.ipe.com/reports/leading-viewpoint-rethinking-materiality-the-missing-link/10048668.article.

Biehl, Christoph F., and Martina N. Macpherson. "Bees and Accountability in Germany: A Multi-Stakeholder Approach." In *The Business of Bees*, edited by Jill F Atkins and Barry Atkins. Sheffield: Routledge, 2016. 277–230

BNP Paribas. "UPM Links EUR 750m Loan to Forest Biodiversity and CO2 Targets," April 22, 2020. https://cib.bnpparibas.com/sustain/upm-links-eur-750m-loan-to-forest-biodiversity-and-co2-targets_a-3-3484.html.

Bradshaw, Corey J. A., Paul R. Ehrlich, Andrew Beattie, Gerardo Ceballos, Eileen Crist, Joan Diamond, Rodolfo Dirzo, et al. "Underestimating the Challenges of Avoiding a

Ghastly Future." *Frontiers in Conservation Science* 1 (January 13, 2021): 615419. https://doi.org/10.3389/fcosc.2020.615419.

BrightTALK. "Natural Capital, Species Extinction & Sustainable Finance - The Impact of SDGs." *ESG Channel*, 2019. https://www.brighttalk.com/webinar/preserving-natural-capital-and-species-sdg-15/.

"Call to Action — Business For Nature." Accessed March 4, 2021. https://www.businessfornature.org/call-to-action.

Cambridge Institute for Sustainability Leadership. "Handbook for Nature-Related Financial Risks: Key Concepts and a Framework for Identification," 2021. https://www.cisl.cam.ac.uk/resources/sustainable-finance-publications/handbook-nature-related-financial-risks.

Climate Bonds Initiative. "Certification under the Climate Bonds Standard." Accessed March 4, 2021. https://www.climatebonds.net/certification.

———. "Labelled Green Bonds Data: Latest 3 Months." Accessed March 4, 2021. https://www.climatebonds.net/cbi/pub/data/bonds.

———. "Post-Issuance Reporting in the Green Bond Market," 2019.

Dasgupta, Sir Partha. "The Economics of Biodiversity: The Dasgupta Review." *HM Treasury*, 2021. https://www.gov.uk/government/publications/final-report-the-economics-of-biodiversity-the-dasgupta-review.

Dutch Central Bank. "Indebted to Nature," no. June (2020).

eit Climate-KIC. "Integrating Nature with Technology to Strengthen Climate Adaptation," 2021. https://www.climate-kic.org/news/integrating-nature-with-technology-to-strengthen-climate-adaptation/.

Enel Group. "Sustainability-Linked Bonds." Accessed March 4, 2021. https://www.enel.com/investors/investing/sustainable-finance/sustainability-linked-finance/sustainability-linked-bonds.

Environmental Finance. "Investing in Nature: Private Finance for Nature-Based Resilience," 2019. https://www.environmental-finance.com/content/research/investing-in-nature-private-finance-for-nature-based-resilience.html.

EU TEG on Sustainable Finance. "USABILITY GUIDE Context and Background Information," no. March (2020).

European Central Bank. "ECB to Accept Sustainability-Linked Bonds as Collateral," 2020. https://www.ecb.europa.eu/press/pr/date/2020/html/ecb.pr200922~482e4a5a90.en.html.

European Commission. "EU Taxonomy for Sustainable Activities." Accessed March 4, 2021. https://ec.europa.eu/info/business-economy-euro/banking-and-finance/sustainable-finance/eu-taxonomy-sustainable-activities_en.

———. "Guidelines on Non-Financial Reporting: Supplement on Reporting Climate-Related Information." *Official Journal of the European Union* (2019): 30.

———. "Guidelines on Non-Financial Reporting." *Official Journal of the European Union* 215, no. 1 (2019): 1–20.

———. "The European Digital Strategy: Shaping Europe's Digital Future," 2020. https://ec.europa.eu/digital-single-market/en/content/european-digital-strategy.

———. "The EU Business @ Biodiversity Platform," 2020. https://ec.europa.eu/environment/biodiversity/business/index_en.htm.

———. "The Just Transition Mechanism: Making Sure No One Is Left Behind." Accessed March 4, 2021. https://ec.europa.eu/info/strategy/priorities-2019-2024/european-green-deal/actions-being-taken-eu/just-transition-mechanism_en.

European Parliament and the Council. "DIRECTIVE 2014/95/EU OF THE EUROPEAN PARLIAMENT AND OF THE COUNCIL of 22 October 2014

Amending Directive 2013/34/EU as Regards Disclosure of Non-Financial and Diversity Information by Certain Large Undertakings and Groups." *Official Journal of the European Union* L330 (2014).

———. "Regulation (2019/2088) on Sustainability-Related Disclosures in the Financial Services Sector." *Official Journal of the European Union* L317 (2019): 1–16.

———. "Regulation (EU) 2020/852 of the European Parliament and of the Council of 18 June 2020 on the Establishment of a Framework to Facilitate Sustainable Investment, and Amending Regulation (EU) 2019/2088." *Official Journal of the European Union*, L198 (2020): 1–31.

Executive Secretary of the Convention on Biological Diversity. "Sustainable Development: Convention on Biological Diversity Report of the Executive Secretary of the Convention on Biological Diversity." *UN Biodiversity Conference* 21, no. 1 (2020): 1–9.

Finance for Biodiversity Pledge. "Finance for Biodiversity Pledge." Accessed March 4, 2021. https://www.financeforbiodiversity.org/.

Finance for the Future. "Rabobank: Building Biodiversity with Impact Loans." Accessed March 4, 2021. www.financeforthefuture.org.

GFC. "China Green Bond Endorsed Project Catalogue (2015 Edition)," October 22, 2015. http://www.greenfinance.org.cn/displaynews.php?cid=79&id=468.

Green Finance Platform. "People's Bank of China Green Bond Endorsed Project Catalogue (2020 Edition)," 2020. https://www.greenfinanceplatform.org/financial-measures-database/peoples-bank-china-green-bond-endorsed-project-catalogue-2020-edition.

Hermes EOS. "Public Engagement Report," 2016.

ICMA. "Climate Transition Finance Handbook Guidance for Issuers," 2020.

———. "Green, Social and Sustainability Bonds." Accessed March 4, 2021. https://www.icmagroup.org/sustainable-finance/#:~:text=Green%2C Social and Sustainability Bonds are any type of bond,environmental and%2For social projects.&text= As the principles are designed,banks are invited to participate.

———. "Green Bond Principles - Voluntary Process Guidelines for Issuing Green Bonds," 2018.

———. "Social Bond Principles." *The Social Bond Principles*, 2020.

———. "Sustainability-Linked Bond Principles," June (2020): 1–11.

———. "Sustainability Bond Guidelines," 2018.

———. "The Role of the Sustainable Bond Markets in Promoting Biodiversity," 2020. https://icma.podbean.com/e/the-role-of-the-sustainable-bond-markets-in-promoting-biodiversity/.

International Capital Markets Association. "Sustainability-Linked Bond Principles," no. June (2020). https://www.icmagroup.org/assets/documents/Regulatory/Green-Bonds/June-2020/Sustainability-Linked-Bond-PrinciplesJune-2020-100620.pdf.

Investec Bank. "Natural Capital, Species Extinction & Sustainable Financial Markets - Capitals Coalition," 2019. https://capitalscoalition.org/events/natural-capital-species-extinction-sustainable-financial-markets/.

IPBES. "Global Assessment Report on Biodiversity and Ecosystem Services of the Intergovernmental Science-Policy Platform on Biodiversity and Ecosystem Services." Bonn, Germany, 2019. https://www.ipbes.net/global-assessment.

IUCN. "The IUCN Red List of Threatened Species," 2020. https://www.iucnredlist.org/.

King, Mervyn, and Jill Atkins. *The Chief Value Officer: Accountants Can Save the Planet.* Greenleaf Publishing, Saltaire, UK, 2016.

Loan Market Association. "Green Loan Principles," 2018. https://www.lma.eu.com/application/files/9115/4452/5458/741_LM_Green_Loan_Principles_Booklet_V8.pdf.

———. "Sustainability Linked Loan Principles." *Loan Market Association*, 2019. https://www.lma.eu.com/application/files/8015/5307/4231/LMA_Sustainability_Linked_Loan_Principles.pdf.

Macpherson, Martina, Andrea Gasperini, and Matteo Bosco. "Artificial Intelligence and FinTech Technologies for ESG Data and Analysis." *SSRN Electronic Journal*, February 15, 2021. https://doi.org/10.2139/ssrn.3790774.

Moody's. "Sustainable Bond Issuance to Hit a Record $650 Billion in 2021," 2021. https://www.moodys.com/research/Moodys-Sustainable-bond-issuance-to-hit-a-record-650-billion--PBC_1263479?cid=YJZ7YNGSROZ5414.

Mountford, Helan, Jan Corfee-Morlot, Molly McGregor, Ferzina Banaji, Amar Bhattacharya, Jessica Brand, Sarah Colenbrander, et al. "Unlocking the Inclusive Growth Story of the 21st Century." *The New Climate Economy*, 2018.

Natixis. "Agrial and Natixis Sign the First Sustainability-Linked Credit Facility for a French Agricultural Cooperative," 2019. https://pressroom-en.natixis.com/news/-agrial-and-natixis-sign-the-first-sustainability-linked-credit-facility-for-a-french-agricultural-cooperative-7615-8e037.html.

Network for Greening the Financial System. "Guide for Supervisors: Integrating Climate-Related and Environmental Risks into Prudential Supervision," no. May (2020): 1–62. https://www.ngfs.net/sites/default/files/medias/documents/ngfs_guide_for_supervisors.pdf.

Nordic Public Issuers Sector. "Position Paper on Green Bonds Impact Reporting," 2020.

OECD. "Biodiversity: Finance and the Economic and Business Case for Action, Report Prepared for the G7 Environment Ministers' Meeting, 5–6 May 2019," 2019. https://doi.org/10.1787/a3147942-en.

Rudgley, Grant and Nina Seega. "Handbook for Nature-Related Financial Risks Key Concepts and a Framework for Identification," 2021.

Reuters. "Enel Ditches Green Bonds for Controversial New Format | Reuters," October 4, 2019. https://www.reuters.com/article/enel-ditches-green-bonds-for-controversi-idUSL5N26O403.

"Sustainable Finance Outlook: Moody's Sees Sustainable Bond Issuance Soaring to $650B in 2021- ESG Today." Accessed March 4, 2021. https://www.esgtoday.com/-sustainable-finance-outlook-moodys-sees-sustainable-bond-issuance-soaring-to-650b-in-2021/?fbclid=IwAR0HWFAxswGiPDhylKoPpXUA3NAwiU54H_tADS-9iX5BVgZEch92DCgHqjM.

SymInvest. "New 'Rhino Bonds' to Allow Investors to Help with Wildlife Conservation | SymInvest - Microfinance Investment Intelligence," July 18, 2019. https://www.syminvest.com/news/new-rhino-bonds-to-allow-investors-to-help-with-wildlife-conservation/2019/7/18/8372.

TCFD. "Task Force on Climate-Related Financial Disclosures." Accessed March 4, 2021. https://www.fsb-tcfd.org/.

The Capitals Coalition. "The Capitals Coalition," 2021. https://capitalscoalition.org/.

TNFD. "TNFD - Taskforce on Nature-Related Financial Disclosures." Accessed March 4, 2021. https://tnfd.info/.

UN Department of Economic and Social Affairs. "Transforming Our World: The 2030 Agenda for Sustainable Development." Accessed March 4, 2021. https://sdgs.un.org/2030agenda.

UNEP. Convention on Biological Diversity (2006). https://www.cbd.int/convention/articles/?a=cbd-02.

World Conservation Monitoring Centre. "Global Biodiversity: Status of the Earth's Living Resources." *Biological Conservation*, 1992. https://doi.org/10.1016/0006-3207(93)90147-s.

World Economic Forum. "The Global Risks Report" 15 (2020): 1–114. http://wef.ch/risks2019.

———. "Vision 2030". January 2020, https://www.weforum.org/projects/frontier-2030.

12

FROM ACTIVE TO PASSIVE

Establishing a Framework for a Biodiversity Index Solution

Erica Zanella and Thomas Montagnon

Active vs Passive

When it comes to investment, there are traditionally two major approaches and belief systems for managing portfolios. Thus, those two manners are usually in contradiction. The first one is active investing: The main goal is to "beat" the market (generating Alpha) by managing your portfolio better than its existing benchmark. In other words, it means that your investment goal will be to beat, for instance, the index FTSE 100 by selecting, on a discretionary basis, the securities that will overperform the performance of the index composed of the top 100 UK stocks in terms of market capitalization. To do so, in most cases, the investors delegate the management of the fund to professional fund managers. Investors usually only buy securities and funds directly managed by such professionals to allocate their capital. If we get take a deeper look at the way the funds are managed, the purpose of active investing is to beat the market. To achieve this, fund managers depend on two big strategies:

i   Stock Picking. This means selecting specific securities among a whole set of possibilities. For instance, pick Royal Dutch Shell rather than British petroleum based on discretionary criteria and subjective opinion by assuming that Royal Dutch Shell will overperform British Petroleum over the long term. Obviously, fund managers base their selections on deep financial, sectorial, market analysis to at the end, issue an opinion on the securities to buy or not buy it.
ii Market Timing. This means investing at a certain moment rather than another. Identify the right momentum of a stock that will overperform. As an example, wait for tomorrow to buy Royal Dutch Shell because today according to the market share value is not a good entry point.

DOI: 10.4324/9781003045557-16

The other philosophy for managing your portfolio or your fund is called passive investing. To some extent, this is called lazy investing. The objective is to capture market performance. For instance, instead of buying a fund that tries to beat the FTSE 100, you will directly buy a fund that replicates the whole financial performance of the Financial Times Stock Exchange (FTSE 100) through an investment vehicle like an exchange-traded funds (ETFs). In that case, the fund manager can buy exactly to same components of the index and respect the weight to structure its funds (synthetic replication). He can also, engage himself to deliver only the performance by using a swap mechanism regarding the underlying securities (synthetic replication).

When it comes to passive investing, you have several underlying strategies to concretely manage your fund.

i   Diversification. The purpose is to build an investment universe as large as possible to maximize the number of securities within your portfolio.
ii Time to market. The purpose is to invest as soon as possible to maximize the time value of money and so the investment duration with the hidden goal to maximize the magic of compounded interests.

Plebiscite since its origin, active management is declining in favour of passive management funds. If we take the example of the US equity market, at the end of 1988, they were 6.5 times as many assets in actively managed US stock portfolios as there were in index funds: and this ratio is decreasing over time. Undoubtedly, in terms of asset under management (AUM), passive investment flow will outperform active flow in the next few years, even active investing continues to be very present on the market with a growing evolution in terms of offerings and investment possibilities (Figure 12.1).

Why such an interest that we can observe since 2007–2008, period of time that reasoning with subprime crisis? Following academic studies and especially SPIVA[1] (S&P indices versus active), that finds that 80% of funds do not outperform the market. Astonishing. But what can explain it? It is important to remind ourselves that market performance corresponds to the evolution of share prices that is the consequence of the meeting of supply and demand. Meaning that when a fund decides to buy Royal Dutch Shell securities, another decides to sell it. That said to run a fund, investment funds are charging high management fees (1.7% – SPIVA). This is indeed one of the factors that affect, by essence, the performance delivered to investors: even if in absolute performance, the funds beat the market. The other factor and reason we can identify is that there is no science and certitude to predict the market performance of a fund over the long term. The best fund this year that outperforms the market will certainly not be the best one next year.

Investors clearly understand that management fees have a large impact over the long term on their performance. As a matter of fact, they want cost-effective funds and transparency for their investments and their capital.

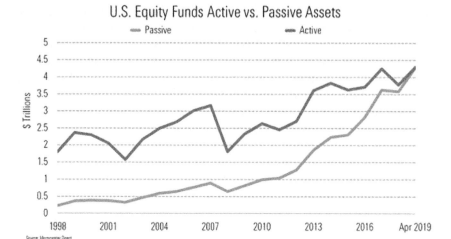

FIGURE 12.1 US Equity Funds (Active vs Passive Assets).
Source: Morningstar.

Rise of Environmental, Social and Governance Investing

In parallel to this growing interest in passive funds, we can also observe another strong trend emerging. Investors now want to understand better where their capital is invested. Indeed, investors not only want to invest in a cost-effective way but clearly also want to have an impact on the economy. The growing expansion of environmental, social and governance (ESG) flows demonstrates that the investors' interests are capitally orientating their capital towards investments that are more meaningful. This statement is visible since subprime crises and has also accelerated since COVID-19 crisis. Can we assume that crisis periods allow awareness for investors? Investors now want to understand better the external factors and take them into consideration within their investment process.

ESG investing is indeed a way to integrate sustainable development issues into the investment selection process. The growing popularity of ethical and green investments has led more and more people to look beyond economic fundamentals when making asset selections. However, assessing a company's behaviour can be a tricky process – after all, there is no single definition of what makes a "good" company. ESG investing uses methods to evaluate a stock beyond purely financial criteria. It also considers the company's actions, for a more coherent overall picture. Some investors use ESG criteria to determine which shares are worthy of their stock. They may, for example, prefer to invest in companies that have a good environmental record because they want their capital to contribute to climate change. Part of the rationale for ESG investment is that a company's good performance on ESG criteria has a positive impact on its economic performance. Indeed, according to investors practising this investment strategy, poor environmental practices, employee mistreatment or mismanagement will ultimately harm a company's financial results. For example, consistent underperformance against environmental regulations can result in fines, loss of business or lack of interest from environmentally conscious investors. ESG investors therefore choose companies that perform in all three areas associated with this strategy because they believe that these companies will perform better economically than others.

ESG criteria can be used in several ways. In theory, fund managers when they are managing a fund can use:

i   Negative/exclusionary screening – some exclusion rules can be settled for companies that are involved in controversial activities like fossils fuels, tobacco or even stem cells. The objective is to "clean" the investment universe to select the stocks that correspond to the strategy you want to set up. This is the most common strategy in today's offerings for investors.

ii   Positive and best-in-class screening. In that case, the stock selection is based on the best performers, that is to say companies that have the best scores in terms of ESG pillars but it can also focus on specific assessments on positive contribution to SDGs or green product involvement.

iii Norms-based screening. For instance, setting exclusionary rules based on international norms, standards and treaties like United Nations (UN) Global Compact, OIT and Organisation for Economic Co-operation and Development (OECD).

iv   Integration of ESG factors. It concerns an integration of some ESG aspects into the traditional financial selection process to enhance the existing rating and orientate the decision-making process.

v   Sustainability-themed investing. In a way, it is linked to an analysis of the Sustainable Development Goals' (SDGs) contribution of a company.

vi   Engagement and proxy voting. Representing investors and shareholders exerted lobbying into executive committee of selected stock to try to the exercise influence into the companies' strategy.

vii Impact/community investing. Setting goals, concrete actions and target that your investment will allow to drive and conduct.

To drive their decisions, investors and fund managers can rely on specific data produced by external rating agencies that provide ESG assessments and ratings but also produce their own internal research. In the ESG assessment landscape, the following criteria are generally used:

•   Environment. This generally involves assessing a company's ability to manage risks and opportunities related to environmental topics such as having a strong commitment and environmental strategy; put in place pollution prevention policies and control; manage atmospheric emissions; and control impact on biodiversity, selling green products and services and eventually the analysis of the environmental impact during the full product lifecycle

- Social. This generally involves assessing a company's ability to manage risks and opportunities related to social issues like respecting fundamental human and labour rights, applying nondiscrimination and diversity policies, promoting social dialogue and collective bargaining or insure health and safety in the office or even promoting career development.
- Governance. It is generally assessing a company's ability to manage risks and opportunities related to governance issues like the independency of the board of directors, put in place audit and internal controls and have a transparent executive remuneration and ability to prevent corruption, anticompetitive and lobbying practices.

As a form of ethical investment, ESG does not neglect financial performance. ESG investors believe that ESG factors will affect the future price of a stock at a given point in time. Above the ethical aspect that is reinforced, ESG investing is also financially very interesting in terms of long-term performance. Indeed, taking into consideration those factors in the investment process allow us to better integrate the risks and opportunities. It materializes the assessment of securities and their impact on the planet, their societal impact and the way the company is governed. Even if active fund managers are using ESG criteria to generate more alpha and drain more and more assets under management. Indeed, in a way, it is for them a source of justification that allows us to charge higher fees because ESG investing needs more research and analysis to select the "right" company to apply the "right" strategy. The trends of transition between active to passive are also visible regarding ESG investing. Indeed, since 2015 we observe a large transition among the allocation of flows into active and passive funds towards ESG (Figure 12.2).

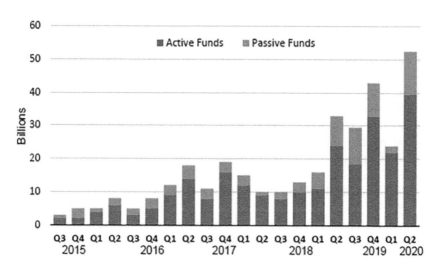

FIGURE 12.2 Integrating ESG into index and passive funds.

We saw along this chapter that ESG is now mainstream in active management and start becoming passive management. Thus, there are some best practices to integrate ESG into passive funds. When an investor wants to buy an index fund or an ETF (the most common investment vehicle when it comes to passive funds), he or she enters in a broad spectrum, landscape and value chain that is more complex than simply buying a fund with a Royal Dutch shell inside it that replicates the FTSE100 index. But in reality, which are the stakeholders in the index creation value chain and where does ESG fit into this?

Let us remind ourselves that taking ESG considerations into account in the construction process is admitting in a sense that financial decision-making data points are not enough to assess the long-term performance of a company. ESG factors are there to readjust the market value of stocks. To that effect, ESG indices are well known and perceived by investors that look for financial performance and "sustainable growth". ESG attracts more and more capital from investors. As of today, passive fund managers, banks, asset owners have their own interest in maintaining their existing assets under the manager on the one hand and draining more on the other hand. Indeed, facing the fundamental trend shift of investors they need to propose competitive solutions that match those news needs coming from investors. To do so, and because ESG indices are considered as one of the best channels to reach AUM, they put in place two big ways to create ESG indices:

i   Derived existing non ESG indices into ESG versions
ii Integrating ESG in the asset selection process.

As said, we can understand that behind any passive fund, there is an underlying index even for ESG. To do so, only index providers can administer indexes they are key actors and stakeholders in the value chain. They can be stock exchanges such as Euronext, Intercontinental Exchange, FTSE Russell and Nasdaq. They can also be independent index providers like MSCI (that provide also ESG data) Standard & Poor's, or Solactive. The last type of index providers can be directly banks like BNP Paribas or JP Morgan who can decide to internalize the process of index administration using their own resources. But how such actors are building indices and how and where ESG factors are integrated? In the construction process, there are a lot of structural activities and stakeholders.[2]

Data Supplies

To set up and create an index, the index provider must use data. In the index construction process, the first step is to define the eligible universe. Meaning determines the "starting point". It will take into consideration the asset class, the market price, the data selection based on sectors, size, if you want to use ESG or not, if you want to use specific financial data like volatility, or dividend yield, etc.

Index Administration

Following the last Benchmark Regulation, index administrators must follow specific rules in order to build indexes and be transparent on the design and the calculation of the index. The administration part takes into consideration all the aspects related to the design and the calculation of the index. On the one hand, the "design phase" englobes all the parts related to research and marketing, methodology, and the governance of the index. This is here that ESG data will be integrated. Indeed, the index providers will define thresholds, baseline exclusions using all the data and ESG research available depending on the thematic they want to tackle.

On the other hand, the "calculation" phase is more related to the final selection and weighting of the index and eventually the rebalancing phases defined by the methodology and the governance to manage new entrants and eventually exit rules.

Diffusion

As soon as the index is structured, the index provider or the administrator of the index has the choice to define the scope of the diffusion of this index. In another way, the index provider can decide to open and make available the index to all the public like one of the last launched by Euronext the ESG Large 80, meaning that every corporate and investment bank can have access to it and structure a financial product on it. But the index provider can directly be asked by an asset manager or asset owner to set up a custom exclusive proprietary index that can only be used by the requester.

Structuration

After setting up the index, the goal of the index provider is to find an investor to structure a product that uses the index as an underlying. As mentioned before, those investors can be asset managers that are managing ETFs but also structured product issuers (certificates, euro medium-term note (EMTN, debts, etc). To some extent, it can also be derivative contracts' issuers (futures, listed or not).

Distribution

After all these steps, products are distributed to institutional or retail investors depending on the complexity and the type of index used. Indeed, when a bank makes the choice to internalize the calculation of an index, it might be used to feed the internal retail distribution channel to propose new offerings and products to their clients so that they can invest it through their life insurance contracts using ETFs or in their stock portfolio account by buying structured products.

Therefore, it is not rare to find several types of financial products that integrate ESG factors, not only ETFs, most known as ETFs! Indeed, even if it is the most common tool for investors regarding passive funds, an investor could have access to other types of products such as index-linked notes and exchange-traded products like warrants and certificates. Into this passive product landscape, the rise of structured products that implies a specific risk yield management using several underlyings, a capital protection and a defined maturity, is very appreciated by investors. Then, derivative products are also emerging. They are structured on ESG indexes and listed such as futures and options or they can be swapped for institutionals but also more solutions for retail investors like credit defaults swaps or contracts for difference (CFDs).

Introduction to Biodiversity Framework Index Concept

Throughout this book, we consider the crucial issue of taking biodiversity into consideration in the investment process. Using the data produced by extra-financial rating agencies, it can be hard to imagine an effective way to integrate this topic using the ESG data available into a passive investing framework. Indeed, how a retail investor can have an impact by just replicating performance? However, doing passive investing must not excuse the investor to have a dedicated impact related to the preservation of biodiversity. Indexes are a tremendous tool to reallocate capital and encourage good behaviours. Indeed, being present on an index or not, a corporate have strong impacts on their market value and share price. It can also increase the cost of capital, thus increasing the financing cost of the companies that might not enter an ESG index.

In this sense, a biodiversity framework made for passive solution makes sense. But how to define a relevant and reliable solution that allows investors to reallocate their capital in favour of biodiversity?

The Solactive Vigeo Eiris Biodiversity Index[3] was created in collaboration between Solactive and Vigeo Eiris (now V.E) and launched in December 2019. The increasing importance of natural capital and the protection of its diversity is a central area of interest and importance for sustainability policies at global level. As stated in the OECD report[4]: *"Biodiversity loss is among the top global risks to society. The planet is now facing its sixth mass extinction, with consequences that will affect all life on Earth, both now and for millions of years to come"*. The interconnection between biodiversity and the economy is also clear.

Solactive and V.E wanted to create an instrument that could highlight the importance of this issue. The objective of the index was to create a selection of companies that integrate the protection of biodiversity in their sustainability strategy to allow investors to benefit from a global trend towards a more sustainable future. The index's constituents are companies with strong policies on biodiversity protection, which deal with the problem of biodiversity loss and take corrective actions to reduce their impacts on the exploited natural environment or that create a positive impact through their activities. In order to do so, the index uses a combination of different data and approaches to have the largest vision on different aspects of the topic. Not only policies and management of biodiversity protection but also positive and negative impacts of companies' activities are considered.

Sector Exclusions

V.E ESG methodology for screening companies is based on a sectorial approach. For each sector, some criteria are activated or deactivated and over- or underweighted depending on the materiality and impacts of company activities. The Biodiversity Index is focused on those sectors for which biodiversity protection is a relevant issue. For this reason, some sectors were excluded from the analysis due to their limited or indirect impact on biodiversity. Among others, some of the sectors that are used by the index methodology are electric and gas utilities, heavy constructions, forest products and paper, and financial services and real estate.[5] The definition of these sectors is the one proper to V.E ESG methodology.

Protection of Biodiversity Assessment

The basement of V.E assessment on biodiversity is the Protection of Biodiversity criteria present in V.E's ESG assessment. The objective of this assessment is to evaluate the company's commitment to prevent risks of endangering biodiversity. The evaluation results in a score scaled from 0 to 100 that is used as a filter in the index construction. In more detail, the score represents the capacity of the company to evaluate its impact on biodiversity and take corrective actions under three main pillars: leadership, implementation and results.

The analysis follows some principles of action that aim to have a complete assessment of the company commitment and actions. Firstly, the company is evaluated based on its capacity in identifying the impacts of its business operations on biodiversity and establishing an evaluation system to assess the health of impacted ecosystems. Secondly, the company is evaluated based on its policies and ability to avoid or reduce the exploitation of sensitive ecosystems. Finally, V.E ESG methodology takes into consideration the presence and the amplitude of corrective measures and policies in case of exploitation to rehabilitate the ecosystem.

For the Biodiversity Index, the threshold used to admit a company in the index is a minimum score of 60 (out of 100). This score represents the highest V.E opinion "Advanced" in the ESG assessment. In case the company have some positive impacts via its sustainable goods and services, as explained in the below section "Positive Impacts Assessment", the threshold score will be moved to 50 (out of 100) associated with the "Robust" opinion by V.E. This allowance is admitted as we consider that the small difference in the Global Biodiversity Score (GBS) is compensated by the positive concrete impacts of company's products or services.

In order to have a more precise analysis, the index includes another filter as a precise indicator of the disclosure of the company's commitment to protecting biodiversity. On V.E methodology, we can find seven levels of commitment disclosure that starts from the lower level when the company do not disclose any commitments to biodiversity protection, to the highest level when the company's commitment towards biodiversity protection covers the main relevant impacts of its activities and in addition the company engages with independent and representative stakeholder in this regard.

In the index methodology, we accept only those companies that have a commitment towards biodiversity protection that is at least general. Below are some examples of companies with a strong commitment to biodiversity protection that are included in the index.[6]

- BillerudKorsnas –Forest Products and Paper, V.E sector
  All forest operations carried out by BillerudKorsnas shall be in accordance with BillerudKorsnas Sustainable Forestry Directive, based on long-term sustainable wood production and maintaining biodiversity in the forest landscape. All wood supply to BillerudKorsnas shall be purchased in accordance with BillerudKorsnas Wood Procurement Directive. BillerudKorsnas requires that all wood supply complies with the demands of Forest Stewardship Council (FSC) controlled wood and Programme for the Endorsement of Forest Certification (PEFC) controlled sources. Moreover, the company recognized that:
  - "The forest is home to many species of fungi, flora and fauna, some of which are affected positively, others negatively".
  - "The forest is a social and cultural asset as an area for recreation and we take this into account".

  Finally, the company sets the following targets:
  - 180 certified forest owners in BillerudKorsnas' group certificates for FSC and PEFC.
  - 100% Biodiversity Index for nature conservation measures
    BillerudKorsnas policies take into consideration degradation, destruction or fragmentation of fragile or specific ecosystem and habitat, impacts on population dynamics and indirect negative effects due to suppliers' operations.
- Hammerson – Financial Services – Real Estate, V.E sector
  In its biodiversity policy, Hammerson states that it ensures that negative impacts on biodiversity are minimized, and opportunities to protect and enhance biodiversity are maximized.
  - Conserve on-site habitat: The company aims to protect and enhance the natural environment by minimizing resource consumption and delivering restorative projects to local biodiversity surrounding Hammerson's centres.
  - Improve site biodiversity: Local Biodiversity Action Plans (LBAPs) set out targets and objectives for the protection and enhancement of priority habitats and species that are important at a local level.

- Undertake ecological impact assessment for biodiversity risks: The company aims to undertake ecological appraisals (and impact assessments if required) of all new developments, in order to identify appropriate mitigation to offset any impacts on biodiversity.
- Engage with stakeholders (including employees) to protect biodiversity: In some cases, the objectives within LBAPs can be to engage with local stakeholders to enable biodiversity projects. An example of this is with our beehives installed at Les Trois Fontaines Shopping Centre in France, City Bzz, a local bee-keeping specialist was engaged to help install and maintain the hives.

- VINCI – Heavy Constructions, V.E sector
Operators of linear infrastructure concessions are primarily concerned with limiting the fragmentation of natural habitats during construction work, focusing their efforts on the ecological transparency of their infrastructure, the reversibility of barriers and the restoration of sensitive environments and ecological connectivity.

  - Loss or degradation and/or fragmentation of ecosystems and habitats on operation sites: VINCI is committed to putting in place specific ecological restoration measures, especially at motorway and quarry worksites
  - Loss or degradation and/or fragmentation of ecosystems and habitats in areas surrounding operations: Vinci reports that operators of linear infrastructure concessions are primarily concerned with limiting the fragmentation of natural habitats during construction work
  - Soil erosion: VINCI Construction is committed to fighting against soil erosion through ecological engineering services offered by Equo Vivo.

VINCI Airports is committed to assessing biodiversity issues at all of its airport sites by 2020.

VINCI has also a Biodiversity Task Force in place, gathering 40 ecology experts and environment managers, responsible for analysing risks and promoting best practices in the company. In addition, VINCI's subsidiary Eurovia has set up a specific partnership with France's Natural History Museum to take into account biodiversity during the different phases of quarry operations.

Of note, VINCI's commitment to promoting and protecting biodiversity in its operations was officially recognized in 2012 by France's Ministry of Ecology, Sustainable Development and Energy, under the National Biodiversity Strategy (SNB).

- Red Electrica – Electric and Gas Utilities, V.E sector
The company's commitment towards biodiversity protection covers the main relevant impacts of its activities:

  - Effects on population's dynamic (breeding, feeding and reproduction behaviour), due to noise, habitats degradation or fragmentation
  - Effects on sensitive or migratory species (due to noise, habitat degradation)
  - Soil erosion (due to draining, use of pesticide, cut of trees).

The company also engages with the Centre for Mediterranean Cooperation (International Union for the Conservation of Nature), the Spanish Ornithological Society and the "Natural Capital in the Spanish Energy Sector" working group. In addition, the company is adhering to the Biodiversity Pact promoted by the Ministry of Ecological Transition. As said in the introduction the index aims to have the most complete view possible on biodiversity, also considering positive and negative impacts of the company's activities. The following two sections are dedicated to detailed activities and filters included in the Index.

Positive Impacts

The positive impact analysis for the Biodiversity Index uses the Sustainable Goods and Services from V.E assessment. As by definition from the V.E methodology, "*Sustainable Goods or Services are those that function in a manner whereby they contribute to sustainable development objectives as outlines by international texts and reference standards[7]*". To be considered as a Sustainable Good or Service, it needs to guarantee a net positive impact for stakeholders that could take the form both of corrective present or past harms or of supporting the progress towards a development goal.

Sustainable Goods and Services as considered in V.E analysis must be associated with the real activity of the company, issuer output and revenues. Charitable donations and philanthropic services are outside of the scope of this analysis.

For this Index, a specific list of Sustainable Goods and Services was selected by V.E experts from the full V.E assessment. The goods and services selected spread from biobased chemicals, pollution abatement technology, water treatment to recycling services and sustainable farming.[8]

It is important to highlight here that this analysis is separate from the V.E ESG methodology, but in the index, these two are used together. In case the company have some positive impacts via its Sustainable Goods and Services, selected from the bespoke list, the threshold on the GBS will be moved from 60 to 50 (out of 100), associated with the "robust" opinion by V.E (Table 12.1).

Negative Impacts

The index methodology integrates into the negative impact part, some exclusions in rules for those activities and events that are considered harmful for biodiversity protection. Two different aspects of analysing the negative impacts are adopted in the index methodology: the Controversial Activities Assessment and the Controversy Risk Assessment of the V.E research.

Controversial Activities Assessment

The Controversial Activities Assessment has the objective to identify the company's involvement in activities that contributes to the degradation of biodiversity or

TABLE 12.1 Example of companies included in the V.E selection for the Index

Company	V.E Sector	Products or Services
Neste	Energy	- Biobased chemicals
Cementos Argos	Building Material	- Afforestation
		- Building materials from wood
Suez	Waste and Water Utilities	- Contaminated site rehabilitation
		- Waste treatment
		- Wastewater treatment
		- Recycling services
		- Waste collection
		- Seawater desalinization
Seche Environnement	Waste and Water Utilities	- Contaminated site rehabilitation
		- Waste treatment
		- Recycling services
		- Waste collection
		- Pollution abatement technologies

The data for the companies listed are based on the V.E Sustainable Goods and Services updated in December 2020. Products and services provided by the company might vary in the future.

that are considered or perceived as controversial. The index uses two Controversial Activities areas: genetically modified organisms (GMOs) and Animal Welfare.

Genetically modified organisms

Genetic engineering is generally perceived to be a new way of manipulating nature. As in the V.E assessment, GMOs can be defined as *"organisms in which the genetic material has been altered in a way that does not normally occur naturally by natural recombination and/or mating"*. Those organisms could be crops, animals and microorganisms, used for human consumption or for other industrial applications. The Biodiversity Index excludes all companies that have an involvement in the production of GMOs for both human consumption and industrial uses. The level of involvement is identified from the revenues associated with these activities. The production of GMOs for medical purposes such as transgenic animals used as models or GM bacteria that produce insulin is excluded from the research.

Animal Welfare

The animal welfare area deals with three different issues that have in common the threat to the well-being of animals: animal testing, fur and intensive farming. In the case of animal farming, the raising of animals in restricted spaces has different effects and concerns both in terms of animal welfare but also safety and quality of the outputs. Animals are unable to behave according to their natural instinct and the close proximity encourages the spread of harmful antigens. This leads to the mass utilization of antibiotics that create potential risks for humans and the environment. In the case of agriculture, intensive farming implies a massive use of fertilizers, pesticides and insecticides. The usage of these products, with the run-off into water sources, has a direct impact on the surrounding ecosystem and biodiversity. The Biodiversity Index excludes all companies that have an involvement in the practices above. As for the GMOs, involvement is measured in terms of revenues associated with the activities.

Controversy Risk Assessment

Another instrument that is used by the index to exclude those companies that have a negative impact on Biodiversity is the Controversy Risk Assessment. The aim is to identify and assess any controversial event that might occur to the company connected to the biodiversity topic. A controversy as from the V.E definition is *"public information from traceable and liable sources that incriminates an issuer on ESG issues within the scope of V.E methodology"*. Such incrimination may relate to specific events or facts, to their conflicting interpretations, legal procedures or nonproven claims. Controversies are assessed based on the severity of the event; the responsiveness of the company is taking actions to remedy or prevent those events and the frequency of occurrence of the controversial events. The index excludes all companies that have at least one controversy identified on the Protection of Biodiversity ESG criteria. Below are some examples of controversies that are flagged that lead to an exclusion of stocks for the Index[9]

- BP to pay USD 71,000 in diesel spill settlement in Iowa
- Pan American Energy (a partly owned BP company) among other companies sued over environmental contamination by a group of indigenous people in Argentina
- BHP loses bid to limit shareholder claims in Samarco dam disaster class action
- US administration seeks to transfer ownership of Arizona's Oak Flat to Resolution Copper despite Apache tribe opposition
- ENI responds to Amnesty International accusation of negligence over oil spills in Nigeria

Conclusion

ESG is more and more important for investors. If at the beginning investor policies were general and focused mainly on the three pillars of ESG, now policies and sustainable investment strategies are getting richer in detail. The strong activity of regulatory frameworks and international agreements is also pushing the investment towards a more precise analysis of the composition of portfolios and funds. On the contrary, for some companies, the cost of taking action and engaging with policies towards a more sustainable future is still high. Incentives to migrate these companies to the new sustainable alignment should be driven not only by regulation and common interests, but also by investment choices.

In this context, the Biodiversity Index wants to highlight and give relevance to some good examples of actors that have already incorporated biodiversity in their agenda with strong commitments and actions, and stimulate others to pursue this goal.

With the development of passive investment, the aim of this index is also to push the market to have an innovative and sustainable way to allocate resources to companies and actors that are making the difference in one or more thematic areas and set a trend for the future towards a more meaningful way of investing.

Notes

1 SPIVA® U.S. Scorecard mid-2020, Berlinda Liu & Gaurav Sinha (2020).
2 For further details, please see the French Financial Market Authority (AMF) "Opportunities and risks in the financial index market", Laurent Grillet Aubert (2020).
3 Solactive (2019): Blog Biodiversity as an Investment Opportunity.
4 OECD (2019); Biodiversity: Finance and the Economic and Business Case for Action, report prepared for the G7 Environment Ministers' Meeting, 5–6 May 2019.
5 Not exhaustive list.
6 The companies listed are part of the Index selection based on ESG filters only with the update of December 2020. The index composition might vary in the future. The financial filters applied by Solactive for the final selection are not used here.
7 The main historical and contemporary reference texts and standards outlining definitions for Sustainable Development used in the V.E methodology and definition are:

   "Our Common Future" – Brundtland Commission – 1987
   "Rio Declaration on Environmental and Development" – United Nations – 1992
   "Millennium Development Goals" – United Nations – 2000
   "Sustainable Development Goals" – United Nations – 2015

8 Not exhaustive list.
9 Controversies remain in V.E database for a certain number of years depending on the severity associated with the research and the updates of the controversy itself. These examples are taken from the V.E data updated in December 2020.

13

BIODIVERSITY AND SUSTAINABILITY RATINGS

From Data to Assessments[1]

Anna Zubets-Anderson and Marie Lehmann

Section 1: The Growing Need for Comprehensive and Reliable Biodiversity Impact Data

ANNA ZUBETS-ANDERSON

Ecosystem Decline Calls for Deeper Understanding of Biodiversity Factors

The ongoing biodiversity decline is calling for a more comprehensive incorporation of nature-related risks into investment decisions. While nature services are critical to well-functioning economies and societies, we have been experiencing biodiversity loss at a rate that leads many experts to believe we are facing the sixth mass extinction on the planet.[2] According to the recent report by Credit Suisse and Responsible Investor,[3] vertebrate populations have declined by almost 70% from 1970, roughly 40% of plants are estimated to be threatened, and over 50% of marine species will be threatened by 2050. Erosion of natural systems is presenting enormous risks to human health, food security, industrial production and social order. These issues also present direct risks to businesses, to the extent that their operations rely on access to water, land and natural capital. While companies affect their ecosystem, they, just like the rest of humanity, ultimately depend on it for their continued survival. A water-polluting business depends on continuing access to water, exposing it to water scarcity issues. A biomass company depends on continued access to logging residues and will likely suffer from the impacts of deforestation. The agriculture business depends on the fertile soil and will be impacted by its depletion. Numerous industries depend on the ecosystem remaining in balance – not to mention employees and communities, whose health is also dependent on it.

The *Global Futures* report, published in February 2020 by World Wildlife Fund for Nature (WWF), Global Trade Analysis Project and the Natural Capital Project,[4] investigates the economic value of "'ecosystem services' – such as the

DOI: 10.4324/9781003045557-17

pollination of crops, protection of coasts from flooding and erosion, supply of water, timber production, marine fisheries and carbon storage" and concludes that in a business–as–usual scenario, the economic loss from the erosion of these systems alone would be almost $10 trillion through 2050. The 2021 report by Credit Suisse and Responsible Investor estimates the total economic value of nature, as a contributor to global economy, at $125 trillion.

In response to the growing environmental crisis and related business risks, many market participants seek to direct capital flows towards projects with environmental benefits and towards companies that manage their environmental footprint. As a result, we have seen tremendous growth in the sustainable finance market and proliferation of responsible investment strategies, with sustainable assets under management now topping $35 trillion globally (Global Sustainable Investment Alliance, 2021[5]).

Dual-Materiality Perspective Is Essential to Biodiversity-Conscious Investment Decisions

Although the interdependencies between natural resource-reliant companies and the health of the ecosystem are becoming increasingly obvious, indicators or measures of biodiversity, and especially biodiversity loss, have not been traditionally fully factored into financial reporting and analysis. Put simply, established traditional accounting frameworks value the industrial process, but not the natural habitat consumed by it. Products, properties, intellectual inventions and even human relationships (e.g. customer contracts) are recognized as assets on the corporate balance sheets. But so far, there has been no mechanism to recognize obligations to, or impact upon, other species and nature at large. As Duncan Austin remarked in his October 2020 article,[6] the "market rests on half of an accounting framework that disconnects it from physical reality";… "we 'value' the sheltering log cabin, but not the corresponding damage to the forest".

Unlike traditional financial information, data that are needed to drive environmentally conscious investment decisions must embrace the concept of dual materiality – meaning that decision-relevant factors are not only those that directly affect the financial performance and long-term value of the company (i.e. financially material factors), but also those that pertain to the company's impact on the ecosystem and the human society.

The entity's impact on society and the environment can and often does eventually become financially material, through channels such as reputational or legal risk. Generally, a company's biodiversity footprint becomes financially material when it is assessed legal fines, is required to remediate impacted areas, faces restrictions in its access to natural capital such as land or water, or suffers reputational damage due to controversial incidents. Traditional accounting frameworks, which focus on financial materiality, often result in reporting of biodiversity-relevant data only after a controversial event, like an oil spill or an adverse government action, happens.

However, investment decisions made through the lens of environmental and social sustainability seek to have a more comprehensive and forward view. This includes information that extends beyond financial materiality and captures the entity's impact on a broader set of stakeholders and not just the shareholders, potentially highlighting a controversial business practice long before it translates into a direct or indirect financial impact. A dual-materiality perspective aims to capture this broader set of biodiversity data – but most corporate disclosure frameworks that embrace the dual-materiality concept are voluntary. Due to inconsistencies amongst companies as to how and whether they adopt the voluntary frameworks, asset managers face biodiversity data that are inconsistent, incomplete or simply non-existent, as is further discussed below.

Further complicating the picture, when it comes to the company's impact on the ecosystem, the question of what to measure and how to measure it is complex. It is context-specific, for both individual industries and specific locations across a company's operations. Relevant metrics may be very different for a utility that is a significant carbon emitter, a wind farm that is threatening wildlife like birds and bats, or a fishery that is dependent on marine natural resources.

Sustainability Rating Providers Seek to Measure Biodiversity Footprint with Varied Approaches

Sustainability assessments (also commonly called Environmental, Social and Governance (ESG) ratings) seek to make responsible investment decisions easier by applying standardized methodologies to diverse ESG data available in the market, to come up with a more easily digestible score (or set of scores). Sustainability assessments generally evaluate how the company manages relationships with its various stakeholders, which usually extend well beyond shareholders and creditors and include customers, employees and communities, amongst others. Such assessments typically include the company's impact on natural habitats. Given the variability of available ESG data from a dual-materiality standpoint, assessment providers may base their evaluations on a broad range of different information sources – including company disclosures, public reports, government, media and company completed questionnaires.

The market of sustainability assessments is relatively young, with best market practices still developing. There are many different providers of ESG assessments, with many different philosophies and methodologies as to what to measure, how to measure it, and how to weigh trade-offs between competing business priorities. They cater to a wide range of users with differing needs – some focusing on financially material data and some on a broader range of considerations as to what constitutes a socially and environmentally responsible business, yet others seeking to align portfolios with specific social and/or environmental agendas. This diversity in end-users drives diversity in methodologies and approaches employed by sustainability assessment providers.

In the widely referenced *Aggregate Confusion: The Divergence of ESG Ratings*, Florian Berg, Julian F. Koelbel and Roberto Rigobon of the MIT Sloan School of Management[7] explore this diversity at length. They evaluate ESG scores from six providers – KLD (MSCI Stats), Sustainalytics, Vigeo Eiris (V.E) (Moody's), RobecoSAM (S&P Global), Asset4 (Refinitiv), and MSCI, and find an average correlation of 0.54, with a range from 0.38 to 0.71, compared to the correlation between traditional credit ratings of 0.99. In this study, they find that biodiversity was considered as a factor by all six providers – indicating that there is at least a consistent recognition that biodiversity footprint is material to business sustainability. But the correlation between Global Biodiversity Scores (GBSs) averaged at 0.43 in 2017, with seven out of ten provider pairs correlating below 0.50 – indicating a low level of agreement between them on issues of biodiversity management.

Sustainability Assessment Example – V.E Biodiversity Score

As one example, Moody's Affiliate, V.E, evaluates biodiversity as one of 38 distinct ESG criteria, and it is weighted differently depending on the sector, with 40 industry-specific models deployed. V.E defines biodiversity as a company's commitment to prevent risks of endangering biodiversity and to manage animal testing (when relevant for the sector). Its approach to scoring the biodiversity factor, similar to other factors, is to evaluate it along three dimensions – quality of leadership (i.e. the extent of company's commitments), quality of implementation of said commitments (i.e. sufficiency of measures put in place) and evaluation of results (i.e. extent and management of biodiversity-related controversies). A high-performing company along this dimension would be expected to identify where and how it impacts biodiversity and establish evaluation systems to assess the health of the ecosystems it affects. It would also be expected to avoid or reduce ecosystem exploitation and to rehabilitate any exploited areas. The importance of the factor would vary by industry. For example, industries that deploy large land areas (like forestry, agriculture, mining and hotels) or have frequent harmful incidents (like the oil industry) are considered to be more exposed. Sectors for which operations require less land or whose facilities are located in less ecologically sensitive places, such as urban areas (e.g. real estate) or industrial zones (e.g. the chemical industry) may be less exposed.

Asset Managers Largely Rely on Their Own Analysis, Engagement with Issuers and Narrowly Focused Measurement Tools

With sustainability assessments diverging, asset managers are largely left to their own devices in determining how to incorporate biodiversity into their investment decisions, especially when part of the goal is in alignment with environmental and social responsibility. And while we see a widespread and growing acknowledgement of biodiversity risks as critically important, the financial community is still in the early phases of learning to understand them. According to the 2021 report by Responsible Investor and Credit Suisse, amongst the 327 investors surveyed from 35 countries, 84% were very concerned about the biodiversity loss, but 91% did not have measurable biodiversity-linked targets and 72% have not assessed their investments' impact on biodiversity. As to the cause, 70% of responders identified data issues as a key barrier to biodiversity-conscious investment decisions.

Consistent with these findings, three investment managers that we interviewed[8] also cited inconsistent and insufficient data as key factors in making their biodiversity evaluation difficult. They further noted that applying standardized methodologies may not yield clear results, because sector- and context-specific nature of biodiversity dependencies makes meaningful measurement of standardized metrics very difficult. They contrasted this with climate issues, the understanding of which is more advanced, and for which standardized metrics are easier to define, due to more homogeneous nature of the impacts being measured.

Highlighting the same issue, the 2019 report by AXA Group and the WWF[9] stated:

> In contrast to climate, standardized data and methodologies do not yet exist for other nature-related risk analysis. There are no "tons of CO_2" to factor in when it comes to mitigating biodiversity loss. As a result, financial institutions are not yet capable of measuring, monitoring or reporting the impacts and dependencies of their portfolios on nature in a harmonized manner. This also prevents them from assessing the ensuing nature-related risks and opportunities and ultimately changing their investment behaviour.

Similarly, a 2020 PRI study of 11 investors[10] noted that they lacked sufficient asset- and company-level data:

> Data is often not fit for purpose. Biodiversity is location specific and varies according to the actual asset at that location. Therefore, it can be challenging to aggregate biodiversity data at an enterprise level.

As a result of these issues, asset managers we interviewed reported applying their own inquiry and evaluation on a case-by-case basis. In some cases, they reported the use of an internally developed questionnaire posed to management of investee companies. In others, they relied on various measurement tools that were narrow- and context-specific, such as measures of deforestation, impacts of palm oil production, or proximity of facilities to species-protected areas.

The asset managers we interviewed expressed hope that as disclosures around biodiversity and natural capital develop, better understanding and more sophisticated standardized assessment tools will follow. And as discussed below, there are signs that the financial community is moving in this direction.

Corporate Disclosures on Biodiversity Are Starting to Develop

Although disclosure is in the early stages of development, there are signs that corporates are starting to address the biodiversity information gap. A 2018 study by Addison, Bull and Milner-Gulland[11] studied the Fortune 100 companies' sustainability reports, finding that almost half (49) mentioned biodiversity in reports, and 31 made clear biodiversity commitments. However, of these only five were "specific, measurable, and time bound". They noted disclosure of a variety of biodiversity-related activities, including impact management, habitat restoration, and investments in biodiversity. However, quantitative metrics were available from only nine companies.

Such inconsistencies in extent and quality of reporting are attributable to the fact that most corporate disclosure frameworks that address companies' impact on the environment are voluntary. They include standards like the Global Reporting Initiative (GRI) and formerly the Carbon Disclosure Project (CDP). For example, the voluntary GRI standard on biodiversity (GRI 304) directs companies to disclose:

- their biodiversity management strategy related to the damage that business activities cause to natural habitats;
- operational details on sites located in, or adjacent to, protected areas;
- description of significant direct and indirect impacts on biodiversity, such as pollution, invasive species and habitat destruction;
- size, location and other descriptors of habitat protection and restoration efforts; and
- total number of species in habitats affected by operations, by level of extinction risk.

Several recently launched initiatives aim to further develop the quality and comprehensiveness of biodiversity-related data available in the market. Perhaps the most significant development is the launch of the Task Force on Nature-related Financial Disclosure (TNFD)[12] in September 2020. The TNFD working group includes members such as the World Bank, the Organisation for Economic Co-operation and Development (OECD), over 30 financial institutions from five continents, and representatives of the governments of UK, France, Peru, Switzerland, Argentina and Mexico. The TNFD will build on the earlier similar work done for climate – by the Task Force on Climate-related Financial Disclosure (TCFD), which in 2017 released its recommendations on climate risk disclosures. TCFD work drove significant improvements in data needed to manage risks stemming from climate change. The TNFD framework may, in a similar way, help improve the availability, quality, comparability, consistency and transparency of biodiversity-related data. In addition, the EU Taxonomy, which is part of the European Commission's Sustainable Finance Action Plan, is expected (in 2021) to address biodiversity in defining which business activities qualify as sustainable.

Also in September 2020, 26 financial firms managing over €3 trillion ($3.5 trillion) in assets, including AXA, HSBC Global Asset Management and Robeco, signed the Finance for Biodiversity Pledge to assess their own biodiversity impact and to set science-based targets and reporting on biodiversity issues by 2024.[13] And earlier in the year, in July 2020, eight Dutch financial institutions formed a Working Group on Biodiversity which will work to enhance understanding of biodiversity-related risks and opportunities.[14]

Looking ahead, momentum is building to close data gaps, thereby enhancing the assessment of companies' management of their biodiversity footprint and nature-related financial risks. Asset managers will be better equipped to make biodiversity-conscious decisions with the further development, standardization and alignment of biodiversity reporting standards.

Section 2: Emerging Innovative Biodiversity Measurement Tools Offer Promise

By Marie Lehmann[15]

As financial reporting around biodiversity risks and dependencies continues to develop, we also see continued innovation with respect to measurement tools that use these data. A number of tools have emerged in the last few years and offer promise. Amongst them are the Exploring Natural Capital Opportunities, Risks and Exposure (ENCORE) tool launched by the UN Environment Programme World Conservation Monitoring Centre (UNEP-WCMC) and the Natural Capital Finance Alliance, the Biodiversity Return on Investment Metric (BRIM) launched by the International Union for Conservation of Nature (IUCN), the GBS developed by CDC Biodiversité, and the University of Cambridge Institute for Sustainability Leadership (CISL)'s Biodiversity Impact Metric.

These tools have a fundamental role to play in promoting the consideration of biodiversity factors across sectors amongst the finance industry and more specifically, to engage businesses. Such tools can help highlight actions taken by organizations to effectively reduce pressures on biodiversity and their contribution to the achievement of global targets such as the Aichi Biodiversity Targets.

Some of these existing tools are presented in more detail below. While these initiatives are promising, they also illustrate the current lack of standardization around biodiversity impact measurement, which is an issue valid for ESG metrics in general as discussed above. In an effort to facilitate alignment, in September 2020, the Partnership for Biodiversity Accounting Financial (PBAF) published the *Common Ground Report on biodiversity impact assessment* – offering some common practices that can be used in a biodiversity impact assessment.[16]

Exploring Natural Capital Opportunities, Risks and Exposure

The ENCORE tool was developed by the UNEP-WCMC in partnership with the Natural Capital Finance Alliance (UNEP-FI and Global Canopy) and launched in November 2018. It is part of a project financed by the Swiss State Secretariat for Economic Affairs (SECO) and the MAVA Foundation whose aim it was to assist financial institutions in better understanding, assessing and integrating natural capital risks into their investment or lending activities.

More particularly, this project focused on how financial institutions can apply this information to screen portfolios for natural capital risks, integrate these insights in risk management processes and help align their portfolios with global/regional biodiversity goals.

ENCORE is an open access, interactive and very visual tool that allows users to assess the impact of businesses on nature, how they depend on it and how environmental degradation could present business risks for companies and therefore financial institutions as a result. Companies can use the tool to identify natural capital risks from a business sector, ecosystem service or natural capital asset lens. ENCORE also provides maps of natural capital assets and drivers of environmental change for location-specific risk assessments.

Biodiversity Return on Investment Metric

The BRIM was launched by the IUCN to assist investors in making investment decisions.

Based on the IUCN Red List of Threatened Species, the BRIM measures the contribution that investments can make to reducing species extinction risk across geographies. It can be used by investors and more broadly finance professionals to target their investments to achieve conservation outcomes (for instance, choose investments in protected areas to mitigate issues such as hunting, deforestation or invasive species that threaten species survival and then assess how their investment is able to reduce the impact of these threats on extinction risk). It also measures the contributions these investments make to global targets such as the Sustainable Development Goals (SDGs).

The BRIM assigns a relative contribution of threats (pressures) to each threatened species' extinction. It provides an ex ante measure (i.e. the potential for reducing extinction risk before investment activities begin) and ex post measure (i.e. the achieved impact of conservation interventions on extinction risk over time).

It is used to analyze and compare potential and achieved a return on investment across a portfolio, to track sectoral impacts on extinction risks, to target interventions at specific sites and/or specific pressures and to also track and develop global targets on slowing extinction risks.

CDC Biodiversité Methodology

Developed by the Paris-based financial institution CDC Biodiversité (Groupe Caisse des Dépôts), the CDC Biodiversité methodology is an innovative methodology that helps firms across all sectors quantify their impacts on ecosystems and put more emphasis on biodiversity factors when defining development strategies. It uses a single indicator called the GBS that is expressed in the surface area of destroyed pristine natural areas. CDC Biodiversité collaborated with several members of the Business for Positive Biodiversity (B4B+) Club to create this score.

The GBS enables one to quantify the biodiversity footprint of organizations and investments along the whole value chain. The results of assessments conducted with the GBS are expressed in the MSA.km2 unit where MSA is the mean species abundance, a metric expressed in percentage characterizing the intactness of ecosystems. MSA values range from 0% to 100%, where 100% represents an undisturbed pristine ecosystem. Stakeholders can then build indicators based on GBS assessment results, for instance, Key Performance Indicators (KPIs) against which to measure corporate performance. Such a KPI could, for instance, be the total biodiversity impact of a business, and it could, for example, be associated with a reduction target by 2030.

The University of Cambridge Institute for Sustainability Leadership's Biodiversity Impact Metric

The CISL's Natural Capital Impact Group launched the Biodiversity Impact Metric in the spring of 2020. It is a practical risk-screening tool that allows supply chain organizations that source agricultural commodities map key biodiversity risk areas across their operations around the world and across different commodities. Based on this metric which is comparable, businesses can prioritize where to act, make better sourcing decisions and develop adequate response strategies enabling them to safeguard natural capital, drive improved business performance and ultimately maintain their license to operate. This tool is particularly useful for firms with complex global supply chains that lack data. The Biodiversity Impact Metric evaluates the impact of companies for specific commodities sourced from a particular location based on the land area needed for production of the commodity, the proportion of biodiversity lost when the land is transformed to produce the commodity – related to the type of land use – and its intensity and the relative global importance of that biodiversity.

To conclude, biodiversity is not yet captured effectively by traditional accounting and disclosure frameworks. Corporates must embrace dual materiality and improve biodiversity disclosures. The financial community has a key role to play in creating a sense of urgency amongst corporations to do so. It is imperative that investment management companies heighten their levels of engagement with companies to entice them to enhance their biodiversity disclosures. Lenders need to better assess the impact on biodiversity of companies' projects prior to offering financing. Governmental and non-governmental organizations need to scrutinize companies' potential harm to biodiversity and disclosures more closely. Finally, there is an urgent need for data providers to improve the quality and comparability of their data as well as the transparency of their methodologies. Close collaboration between all these actors will be crucial in order to avoid them working in silos and ultimately reverse *biodiversity* loss and put nature and ecosystems on a path to recovery within the next ten years.

Summary

- Assessment and measurement of biodiversity footprint are essential to understanding a company's sustainability profile.
- Traditional accounting and disclosure frameworks do not sufficiently capture biodiversity-related information from a dual-materiality perspective.
- Limited company-level data and different approaches in ESG assessment methodologies can present a challenge to asset managers seeking to evaluate target companies' biodiversity factors.
- Continued improvement in the quality, transparency and comparability of biodiversity data will bring a sharper focus on protection of biodiversity from decline and extinction.
- A number of recent developments around standardization of disclosures and metrics set the direction for the future, towards biodiversity-related data that is more comprehensive, consistent and robust.

Notes

1 © Moody's Corporation and/or its affiliates. Reprinted with permission. All Rights Reserved. The full terms and conditions applicable to this chapter are available at the following link: moodys.com/disclaimer.
2 See, for example, *Biological annihilation via the ongoing sixth mass extinction signaled by vertebrate population losses and declines* by Gerardo Ceballos, Paul R. Ehrlich, and Rodolfo Dirzo (https://www.pnas.org/content/114/30/E6089).
3 Unearthing investor action on biodiversity, Credit Suisse and RI, January 2021 (https://www.esg-data.com/product-page/unearthing-investor-action-on-biodiversity?utm_source=Responsible+Investor+Membership&utm_campaign=cb473727b2-EMAIL_CAMPAIGN_2019_09_10_03_56_COPY_02&utm_medium=email&utm_term=0_c06c86fea3-cb473727b2-293916591).
4 Retrieved from https://wwfint.awsassets.panda.org/downloads/global_futures_summary_report.pdf.
5 Downloaded from http://www.gsi-alliance.org/wp-content/uploads/2021/07/GSIR-2020.pdf.
6 *Should ESG view sustainability as a quicksand problem?*, Duncan Austin, October 12, 2020, Responsible Investor.
7 Retrieved from https://papers.ssrn.com/sol3/papers.cfm?abstract_id=3438533.
8 We discussed these issues with three asset managers from three major institutions, asking each how they go about evaluating investees' biodiversity footprint, their views on the state of information available, the assessments and tools that they use in their evaluation, and their expectations for the future.

9 Retrieved from https://wwfeu.awsassets.panda.org/downloads/report_wwf_france____axa_into_the_wild_may_2019__dv_1.pdf.

10 UN Principles for Responsible Investment *Investor action on biodiversity: Discussion paper;* retrieved from https://www.unpri.org/download?ac=11357.

11 Using conservation science to advance corporate biodiversity accountability by Prue F. E. Addison Joseph W. Bull E. J. Milner-Gulland. First published: 15 July 2018 https://doi.org/10.1111/cobi.13190.

12 https://www.responsible-investor.com/articles/what-a-task-force-on-nature-related-financial-disclosures-will-achieve.

13 https://www.environmental-finance.com/content/news/26-firms-commit-to-biodiversity-impact-and-disclosure-pledge.html.

14 https://www.environmental-finance.com/content/analysis/biodiversity-lessons-from-the-dutch-working-group.html.

15 The views expressed in this section are wholly those of the author. They do not necessarily represent the views of the author's employer or any of its affiliates; and accordingly, such employer and its affiliates expressly disclaim all responsibility for the content and information contained herein.

16 https://www.environmental-finance.com/content/news/biodiversity-accounting-initiative-outlines-initial-guidelines.html.

14

ASSESSING FINANCIAL EXPOSURE TO BIODIVERSITY RISKS THROUGH CORPORATE FACILITY MAPPING[1]

Léonie Chatain, Nathalie Borgeaud and Natalie Ambrosio Preudhomme

The current rate of extinction of species is estimated at 100 to 1,000 times higher than natural background rates, leading some scientists to argue that we are on the verge of or even in the midst of sixth mass extinction.[2] The latest Intergovernmental Science-Policy Platform on Biodiversity and Ecosystem Services (IPBES) states in its 2019 report that nature is declining at rates unprecedented in human history.[3] As with climate change, this leads to global impacts and is influenced by human and business activity. Businesses contribute to biodiversity loss with their impacts on ecosystems, yet they also rely on nature for their operations, making them dependent on biodiversity. We use the following three pillars to understand businesses' relationship to biodiversity and explain each briefly below: business impacts on biodiversity, business dependencies on biodiversity and governance of biodiversity risks.

Business Impacts on Biodiversity

At the root of the biodiversity crisis are five drivers of biodiversity loss, identified by the IPBES and listed here in declining order of impact: changes in land and sea use, direct exploitation of organisms, climate change, pollution and invasive species. These five direct drivers result from underlying causes including production and consumption patterns, human population dynamics, trade, technological innovations and governance, from local to global levels. IPBES defines land and sea use changes as the expansion of agriculture and cities, fragmentation, land degradation as well as increasing management of landscapes and oceans. Overexploitation of animals, plants and other organisms occurs primarily through harvesting, logging, hunting and fishing, according to IPBES.[4] Land and sea use changes together with direct exploitation account for more than 50% of the global impact of humans on land, in freshwater and in the sea. The products we

DOI: 10.4324/9781003045557-18

consume and their supply chains, including material inputs and how these are extracted and manufactured, have countless impacts on nature. The case study in this chapter will explore corporate facilities' proximity to areas of biodiversity significance based on if they're in protected zones, as one indicator of business impacts on biodiversity.

Business Dependencies on Nature

While this chapter will focus on business impacts on biodiversity, it's also important to understand that the economy is dependent on biodiversity and nature, as natural ecosystems provide essential services to businesses. Two main types of natural services are particularly important to businesses: provisioning and regulating services. Provisioning services relate to production inputs. Water, food, fiber and other raw materials are important inputs for many primary sectors and processing operations. Shortages in these materials would lead to risks in other sectors such as consumer goods, through the supply chain. Regulating services are the ecosystem processes that facilitate or moderate natural phenomena. For example, pollination and pest control are essential for agriculture, while natural flood protection is key to telecommunication networks and erosion protection through adequate vegetation cover is important to many utilities.

Half of the global gross domestic product (GDP), €40 trillion, depends on nature, as the European Union (EU) Commission acknowledges in its Biodiversity Strategy for 2030.[5] An analysis from the Natural Capital Finance Alliance showed that 74% of the market capitalization of the Financial Times Stock Exchange (FTSE) 100 is associated with production processes highly dependent on natural capital.[6] Recognizing the significant dependence of sectors such as agriculture, construction and consumer goods on nature, the World Economic Forum highlighted biodiversity loss as one of the top five risks in their 2020 Global Risks Report.[7] The loss of ecosystem services can threaten companies' production processes and supply chains and therefore directly influence their financial revenues.

Governance of Biodiversity Risks

While it's not the focus of this chapter, the third pillar of businesses' relationships with biodiversity is their governance of biodiversity risks. A company's impacts on both biodiversity and its dependence on natural capital will be affected by the governance, which will in turn drive the impacts a company incurs from these risks. Governance includes a company's engagement in conservation initiatives and its efforts to reduce species and biodiversity loss throughout the value chain.

New Policies and Regulations – Focus on Europe

Biodiversity loss is a growing concern for policy makers and regulators around the world. In Europe, regulators on the national and EU level have begun to give more attention to the question of reporting and disclosure of corporate information on biodiversity management. In France, the landmark climate risk disclosure law, Article 173 of the Law on Energy Transition for Green Growth, adopted in 2015, will be replaced by Article 29, which adds the requirement for firms to disclose their impact and dependence on biodiversity, as well as their governance of these risks, beginning in 2022.[8]

The Europe 2030 Biodiversity Strategy already lays out commitments to establish protected areas for at least 30% of land and sea in Europe, including 10% as "strictly protected areas."[9] Protected areas are defined by the International Union for Conservation of Nature (IUCN) as "a clearly defined geographical space, recognized, dedicated and managed through legal or other effective means, to achieve the long-term conservation of nature with associated ecosystem services and cultural values."[10] (Dudley 2008). This broad definition does not exclude areas where economic activities are happening, as these areas are meant to exist not in isolated locations, but within the broader socioeconomic context.[11] Rather, this classification means that such protected areas are subject to specific conservational goals, based on their precise characteristics. For example, the EU also has a target for "strictly protected areas," defined as "accessible to humans" but leaving "natural processes essentially undisturbed to respect the areas' ecological requirements."[12] While the EU Commission is still refining its definition of protected areas,[13] it is likely to exclude some economic activities, especially those with the most direct impacts on nature, such as manufacturing and mining.

The EU taxonomy for sustainable activities, adopted by the parliament in June 2020, includes a list of economic activities considered environmentally sustainable for investment purposes.[14] For a company's activities to fall within this list, they must meet the criteria for doing no significant harm to biodiversity. The first company reports and investor disclosures using the EU Taxonomy are due in January 2022. These will be required as part of the EU Non-financial Reporting Directive (NFRD).[15] The NFRD is also expected to request disclosure on key points such as proximity to biodiversity-protected zones, deforestation or water stress.[16] Likewise, the EU Sustainable Finance Reporting Directive (SFRD) that came into effect in March 2021 mandates financial institutions to report on the sustainability of their investments and includes biodiversity indicators.[17]

In the same spirit, in fall 2020, the European Central Bank (ECB) opened a draft guide on climate-related and environmental risks for consultation.[18] The guide describes the ECB's expectations for banks' risks management frameworks to integrate how they will be affected by environmental and climate risks such as those driven by biodiversity loss or water stress. Disclosing these risks with meaningful, comparable metrics will increase transparency in the financial system.

To meet this growing demand, investors and corporates jointly call for the implementation of quantitative, biodiversity-related metrics, footprint assessment tools and measurable science-based targets.[19] On the financial side, Global Canopy, the United Nations Development Programme (UNDP), the United

Nations Environment Programme Finance Initiative (UNEP FI), and the World Wide Fund for Nature (WWF) launched the Task Force for Nature-related Financial Disclosure (TNFD) in July 2020.[20] The TNFD was aimed to support the redirecting of finance flows toward nature-positive investments by providing a reporting framework for biodiversity risks.[21] As of April 2021, an informal working group including financial institutions, business and government participants and a technical expert group has been developing the scope for the initiative. These developments highlight the growing need for ongoing research to develop such tools and metrics.

Understanding and Assessing Business Impacts on Biodiversity

Biodiversity Significance

One of the approaches for understanding financial exposure to biodiversity impact risk is to map the footprint of business operations and identify locations that operate near areas of high biodiversity importance. The IUCN classifies areas of high biodiversity value, including areas important to threatened species, migratory species, critical habitats or key ecosystems.

This case study looks specifically at protected areas classified by UNEP and IUCN as one type of area with biodiversity significance. However, it is important to note that a protected area is not necessarily an area of high biodiversity significance, and conversely, there might be areas with high and valuable biological diversity which are not part of a recognized protected area. Therefore, a corporation can have a negative impact on biodiversity outside of the protected zones, and it will not be captured by this analysis. Similarly, as this case study focuses only on protected areas, it does not include areas listed as threatened species zones. Ongoing analyses by Moody's ESG Solutions, powered by Four Twenty Seven, capture the presence of corporate facilities in other types of areas with high biodiversity significance. For example, we are currently developing a biodiversity significance indicator that considers *contextual intactness*, defined as the importance of a location relative to other areas across the globe with similar species composition.[22]

As we expect to see changes in regulation and consumer preferences, companies with operations in areas of high biodiversity significance are likely to face increasing reputation risk and will need to adapt to an economy "which conserves and restores biodiversity."[23] The Amazon deforestation provides an example of how regulations and changing consumer behavior can translate to financial risk for investors in companies that have operations in areas of biodiversity significance.[24] In response to the increasing deforestation in the Brazilian Amazon forest, the Norwegian pension fund Storebrand expressed its concern to Brazilian embassies on the impact on investing conditions.[25] The fund committed to zero deforestation by 2025, defining deforestation as a risk for companies and shareholders, which will have implications for companies contributing to or benefiting from deforestation, such as companies linked to commodities, particularly palm oil, soy, timber or cattle products.[26]

Leveraging Four Twenty Seven's database[27] on corporate facilities, in a June 2020 study, The Dutch Central Bank (DNB) found that Dutch financial institutions have EUR 308 billion in shares in companies that have some of their facilities in protected or valuable areas and provided them EUR 81 billion in loans.[28] This equates to a striking 71% of the total equity portfolio of Dutch financial institutions and 40% of the Dutch banks' major loans. The DNB report identifies proximity to protected areas as a reputational risk for financial institutions invested in companies that operate in protected areas.[29] The report uses the controversy around British oil company SOCO's exploration activities in the Virunga National Park in the Democratic Republic of Congo as an example of reputation risks of biodiversity loss. This park is home to endangered mountain gorillas[30] and in its campaign against the project, the WWF directly targeted the corporations' investors,[31] putting them in a difficult position to justify and report on their engagement and vote action with the company.

Approach: Identifying Corporate Operations in Protected Zones

This chapter builds on the research shared in the DNB report, providing an analysis of 720 companies' proximity to protected areas, as a proxy for areas with high biodiversity significance, based on the location of their corporate facilities. For each company, we identified if its European facilities fall within a protected zone. To develop this analysis, we matched Four Twenty Seven's database on the precise location of corporate facilities with data on terrestrial-protected areas. The latter comes from the World Database on Protected Areas (WDPA) developed by UNEP and IUCN and includes a set of areas with different conservational goals. In a significant number of these areas, economic activities are authorized with various levels of restrictions. As these zones host valuable ecosystems, the presence of facilities increases a company's potential impacts on biodiversity, exacerbating its risk.

Currently, companies are often under added pressure from their stakeholders, including nongovernmental organizations (NGOs), local regulators and investors, to conduct their operations with additional care in areas listed by IUCN even when the areas aren't specifically protected. For example, the International Finance Corporation Performance Standard #6[32] focuses on Biodiversity Conservation and Sustainable Management of Living Natural Resources and the NFDR and SFRD regulations discussed above include disclosures on biodiversity. As Europe continues toward its biodiversity goals, additional areas are likely to receive protected status in the future. Thus, companies that have business activities in locations that will be granted protected area status in the future may have to relocate or adjust, involving additional costs.

   This analysis brings insights on the proximity to protected areas, as one criterion of biodiversity significance to help inform the understanding of interactions between businesses and biodiversity.

Findings: Differing Proximity to Protected Zones based on Sectors

Overall, our analysis found that 6% of the 107,207 assessed facilities are in a protected area. 412 of the 720 companies included in the study have at least one site within a protected area. This average figure hides some level of discrepancies between sectors, as there is a larger share of facilities from the utilities and energy sectors with facilities in protected areas. These two sectors have 10% and 8%, respectively, of their facilities within protected areas (see Figure 14.1). Their facilities include water supply facilities, industrial sewage systems, refuse systems and electrical transmission or distribution facilities. Sewage and refuse systems are of particular concern regarding their potential polluting impact on the surrounding ecosystems.

   Consumer services, capital goods and the food, beverage and tobacco sectors are also among the most exposed sectors, based on their percentage of facilities in protected areas. The food sector is mainly known for its impacts on biodiversity

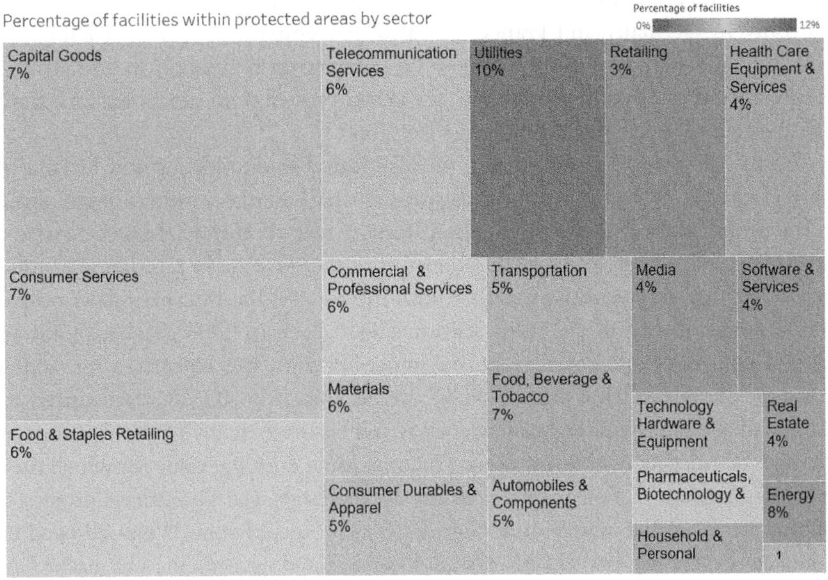

FIGURE 14.1   This heat map represents the percentage of facilities located within protected areas. The size of the boxes corresponds to the number of assessed facilities in the sector and the color illustrates the percentage of facilities within protected areas.

Source: Moody's ESG Solutions, powered by Four Twenty Seven; and the WDPA, developed by UNEP-WCMC and IUCN.

due to intensive agriculture and fishing. However, most of the risk lies within the corporations' supply chain and is not captured within this analysis.

The consumer services facilities in the Four Twenty Seven's database are mainly retail sites. One way in which retail sites likely impact biodiversity is through their land use, as well as the infrastructure supporting the retail activity, such as transportation infrastructure. In France, the new Governmental Biodiversity plan calls for zero net land transformation. Achieving this goal by 2030 will mean reducing land conversion by 70% while bringing 5,500 hectares back to nature every year ("renaturation strategy"). As such, the parliament adopted a law in April 2021 prohibiting the construction of new large shopping centers in natural or agricultural areas.[33] Transportation infrastructure is known to represent 28% of land use in France and is therefore at the center of those concerns.[34] For example, the Notre Dame des Landes controversy over the building of a new airport in France on wetlands that had biodiversity value lasted over 20 years and was settled by a definitive no-go in 2018, under the pressure of the Minister for Ecological Transition, Mr. Hulot.[35]

Our analysis shows that most of the capital goods sector's facilities located in the protected areas are construction and manufacturing sites. These types of sites are likely to have a high water consumption and to generate water and air pollution that affects ecosystems. As illustrated by the map below (Figure 14.2), of assessed manufacturing sites, those within protected areas are mainly located not only in Germany and France, but also in Denmark, the United Kingdom and Italy. These sites could be exposed to increasing regulation in and around the protected areas and may already face certain restrictions meant to limit their disturbance of species and habitat in these areas.

Within the capital goods sector, we also found some mining sites located in protected areas. Most of these mining sites are used by large multinationals for the extraction of sand, gravel or dimension stone. Given their impact on ecosystems, mining sites are likely to be at the forefront of the increase in regulation around nature protection. Working together with the IUCN, the International Council on Mining and Metals (ICMM) acknowledged back in 2003 that "exploration and mining development may be incompatible with the objectives for which areas are designated for protection."[36] In response, the ICMM committed to "respect legally designated protected areas and ensure that any new operations or changes to existing operations are not incompatible with the value for which they were designated."[37] For example, in the Netherlands, the Grensmaas project, a public/private collaboration in a Natura 2000 protected zone,[38] was allowed to continue extracting gravel only after a long-awaited agreement was reached in 2017. The group committed to national and regional authorities that it would restore over 1,000 hectares, with a focus on reducing flood risk in the area.[39]

As mentioned above, increasing coverage and requirements of protected areas is a key aspect of the European Green Deal Strategy.[40] This analysis shows that a significant number of the assessed large corporations own sites in these European-protected areas. As new sets of regulations are expected, we may see

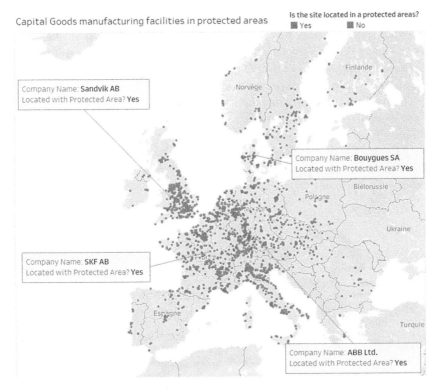

FIGURE 14.2   This map represents the European manufacturing facilities of the analyzed companies. Red dots represent the sites located in protected areas and green dots represent the sites outside of protected areas.

Source: Moody's ESG solutions, powered by Four Twenty Seven; and the WDPA, developed by UNEP.

increasing tensions and impacts on the companies' activities in these areas. Companies and financial institutions will benefit from paying attention to their impact on biodiversity based on the location of their assets and those in their portfolios. By understanding their exposure to these risks, companies and their investors can better comply with emerging reporting requirements, respond to new regulations and take action to reduce their impacts on biodiversity.

Conclusion

While Europe is at the forefront of regulatory discussions for biodiversity protection, policy makers around the world are growing increasingly aware that global biodiversity loss is a systemic crisis with a magnitude compared to that of climate change. The Convention for Biological Diversity (CBD) is currently preparing to adapt a post-2020 Global Biodiversity Framework that is to be set at the COP15 planned in Kunming, China, in October 2021[41] and is already anticipated as a "historic milestone in the history of biodiversity governance."[42] Likewise, similar to the Task Force on Climate-related Financial Disclosure (TCFD), over the next several years we can expect the TNFD initiative to catalyze increased attention to the development of guidelines and methodologies to measure and disclose the impact of biodiversity loss.

The biodiversity significance indicator explored in this chapter contributes to the emerging conversation on metrics for understanding biodiversity risks for companies and their investors. It provides an important starting point for assessing one type of corporate impact on biodiversity, which will complement further research needed to understand the many dimensions of this risk and develop consistent, comparable metrics for assessment and disclosure.

Notes

1 "© Four Twenty Seven, Inc. Reprinted with permission. All Rights Reserved. The full terms and conditions applicable to this chapter are available at the following link: 427mt.com/copyright."
2 https://science.sciencemag.org/content/269/5222/347.
3 https://ipbes.net/sites/default/files/2020-02/ipbes_global_assessment_report_summary_for_policymakers_en.pdf.
4 Cf. ipbes_global_assessment_report_summary_for_policymakers_en.pdf page 14.
5 https://ec.europa.eu/info/strategy/priorities-2019-2024/european-green-deal/actions-being-taken-eu/EU-biodiversity-strategy-2030_en.
6 https://naturalcapital.finance/blog/new-analysis-of-natural-capital-dependencies-launched-in-london-as-central-banks-warn-of-obvious-physical-risks/.
7 https://www.weforum.org/reports/the-global-risks-report-2020.
8 https://globalcanopy.org/insights/insight/frances-article-29-biodiversity-disclosure-requirements-sign-of-whats-to-come/.
9 https://ec.europa.eu/info/strategy/priorities-2019-2024/european-green-deal/actions-being-taken-eu/EU-biodiversity-strategy-2030_en, p.5.
10 Cited by UNEP-WCMC (2019). User Manual for the World Database on Protected Areas and world database on other effective area-based conservation measures: 1.6. UNEP-WCMC: Cambridge, UK. Available at: http://wcmc.io/WDPA_Manual.
11 https://www.eea.europa.eu/themes/biodiversity/europe-protected-areas.
12 https://biodiversity.europa.eu/protected-areas/introduction.
13 https://eur-lex.europa.eu/resource.html?uri=cellar:a3c806a6-9ab3-11ea-9d2d-01aa75ed71a1.0001.02/DOC_1&format=PDF, p.5.
14 https://ec.europa.eu/info/sites/info/files/business_economy_euro/banking_and_finance/documents/200309-sustainable-finance-teg-final-report-taxonomy_en.pdf.
15 https://ec.europa.eu/info/sites/info/files/business_economy_euro/banking_and_finance/documents/200610-sustainable-finance-teg-taxonomy-green-bond-standard-faq_en.pdf.
16 https://eba.europa.eu/esas-consult-environmental-social-and-governance-disclosure-rules.
17 https://eur-lex.europa.eu/legal-content/EN/TXT/?uri=CELEX%3A02019R2088-20200712.
18 https://www.bankingsupervision.europa.eu/legalframework/publiccons/pdf/-climate-related_risks/ssm.202005_draft_guide_on_climate-related_and_environmental_risks.en.pdf.
19 https://www.responsible-investor.com/articles/we-need-sound-metrics-to-reverse-biodiversity-loss-at-a-global-scale.

20 https://tnfd.info/how-it-works/.
21 https://tnfd.info/why-a-task-force-is-needed/.
22 Mokany, K., Ferrier, S., Harwood, T.D., Ware, C., Di Marco, M., Grantham, H.S., Venter, O., Hoskins, A.J. and Watson, J.E., 2020. Reconciling global priorities for conserving biodiversity habitat. Proceedings of the National Academy of Sciences, 117(18), pp. 9906–9911.
23 https://www.pwc.ch/en/publications/2020/nature-is-too-big-to-fail.pdf.
24 https://www.responsible-investor.com/articles/investors-take-a-stand-against-amazon-deforestation.
25 Ibid.
26 https://www.storebrand.no/en/asset-management/sustainable-investments/exclusions/deforestation-policy/.
27 Four Twenty Seven, an affiliate of Moody's, maintains a growing database of over 2 million corporate facilities globally, owned by about 5,000 of the largest publicly listed companies. We score each facility on its exposure to physical climate hazards, and also leverage our database for analysis on biodiversity risks.
28 https://www.dnb.nl/en/binaries/Indebted%20to%20nature%20_tcm47-389172.pdf.
29 p.22.
30 https://www.theguardian.com/sustainable-business/soco-international-oil-exporation-drc-virunga-gorilla-park.
31 https://www.wwf-congobasin.org/?217136/Increased-risk-to-shareholders-over-Socos-controversial-exploration-plans-in-Virunga.
32 https://www.ifc.org/wps/wcm/connect/topics_ext_content/ifc_external_corporate_site/sustainability-at-ifc/policies-standards/performance-standards/ps6.
33 https://www.leparisien.fr/economie/projet-de-loi-climat-les-grands-centres-commerciaux-cest-fini-19-04-2021-GQKJV26Z2BE4ZKKMZGLN2SK2A4.php.
34 https://www.strategie.gouv.fr/sites/strategie.gouv.fr/files/atoms/files/fs-dp-artificialisation-juillet-2019_0.pdf.
35 https://www.lemonde.fr/planete/article/2018/01/17/le-gouvernement-annonce-l-abandon-du-projet-d-aeroport-a-notre-dame-des-landes_5243002_3244.html.
36 https://www.icmm.com/website/publications/pdfs/mining-principles/position-statements_protected-areas.pdf.
37 Ibid.
38 Natura 2000 sites have been designated specifically to protect core areas for a sub-set of species or habitat types listed in the EU Habitats and Birds Directives. They are deemed to be of European importance because they are endangered, vulnerable, rare, endemic or present outstanding examples of typical characteristics of one or more of Europe's nine biogeographical regions. For more information: https://ec.europa.eu/environment/nature/natura2000/faq_en.htm#1-0.
39 https://ec.europa.eu/environment/nature/natura2000/management/docs/NEEI%20case%20studies%20-%20Final%20booklet.pdf.
40 https://ec.europa.eu/info/strategy/priorities-2019-2024/european-green-deal/actions-being-taken-eu/eu-biodiversity-strategy-2030_fr.
41 https://www.cbd.int/meetings/COP-15.
42 https://www.iddri.org/en/publications-and-events/blog-post/search-pillars-kunming-what-ambition-biodiversity-cop15-october.

15

HOW TO IMPROVE BIODIVERSITY-RELATED INFORMATION

Andrea Gasperini and Sonia Artuso

Introduction

The health crisis has deeply affected our system and has brought to light many weaknesses and shortcomings that everyone has become suddenly aware and afraid of. In the short term, also the institutions called to greening the economy operate in areas that require immediate intervention to restore normal activities and the life that every human being has currently lost in the lockdown situation. The longer-term vision and planning/strategy must necessarily be considered to define a re-start that include also climate change and biodiversity among the core elements.

COVID-19 and Renovated Awareness

The European Green Deal[1] of the European Union (EU) first, and the health and economic crisis due to the COVID-19 pandemic then, make clear the urgent action to tackle with the climate change and biodiversity issues. The interaction effects of the two in the short and in the long term can no longer be considered a secondary problem. There are now many studies that underline the clear link between climate, nature and health.[2] Climate change, human activities and loss in biodiversity increase the contact rate between infected wildlife and humans. The contact rate grows as roadbuilding, expansion of urban centres and settlements increase, and ultimately, deforestation and virus spillovers[3] take off.

The Intergovernmental Panel on Climate Change (IPCC)[4] and the Intergovernmental Science-Policy Platform on Biodiversity and Ecosystem Services (IPBES)[5] in their various special reports highlighted how the emissions and the impacts of anthropogenic activities[6] destroy the biosphere and the ecological system and damage the entire planet's health, not only that humans' one. In the past,

DOI: 10.4324/9781003045557-19

Year	Anthropomass	Wild Mammalian Zoomass	Elephants	Domesticated Animals	Cattle
1900	13	10	3	35	23
2000	55	5	0,3	120	80

Vaclav Smil. Harvesting the biosphere. What We Have Taken from Nature. The MIT Press (reprinting by the authors)

FIGURE 15.1 Anthropomass and Zoomass of Wild and Domesticated Animals, 1900–2000 (in MT C).

Vaclav Smil. Harvesting the biosphere. What We Have Taken from Nature. The MIT Press.

studies had already grabbed the meaning of the unequivocal impact of human's activity, despite the fact that at the beginning of the 20th century, it was estimated that mankind was a literally lesser burden on Earth (Figure 15.1).[7]

The IPBES defines the collapse of ecosystems as one of the future global challenges, and it estimates that the current biodiversity trend undermines the progress towards 80% of the SDG's targets. Depleting vital habitat and ecosystem services threatens the integrity and stability of the planet. Clear examples of these catastrophic consequences are the loss of capacity of the natural carbon sinks and the albedo effect that could exacerbate the climate crisis and compromise the Paris Agreement's achievements. The degradation of ecosystem services is estimated as an annual loss of at least US$ 479 billion per year, and more than half of the world's GDP is moderately or highly dependent on ecosystem services.[8] The urgent economic recovery needs to start from those sectors that present more just and inclusive activities with low environmental impact, resilient to climate change and well-suited to eradicate biodiversity loss. Nature is vital, and that is why, biodiversity loss is stated, in the last World Economic Forum (WEF) Global Risks Report,[9] as one of the top five environmental risks.

The current global crisis calls for a systemic approach that pays attention to the different dimensions of sustainable development in the medium and long term. In Europe, environmental action has been defined as primary and urgent and the activities connected to this action have not stopped, even in the peak of the pandemic. In fact, in the first half of the year 2020, the milestones of the European Green Deal were presented, including the proposed European Climate Law,[10] the regulation on the EU Taxonomy for Sustainable Activities[11] and the EU Biodiversity Strategy for 2030.[12]

A global call to action arises for institutions, countries, corporates and citizens. Bold policy, such as the European Green Deal, will not be enough. The Post-2020 Global Biodiversity Framework, initially expected in October 2020 in Kunming China but rescheduled from 17 to 30 May 2021 due to the COVID-19 pandemic,[13] will have to be ambitious able to update Aichi Biodiversity Targets[14] to define procedures to make effective the eradicating the biodiversity loss and restoring its actions.

A crucial role will be played by the global biodiversity finance.[15] A positive outcome will be related to an efficient exchange of ESG – environmental, social and corporate governance – information between companies, financial analysts and investors, in order to systematically integrating sustainability – climate and biodiversity information included – into business strategy, decision-making and risk management.

However, current metrics often seem insufficient and companies face many difficulties while disclosing non-financial information. With the outbreak of the COVID-19 crisis, among the current ESG metrics, the social ones do not represent the reality that many companies are facing. Note that among the environmental issues, biodiversity plays the role of great absence from the usual reports. In an attempt to measure global biodiversity finance flows, the OECD's Report[16] aims to address information gap by providing a more comprehensive overview and an aggregate estimate of global biodiversity finance and biodiversity harmful spending. Based on currently available data, global biodiversity finance is estimated at USD 78–91 billion per year (2015–2017 average). Public domestic expenditure counts for USD 67.8 billion per year; meanwhile, governments spend approximately USD 500 billion per year in support that is potentially harmful to biodiversity, that is five to six times more than total spending for biodiversity. Various initiatives are underway to improve the assessment, tracking and reporting of biodiversity finance flows. Nevertheless, data gaps and inconsistencies persist. To address an improving challenge in the assessment, tracking and reporting of biodiversity finance flows, the Convention on Biological Diversity (CBD) provides five key recommendations, among which improving the consistency and transparency of the reported data by adapting the financial reporting framework to request further granularity. Specifically, the template of the CBD financial reporting framework could be adapted to encourage countries to:

- Report quantitative data on biodiversity expenditure by individual category (e.g. government budgets, private, NGO), rather than reporting only the total amount.
- Provide supplementary information on methods used to estimate finance flows, by category.
- Distinguish between expenditure allocated to promote the conservation and sustainable use of ocean/marine biodiversity (SDG 14) and terrestrial biodiversity (SDG 15).[17]

A strong contribution to the theme of reporting comes from the Recommendations of the Task Force on Climate-related Financial Disclosures (TCFD) of Financial Stability Board; this is an important step towards better and more comprehensive non-financial accounting of the environmental dimension. The TCFD focused on the risks of climate change and exposure to these risks by companies; they are invited to actively use scenario analysis to evaluate effective corporate resilience policies that can cope with different climate change trends. This initiative has great potential to be applied to manage biodiversity risks and opportunities: a Task Force on Nature-related Financial Disclosures (TNFD)[18] is claimed to build on lessons from implementation of the TCFD recommendations by developing an approach for disclosure on biodiversity. Disclosure alone is not enough to integrate biodiversity into financial decision-making across portfolios, but it is definitely a first good step to start. In future, the efforts by the finance sector will aim to measure the impacts of financial flows on biodiversity.

It is often found that the attention of the TCFD[19] and the European Commission with Action Plan on Financing Sustainable Growth[20] is mainly focused on environmental issues and limited attention is paid to the social one. The reason is that resources are increasingly scarce for everyone and this entails a priority action on the planet in order to ensure the survival of species (not just the human one) and therefore a harmonious existence and sustainable development of the other dimensions identified by the UN: People, Prosperity, Peace and Partnership (Figure 15.2).

The biosphere is the basis of our entire socio-economic system. The definition of sustainable development[21] has already been envisaged to ensure that the humanity meets the needs of the present without compromising the ability of future generations to meet their own needs. It also means to respect the limits, not absolute limits, but limitations imposed by the present state of technology and

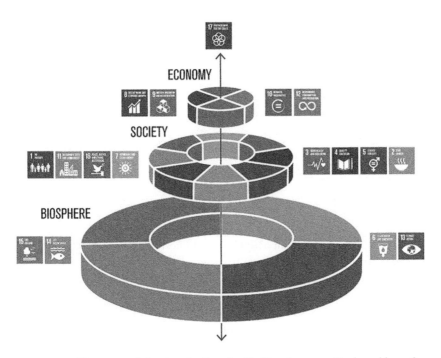

FIGURE 15.2 New way of viewing the Sustainable Development Goals and how they are all linked to food.

Johan Rockström and Pavan Sukhdev. Azote for Stockholm Resilience Centre, Stockholm University.

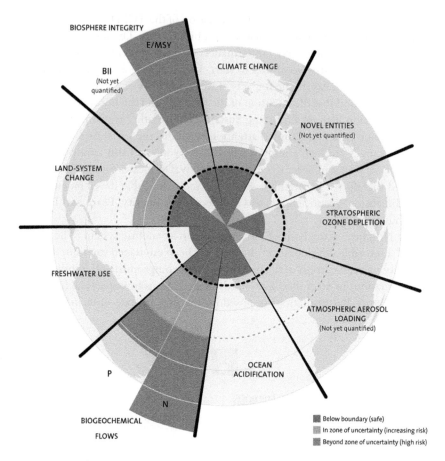

FIGURE 15.3 Planetary boundaries: exploring the safe operating space for humanity. Rockström, J., W. Steffen, K. Noone, Å. Persson, et.al. 2009. Planetary boundaries: exploring the safe operating space for humanity. Ecology and Society (J. Lokrantz/Azote based on Steffen et al. 2015).

social organization on environmental resources by the ability of the biosphere to absorb[22] the effects of human activities. As indicated by the Stockholm Resilience Centre, the limits of the planet have already been irreversibly exceeded, the fact that is creating many difficulties for the system of the Earth, highlighted by the recent reports from the IPCC and IPBES (Figure 15.3).

The current crisis should therefore be considered by companies, investors, analysts and other market players as an opportunity to change mindset and to broaden the use of ESG metrics and materiality rationale as an activity to inform corporate strategy, not just to report and to use ESG disclosure for orientating capital flows towards climate and biodiversity investment to finance the economic recovery.

The Post-2020 Biodiversity Framework and the Green Oath to "Do Not Harm"

The EU aim is to improve post-2020 global framework at the 15th Conference of the Parties to the Convention on Biological Diversity. European ambition is clear and in line with 2030 Agenda for Sustainable Development and with the objectives of the Paris Agreement on Climate Change: reverse biodiversity loss, build and ensure that by 2050 all of the world's ecosystems are restored, resilient and adequately protected.

The EU Biodiversity Strategy for 2030[23] addresses biodiversity loss, sets out an enhanced governance framework to fill remaining gaps and ensures the full implementation of EU legislation. It will require action by citizens, businesses, social partners and the research and knowledge community, as well as strong partnerships between local, regional, national and European levels. This strategy is in line with the ambitions and commitment with the European Green Deal, a central element of the EU's recovery plan. It will be crucial to prevent and build resilience to future zoonosis outbreaks and to provide immediate business and investment opportunities for restoring the EU's economy.

EU plans to improve and to widen the European network of protected area. The global Aichi Biodiversity Targets for protected areas cover 17% on land and 10% at sea, and these do not guarantee an adequate protection of nature, as scientific studies' figures range from 30% to 70%. Below are the European Nature Protection key commitments by 2030:

- Legally protect a minimum of 30% of the EU's land area and 30% of the EU's sea area and integrate ecological corridors, as part of a true Trans-European Nature Network.
- Strictly protect at least a third of the EU's protected areas, including all remaining EU primary and old-growth forests.
- Effectively manage all protected areas, defining clear conservation objectives and measures, and monitoring them appropriately.

The EU Nature Restoration Plan will improve existing and new protected areas. It will support the recovery of nature, limiting soil sealing and urban sprawl, and tackling pollution and invasive alien species. Below are the European Nature Restoration Plan key commitments by 2030:

- Legally binding EU nature restoration targets to be proposed in 2021, subject to an impact assessment. By 2030, significant areas of degraded and carbon-rich ecosystems are restored; habitats and species show no deterioration in conservation trends and status; and at least 30% reach favourable conservation status or at least show a positive trend.
- The decline in pollinators is reversed.

- The risk and use of chemical pesticides are reduced by 50%, and the use of more hazardous pesticides is reduced by 50%.
- At least 10% of agricultural area is under high-diversity landscape features.
- At least 25% of agricultural land is under organic farming management, and the uptake of agro-ecological practices is significantly increased.
- Three billion new trees are planted in the EU, in full respect of ecological principles.
- Significant progress has been made in the remediation of contaminated soil sites.
- At least 25,000 km of free-flowing rivers are restored.
- There is a 50% reduction in the number of Red List species threatened by invasive alien species.
- The losses of nutrients from fertilizers are reduced by 50%, resulting in the reduction of the use of fertilizers by at least 20%.
- Cities with at least 20,000 inhabitants have an ambitious Urban Greening Plan.
- No chemical pesticides are used in sensitive areas such as EU urban green areas.
- The negative impacts on sensitive species and habitats, including on the seabed through fishing and extraction activities, are substantially reduced to achieve good environmental status.
- The bycatch of species is eliminated or reduced to a level that allows species recovery and conservation.

Moreover, the new European biodiversity governance framework will help map obligations and commitments and set out a road map to guide their implementation. The European Commission will put in place a monitoring and review mechanism. This will include a clear set of agreed indicators and will enable regular progress assessment and set out corrective action if necessary. It will support administrative capacity building, transparency, stakeholder dialogue and participatory governance at different levels.

To ensure that the environmental and social interests are fully embedded into business strategies, the Commission has put forward a new initiative on sustainable corporate governance in 2021, in order to address human rights and environmental duty of care and due diligence across economic value chains proportionally. In addition, the Non-Financial Reporting Directive[24] is being reviewed to improve the quality and scope of non-financial disclosures, including on environmental aspects such as biodiversity.

Meeting the EU Biodiversity Strategy will require mobilizing private and public funding at national and EU level, including the Next Generation EU of €750 billion, as well as targeted reinforcements to the long-term EU budget for 2021–2027. It will bring the total financial firepower of the EU budget to €1.85 trillion through a range of different programmes.[25] Moreover, as nature restoration will make a major contribution to climate objectives, a significant proportion of the 30% of the EU budget dedicated to climate action will be invested on biodiversity and nature-based solutions.

The EU sustainable finance taxonomy[26] will be addressed towards a green recovery and the deployment of nature-based solutions. By 2023, the European Commission will adopt a delegated act under the Taxonomy Regulation to establish a common classification of economic activities that substantially contribute six environmental objectives among which to protecting and restoring biodiversity and ecosystems. Art.15 of Regulation (EU) 2020/852 stated:

An economic activity shall qualify as contributing substantially to the protection and restoration of biodiversity and ecosystems where that activity contributes substantially to protecting, conserving or restoring biodiversity or to achieving the good condition of ecosystems, or to protecting ecosystems that are already in good condition, through:

a   nature and biodiversity conservation, including achieving favourable conservation status of natural and semi-natural habitats and species, or preventing their deterioration where they already have favourable conservation status, and protecting and restoring terrestrial, marine and other aquatic ecosystems in order to improve their condition and enhance their capacity to provide ecosystem services;

b   sustainable land use and management, including adequate protection of soil biodiversity, land degradation neutrality and the remediation of contaminated sites;

c   sustainable agricultural practices, including those that contribute to enhancing biodiversity or to halting or preventing the degradation of soils and other ecosystems, deforestation and habitat loss;

d   sustainable forest management, including practices and uses of forests and forest land that contribute to enhancing biodiversity or to halting or preventing degradation of ecosystems, deforestation and habitat loss;

e   enabling any of the activities listed in points (a) to (d) of this paragraph in accordance with the definition of the enabling activities (Art.16).

Economic activities will be considered eco-sustainable if they meet the following requirements:

- to contribute substantially to the achievement of at least one of the six environmental objectives (condition of substantial contribution);
- to not cause significant damage to any of the environmental objectives (principle of do no significant harm or DNSH);
- to be carried out in compliance with the minimum social safeguards (condition of minimum social safeguards);
- to comply with the technical evaluation criteria.

For each environmental objective, regulatory technical standards must be established to determine whether economic activities contribute substantially to that objective, are carried out in compliance with the minimum social guarantees and do not significantly damage any of the other environmental objectives of the regulation. These criteria must take into account the life cycle of the products and services provided (production, use and end of life) in assessing the environmental impact of economic activity, and therefore, they must be oriented towards an assessment of the impact in the long term.

In establishing and updating the technical screening criteria, the European Commission will have to take into account the current legislation, consistent with the current classifications of environmental protection activities (CEPA)[27] and resource management activities (CReMA)[28] and in general with the communication made in July 2018 on *"public procurement for a better environment"*.

This will be further supported by a Renewed Sustainable Finance Strategy[29] to ensure that the financial system contributes to mitigating existing and future risks to biodiversity and better reflect how biodiversity loss affects companies' profitability and long-term prospects. The European Commission has provided a Sustainable Finance Platform[30] to guarantee a constant and adequate process of updating the technical evaluation criteria which involves the involvement of stakeholders, as well as experts who have proven knowledge and experience in the relevant sectors both for the public sector and for the private one.

The Commission will further promote tax systems and pricing that reflect environmental costs, including biodiversity loss. This should encourage changes in national fiscal systems to shift the tax burden from labour to pollution, underpriced resources and other environmental externalities. The "user pays" and "polluter pays" principles have to be applied to prevent and correct environmental degradation.

Biodiversity Materiality on Business

Biodiversity – the diversity within species, between species and of ecosystems – is declining faster than at any time in human history. IPBES Global Report announced that much of nature has already been lost, and what remains is continuing to decline. To date, 70% of land systems, 50% of freshwater and 40% of oceans and seas have been significantly altered. As for the value of that loss, previous estimates of nature's value in monetary terms put it at USD 125–145 trillion/year in 2011 (Figure 15.4).

The IPBES Global Assessment Report identifies five main drivers of biodiversity loss: changes in land and sea use; overexploitation of organisms; climate change; pollution; and invasive alien species. Climate change is currently responsible for between 11% and 16% of biodiversity loss. This share is expected only to increase, and it has the potential to trigger irreversible biome-scale ecosystem disruptions. The recent study of WEF[31] relied on the lens of the 44 threats to biodiversity identified by the International Union for Conservation of Nature's

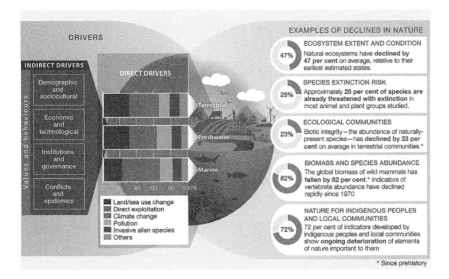

FIGURE 15.4   Examples of global declines in nature, emphasizing declines in biodiversity, that have been and are being caused by direct and indirect drivers of change.

IPBES. The global assessment report on biodiversity and ecosystem services. 2019.

(IUCN) Red List of Threatened Species, the world's most comprehensive inventory of the global status of nature conservation, to prioritize the most pressing threats for business to address. Fifteen business-related threats to biodiversity have been prioritized by taking into account three criteria:

a   the importance of the threat to biodiversity loss;
b   the role of business in causing the threat, and hence the potential of business to address it; and
c   the potential of the threat to disrupt business activities.

The prioritized biodiversity threats all relate to just three socio-economic systems (Figure 15.5). These systems are:

The global food, land and ocean use system generates around $10 trillion annually (12% of global GDP), as well as up to 40% of employment, and it provides the food and clothes that sustain humans in their daily lives and is crucial for the livelihoods of millions of people, particularly in low-income countries.

The activities and supply chains of this system impact around 72% of all threatened and near-threatened species, as classified by the IUCN Red List.[32] Agriculture and land use alone are responsible for around 30% of global greenhouse gas (GHG) emissions.

The impact of humans on the ocean is expanding. Fishing fleets are targeting new species and expanding to new areas, raising the total area fished from 60%

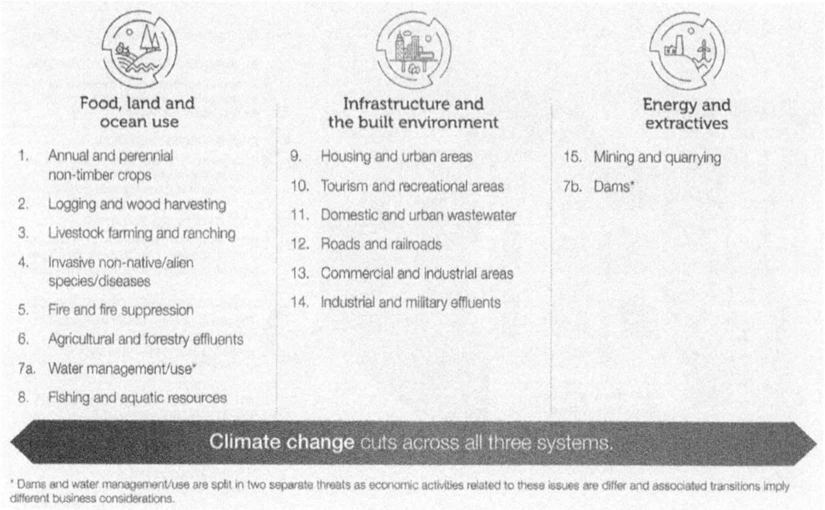

	Food, land and ocean use			Infrastructure and the built environment			Energy and extractives
1.	Annual and perennial non-timber crops		9.	Housing and urban areas		15.	Mining and quarrying
2.	Logging and wood harvesting		10.	Tourism and recreational areas		7b.	Dams*
3.	Livestock farming and ranching		11.	Domestic and urban wastewater			
4.	Invasive non-native/alien species/diseases		12.	Roads and railroads			
5.	Fire and fire suppression		13.	Commercial and industrial areas			
6.	Agricultural and forestry effluents		14.	Industrial and military effluents			
7a.	Water management/use*						
8.	Fishing and aquatic resources						

Climate change cuts across all three systems.

*Dams and water management/use are split in two separate threats as economic activities related to these issues are differ and associated transitions imply different business considerations.

FIGURE 15.5 Threats prioritized for business action all relate to three socio-economic systems.

WEF. The Future of Nature and Business. 2020.

to 90% of the world's oceans. As a result of industrial fishing, 93% of fish stocks today are fished at or beyond maximum sustainable levels.

The built environment system accounts for a 40% of global GDP, and it is of crucial importance to the global economy. Global spending on construction alone is estimated to have exceeded $13 trillion in 2019, around 15% of global GDP, and contributed to around 7% of global employment. The threats emerging from the infrastructure and the built environment system together impact 29% of the IUCN's list of threatened and near-threatened species. Cities are responsible for 75% of global GHG emissions, primarily through transportation and buildings. Continued expansion of cities could lead to the loss of around 2 million hectares of agricultural land every year.

The 23% of global GDP and the 16% of employment originate from the energy and extractives system. It has also created a significant burden for biodiversity and is responsible for threats that impact around 18% of species on the IUCN's list. Global resource extraction has tripled from 27 billion tonnes in 1970 to 92 billion tonnes in 2017, but 840 million people still lack access to electricity. Identified oil, gas, metal and mineral reserves are increasingly difficult to extract, and natural resource extraction and processing make roughly 50% of the total GHG emissions. Under business-as-usual projections, global energy demand will rise by 40% through 2050, and materials use will rise by 110% through 2060 (Figure 15.6).

Biodiversity and ecosystem services are vital for life on Earth. They influence the functioning of our society and economy, health, and safety. Importantly,

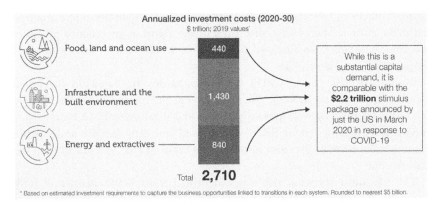

FIGURE 15.6 Capital investment required to capture opportunities in the three systems is around $2.7 trillion.

WEF. The Future of Nature and Business. 2020.

natural capital, ecosystems, biodiversity and their services are all interrelated and connected. Thus, it is obvious that biodiversity creates flows of ecosystem services, which benefit and create value for business and society, through which financial institutions are ultimately influenced.[33]

The report underlines that climate-related risk and nature-related risk are not separate entities; nature loss decreases climate resilience, and climate change exacerbates drivers of nature loss. The concept of the double materiality also for biodiversity issue, previously absent, is defined for climate change information by the EU group of Technical Experts on Sustainable Finance (TEG):

• Information on biodiversity communicated, if necessary, to understand the internal impacts on company's performance and outcome.
• Biodiversity information must even be disclosed, if necessary, to understand the external impacts of the company's activities.

This materiality must be regularly identified, assessed and disclosed by business. In order to integrate nature risks and opportunities and to enable more efficient and effective integration into business decision-making, nature-related risks can be incorporated within ERM[34] and ESG processes, investment decision-making, and financial and non-financial reporting. The TCFD framework, still missing a new TNFD one, could be used to manage nature risks by relying on the main aspects as stated in the WEF Nature Risk Rising Report:

Financial materiality: The TCFD moves beyond non-financial sustainability metrics and requires assessment and disclosure of potential financial impacts. Impact valuation of land-use restriction or the insurance increased costs due to settlements from pollution can be added.

The TCFD recommends that disclosures are made in audited annual financial filings under the laws of the jurisdictions in which they operate. Thus, the chief financial officer and the chief risk officer increase their responsible range of action and make climate and biodiversity issues to the rigorous governance processes that inform mainstream financial filings. This would raise action on nature-related risks alongside climate.

Business-centric: The TCFD's recommendations are based on the broad themes of governance, strategy, risk management and metrics and targets. These make this framework well-known and able and to allow risks to be incorporated into companies' own ERM systems and not only in core and climate business risk processes, but also into different types of risks assessment such the Nature's one.

The five most common risk types identified from WWF Nature of Risk Report[35] were physical, regulatory and legal, market, reputational, and financial risk.

- Physical risks arise from material destruction causing economic and financial losses for businesses and investors. These kinds of risks can be further classified, as for climate ones, into event-driven or acute or longer-term in nature or chronic ones.
- Regulatory and legal risks relate to laws, policies, regulations and court actions that affect the operations of businesses.
- Market risks relate to product and service offerings, customer preferences and other market factors that can affect corporate performance.
- Reputational risks relate to a company's brand, image and relationship with customers, the general public and other stakeholders.
- Financial risk is divided into financing risk whether the risk accrues to businesses, and financier risk whether the risk accrues to financial institutions.

To be aligned to the European double materiality rationale, the further distinction of threats and/or consequences of the five identified risks is useful. The analytical value of this difference is found in two elements of risk for businesses: (1) how a risk might arise (the threat), but also (2) how it becomes material to the business or investors (the consequence). Below are the most commonly cited nature-related threats to business, followed by the consequences of these nature-related risks (Figures 15.7 and 15.8).

Change Mindset to Use ESG Metrics on Biodiversity

The Paris Agreement on Climate Change was adopted in 2015. This agreement, under the United Nations Framework Convention on Climate Change (UNFCCC), produced a global consensus on taking ambitious action to hold the increase in the global average temperature to well below 2°C above pre-industrial levels and to pursue efforts to limit the increase to 1.5°C, recognizing that this would significantly reduce the risks and impacts of climate change and increase the ability to adapt to it.[36]

RISK TYPES	THREAT TYPE	TOTAL	
Physical Risk		11	
	Acute events; damage from natural/man-made hazards	11	
	Biodiversity loss and decreasing species richness	7	
	Scarcity of water	4	
	Availability, reliability, and security of energy	4	
	Habitat loss	2	
	Air pollution	2	
	Water pollution	2	
Regulatory & Legal Risk		14	
	Litigation, damages, and/or compensation	11	
	Pricing or other regulations for emissions (GNG*/other)	10	
	Restrictions on land and ES access	6	
	Air pollution regulation	6	
	Non-hazardous waste management	6	
	Soil pollution regulation	6	
	Resource quotas for ES use	4	
	Unsustainable practices	4	
	Changing liability regimes	3	
	Hazardous waste management	3	
	Water pollution regulation	3	
	Changes in disclosure requirements	2	
Market Risk		10	
	Changing consumer preferences	7	
	Inability to attract co-financiers due to uncertainty	2	
	Purchaser requirements	2	
Reputational Risk		13	
	Negative press coverage	3	
	Divestment or other stakeholder campaigns	3	
	Impacts on World Heritage Sites or protected areas	2	
	Impacts on species on IUCN** Red List	2	

■ Physical Risk   Regulatory & Legal Risk   ■ Market Risk   ■ Reputational Risk

*GHG - Greenhouse gas
**IUCN - International Union for Conservation of Nature

FIGURE 15.7 Top identified nature-related threats.

RISK TYPES	CONSEQUENCE TYPE	TOTAL	
Physical Risk	Disruptions to business operations	7	
	Labor shortages	5	
Regulatory & Legal Risk	Unexpected costs of compliance/fines for noncompliance	9	
	Stranded assets	4	
Market Risk	Changes in the cost and availability of resources	4	
Reputational Risk	Lost sales due to negative perceptions of the institution	3	
Financial Risk	Increased cost of capital or lending requirements	5	
	Write-downs of asset value and write-offs of assets	5	
	Increased insurance claims	4	
	Higher premiums; loss of insurance value	4	
	Increased risk of default	3	
	Loss of investment value related to reputational risks	2	
	Changes in market value of the business	2	

■ Physical Risk   Regulatory & Legal Risk   ■ Market Risk   ■ Reputational Risk   ■ Financial Risk

FIGURE 15.8 Top identified nature-related consequences.

WWF. Nature of Risk: A Framework for Understanding Nature-Related Risk to Business 2020.

The issues of biodiversity and climate are intricately connected, with climate change expected to become an increasingly important driver of biodiversity loss. Recent research assessed by the Intergovernmental Panel on Climate Change (IPCC) has emphasized significant differences in the outcomes for biodiversity depending on the global warming.[37]

The scale and pace of the decline is why the danger to biodiversity from human activity is listed in the World Economic Forum's Global Risks Report 2020 based on a survey of more than 800 *"renowned experts and decision-makers"*. Biodiversity loss was identified as the fourth most likely global risk over the next 10 years and the third most serious in terms of potential impact. Both rankings are significantly higher than in previous years.[38]

As stated below, from Principles for Responsible Investment, although biodiversity is not an explicit concern in many financial regulations, it is a significant source of financial risks and sustainability impact, so it should be considered as part of existing commitments, such as the UK Pension Fund. Act clarification on fiduciary duty and ESG and the EU regulation on sustainability-related disclosures in the financial sector. Where biodiversity-focused legislation is lacking and government action is limited, investors should advocate more for strong public policies.

For investors, a strong perception of the potential impact that biodiversity loss might have on the risk-return profile of investees, as well as a whole portfolio, will be important since exposures to some sectors may lead to those assets becoming stranded if not correctly managed. Engagement with companies and data service providers is crucial to boost the provision of more meaningful and reliable biodiversity data. Access to better biodiversity data, material data sets and the standardization of key metrics will help investors classify and evaluate their portfolios' biodiversity exposure.[39]

Many investors highlight a lack of accessibility to suitable biodiversity data to assess company performance and evaluate investment impact. Data are often not fit for purpose, and biodiversity-related investments are relatively undeveloped, with a limited track record compared to climate-related investments. Biodiversity-related investments are relatively immature, with a limited track record compared to climate-related investments. Therefore, the proposition looks risky for investors, and the rationale for investment is weak. The lack of readily available data, metrics and company research means that investors wishing to understand the risk exposure and opportunities linked to biodiversity have to develop in-house, bespoke tools.

This also creates higher entry costs into, for example, biodiversity-themed funds.

The Disclosure of Biodiversity

As of September 2019, 898 organizations globally have declared their support for the TCFD and reporting on the "E" factor of the acronym "ESG" has been prevalent by data on greenhouse gas emissions. Until now not enough companies are disclosing decision-useful climate-related financial information: (i) given the speed at which changes are needed to limit the rise in the global average temperature – across a wide range of sectors – more companies need to consider the potential impact of climate change and disclose material findings; (ii) more clarity is needed on the potential financial impact of climate-related issues on companies; (iii) among the companies using scenarios, the majority do not disclose information on the resilience of their strategies; and (iv) involvement of multiple functions is critical to mainstreaming climate-related issues, especially the involvement of the risk management and finance functions.[40]

Based on findings from an online survey proposed to investment professionals from the Global Sustainable Investment Alliance (GSIA) during the month of October 2019, it is highlighted that while the number of organizations supporting the TCFD recommendations has grown, survey respondents are generally dissatisfied with publicly traded companies' climate-related disclosure. Among the different organizational types, service providers and asset management firms were most likely to be dissatisfied (67% and 63% "very" or "somewhat" dissatisfied, respectively). Meanwhile, financial advisors/planners and those in the "other" category were most likely to be satisfied (32% and 23%, respectively) (Figure 15.9).[41]

Investors and regulators are increasingly turning their attention to assets such as water, soil and biodiversity (living organisms). Such assets – collectively known as natural capital – provide humans with a wide range of further goods and services – including food, medicines, flood protection and pollination. That is why, the financial community is stating growing concern about the economic consequences of the loss of these natural assets.[42]

Since Socially Responsible Investment (SRI) has swept across the financial world, the "E" in ESG has become nearly synonymous with attempts to mitigate climate change. A reason for that is a lack of data and measurement standards. While climate-conscious investors can look at metrics such as "CO_2 equivalent" – which provides a standardized way to quantify greenhouse gas emissions – there is no similar measurement for biodiversity yet.

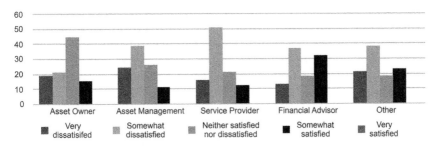

FIGURE 15.9 How satisfied are you with the climate-related disclosure of publicly traded companies?

Source: Global Sustainable Investment Alliance December 2019.

The UNEP FI recently said it was teaming up with the governments of the UK and Switzerland, WWF and others to develop a Task Force on Nature-related Financial Disclosures (TNFD).[43] The body is modelled on the Taskforce on Climate-related Financial Disclosures (TCFD) headed by former Bank of England Governor Mark Carney, which set guidelines for how companies should disclose their carbon emissions.

Biodiversity loss threatens the sustainability of global economies and societies. Acknowledging this, corporate companies are beginning to make first efforts to understand and be aware of their impacts on biodiversity and how to monitor and disclose them in sustainability reports.

All businesses should account for ecological risks to their operations and reputation, yet few do: a recent study of Prue F. E. Addison, Joseph W. Bull and E. J. Milner-Gulland[44] assessed the top 100 (Fortune 100) of the 2016 Fortune 500 Global companies' sustainability reports to gauge the current state of corporate accountability about biodiversity. Almost half (49) of the Fortune 100 mentioned biodiversity in reports, and 31 made clear biodiversity commitments, but only 5 (Walmart, Hewlett Packard, AXA, Nestlé and Carrefour) of them were specific, measurable and time-bound.

The companies disclose many biodiversity-related activities (e.g. managing impacts, restoring and investing in biodiversity), but only nine companies provided quantitative indicators to verify the magnitude of their activities (e.g. area of habitat restored). No companies reported quantitative biodiversity outcomes, making it difficult to determine whether business actions were of sufficient magnitude to address impacts and were achieving positive outcomes for the environment.

An additional challenge is that biodiversity impacts and reliance vary among companies and sectors, making comparisons difficult. The research shows that many companies measure and report on land use and water use, thus referring to important drivers of biodiversity loss; yet, they do not make the potentially important link with biodiversity.

Action on biodiversity is also far less common than climate change action – mentions of biodiversity, ecosystem services and natural capital by PRI signatories in their reporting are low in comparison with climate and water (Figure 15.10).[45]

Biodiversity is not often explicitly addressed, and reported on, in sustainability reports, and even when it is, there appeared to be a lack of coherence and consistency across reports. One explanation may be that this is due to the complexity associated with the term and associated misconceptions about the relevance of biodiversity for a company. There appears to be a lack of overall understanding of the potential links between biodiversity and business risks and opportunities. The resulting inconsistency of terms used prevents effective data comparison across companies and the derivation of associated policy recommendations.

An additional challenge is that biodiversity impacts and dependencies vary among companies and sectors, making comparisons difficult.

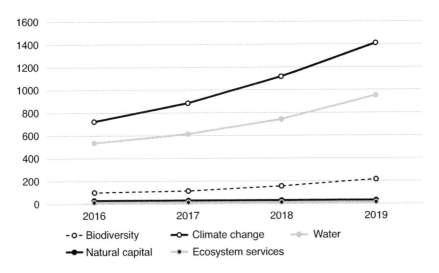

FIGURE 15.10 Mentions of biodiversity, climate change and water by PRI signatories in their reporting from 2016 to 2019.

Source: PRI, "investor action on biodiversity: discussion paper" webinar 1/9/2020.

TABLE 15.1 Twenty targets, under five strategic goals

Strategic goal	Activities
A	Address the underlying causes of biodiversity loss by mainstreaming biodiversity across government and society
B	Reduce the direct pressures on biodiversity and promote sustainable use
C	Improve the status of biodiversity by safeguarding ecosystems, species and genetic diversity
D	Enhance the benefits to all from biodiversity and ecosystem services
E	Enhance implementation through participatory planning, knowledge management and capacity building

Source: https://www.cbd.int/sp/targets/.

Attention to the biodiversity disclosures is growing in:

- **Beyond the Strategic Plan for Biodiversity 2011–2020:** In 2010, Parties to the Convention on Biological Diversity (CBD) adopted the Strategic Plan for Biodiversity 2011–2020, a ten-year framework for action to safeguard biodiversity and the benefits it provides to people. As part of the Strategic Plan 20 for Biodiversity 2011–2020 (SPB), ambitious but realistic targets, known as the Aichi Biodiversity Targets, were adopted (Table 15.1).

  The Global Biodiversity Outlook 5 (GBO-5),[46] published by the UN Convention on Biological Diversity (CBD), offers an authoritative overview of the state of nature. It is a final report on progress against the 20 global biodiversity targets agreed most of the "Aichi objectives" will not be achieved by 2020 and the planet is about to face an unprecedented environmental crisis, with a very high number of species on the verge of extinction. Biodiversity is declining at an extraordinary rate, and the pressures driving this decline are intensifying.[47]

The city of Kunming in south-western China was scheduled to host the 15th conference of the parties to the UN Convention on Biological Diversity (CBD), the most important biodiversity meeting in a decade, in October 2020, to negotiate the adoption of the post-2020 Global Biodiversity Framework, setting the course of action for a "Paris moment" for nature and set new targets, encouraging increased government action on nature loss. The 15th meeting of the Conference of the Parties to the Convention on Biological Diversity (CBD) has been rescheduled to take place from 17 to 30 May 2021 due to the COVID-19 pandemic.[48]

- *UN Agenda 2030 for Sustainable Development*: An important trend is the increasing reference made in companies' sustainability reports to the Agenda 2030 and the Sustainable Development Goals (SDGs). Many companies are now using the SDGs as a strategic planning tool, and investors are looking at a commitment to the Goals as a risk measure.

  The 2030 Agenda, agreed by the 193 States Members of the United Nations, sets out an ambitious framework of universal and indivisible goals and targets to address a range of global societal challenges. Biodiversity and ecosystems feature prominently across many of the SDGs and associated targets. They contribute directly to human well-being and development priorities.

  Biodiversity is at the heart of many economic activities, particularly those related to crop and livestock agriculture, forestry and fisheries. Globally, nearly half of the human population is directly dependent on natural resources for its livelihood, and many of the most vulnerable people depend directly on biodiversity to fulfil their daily subsistence needs.

  The Strategic Plan for Biodiversity 2011–2020 and its Aichi Biodiversity Targets adopted under the Convention on Biological Diversity has been recognized as setting the global framework for priority actions on biodiversity. The SDGs and the SPB are mutually supportive and reinforcing, as implementation of one contributes to the achievement of the other.[49]

  The conservation and sustainable use of biodiversity may therefore be regarded as foundational to the whole 2030 Agenda. Sustainable Development Goals 14 and 15 directly address biodiversity in aquatic and terrestrial environments, respectively. Beyond these, the achievement of many other Goals is either directly or indirectly dependent on biodiversity. This recognition aids the mainstreaming of biodiversity into the relevant sectors and provides incentives for its conservation and sustainable use.[50]

- *Natural capital protocol*: Recent work of the Natural Capital Coalition is a framework designed to help generate credible and actionable information for business managers, suggesting a standardized approach to identify, measure and value business impacts and reliance on natural capital and ecosystem services, to inform and improve internal management decision-making. Once considered a separate issue to climate change, biodiversity loss is now regarded as an equally urgent crisis, and its connection to climate adaptation and mitigation is increasingly understood. Businesses are beginning to recognize this and are looking for ways to understand the value of their impacts and dependencies on biodiversity.

A Biodiversity Guidance was developed jointly from Natural Capital Coalition and Cambridge Conservation Initiative as a companion to the Natural Capital Protocol, enabling businesses to better incorporate biodiversity into natural capital assessments and decision-making.[51] It guides companies through the process of including the value of biodiversity in their natural capital assessments and how to operationalize this information in internal decision-making.

The Biodiversity Guidance is applicable to all business sectors, at any geography and any organizational level. It is designed to work in four stages, "Why" (Framing Guidance), "What" (Scoping Guidance), "How" (Measure and Value Guidance) and "What Next" (Application Guidance).

In March 2020, the Natural Capital Coalition in collaboration with the Cambridge Conservation Initiative presented the "Framing Guidance" part of a series of Biodiversity Guidance to accompany the Natural Capital Protocol that helps to identify and describe biodiversity-related impacts, dependencies, risks and opportunities relevant to the business.[52]

- *EU regulation:* In its communication of 8 March 2018, the European Commission published its Action Plan on financing sustainable growth,[53] launching an ambitious and comprehensive strategy on sustainable finance. The establishment of a unified classification system for sustainable activities is the most important and urgent action envisaged by the action plan, and as a first step, clear guidance on activities that qualify as contributing to environmental objectives would help inform investors about the investments that fund environmentally sustainable economic activities.

In order to determine the environmental sustainability of a given economic activity, an exhaustive list of six environmental objectives has been established: (i) climate change mitigation; (ii) climate change adaptation; (iii) the sustainable use and protection of water and marine resources; (iv) the transition to a circular economy; (v) pollution prevention and control; and (vi) the protection and restoration of biodiversity and ecosystems.[54]

The EU Taxonomy (Regulation (EU) 2020/852) is a tool to help investors, companies, issuers and project promoters focus their investments and the use of private finance to delivering a low-carbon, resilient and resource-efficient economy. It sets performance thresholds ("technical screening criteria") for economic activities which:

- make a substantive contribution to one of six environmental objectives;

- do no significant harm (DNSH) to the other five, where relevant;
- meet minimum safeguards.

Regarding the protection and restoration of biodiversity and ecosystems, Article 15 defines which is considered an economic activity that contributes substantially to protecting, conserving or restoring biodiversity or to achieving the good condition of ecosystems, or to protecting ecosystems that are already in good condition.

An economic activity can contribute substantially to the environmental objectives in several ways as nature and biodiversity conservation, sustainable land use and management, sustainable agricultural practices and sustainable forest management.

- *ESA Joint Consultation Paper "ESG disclosure":* Draft regulatory technical standards with regard to the content, methodologies and presentation of disclosures of Regulation (EU) 2019/2088

The European Supervisory Authorities (ESAs) launched in April 2020 a consultation paper setting out the proposed Regulatory Technical Standards (RTS) on content, methodologies and presentation of disclosures of sustainable investment under the Sustainable Finance Disclosure Regulation (SFDR).

Sustainable investment means an investment in an economic activity that contributes to an environmental objective, as measured, for example, by key resource efficiency indicators on the use of energy, renewable energy, raw materials, water and land, on the production of waste, and greenhouse gas emissions, or on its impact on biodiversity (Table 15.2).[55]

TABLE 15.2 Climate and other environment-related indicators

Adverse sustainability indicator		Metric (expressed in market value)
Biodiversity	1. Biodiversity and ecosystem preservation practices	1. Share of all investments in investee companies that do not assess, monitor or control the pressures corresponding to the indirect and direct drivers of biodiversity and ecosystem change 2. Share of all investee companies that do not assess, monitor or control the pressures corresponding to the indirect and direct drivers of biodiversity and ecosystem change
	2. Natural species and protected areas	1. Share of investments invested in investee companies whose operations affect IUCN Red List species and/or national conservation list species 2. Share of investments in investee companies with operational sites owned, leased, managed in, or adjacent to, protected areas and areas of high biodiversity value outside protected areas

ESA: Annex 1 Template principal adverse impacts statement.

Necessary Meaningful Data

Biodiversity is currently not perceived by most businesses as directly impacting them. There is a need to improve the understanding of how biodiversity underpins the provision of ecosystem services and benefits that are critical for business operations and business models, and to get this understanding to the forefront of business discussions. Access to better biodiversity data, relevant data sets and the harmonization of indicators will help investors identify and assess their portfolios' biodiversity exposure.

According to the PRI "*Investor Action on Biodiversity: Discussion paper*"[56] below presented, the three enabling factors for biodiversity analysis are appropriate: (i) targets and standards, (ii) metrics by which performance can be measured; and (iii) data to populate those metrics.

- *Targets and Standards*: Although governments agreed to the Aichi Biodiversity Targets through the Convention on Biological Diversity, they have not gained traction within the private sector, nor do they readily lend themselves to holding businesses to account on their performance in managing biodiversity outcomes. The lack of broadly agreed biodiversity metrics for governments and businesses has hampered efforts to develop a globally agreed target on biodiversity, around which a broad range of stakeholders can coalesce.

  International targets exist to direct governments and inspire society to take steps towards the conservation of biodiversity in the broader context of global sustainable development (e.g. the Convention on Biological Diversity Aichi targets (CBD 2011) and post-2020 biodiversity targets, the Sustainable Development Goals (SDGs) Agenda 2030, the EU Taxonomy, the Planetary Boundaries, ISO 14001 and EMAS).

- *Metrics*: Metrics are necessary to ensure the biodiversity protection and must be integrated into all investments analysis, but as outlined above, the lack of consistent and uniform metrics to assess company performance about biodiversity is identified as a key barrier by the investors. Proxies for measuring impact are available, such as the potential overlap of company operations with ecologically sensitive areas, and work is underdevelopment to establish metrics that give insight into performance on biodiversity and portfolio impact.[57]

  Quantifying biodiversity-related risks and opportunities presents a major challenge. Standardized methodologies, such as carbon footprinting in the context of climate-related risk analysis, are in early stages of development and are unlikely to become as universally applicable across sectors and asset classes as certain climate-related metrics.[58]

  Tools that give insight into actual impact and performance at the corporate or portfolio level are limited. Some investors have developed bespoke scoring methods, while others obtain biodiversity information from third parties such as research and data providers.

- *Data:* There is a lack of access to appropriate asset and company-level data as an issue for assessing company performance and evaluating fund or investment impact. This indicates that even if metrics were established through the processes outlined above, that data gaps would need to be filled in parallel.

  Data are often not fit for purpose. Biodiversity is location-specific and varies according to the actual asset at that location. Therefore, it can be challenging to aggregate biodiversity data at an enterprise level. This is a major challenge for sectors which have extended, complex, natural resource-based supply chains. Biodiversity risk and impact are also measured differently within companies and sectors.

  Tools that give insight into actual impact and performance at the corporate or portfolio level are limited.

  ESG data providers currently focus on management measures which are proxies for performance, but give limited insight into the impact of companies on the ground and how well these are managed over time.

  There is also significant variation in how data providers address biodiversity within their research, such as the level of information and wide-ranging nature of questions asked of companies.

  Addressing this barrier will therefore require action by data providers to ensure the inclusion of biodiversity considerations within their ESG criteria and rating methodologies, as well as improved regulatory drivers for companies in the real economy to disclose biodiversity performance in a standardized way.

Conclusion

A recent study published on Science[59] in July 2020 stated that the gross estimated costs of prevention future zoonotic pandemics before they start take $22 to $31 billion per year. Reduced deforestation has the ancillary benefit of around $4 billion per year in social benefits from reduced greenhouse gas emissions, so net prevention costs range from $18 to $27 billion per year. The study outlines how COVID-19 has shown us the immense potential cost of a pandemic. The world may lose at least $5 trillion in GDP in 2020, and the willingness to pay for the lives lost constitutes many additional trillions. An important information that the study revealed is that a year's worth of these preventive strategies would only need to reduce the likelihood of another pandemic like COVID-19 in the next year by about 27% below baseline probability in the most likely scenario.

The sustainable growth of the pharmaceutical industry, as reported in the WEF Nature risk rising report, depends on the development of new drugs[60] and treatments to drive future revenues. As much as 50% of prescription drugs are based on a molecule that occurs naturally in a plant, while 70% of cancer drugs are natural or synthetic products inspired by nature.

The industry is particularly dependent on biodiverse tropical rainforests for new discoveries, with 25% of drugs used in modern medicine derived from rainforest plants. As tropical forests face threats from felling and wildfires, pharmaceutical companies face losing a vast repository of undiscovered genetic materials that could lead to the next medical – and commercial – breakthrough. Only 15% of an estimated 300,000 plant species in the world have been evaluated to determine their pharmacological potential. According to some estimates, the industry is already losing one potential major drug every two years.

So, a lot of efforts will be taken in order to monitor and tackle with future huge disaster like COVID-19 ones. The UN Sendai Framework 2015–2030 promotes a global culture of disaster risk reduction. The Sendai Framework has seven strategic targets and 38 indicators for measuring progress on reducing disaster risk and losses. These indicators align implementation of the Sendai Framework with implementation of the SDGs and the Paris Agreement on Climate Change. The issues of disaster risk governance – identifying and acknowledging, planning and acting on disaster risk – have come into sharp focus this year, as evidence accumulates of the failure of many countries to heed the many warnings in recent years, and prepare for global threats such as a major pandemic like COVID-19. Only a few of the 86 national strategies for disaster risk reduction developed to date make adequate inclusion of epidemic and pandemic risk management, including prevention and preparedness measures.

Better communication of climate and biodiversity information by companies can contribute to the implementation of Sendai Framework for Disaster Risk Reduction 2015–2030.[61] This comprehensive strategy sets goals and priorities for governments to deal with increasingly intense and frequent disasters. In addition, climate change, biodiversity loss and health threats, as a source of financial instability, have come under the hood of central banks, regulators and supervisors, responsible for maintaining and monitoring stability in the markets. The effort to consider the climate and biodiversity element in the risk analysis, and therefore in facilitating the inflow of capital into green and social investments, has seen the establishment of the Central Banks and Supervisors Network for Greening the Financial System (NGFS)[62] in December 2017. Biodiversity together with climate change can be considered a green swan event[63] that can cause systemic financial crisis. Physical and temporary climate risks create complex, broad and non-linear knock-on effects that can lead to catastrophic and irreversible impacts whose externalities are difficult to estimate.

Notes

1 This growth strategy aims to transform the EU into a just and prosperous society, with a modern and efficient economy, which in 2050 no longer generates net greenhouse gas emissions and with economic growth decoupled from resource use. It aims to protect, conserve and improve the EU's natural capital and to protect citizens' health and well-being from environmental risks. The Green Deal is an integral part of the Commission's strategy to implement the 2030 Agenda, and for this reason, it foresees that at the same time, this transition must be fair and inclusive. Ref. https://ec.europa.eu/info/publications/communication-european-green-deal.

2 The Lancet (11/2019), The 2019 report of The Lancet Countdown on health and climate change: Ensuring that the health of a child born today is not defined by a changing climate, Vol. 394, www.thelancet.com. Accessed June 30, 2020.

Harvard T.H. Chan School of Public Health (04/2020), Exposure to air pollution and COVID-19 mortality in the United States: A nationwide cross-sectional study, https://projects.iq.harvard.edu/covid-pm. Accessed August 14, 2020.

Joule (06/2020), The Short-run and Long-run Effects of Covid-19 on Energy and the Environment, https://doi.org/10.1016/j.joule.2020.06.010. Accessed August 14, 2020.

Science (07/2020) Ecology and economics for pandemic prevention, DOI: 10.1126/science.abc3189. Accessed August 14, 2020.

3 MERS, SARS, Swine Flu and Covid-19 are all zoonotic viruses.

4 The Intergovernmental Panel on Climate Change (IPCC), The IPCC Special Report on Global Warming of 1.5°C was formally approved by the world's governments in 2018, https://www.ipcc.ch/sr15/. Accessed June 30, 2020.

5 The Intergovernmental Science-Policy Platform on Biodiversity and Ecosystem Services (IPBES), Global Assessment Report on Biodiversity and Ecosystem Services, https://ipbes.net/global-assessment. Accessed August 14, 2020.

6 The *Anthropocene* is a proposed geological epoch dating from the commencement of significant human impact on Earth's geology and ecosystems, including, but not limited to, anthropogenic climate change. Neither the International Commission on Stratigraphy (ICS) nor the International Union of Geological Sciences (IUGS) has officially approved the term as a recognized subdivision of geologic time, although the Anthropocene Working Group (AWG) of the Subcommission on Quaternary Stratigraphy (SQS) of the ICS voted in April 2016 to proceed towards a formal golden spike (GSSP) proposal to define the Anthropocene epoch in the geologic timescale and presented the recommendation to the International Geological Congress in August 2016. http://quaternary.stratigraphy.org/working-groups/anthropocene/. Accessed August 14, 2020.

7 Vaclav Smil (2013) Harvesting the biosphere. What We Have Taken from Nature, The MIT Press, ISBN: 9780262018562.

8 World Economic Forum (WEF) (01/2020) Nature risk rising: why the crisis engulfing nature matters of business and the economy, https://www.weforum.org/reports/-nature-risk-rising-why-the-crisis-engulfing-nature-matters-for-business-and-the-economy. Accessed August 14, 2020.

9 World Economic Forum (WEF) (2020) Global Risks Report, http://www3.weforum.org/docs/WEF_Global_Risk_Report_2020.pdf.

10 https://ec.europa.eu/clima/policies/eu-climate-action/law_en.

11 https://ec.europa.eu/info/publications/sustainable-finance-teg-taxonomy_en.

12 https://ec.europa.eu/info/sites/info/files/communication-annex-eu-biodiversity-strategy-2030_en.pdf.

13 Reuters, "China says UN biodiversity summit rescheduled for May 2021", https://news.yahoo.com/china-says-un-biodiversity-summit-023720577.html.

14 The Strategic Plan for Biodiversity includes five strategic goals (A–E) and 20 time-bound, measurable targets to be met by the year 2020 (*Aichi Biodiversity Targets*) valid for the entire United Nations system and all other partners engaged in biodiversity management and policy development.

- Strategic Goal A: Address the underlying causes of biodiversity loss by mainstreaming biodiversity across government and society
- Strategic Goal B: Reduce the direct pressures on biodiversity and promote sustainable use
- Strategic Goal C: Improve the status of biodiversity by safeguarding ecosystems, species and genetic diversity
- Strategic Goal D: Enhance the benefits to all from biodiversity and ecosystem services

- Strategic Goal E: Enhance implementation through participatory planning, knowledge management and capacity building
https://www.cbd.int/sp/targets/. Accessed August 14, 2020

15 OECD (04/2020) A Comprehensive Overview of Global Biodiversity Finance, https://www.oecd.org/environment/resources/biodiversityfinance.htm. Accessed August 14, 2020.
16 Ibid.
17 https://www.un.org/sustainabledevelopment/sustainable-development-goals/.
18 UNEP Finance Initiative (June 2020) Beyond business as usual biodiversity targets and finance, https://www.unepfi.org/wordpress/wp-content/uploads/2020/06/Beyond-Business-As-Usual-Full-Report.pdf. Accessed August 14, 2020.
19 IOSCO - Statement on Disclosure of Esg Matters by Issuers – 2019.
20 EC Action Plan: Financing Sustainable Growth - Brussels, 8.3.2018 COM (2018) 97.
21 WCED (1987) Our Common Future. http://www.un-documents.net/our-common-future.pdf. Accessed August 14, 2020.
22 Humans use as much ecological resources as if we lived on 1.6 Earths. The *Ecological Footprint* is the only metric that compares the resource demand of individuals, governments and businesses against what Earth can renew. https://www.footprintnetwork.org/. Accessed August 14, 2020.
23 https://ec.europa.eu/info/sites/info/files/communication-annex-eu-biodiversity-strategy-2030_en.pdf.
24 https://ec.europa.eu/info/law/better-regulation/have-your-say/initiatives/12129-Revision-of-Non-Financial-Reporting-Directive.
25 https://ec.europa.eu/info/files/eu-budget-powering-recovery-plan-europe_en.
26 https://ec.europa.eu/info/business-economy-euro/banking-and-finance/sustainable-finance/eu-taxonomy-sustainable-activities_en.
27 https://communities.unescap.org/system/files/seea-cf_4_classification-environmental_activities.pdf.
28 https://www.dst.dk/en/Statistik/dokumentation/nomenklaturer/ressourceforvaltningsaktiviteter--crema-.
29 https://ec.europa.eu/info/consultations/finance-2020-sustainable-finance-strategy_en.
30 https://ec.europa.eu/info/files/international-platform-sustainable-finance-factsheet_en.
31 World Economic Forum (WEF) (70/2020) The Future of Nature and Business, http://www3.weforum.org/docs/WEF_The_Future_Of_Nature_And_Business_2020.pdf. Accessed August 15, 2020.
32 https://www.iucnredlist.org/.
33 DNB (07/2020) Biodiversity Opportunities and Risks for the Financial Sector, https://www.dnb.nl/binaries/Biodiversity%20opportunities%20risks%20for%20the%20financial%20sector_tcm46-389029.pdf. Accessed August 15, 2020.
34 Enterprise risk management.
35 WWF (09/2019) Nature of Risk: A Framework for Understanding Nature-Related Risk to Business, https://c402277.ssl.cf1.rackcdn.com/publications/1255/files/original/WWF_Nature_of_Risk.FINAL2.pdf?1568216828. Accessed August 15, 2020.
36 UNFCCC (2015). Paris Agreement. https://unfccc.int/files/essential_background/convention/application/pdf/english_paris_agreement.pdf.
37 IPCC, 2018: Summary for Policymakers, https://www.ipcc.ch/sr15/chapter/spm/b/spm2/.
38 World Economic Forum, 2020, "The Global Risk Report 2020", http://www3.weforum.org/docs/WEF_Global_Risk_Report_2020.pdf.
39 The EU Taxonomy, the SDGs and bond standards also have a role to play in setting the ambition for managing biodiversity and reducing biodiversity loss. Current disclosure guidance through the Global Reporting Initiative and the CDP Forests 2020

questionnaire are limited in the biodiversity measures they consider, or the sectors addressed for investors.

40 Task Force on Climate-related Financial Disclosure (TCFD), Status report June 2019, https://www.fsb-tcfd.org/wp-content/uploads/2019/06/2019-TCFD-Status-Report-FINAL-053119.pdf.

41 Global Sustainable Investment Alliance, December 2019, "Sustainable Investor Poll on TCFD Implementation", "... *the survey was distributed by JSIF, RIA Australasia, RIA Canada, UK SIF, US SIF, and VBDO to their respective memberships. Overall, 272 individuals responded to the survey*", http://www.gsi-alliance.org/wp-content/uploads/2019/12/Global-Sustainable-Investment-Alliance-TCFD-Poll.pdf.

42 Biodiversity: the next frontier for ESG data ENVIRONMENTAL FINANCE spring 2020 Graham Cooper reports, https://www.environmental-finance.com/content/analysis/the-esg-data-files-part-nine-biodiversity-the-new-frontier.html.

43 https://tnfd.info/.

44 Prue F. E. Addison, Joseph W. Bull and E. J. Milner-Gulland, 2018, "Using conservation science to advance corporate biodiversity accountability"; https://conbio.onlinelibrary.wiley.com/doi/pdf/10.1111/cobi.13190.

45 PRI, webinar 1/9/2020, Biodiversity: "What are the pathways for priority sectors and what are investors doing?", https://www.brighttalk.com/webcast/17701/429663/-biodiversity-what-are-the-pathways-for-priority-sectors.

46 UN Convention on Biological Diversity, 9/2020, "Global Biodiversity Outlook 5", https://www.cbd.int/gbo/gbo5/publication/gbo-5-en.pdf.

47 WWF (2020) "Living Planet Report 2020 - Bending the curve of biodiversity loss", Almond, R.E.A., Grooten M. and Petersen, T. (Eds). WWF, Gland, Switzerland, https://www.zsl.org/sites/default/files/LPR%202020%20Full%20report.pdf.

48 Reuters, "China says UN biodiversity summit rescheduled for May 2021", https://news.yahoo.com/china-says-un-biodiversity-summit-023720577.html.

49 Convention on Biological Diversity, "Biodiversity and the 2030 agenda for sustainable development", https://www.cbd.int/development/doc/biodiversity-2030-agenda-technical-note-en.pdf.

50 Convention on Biological Diversity, 2020, "Global Biodiversity Outlook 5",

> Examples of where biodiversity is a key factor for the achievement of other SDGs are Goal 2 (Zero Hunger). All food systems depend on biodiversity and a broad range of ecosystem services that support agricultural productivity, soil fertility, and water quality and supply and Goal 6 (Clean water and sanitation). Healthy ecosystems underpin the delivery of water supplies, water quality, and guard against water-related hazards and disasters. Some SDGS address the drivers of biodiversity loss, such as climate change (Goal 13), pollution (Goals 6, 12 and 14) and overexploitation (Goals 6, 12, 14 and 15). Achieving these Goals would therefore contribute to the conservation of biodiversity. Greater access to education (Goal 4) builds human capital and thereby enables effective action, including collective action, to be taken. In addition, education, especially for women and girls, has been shown to reduce fertility rates and, therefore, this goal may have an indirect effect on biodiversity by reducing population growth, a pressure on biodiversity.
>
> https://www.cbd.int/gbo/gbo5/publication/gbo-5-en.pdf

51 Capitals Coalition and Cambridge Conservation Initiative. 2020. "Integrating biodiversity into natural capital assessments". (Online) available at: www.capitalscoalition.org, https://vimeo.com/463515491.

52 Cambridge Conservation Initiative and Capital Coalition, 3/2020, "Framing Guidance Part of a series of Biodiversity Guidance to accompany the Natural Capital Protocol", https://naturalcapitalcoalition.org/wp-content/uploads/2020/03/FramingGuidance_ConsultationMarch2020.pdf.

53 European Commission, 8.3.2018, "Action Plan: Financing Sustainable Growth" https://eur-lex.europa.eu/legal-content/EN/TXT/PDF/?uri=CELEX:52018DC0097&from=EN.

54 "Official Journal L 198 of the European Union, 22 June 2020, *'Biodiversity' means the variability among living organisms arising from all sources including terrestrial, marine and other aquatic ecosystems and the ecological complexes of which they are part and includes diversity within species, between species and of ecosystems*" Regulation (EU) 2020/852 of the European Parliament and of the Council of 18 June 2020 on the establishment of a framework to facilitate sustainable investment, and amending Regulation (EU) 2019/2088, https://eur-lex.europa.eu/legal-content/EN/TXT/PDF/?uri=OJ:L:2020:198:FULL&from=EN.

55 Other sustainable investments are in economic activities that contribute to a social objective, in particular, an investment that contributes to tackling inequality or that fosters social cohesion, social integration and labour relations, or an investment in human capital or economically or socially disadvantaged communities, provided that such investments do not significantly harm any of those objectives and that the investee companies follow good governance practices, in particular with respect to sound management structures, employee relations, remuneration of staff and tax compliance.

56 Principles for Responsible Investment, 9/2020, "Investor action on biodiversity: discussion paper", https://www.unpri.org/sustainability-issues/environmental-social-and-governance-issues/environmental-issues/biodiversity.

57 Several biodiversity measurement approaches are being developed, including some targeted specifically at the finance sector (The Global Biodiversity Score (GBS), Biodiversity Footprint for Financials (BFFI), Species threat abatement and recovery metric (STAR), Net Environmental Contribution (NEC)).

58 Point of No Returns – Share ACTION, Part IV – Biodiversity An assessment of asset managers' approaches to biodiversity, Metrics, risk assessment and integration, 5.1 – The vast majority of asset managers do not integrate biodiversity-related metrics into investment processes.

59 Science (07/2020) Ecology and economics for pandemic prevention, DOI: 10.1126/science.abc3189. Accessed August 14, 2020.

60 No other sector spends as much on R&D as pharmaceuticals.

61 https://www.undrr.org/.

62 https://www.ngfs.net/en.

63 Rif. The green swan: Central banking and financial stability in the age of climate change. BIS. https://www.bis.org/publ/othp31.pdf.

References

BCG, NABU, Birdlife international, 9/2020, "The biodiversity imperative for business: Preserving the foundations of our well-being", https://web-assets.bcg.com/2a/f5/e95293214c29877c11251290ebca/2020-09-the-biodiversity-imperative-for-business-final2-002.pdf

Commission, Factsheet, 5/2020, "EU 2030 Biodiversity strategy – Bringing nature back into our lives", file:///C:/Users/Utente/Downloads/factsheet-EU-biodiversity-strategy_en.pdf.pdf

Communication from the commission to the European Parliament, the Council, the European Economic and Social Committee and the Committee of the Regions, Brussels, 20.5.2020 COM (2020) 380 final, "EU Biodiversity strategy for 2030 bringing nature back into our lives", https://eur-lex.europa.eu/resource.html?uri=cellar%-3Aa3c806a6-9ab3-11ea-9d2d-01aa75ed71a1.0001.02/DOC_1&format=PDF

Convention on Biological Diversity, 7/2018 "Guidance for reporting by businesses on their actions related to biodiversity", https://www.cbd.int/doc/c/ff6d/906c/ebebc273f27f8e9416bba00b/sbi-02-04-add2-en.pdf

Convention on Biological Diversity, 2/2020, "zero draft of the post-2020 global biodiversity framework", https://www.cbd.int/doc/c/efb0/1f84/a892b98d2982a829962b6371/wg2020-02-03-en.pdf

Convention on Biological Diversity, 8/2020 "Global Biodiversity Outlook 5", https://www.cbd.int/gbo5

Convention on Biological Diversity, "Strategic plan for biodiversity 2011–2020 and the Aichi targets", https://www.cbd.int/doc/strategic-plan/2011-2020/Aichi-Targets-EN.pdf

Environmental Finance, 4/2020, "The ESG data files, part nine: Biodiversity - the new frontier", https://www.environmental-finance.com/content/analysis/the-esg-data-files-part-nine-biodiversity-the-new-frontier.html

EU Business & Biodiversity Platform, 12/2019, "Assessment of biodiversity measurement approaches for businesses and financial institutions", https://ec.europa.eu/environment/biodiversity/business/assets/pdf/European_B@B_platform_report_biodiversity_assessment_2019_FINAL_5Dec2019.pdf

GOV.UK, 4/2020 "The Dasgupta review – Independent review on the economics of biodiversity. Interim report", https://assets.publishing.service.gov.uk/government/uploads/system/uploads/attachment_data/file/882222/The_Economics_of_Biodiversity_The_Dasgupta_Review_Interim_Report.pdf

Harold Levrel, 10/2007, "Selecting indicators for the management of biodiversity", Institut français de la biodiversité, https://www.isprambiente.gov.it/files/biodiversita/Levrel_2007_Selecting_indicators.pdf

ipbes, 2019, "Global assessment report on biodiversity and ecosystem services", https://ipbes.net/global-assessment

Joel Houdet, Endangered Wildlife Trust, "Biodiversity indicators for management & disclosure", https://ec.europa.eu/environment/biodiversity/business/assets/pdf/2019/Biodiversity%20Indicators%20for%20Management%20and%20Disclosure.pdf

MATTM, 9/2020, "Global biodiversity framework post-2020", https://www.minambiente.it/pagina/global-biodiversity-framework

McKinsey&company, 9/2020, "Valuing nature conservation. A methodology to evaluate where safeguarding natural capital could have the biggest impact on climate, economies and health", https://www.mckinsey.com/~/media/McKinsey/Business%20Functions/Sustainability/Our%20Insights/Valuing%20nature%20conservation/Valuing-nature-conservation.pdf

Natural Capital Coalition, 7/2016 "Natural capital protocol principles and framework", https://naturalcapitalcoalition.org/wp-content/uploads/2016/07/Framework_Book_2016-07-01-2.pdf

NatureServe, 3/2020, "A biodiversity observation data standard for the NatureServe network", https://www.natureserve.org/sites/default/files/publications/files/ods_wg_final_report.pdf

OECD, 4/2020, "A comprehensive overview of global biodiversity finance final report", https://www.oecd.org/environment/resources/biodiversity/report-a-comprehensive-overview-of-global-biodiversity-finance.pdf

OECD, 4/2020, "Tracking economic instruments and finance for biodiversity 2020", http://www.oecd.org/environment/resources/tracking-economic-instruments-and-finance-for-biodiversity-2020.pdf

OECD International Expert Workshop, 2/2019, "The post-2020 biodiversity framework: Targets, indicators and measurability implications at global and national level", http://www.oecd.org/environment/resources/biodiversity/Summary-Record-OECD-workshop-The-Post-2020-Biodiversity-Framework-targets-indicators-and-measurability-implications.pdf

Prue F. E. Addison, Joseph W. Bull and E. J. Milner-Gulland, "Using conservation science to advance corporate biodiversity accountability", https://conbio.onlinelibrary.wiley.com/doi/full/10.1111/cobi.13190

PwC & WWF, 9/2020, "Leading the way to a green and resilient economy. A Swiss-quality approach to sustainable finance", https://www.pwc.ch/en/publications/2020/-the-way-to-a-green-resilient-economy.pdf

ShareAction, 6/2020, "Point of No Returns Part IV – Biodiversity An assessment of asset managers' approaches to biodiversity", https://shareaction.org/wp-content/uploads/2020/06/ShareAction-Biodiversity-Report-Final.pdf

Sole 24 Ore, 6/2020, "Gli indicatori per misurare l'allarme globale sulla biodiversità", https://www.infodata.ilsole24ore.com/2020/06/05/gli-indicatori-misurare-lallarme-globale-sulla-biodiversita/

Sole 24 Ore, 10/2020, "Biodiversità, mancati tutti gli obiettivi. Il Living Planet Index spiegato bene", https://www.infodata.ilsole24ore.com/2020/10/03/biodiversita-mancati-tutti-gli-obiettivi-ll-living-planet-index-spiegato-bene/

The Energy & Biodiversity Initiative's, 1/2003, "Biodiversity Indicators for Monitoring Impacts and Conservation Actions", https://shift.tools/resources/1674

The Paulson Institute, The Nature Conservancy and the Cornell Atkinson Center for Sustainability, 2020, "FINANCING NATURE: Closing the global biodiversity financing gap full report", file:///C:/Users/Utente/Downloads/CBD-Full-Report-Endorsements-.pdf

The University of Cambridge Institute for Sustainability Leadership (CISL), 2016, "Biodiversity and ecosystem services in corporate natural capital accounting synthesis report", https://www.cisl.cam.ac.uk/resources/publication-pdfs/biodiversity-and-ecosystem-services-in-corporate-natural-capital-accounting-synthesis-report

The University of Cambridge Institute for Sustainability Leadership (CISL), 7/2017, "Healthy ecosystem metric framework: Biodiversity impact", https://www.cisl.cam.ac.uk/resources/publication-pdfs/healthy-ecosystem-metric-framework.pdf

The University of Cambridge Institute for Sustainability Leadership (CISL), 2020, "Measuring business impacts on nature. A framework to support better stewardship of biodiversity in global supply chains", https://www.cisl.cam.ac.uk/resources/-publication-pdfs/measuring-business-impacts-on-nature.pdf

The World Bank Group, 2020, "Mobilizing private finance for nature", https://greenfinanceplatform.org/sites/default/files/downloads/resource/FinanceforNature28Sepwebversion.pdf

UN Environment Program, 6/2020, "Beyond 'Business as Usual': Biodiversity targets and finance managing biodiversity risks across business sectors", https://naturalcapital.finance/wp-content/uploads/2020/06/Beyond-Business-As-Usual-Full-Report.pdf

WEF, 1/2020, "Nature risk rising: Why the crisis engulfing nature matters for business and the economy", http://www3.weforum.org/docs/WEF_New_Nature_Economy_Report_2020.pdf

WWF, 2/2020, "GLOBAL FUTURES: Assessing the global economic impacts of environmental change to support policy-making", https://c402277.ssl.cf1.rackcdn.com/publications/1299/files/original/Summary_Report.pdf?1581456250

WWF (2020) Living Planet Report 2020 - Bending the curve of biodiversity loss. Almond, R.E.A., Grooten M. and Petersen, T. (Eds). WWF, Gland, Switzerland, https://f.hubspotusercontent20.net/hubfs/4783129/LPR/PDFs/ENGLISH-FULL.pdf

16

GREEN BONDS FROM AN INTEGRATED THINKING PERSPECTIVE

Wayne van Zijl, Dannielle Cerbone and Warren Maroun

What Are Green Bonds?

Green Bonds are defined by the International Capital Market Association (ICMA) as

> any type of bond instrument[1] where the proceeds will be exclusively ap-
> plied to finance or re-finance, in part or in full, new and/or existing eligi-
> ble Green Projects.
>
> *[1]*

'Green Projects' refer to projects that have clear, measurable environmental benefits and include objectives such as climate change mitigation, climate change
adaptation, natural resource conservation, biodiversity conservation and pollution prevention and control [1]. Each green bond will have selection criteria set
by the issuer.

Sustainability Bonds and social Bonds have also emerged. The former are
bonds which directly aim to address or mitigate a specific social issue and/or seek
to achieve positive social outcomes [2]. Bonds which intentionally mix 'green'
and social projects are referred to as sustainability bonds [3].

Green bonds were issued as early as 2007, with the European Investment
Bank (EIB) leading the movement with its 2007 *Climate Awareness Bond* [4].
This oversubscribed bond funded 14 projects in six countries at a total of EUR
600 million (USD 732 million[2]) and focused on renewable energy and energy
efficiency projects.

Despite the success of the EIB's green bond issue, the market for green bonds
remained limited.

Without clear principles, most green bond issuances were self-defined and self-
reported [5]. Interest in green bonds was dampened by investor concerns regarding

DOI: 10.4324/9781003045557-20

definitions, standards and potential reputational risk from 'greenwashing' if proceeds are not used for their intended purposes [6, 7]. A key catalyst for subsequent market development was the introduction of the Green Bond Principles in January 2014 by the ICMA, which forms the foundation for many of the existing green labels [8]. Since then, the market for labelled green bonds has expanded dramatically, as shown in Figure 16.1 [9].

Green bond issuances have more than doubled from 2014 to 2019. In 2019, total issuances amounted to USD 255 billion.[3] Most issuances have been used to finance clean and efficient energy projects, with investment into climate change mitigation and adaptation projects being relatively limited [9, 10, 11]. The decline in issuances from 2019 to 2020 is probably because of the COVID-19 pandemic and its impact on the global economy [for details see 12].

The five-year uptake in green bonds can be attributed to several benefits for both issuers and investors [5]. For issuers, green bonds can align with long-term project maturities, lower the cost of debt, reduce firm-level environmental footprints and improve financial performance. Green bonds are sought out especially by environmentally conscious investors who wish to ensure their capital is invested in green projects and increase their exposure to less volatile instruments. Institutional investors' mandates may also encourage or require investments in green bonds [13]. This is in keeping with the growing view that environmental, social and governance matters must be factored into investment and capital allocation decisions [14–16].

To be successful, Mathews and Kidney [17] argue that green bonds must generate a return for all participants and not expose investors to worse risk-reward profiles than conventional corporate and government bonds would. Investors are

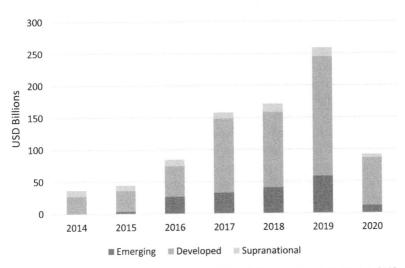

adapted from Climate Bonds Initiative [10]

FIGURE 16.1 Green bonds issued from 2014 to 2020.

presented with environmentally friendly investment opportunities of equivalent risk-reward profiles, compared to environmentally neutral or harmful projects. The favourable economic position, coupled with external pressures to supporting green initiatives, should encourage the financing and development of environmental projects [18].

The World Bank Group [18] considers green bonds a vital component of the transition to a low-carbon economy. As green bonds gain momentum, it is hoped that they will become a generally accepted and common feature of project financing. The following section provides a brief overview of the academic literature dealing with green bonds.

A Brief Review of the Prior Literature

The green bond research has 4 focus areas, namely:

1. macroeconomic conditions affecting the green bond market and its growth determinants [11, 19],
2. green bond pricing with a primary focus on the 'green bond premium'[4] [7, 20],
3. risks that issuers are attempting to remedy [21] and
4. the environmental integrity of green bonds [22].

At a macroeconomic level, Chiesa and Barua [23] explore the factors affecting the size of green bond issuances in emerging and mature markets. They find issue size is positively related to the coupon rate, credit rating, collateral availability and the issuer's sector and financial health. In addition, issuances in emerging markets which are internationally orientated and denominated in Euro are larger. These features offer investors more reliable returns, leading to larger issue sizes because of greater investor demand.

Banga [24] and Deschryver and De Mariz [25] investigate the barriers to and drivers of green bond issuances. The main drivers of the demand for green bonds include increased climate-awareness from investors, the commitment of policy-makers to counter climate change and prevailing macroeconomic conditions. Impediments to the green bond market, especially in developing economies, include a lack of knowledge about how green bonds work, inappropriate institutional arrangements for green bond management, minimum issue sizes, the currency of issuance and high transaction costs.

Tripathy [21] discusses how green bonds extend the ambit of finance practitioners to include environmental and climate change experience. The green bond market is found to extend financial and market logics by forcing financial modelling to include climate risk scenarios, possible economic and policy actions and the associated financial implications.

Prior research on the green bond premium compares yield spreads between green and conventional bonds to identify any price differentials [7, 20, 26]. There appears to be a negative price premium in the primary issuance market but not in the secondary markets [7]. The negative bond premium suggests that investors are motivated by considerations other than underlying environmental considerations [7, 27] and that the bonds are more convenient for issuers [26, 28].

Importantly, the fact that a bond is 'green' does not necessarily mean that it carries lower risk or guarantees a higher financial return for investors. The market for green bonds is characterised by more volatility clustering than the conventional bond market, something which could be a key factor behind the increase in issuance of green bonds and how they are priced by investors [29].

Environmental Bonds – The Case of South Africa

Much of the green bond research focuses on the financial features of green bonds with an emphasis on developed economies and large issuances in emerging markets. To provide a more detailed account of green bonds, details on the nature and functioning of green bonds in South Africa are considered.

The jurisdiction has a long history of promoting different types of environmental and social reporting [14, 30, 31]. Most recently, it was the first country to introduce requirements for companies to prepare integrated reports as part of its codes on corporate governance [32] and the listing requirements of the local stock exchange [33]. Coupled with a relatively mature capital market and commitment to responsible investment [34], South Africa offers an excellent case for providing insights into green bonds that are not from mainstream and wealthy countries.

Despite the sophistication of its capital market, codes on corporate governance and financial reporting regulations, South Africa is a developing country. The country was thought to be a significant growth opportunity, characterised by strong democratic systems, a growing population, rapid urbanization and an expanding middle-class. During the 1990s and early 2000s, South Africa was seen as the economic powerhouse of and gateway into Africa. Unfortunately, the last ten years have seen a steady decline for the South African economy [35, 36]. The country has been plagued by maladministration and corruption which contributed to major rating agencies downgrading South Africa to sub-investment status. High-profile corporate scandals and audit failures have shaken confidence in the local capital market which reported below-inflation returns over the last five years [37–39]. The poor performance by the Johannesburg Stock Exchange (JSE) and a decline in capital investment can be attributed to regulatory uncertainty about asset ownership, taxation and the state's handling of the fiscus [40].

Given the country's economic woes, regaining the confidence of local and international investors is paramount. At the same time, significant social and environmental challenges must be confronted [41]. The country ranks among the worst in the world when it comes to income inequality, crime, education and access to healthcare [42–45]. Located in a region which is historically semi-arid, South Africa is especially vulnerable to the effects of climate change [46, 47].

As a result, South Africa has devoted considerable attention to codes on corporate governance which call for the concurrent management of economic, environmental and social issues [14, 32, 41]. It has played a leading role in the development and application of integrated thinking and reporting in an effort to promote more socially and environmentally responsible business and advance sustainable development [48]. As part of this, the country has called on its institutional investors and large asset owners to focus specially on social indicators, environmental impact and long-term sustainability when evaluating projects and making investments [32, 34]. In this context, South Africa is one of only three African countries to have issued green bonds[5] [10, 49]. The total value of green bonds issued in Africa is reported in Figure 16.2.

Even though South Africa is no longer the largest economy in Africa,[6] it has issued USD2.2Bn of the continent's cumulative USD 2.7 billion in green bonds [10]. South Africa's City of Johannesburg Municipality was the first organisation in the country to issue a green bond. In 2014, the city issued a green bond to the value of ZAR 1.46 billion. Three years later, the City of Cape Town Municipality also issued green bonds but to the value of ZAR 1 billion [49].

Both of these bonds were listed on the JSE. At the time of their issuances, the JSE did not have a dedicated green bond segment. This segment was launched by the JSE only in late 2017 [50]. Both cities have not listed their bonds on the JSE's green bond segment.

The City of Cape Town's bond is listed on the ICMA's database of green bonds. The City of Johannesburg's green bond is not listed by the ICMA [51]. The database does, however, show Nedbank, one of the country's largest banks, as having a green bond. Nedbank's green bond (ZAR 2.662 billion) is also listed on the JSE's green bond segment as is a bond issued by Growthpoint (ZAR 1.1 billion). Growthpoint's bond is not included in the ICMA database.

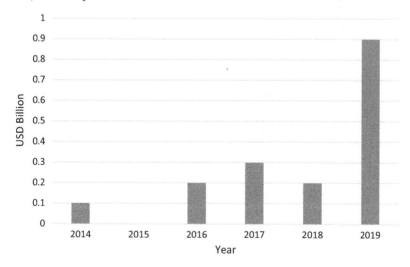

FIGURE 16.2 African green bonds issued per year.

The above inconsistencies underscore a general observation noted while writing this paper. Accessing data and details of green bonds in South Africa is not straightforward. Information is scarce and listings are inconsistent. In addition, green bonds do not frequently appear in popular financial press and forums.

Accounting for Green Bonds as Part of an Integrated Value Creation Process

The technical features of green bonds have been considered in some detail (see Section "A Brief Review of the Prior Literature"), but there is relatively little on how green bonds form part of the broader value creation process and their relevance for stakeholders. The guidance provided by the International Integrated Reporting Council (IIRC) can, however, be applied to address this limitation.

Figure 16.3 shows how different capitals are used by organisations. These are the inputs into their business models. Based on strategic objectives and prevailing risks and opportunities, the capitals are required to achieve specific business objectives and produce output for investors and non-investor stakeholders. The outputs have consequences or outcomes which are also evaluated from a multi-capital perspective [52].

Governing bodies monitor how the capitals are used and affected by the business model. Performance is gauged from an economic, social and environmental perspective and used to evaluate the business outlook. In turn, strategies, risk mitigation, business models and operating activities are revised to ensure long-term and sustainable value creation for stakeholders [52].

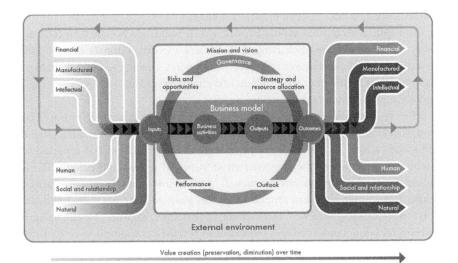

FIGURE 16.3 The value creation process.

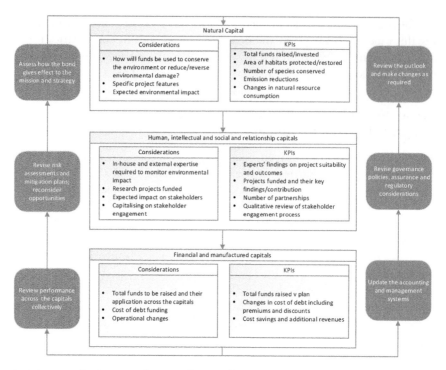

FIGURE 16.4 An integrated approach to evaluating green bonds.

Adapting the principles outlined by the IIRC, Figure 16.4 provides examples of the factors to consider when evaluating and reporting on the relevance of green bonds in the context of an organisation's business model. Possible key performance indicators (KPIs) are also provided.

We begin with natural capital because green bonds are designed to deal directly with environmental challenges. Presenting the direct impact of the bonds on natural capital also ensures that governing bodies, financiers and stakeholders understand and remember the fundamental characteristics of the bonds and their underlying environmental objectives.

The organisation should have a clear understanding of how the bonds will be used to achieve specific environmental objectives. Details on the nature, period and scope of projects funded by the bonds should be evaluated and reported to stockholders, including the expected environmental impact and benefits. KPIs should focus directly on environmental performance and comparing actual results from environmental initiatives to the planned outcomes set when the bonds were originated. These can include, for example, measures for the habitats and species being conserved and reduction in resource consumption or harmful emissions.

To achieve favourable outcomes, investments in human, social and intellectual capital will be required. Specialists must be engaged to evaluate projects supported directly or indirectly by the green bonds. The experts can review project feasibility and appropriateness against predetermined environmental objectives. They can examine the expected outcomes, comment on the suitability of natural capital performance indicators and assist with monitoring performance.

In some cases, research may be required to develop solutions for addressing an entity's environmental challenges. The organisation may need to partner with think tanks, universities and NGOs to achieve its objectives or may finance these entities to complete specific studies as part of its broader environmental protection programme. The number of partnerships, their research outputs and the impact of their findings are possible KPIs.

Stakeholders should be co-opted in planned activities. For example, where bonds are used to finance clean energy projects, infrastructure development or eco-tourism, the impact on stakeholders should be considered. Gaining their support can be a key factor in achieving success. As a result, the number of stakeholder engagements and qualitative assessments of their achievements and failures should be included as KPIs.

As discussed in Sections "What Are Green Bonds?" and "A Brief Review of the Prior Literature", green bonds must still generate a reasonable financial return for their holders. For the issuer, a key consideration is the funds required and how these will be used in connection with each of the capitals. Projects funded by green bonds will typically require significant purchases of materials, labour, land and machinery. The direct and indirect investment in natural, human, intellectual and social capitals must also be factored into the project budget.

The cost of debt is a critical part of evaluating the project's financial return. Differences between the charge on the green bond and equivalent 'conventional' forms of financing should be evaluated and reported. For example, a premium on the bond price could be an intangible benefit. In substance, bondholders are making an additional contribution to the project's conservation or restoration of natural capital over the term of the bond. Conversely, a discount may be indicative of, *inter alia,* additional project-specific risks, a mismatch of the bond's objective with its planned activities or the fact that views of the targeted financial capital providers are not aligned with the those of the organisation.

As part of the project evaluation, the impact on financial performance should be assessed. For example, bonds used to develop and implement new production techniques, lower emissions or reduce energy consumption will have direct and indirect cost and revenue implications. These should be quantified and reported in conjunction with the performance indicators for the other capitals.

Figure 16.3 is not intended to suggest that the capitals are considered sequentially. In practical terms, the evaluation of each capital will take place concurrently and inform a comprehensive assessment of the green bonds and their planned and actual economic, social and environmental impacts. This type of multi-capital assessment can highlight additional risks and opportunities associated with or arising from the green bond issue and lead to a refinement of risk-mitigation policies. The relevance of the bonds for the organisation's broader strategy should also be kept in mind.

The accounting and management systems may need to be updated to provide the information necessary for a thorough review of how green bonds enable value creation. The process followed to collect the required data, analyse it and report key findings to governing bodies should be assessed. Where necessary, internal controls can be updated to ensure that performance across the capitals is being monitored and reported accurately and completely. This can include the use of formal assurance services to ensure that green bonds comply with the requirements stipulated by the relevant bodies such as the ICMA and the applicable exchanges.

Finally, the organisation reflects on how its activities, including the issuing of green bonds, impact the different capitals and the entity's outlook. Where necessary, business processes, risk management and strategies are revised, taking performance assessments and the legitimate interests of the investor and non-investor stakeholders into consideration.

Summary, Conclusion and Areas for Future Research

Since 1880, the seven warmest years on record have all occurred since 2010 [53]. The rising temperature and increasing acidity of ocean water are direct consequences of human activity [54, 55]. The same is true for what scientists are describing as the sixth period of mass extinction [56]. As a result, climate change, habitat destruction and loss of species are not only concerns for the biologist or planetary scientists. They are the greatest governance, accounting and finance challenges facing the global community [57–59].

The effects of climate change and biodiversity loss will be devastating, with the direct and indirect cost disproportionately borne by the world's poorest populations [60]. Immediate action by business leaders and investors is required to avert the 'biological annihilation' [56] predicted by the scientific community. This includes determining how to encourage projects which can help to conserve habitats, reduce greenhouse gases and lower the consumption of natural resources [61].

Green bonds are one mechanism which can be used by the private and public sector to finance environmentally friendly initiatives such as clean energy production, waste reduction and sustainable agriculture. A growing body of academic work considers how green bonds are priced and the factors which contribute to or hinder the growth of the green bond market. This chapter complements the prior research by providing recommendations for evaluating how green bonds form an integral part of an organisation's value creation process.

Using the guidance provided by the IIRC, the chapter proposes that companies and their financiers take a multi-capital approach to evaluating green bonds and reporting their relevance to stakeholders. Key features of the proposed model include:

- Evaluating how green bonds impact and require different types of capital including natural, human and intellectual capitals in addition to financial capital;
- Setting KPIs to evaluate outcomes for each capital and identify under-performance;
- Using performance evaluations to refine risk assessments and mitigation strategies and determine how green bonds enable or frustrate the achievement of strategic objectives;
- Ensuring that the accounting, management and internal control systems are updated to provide the necessary information to evaluate performance and ensure compliance with any contracts, regulations and stakeholder relationships based on the features of a green bond and
- Reflecting on how green bonds affect the different capitals over time, fluctuations in performance indicators and the need for changes to business processes, operations and strategic positions.

The chapter takes a normative stance on the accounting for and reporting on green bonds. Additional research will be required to test the application of the proposed model. Future researchers can also focus on the factors which motivate individual companies to issue green bonds, their experiences with this type of financing and the extent to which the green bonds have contributed to positive environmental outcomes. As explained by King and Atkins [48], accountants may not have the scientific skills and experience to combat habitat destruction and extinction of species, but they still have a role to play in helping to save the planet.

Notes

1 A bond instrument is similar to a loan, however, instead of a single investor providing the entire capital requirement, it is broken into small equal parts that many investors can invest [15].
2 Converted at December 2020 exchange rate of 1:1.22 (EUR:USD).
3 Green bonds and loan issuances.
4 The "green bond premium" refers to the difference in yields between a green bond and an equivalent synthetic conventional bond.
5 Other than South Africa, only Morocco and Nigeria have green bonds outstanding.
6 Nigeria overtook SA in 2019 as the largest economy in Africa.

References

1. ICMA, *Green Bond Principles 2018: Voluntary Process Guidelines for Issuing Green Bonds.* 2018. p. 8.
2. ICMA, *Social Bond Principles: Voluntary Process Guidelines for Issuing Social Bonds.* 2020. p. 8.
3. ICMA, *Sustainability Bond Guidelines.* 2018. p. 8.
4. EIB, *EIB CAB Newsletter 10th Anniversary.* 2017.

5. MacAskill, S., et al., *Is there a green premium in the green bond market? Systematic literature review revealing premium determinants.* Journal of Cleaner Production, 2021. **280**: p. 124491.

6. Wood, D. and K. Grace, *A brief note on the global green bond market.* Initiative for Responsible Investment at Harvard University, 2011.

7. Ehlers, T. and F. Packer, *Green bond finance and certification.* BIS Quarterly Review September, 2017.

8. ICMA, *Green bond principles 2014: Voluntary process guidelines for issuing green bonds.* 2014. p. 8.

9. Climate Bonds Initiative, *Green bonds reach record $255bn for CY 2019.* 2020, Climate Bonds Initiative.

10. Climate Bonds Initiative. *Interactive data platform.* 2020 [cited 2020 14 December 2020]; Available from: https://www.climatebonds.net/market/data/.

11. Tolliver, C., A.R. Keeley, and S. Managi, *Drivers of green bond market growth: The importance of Nationally Determined Contributions to the Paris agreement and implications for sustainability.* Journal of Cleaner Production, 2020. **244**: p. 118643.

12. de Villiers, C., D. Cerbone, and W. Van Zijl, *The South African government's response to COVID-19.* Journal of Public Budgeting, Accounting & Financial Management, 2020.

13. Chatzitheodorou, K., et al., *Exploring socially responsible investment perspectives: A literature mapping and an investor classification.* Sustainable Production and Consumption, 2019. **19**: p. 117–129.

14. Maroun, W. and D. Cerbone, *Corporate Governance in South Africa.* Vol. 2. 2020: Walter de Gruyter GmbH & Co KG.

15. Edelman, *Edelman Trust Barometer Special Report: Institutional Investors U.S. Results.* Edelman, available at: https://www.edelman.com/sites/g/files/aatuss191/files/2018-11/Edelman_Trust_Baromter_Institutional_Investor_US_Results_0.pdf, 2018.

16. Atkins, J. and M. Macpherson, *Developing a Species Protection Action Plan – An Integrated Approach for Taxonomies, Reporting and Engagement for the Financial Services Sector.* 2019, Concept Paper circulated and presented at Investec Bank's Natural Capital, Species Extinction & Sustainable Financial Markets Event, 30th May.

17. Mathews, J.A. and S. Kidney, *Financing climate-friendly energy development through bonds.* Development Southern Africa, 2012. **29**(2): p. 337–349.

18. World Bank Group. *What Are Green Bonds?* 2015; Available from: http://documents.worldbank.org/curated/en/400251468187810398/What-are-green-bonds.

19. Cochu, A., et al., *Study on the potential of green bond finance for resource-efficient investments.* Report, European Commission, 2016.

20. Zerbib, O.D., *The green bond premium.* Available at SSRN 2890316, 2017.

21. Tripathy, A., *Translating to risk: The legibility of climate change and nature in the green bond market.* Economic Anthropology, 2017. **4**(2): p. 239–250.

22. Shishlov, I., R. Morel, and I. Cochran, *Beyond transparency: Unlocking the full potential of green bonds.* Institute for Climate Economics, 2016: p. 1–28.

23. Chiesa, M. and S. Barua, *The surge of impact borrowing: The magnitude and determinants of green bond supply and its heterogeneity across markets.* Journal of Sustainable Finance & Investment, 2019. **9**(2): p. 138–161.

24. Banga, J., *The green bond market: A potential source of climate finance for developing countries.* Journal of Sustainable Finance & Investment, 2019. **9**(1): p. 17–32.

25. Deschryver, P. and F. De Mariz, *What future for the green bond market? How can policymakers, companies, and investors unlock the potential of the green bond market?* Journal of Risk and Financial Management, 2020. **13**(3): p. 61.

26. Gianfrate, G. and M. Peri, *The green advantage: Exploring the convenience of issuing green bonds.* Journal of Cleaner Production, 2019. **219**: p. 127–135.

27. Horsch, A. and S. Richter, *Climate change driving financial innovation: The case of Green Bonds.* The Journal of Structured Finance, 2017. **23**(1): p. 79–90.

28. Zerbib, O.D., *The effect of pro-environmental preferences on bond prices: Evidence from green bonds.* Journal of Banking & Finance, 2019. **98**: p. 39–60.

29. Pham, L., *Is it risky to go green? A volatility analysis of the green bond market.* Journal of Sustainable Finance & Investment, 2016. **6**(4): p. 263–291.

30. Atkins, J. and W. Maroun, *Integrated reporting in South Africa in 2012: Perspectives from South African institutional investors.* Meditari Accountancy Research, 2015. **23**(2): p. 197–221.

31. de Villiers, C., L. Rinaldi, and J. Unerman, *Integrated reporting: Insights, gaps and an agenda for future research.* Accounting, Auditing & Accountability Journal, 2014. **27**(7): p. 1042–1067.

32. IOD, *King IV Report on Corporate Governance in South Africa.* 2016: Lexis Nexus South Africa, Johannesburg, South Africa.

33. JSE *Listing Requirements.* 2016.

34. IOD, *Code for Responsible Investing in South Africa.* 2011: Lexis Nexus South Africa, Johannesburg, South Africa.

35. Mogapi Eunivicia, M., M. Sutherland Margaret, and A. Wilson-Prangley, *Impact investing in South Africa: Managing tensions between financial returns and social impact.* European Business Review, 2019. **31**(3): p. 397–419.

36. Roberts, L., W. van Zijl, and D. Cerbone, *The Integrated Reporting Committee of South Africa: On the balance of integrated reporting,* in *The Routledge Handbook of Integrated Reporting,* C.d. Villiers, P.-C.K. Hsiao, and W. Maroun, Editors. 2020, UK: Routledge.

37. White, R. *Moody's drops SA's credit rating to junk status.* 2020 29 May 2020]; Available from: https://ewn.co.za/2020/03/28/moody-s-drops-sa-s-credit-rating-to-junk-status.

38. Writer, S., *What South Africa lost in the "9 wasted years" under Zuma,* in *BusinessTech.* 2019, BusinessTech: South Africa.

39. Writer, S., *Government database to track all public servants accused of fraud and corrup,* in *Businesstech.* 2020, Businesstech.

40. Writer, S., *South Africa takes a step closer to land expropria,* in *BusinessTech.* 2020, BusinessTech.

41. King, M., *Integrated reporting and corporate governance in South Africa.* 2018: IRCSA Annual Conference, The Johannesburg Stock Exchange, South Africa.

42. Writer, S., *South Africa ranked among unsafest countries in the world – as citizens live in fear,* in *BusinessTech.* 2020.

43. The Guardian, *Inequality index: where are the world's most unequal countries?,* in *The Guardian.* 2017.

44. Economist, *Education - South Africa's youngsters are let down by a lousy education system,* in *Economist.* 2019.

45. Economist, *South Africa has one of the world's worst education systems,* in *Economist.* 2017.

46. Silverstein, K., *For Southern Africa, climate change is real as prolonged droughts are creating food shortages,* in *Forbes.* 2019.

47. Archer, E., et al., *'Farming on the edge' in arid western South Africa: Climate change and agriculture in marginal environments.* Geography, 2008. **93**(2): p. 98.

48. King, M. and J. Atkins, *The Chief Value Officer. Accountants Can Save the Planet.* 2016, Abingdon, Oxon: Greenleaf Publishing Limited.

49. Ngwenya, N. and M.D. Simatele, *The emergence of green bonds as an integral component of climate finance in South Africa*. South African Journal of Science, 2020. **116**(1–2): p. 1–3.

50. JSE, *Press release: JSE launches Green Bond segment*. 2017.

51. ICMA, *Green, social and sustainability bonds database*. 2020, ICMA.

52. IIRC *The International Framework: Integrated Reporting*. 2013.

53. NOAA National Centers for Environmental Information. *State of the Climate: Global Climate Report for 2019*. 2020 April 6, 2020]; Available from: https://www.ncdc.noaa.gov/sotc/global/201913/supplemental/page-1.

54. Kellogg, W.W., *Climate change and society: consequences of increasing atmospheric carbon dioxide*. 2019: Routledge.

55. USGCRP, *Climate Science Special Report: Fourth National Climate Assessment, Volume I*. 2017, U.S. Global Change Research Program.

56. Ceballos, G., P.R. Ehrlich, and R. Dirzo, *Biological annihilation via the ongoing sixth mass extinction signaled by vertebrate population losses and declines*. Proceedings of the National Academy of Sciences, 2017.

57. Melillo, J.M., T. Richmond, and G. Yohe, *Climate change impacts in the United States*. Third national climate assessment, 2014. **52**.

58. Stern, N.H., *The Economics of Climate Change: The Stern Review*. 2007, Cambridge University Press.

59. Atkins, J. and B. Atkins, *Around the World in 80 Species. Exploring the Business of Extinction*. Around the World in 80 Species. 2019, London: Routledge. 434.

60. Hallegatte, S., et al., *Shock Waves: Managing the Impacts of Climate Change on Poverty*, 2016, Washington: International Bank for Reconstruction and Development/The World Bank.

61. United Nations, *The Paris Agreement,* 2015: in UNFCCC, COP Report No. 21, Addenum, at 21, U.N. Doc. FCCC/CP/2015/10/Add, 1 (Jan. 29, 2016).

17

THE WILDLIFE CONSERVATION BOND

Exploring New Market Mechanisms for Protecting Endangered Species

Nnamdi Okolo

Introduction

In the past decade, human intervention in biodiversity and conservation of wildlife has become a central focus in sustainability[1] and international legislative policies.[2] This prioritization of conservation has arisen due to an overexploitation from international trade of endangered species and related extinction concerns. Over 5,800 species of animals and 30,000 species of plants have been overexploited as a result of international trade.[3] The dynamics of some of these endangered species are critical and require radical considerations.

Despite global efforts in sustainable recovery of biota, implementing related international legislative policies at local levels is often weak.[4] In addition, there is insufficient information[5] about the distribution of these threatened species to aid conservation NGOs and related partners. Intensified poaching activities and poor local community inclusion also pose further challenges.[6]

High profile endangered species like lions, elephants and rhinoceros now need to be kept in fully protected areas (PAs)[7] and provided with needed security to aid recovery. Yet, inadequate financial resources undermine effective management for both state and private PAs.[8] Hence, these species still remain vulnerable to illicit activities; mainly poaching, which often results in the death of the protected population.

According to research on PAs carried out in Africa using data for lions, it was estimated that there is a total funding deficit of between $1.2 billion and 2.4 billion annually in the overall African conservation of wildlife. Yet, PAs currently receive only $380 million, a fraction of the deficit.[9] The funding concerns have led to increased calls[10] for sustainable funding innovations to encourage further investment in PAs.

DOI: 10.4324/9781003045557-21

This chapter introduces the most recent funding mechanism and collaborations: the Conservation Wildlife bond (CWB) or more narrowly called the Rhino Impact Bond (RIB). The RIB is designed to leverage private market investments using market principles to support the ongoing counter-poaching activities, to increase rhino growth and improve management of rhinos in PAs.

Dilemma of an Illegal Trade in Rhino Horn and Conservation

Around the world, elephant ivory and keratin from rhino horns maintain high commercial interest, due to the associated aesthetic qualities, durability and alleged health related benefits. Although Asia is often blamed for most of the demand,[11] reports from the EU-TWIX[12] database suggest that the EU also imports and aids the transit route for the supply of illegal wildlife products like ivory and rhino horns. Most of the current global supply of these stocks come from the southern parts of Africa.[13]

More specific to rhinos is that obtaining rhino horn stock for international or local trade involves a dehorning process. After the dehorning process, the rhinoceros may regrow its horns. However, this takes a lengthy period of about three to four years, and this slow regrowth is at odds with the intense demand for rhino horn. Such unyielding pressures on rhino horn along with other factors discussed later in this chapter create an incentive for poaching activities. For these reasons, the Rhino horn market has long been widely considered unethical and unsustainable.[14]

Over the years, several international and local legislations have placed bans on rhino horn trade. Most recently, Chinese who are members of the CITES[15] countries accepted to apply this ban on its international rhino horn and ivory imports, a decision supported by the WWF.[16] However, the enforcement of these bans at the local level especially in Africa appear to be ineffective, allowing for the emergence of an illegal market where scarcity further hikes rhino horn prices.[17] The total value of the illegal international trade of rhino horn is estimated to be between $64 million and $190 million, where the trade per kilogram ranges from $35,000 to $65,000 and the supply goes for around $5,000 to $13,000 per kilogram.[18,19] The large differentials provide an economic incentive for poachers. Poaching involves the capture and killing of these rhinos in PAs and now appears to be the primary source of supply for the illegal rhino horn market. These deaths have continued to deplete the rhino species population. In Southern Africa, there are only about 5500 black rhinos left, and the northern white Rhino (Ceratotherium simum cottoni) is functionally extinct[20] with just two left under 24-hours surveillance on state PA in Kenya.

However today, Southern Africa remains home to the largest proportion of the remaining rhinoceros population. Over the last 15 years, the PAs especially in South Africa and Kenya have remained subject to these nefarious poaching activities. The declining number of rhinos has wider negating implications, influencing the PA owners, rhino management, local communities and overall conservation. In South Africa, 25% of the remaining rhino population is owned and managed by small private PA owners.[21] However, the present crisis and bans have made owning the rhinos for trading horns less lucrative, and this has led to reluctance in re-investing in rhinos. The lacklustre responses towards fighting poaching activities by private PA owners can be attributed to increased costs in security and effective breeding of rhinos. As a result, some private PA owners have sought to exit the ivory market while others struggle to meet these financial challenges. Larger private and state PA-managed sites have also been affected, as they have to reallocate significant portions of income to enhance the security of their current rhino population. These actions come at the expense of other aspects in their conservation budgets. Furthermore, the declining demand for rhino livestock by smaller private owners will also see a consistent fall in re-sources generated from related sales revenues.[22]

In the extinction crisis, military approaches are used for drastic human intervention to deter poaching activities.[23] This is often discussed in mainstream conservation as 'green militarisation' or 'war for biodiversity'. In parts of Africa and India, joint collaborations by the UN Peacekeeping Operations and local anti-poaching unit[24] activities have been conducted. Given the nature of the extinction crisis, such efforts may appear justified. Yet, the shift towards greater physical force[25] gives rise to other concerns. For instance, there have been cases of PA rangers themselves switching to poaching and vice versa. Further empowerment with physical force can result in counter-productivity that can also transpire into other societal risks. For instance, armed engagements between poachers and rangers is known to result in social unrest to local communities. However, these considerations are beyond the scope of this chapter.

By 2017, the concerns in rhino decline in South Africa led to the development of the 'African Rhino range states' African rhino conservation plan. The committee planned to develop an international collaboration for effective human intervention in the conservation of rhinos. Key areas defined for necessary human intervention and collaborations were: growth in number of rhinos, sustainable financing, staff development and social and political support. Debates on these aspects, new sciences together with best practices in biological management of rhinos led to considerations of the Rhino impact bond (RIB) concept. The impact bond is an emerging concept but is well considered in contemporary mainstream social policies for providing sustainable alternate financing in welfare, unemployment and resolving social structural issues.

At the time of this work, the first RIB had completed the development phase and the pilot phase is set to begin.

Introduction of Rhino Impact Investment Project (Rhino Impact Bond)

The impact bond is a funding concept gaining traction in areas of sustainability, particularly in areas of welfare state and unemployment in developed societies.

A unique feature of the impact bond is its ability to create a cohesive collaboration between stakeholders with diverse interest, while allowing greater level of autonomy to NGOs for the use and management of financial resources. Hence, the stakeholders are able to focus on their competences to effectively achieve a common objective.

Contrary to private philanthropic donations or conventional state grants, the impact bond attempts to direct financial resources from the capital market into areas that are considered for state intervention. This concept and stakeholders are further explained in the following section. While the impact (social) bond (SIB) focuses on providing funding for innovative social/state intervention, the RIB scope focuses on conservation as it relates to rhino extinction. In this way, it attempts to replicate the collaborative environment of the SIB. Its purpose is mainly directed at addressing funding constraints experienced in rhino PAs in an innovative effective manner. Consequently, this means supporting counter-poaching efforts, meeting increased security costs and staff training to facilitate the overall growth in the Rhino population under the selected PAs.

The stakeholders involved in the first RIB-SA include donors (outcome payment funders), market investors (financial institutions), private and state owned PAs, and evaluators and an intermediary. The roles of the RIB stakeholders are discussed in the following sub-section with a diagram to explain the cash flow.

Stakeholders in RIB

Outcome Payment Funders:

The outcome payment funders (OPF) in a RIB are philanthropic donors, NGOs and state grant commissioners. They take a risk averse position in the contract, only making payments to market investors if the predefined measurable outcomes are achieved by the implementing partners. By so doing, they can achieve the following:

- Save costs from misuse of funds by implementing partners often associated with grant-funding
- Gain evidence of effective delivery of the desired outcomes
- Optimal use of state and philanthropic resources

The OPFs in the pilot RIB are the Royal Foundation of the Duke and Duchess of Cambridge and the Duke and Duchess of Sussex, Global Environment Facility (GEF), IWT Challenge Fund[26] and UfW[27]

Market Investors: The market investors attempt to earn economic and reputational value from providing upfront financial resources to implementing partners (Conservation NGOs-PAs). If outcomes meet the predetermined targets, market investors are rewarded with a premium with the initial financial resources for taking on the financial risk of the project. The premium along with the financial risk creates a risk/return profile to the RIB contract, serving as incentives to investors. In contrast, if outcomes fall below the predetermined targets, investors are exposed to losing a significant amount of their initial funds. Using market principles with the contract allows investors to

- Consistently monitor and manage the performance of the implementing partners (Conservation NGOs-PAs).
- Provide advisory functions to implementing partners on the use of resources and receive intermittent reports and updates on performances.

The mainstream market investor for the RIB is Credit Suisse managed through Conservation Alpha, a special purpose vehicle (SPV). Conservation Alpha aims to carry out monitoring functions and risk management on the implementing partners.

Implementing Partners: Implementing partners often have the expertise to implement and execute the intervention projects. However, they often lack the financial capacity needed to expedite these actions. In the RIB, there are five state and private 'investment ready' Pas in South Africa and Kenya. The implementing partners include the ZSL,[28] GEF,[29] UNDP[30] Oak Foundation, Rufford Foundation and IWT Challenge Fund, and both parties adhere to their respective national sustainable development objectives. Their role is to

- Ensure that the funds are appropriately distributed and used for the projects.

Intermediaries: The implementing partners also play the functions of the intermediary.
   The roles are:

- To carry out due diligence on PAs to ensure that they possess high level performances, quality and are investment ready. The evaluation and selection process of the PAs were mainly based on track records in rhino managements.
- They serve as the brokers of the contract. In the RIB, they linked the OPF and implementing partners to private investors.

Beneficiaries: The beneficiaries are the groups that experience adverse conditions. In the RIB, the rhinos are the direct subjects along with local communities who may be affected by the unrest from poaching activities. However, there are diverse forms of benefits to the individual stakeholders in the RIB arrangement.

Evaluators: The role of the evaluators is to independently assess the performances of the implementing partners (Conservation NGOs and PAs) against the predetermined target. The results from the assessments are used as the primary determinant for the payments made by the OPFs to private investors. Evaluators in impact bonds are often academics, auditors or intermediaries possessing prior competence in evaluation processes; they usually charge a fee for the service paid by the OPF. Evaluators of the RIB will attempt to vigorously assess and give a

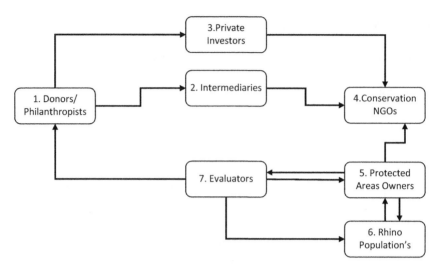

FIGURE 17.1 Illustration of RIB stakeholder interaction.

verdict on the performance of the RIB contract, which is primarily the growth in number of rhinos on a given PA and other enabling targets such as improved rhino management on Pas. The reported results become crucial in release of payouts from OPFs (Figure 17.1).

Critique of RIB and NGO-Company Engagement in Biodiversity

The RIB funding mechanism has huge potential in conservation of wildlife; it can also be deployed vastly in other areas of biodiversity. However, since the inception of the impact bond, the mechanism has been critiqued for its neoliberal roots and ethical concerns in sustainability. The SIB, the first impact bond, focuses on human well-being; critics[31,32]argue the uncertainty around human nature compromises the potential and legitimacy of the concept at least in human areas of welfare and social reforms. They conclude that without robust restructuring, the SIB may be unlikely to develop into a conventional 'tradeable' financial instrument. Other critics argue that using market principles in areas of human state intervention programmes can complicate funding to NGOs and can have negating implications on the well-being of beneficiaries.[33] However, both critics and proponents appear confident that the SIB can be a mechanism deployed in 'testing' of human social intervention; where it can serve as justification for scalability of a given social intervention.

These concerns of SIB do not wholly apply to the RIB. In contrast, the RIB possesses the potential to become a well-developed financial instrument, given the nature of its scope in conservation. First, the RIB is focused on recovery and protection of the rhino species (non–human) using sustainable strategies.

Furthermore, defining predetermined targets and measurability are less complex. This makes structuring and setting up a RIB or an impact bond in conservation easier, reducing the transaction costs[34] of the contract.

Extinction and conservation challenges (non-human) are generally better understood when compared to challenges experienced in human social intervention. Therefore, the risk and uncertainties associated with outcomes are also lower than in a SIB. This enhances reliability for market investor stakeholders when developing financial forecasts and modelling tools to assess the data of the given species in the contract.

Implementing NGOs in SIB have come under scrutiny: that the pressures (of monitoring and formalized reporting) from using market financial resources can compel NGO managers to manipulate data of the human beneficiaries. Again, these concerns are limited to the nature of SIB in human social intervention. For RIB and conservation of wildlife, evidences of growth in species and well-being of non-human beneficiaries are more self-evident.

Owing to these highlights, there has been a sense of optimism on the first RIB pilot project among both RIB stakeholders and the public. If the mechanism achieves the predetermined outcomes by the end of the five-year contract, it may go on to play a crucial role in providing financial resources for rhino management, wider extinction and biodiversity challenges.

Prior to the RIB development, there had been an evolving narrative[35] existing between conservation NGO-company engagements in species protection. These interactions had seen both stakeholders shift towards more collaborations. Conservation NGOs provided strategies to corporations that allow for better contribution in areas of conservation and biodiversity. However, such contributions from corporations had been reflexive and mainly philanthropic/voluntary supports. The RIB introduces a dynamic change in the narrative NGO-company engagement. First, the RIB shifts focus towards effectiveness and results in the conservation NGO-company engagement. The RIB also provides the conservation NGOs with greater autonomy in defining its use of financial resources and enhancing 'integrated-thinking' in NGO-company engagements. In addition, the corporations (here financial institutions) seek ways to influence NGOs into conscientious use of scarce resources through monitoring. This enhances the quality of the interaction between both parties. Another distinct aspect in the evolving narrative emanating from the RIB is that it alters the nature of the existing reports and disclosures to its emerging stakeholders. While these aspects in the NGO-company engagement can easily be considered beneficial in the extinction crisis, it requires critical considerations and further research.

Without undermining the RIB potentials in the short term, the risk and return profile creates commodification in areas of wildlife. It gives grounds for conservation organisations, agents of non-human beneficiaries to shift away from direct state support and philanthropic aid towards market territory and financial liberation. Market liberations may be beneficial in the short term; however, as conservation NGO-PAs adapt in the long-term, it can have negating effects to their structure and wider society. These effects often ensue in areas of accountability, ideological drifts or operational and cultural changes.

In addition, stricter monitoring conditions, investment readiness and formalized reporting disclosures are all crucial considerations when adhering to market principles. Yet, these features may be inferior to Conservation NGOs and PAs. This may blur reporting channels for conservation. In addition, 'investment readiness' and due diligence are crucial aspects to the RIB; however, these aspects can create a barrier for private entrepreneurs with less historical track record, making them appear less investment worthy. The emphasis on these naive aspects can be in contrast to promoting the culture and values of entrepreneurial skill, and innovations may also pose longer term challenges to conservation and restrict development for Conservation NGO-company engagement.

Conclusion

Society is currently experiencing the sixth period of extinction on earth, and over the years, corporations have played a role in biodiversity loss. The funding concerns in biodiversity only exacerbate the challenges in the on-going extinction crisis. Corporations and the financial market have also been influential to the build of the current crisis. Global markets have expanded through the economic activities of these institutions; some of these activities involve development of new technologies such as rifles and steel traps which have lowered the cost of harvesting wildlife and have facilitated poaching. In addition, while improved transport systems aid social and economic development, it also makes tracking illegal trade more challenging. This makes effective contribution by these corporations compelling. The chapter provided a summary of the RIB, a nascent funding mechanism capable of transferring private financial resources into rhino management and conservation. Despite neoliberal concerns, the RIB encourages the use of market principles and ideologies to resolve challenges in social aspects of society, biodiversity in this scope. While the fundamentals of the RIB may create these concerns, there is still insufficient validity to support these arguments. The risks/return profile and reliability of data forecast can be appealing for responsible sustainable investments. However, the RIB can create longer term alterations in strategy, accountability and ideologies of not only conservation NGO-PAs but for private investors. It is the wider implications of the RIB that require critical thinking and further research.

Notes

1 Nellemann, C., Henriksen, R., Raxter, P., Ash, N. and Mrema, E., 2014. *The Environmental Crime Crisis: Threats to Sustainable Development from Illegal Exploitation and Trade in Wildlife and Forest Resources.* United Nations Environment Programme (UNEP).
2 Tittensor, D.P., Harfoot, M., McLardy, C., Britten, G.L., Kecse-Nagy, K., Landry, B., Outhwaite, W., Price, B., Sinovas, P., Blanc, J. and Burgess, N.D., 2020. Evaluating

the relationships between the legal and illegal international wildlife trades. *Conservation Letters*, p. e12724.

3 https://www.cites.org/eng/disc/species.php.

4 Wright, O.T., Cundill, G. and Biggs, D., 2018. Stakeholder perceptions of legal trade in rhinoceros horn and implications for private reserve management in the Eastern Cape, South Africa. *Oryx, 52*(1), pp. 175–185.

5 Wright, O.T., Cundill, G. and Biggs, D., 2018. Stakeholder perceptions of legal trade in rhinoceros horn and implications for private reserve management in the Eastern Cape, South Africa. *Oryx, 52*(1), pp. 175–185.

6 Child, B., 2012. The sustainable use approach could save South Africa's rhinos. *South African Journal of Science, 108*(7–8), pp. 21–25.

7 Protected Areas are locations like parks and reserves where animals are kept and managed. They are either private or state owned and the management is fundamental for recovery of biodiversity.

8 Balfour, D., Shaw, J., Banasiak, N., le Roex, N., Rusch, U. & Emslie,R. 2019. Concise best practice guidelines for the biological management of African rhino. WWF-SA. 123pp.

9 Lindsey, P.A., Miller, J.R., Petracca, L.S., Coad, L., Dickman, A.J., Fitzgerald, K.H., Flyman, M.V., Funston, P.J., Henschel, P., Kasiki, S. and Knights, K., 2018. More than $1 billion needed annually.

10 Wright, O.T., Cundill, G. and Biggs, D., 2018. Stakeholder perceptions of legal trade in rhinoceros horn and implications for private reserve management in the Eastern Cape, South Africa. *Oryx, 52*(1), pp. 175–185.

11 Wright, O.T., Cundill, G. and Biggs, D., 2018. Stakeholder perceptions of legal trade in rhinoceros horn and implications for private reserve management in the Eastern Cape, South Africa. *Oryx, 52*(1), pp. 175–185.

12 Trade In Wildlife Information Exchange 2018.

13 Child, B., 2012. The sustainable use approach could save South Africa's rhinos. *South African Journal of Science, 108*(7–8), pp. 21–25.

14 Tittensor, D.P., Harfoot, M., McLardy, C., Britten, G.L., Kecse-Nagy, K., Landry, B., Outhwaite, W., Price, B., Sinovas, P., Blanc, J. and Burgess, N.D., 2020. Evaluating the relationships between the legal and illegal international wildlife trades. *Conservation Letters*, p. e12724.

15 Convention on International Trade in Endangered Species of Wild Fauna and Flora is a multilateral treaty with members pledging to protect endangered species.

16 World Wide Fund for nature supporting vital conservation work and tackling climate change.

17 Leader-Williams, N., 1992. *The World Trade in Rhino Horn: A Review.* Cambridge: Traffic International.

18 Nellemann, C., Henriksen, R., Raxter, P., Ash, N. and Mrema, E., 2014. *The Environmental Crime Crisis: Threats to Sustainable Development from Illegal Exploitation and Trade in Wildlife and Forest Resources.* United Nations Environment Programme (UNEP).

19 Gwin, P., 2012. Rhino wars. *National Geographic, 221,* pp. 106–120.

20 Callaway, E., 2016. Stem-cell plan aims to bring rhino back from brink of extinction. *Nature, 533*(7601).

21 Wright, O.T., Cundill, G. and Biggs, D., 2018. Stakeholder perceptions of legal trade in rhinoceros horn and implications for private reserve management in the Eastern Cape, South Africa. *Oryx, 52*(1), pp. 175–185.

22 Child, B. 2012 the sustainable use approach could save South Africa's rhinos. *South African Journal of Science.*

23 Duffy, R., 2017. We need to talk about the militarization of conservation. *Green European Journal* https://www.greeneuropeanjournal.eu/we-need-to-talk-about-militarisation-of-conservation/.

24 For instance in Rhino Conservation in Kaziranga National park, India.
25 Shoot to kill, surveillance techniques, drones and traps.
26 IWT (illegal Wildlife Trade) Challenge Fund is an agent of the UK government responsible for funding and support projects in conservation.
27 United for Wildlife (UfW) is an collaboration between seven of the largest international conservation organisations.
28 Zoological Society of London (ZSL) support conservation of species.
29 Global Environment Facility.
30 United Nations Development Programme.
31 The SIB is considered to be a strand of neoliberalism and New Public Management (NPM) and has faced criticism from cautionary narrative SIB scholars.
32 Cooper, C., Graham, C. and Himick, D., 2016. Social impact bonds: The securitization of the homeless. *Accounting, Organizations and Society*, *55*, pp. 63–82.
33 Andreu, M., 2018. A Responsibility to Profit? Social Impact Bonds as a Form of "Humanitarian Finance". *New Political Science*, *40*(4), pp. 708–726.
34 Transaction costs in the impact bond contracts go beyond financial resources; to resources used to set up the SIB including staff time, administration and reversals between stakeholders in the arrangement.
35 Atkins, J., Maroun, W., Atkins, B.C. and Barone, E., 2018. From the big five to the big four? Exploring extinction accounting for the rhinoceros. *Accounting, Auditing & Accountability Journal*.

References

Andreu, M., 2018. A responsibility to profit? Social impact bonds as a form of "humanitarian finance". *New Political Science*, *40*(4), pp. 708–726.

Atkins, J. F., Maroun, W., Atkins, B. C., Barone. E. (2018) "From the Big Five to the Big Four? Exploring Extinction Accounting for the Rhinoceros?", *Accounting, Auditing & Accountability Journal*, Vol. 31 No. 2, pp. 1-31.

Atkins, J. F. and Maroun, W. (2018) "Integrated Extinction Accounting and Accountability: Building an Ark", *Accounting, Auditing & Accountability Journal*, Vol. 31 No. 3, pp. 1-41.

Balfour, D., Barichievy, C., Gordon, C. and Brett, R., 2019. A theory of change to grow numbers of African Rhino at a conservation site. *Conservation Science and Practice*, *1*(6), p. e40.

Balfour, D., Shaw, J., Banasiak, N., le Roex, N., Rusch, U. & Emslie, R. 2019. Concise best practice guidelines for the biological management of African rhino. WWF-SA. 123pp.

Burand, Deborah. "Globalizing social finance: How social impact bonds and social impact performance guarantees can scale development." *NYUJL & Bus.* 9 (2012): 447.

Callaway, E., 2016. Stem-cell plan aims to bring rhino back from brink of extinction. *Nature*, *533*(7601).

Child, B., 2012. The sustainable use approach could save South Africa's rhinos. *South African Journal of Science*, *108*(7–8), pp. 21–25.

Cooper, C., Graham, C. and Himick, D., 2016. Social impact bonds: The securitization of the homeless. *Accounting, Organizations and Society*, *55*, pp. 63–82.

D'Aprix, R., 2006. Throwing rocks at the corporate rhinoceros. *The IABC Handbook of Organizational Communication*, O'Reilly Online Learning, p. 227.

Duffy, R., 2017. We need to talk about the militarization of conservation. *Green European Journal*. https://www.greeneuropeanjournal.eu/we-need-to-talk-about-militarisation-of-conservation/

Gwin, P., 2012. Rhino wars. *National Geographic, 221*, pp. 106–120.

Leader-Williams, N., 1992. *The World Trade in Rhino Horn: A Review*. Cambridge: Traffic International.

Lindsey, P.A., Miller, J.R., Petracca, L.S., Coad, L., Dickman, A.J., Fitzgerald, K.H., Flyman, M.V., Funston, P.J., Henschel, P., Kasiki, S. and Knights, K., 2018. More than $1 billion needed annually to secure Africa's protected areas with lions. *Proceedings of the National Academy of Sciences, 115*(45), pp. E10788–E10796.

Nellemann, C., Henriksen, R., Raxter, P., Ash, N. and Mrema, E., 2014. *The Environmental Crime Crisis: Threats to Sustainable Development from Illegal Exploitation and Trade in Wildlife and Forest Resources*. United Nations Environment Programme (UNEP).

New 'rhino bonds' to allow investors to help with wildlife conservation, Published Thu, Jul 18 20199:24 AM EDT Spriha Srivastava@spriha

Novacek, M.J. and Cleland, E.E., 2001. The current biodiversity extinction event: Scenarios for mitigation and recovery. *Proceedings of the National Academy of Sciences, 98*(10), pp. 5466–5470.

Sacré, V., 2016. EU–TWIX: Ten years of information exchange and cooperation between wildlife law enforcement officials in Europe. In *Handbook of Transnational Environmental Crime*. Edward Elgar Publishing House.

Tittensor, D.P., Harfoot, M., McLardy, C., Britten, G.L., Kecse-Nagy, K., Landry, B., Outhwaite, W., Price, B., Sinovas, P., Blanc, J. and Burgess, N.D., 2020. Evaluating the relationships between the legal and illegal international wildlife trades. *Conservation Letters*, p. 12724.

Wright, O.T., Cundill, G. and Biggs, D., 2018. Stakeholder perceptions of legal trade in rhinoceros horn and implications for private reserve management in the Eastern Cape, South Africa. *Oryx, 52*(1), pp. 175–185.

18

EXPLORING A MECHANISM WITH EMANCIPATORY POTENTIAL FOR 'BUSINESS AND BIODIVERSITY' IN CHINA

'Ant Forest'

Longxiang Zhao

Introduction

The creation of the 'Strategic Plan for Biodiversity' by the Convention on Biological Diversity (CBD) has been identified as the 'United Nation's Decade on Biodiversity' (UNDB, n.d.). Studies (WWF, 2018, 2020a) indicate that despite various policy commitments (e.g. Aichi Targets) being established to aim to slow down or alter the rate of species extinction, the trend of biodiversity decline continues, and the dominant drivers of the current biodiversity decline remain the same. Further, climate change is gradually creating significant impact on species, even at a genetic level. A dramatic move towards more ambitious and well-defined goals is urgently needed to stop the current severe decline of biodiversity. Not only is species extinction a crisis requiring urgent transformation, but wildlife populations are also at stake: the population of mammals, birds, amphibians, reptiles and fish have declined by 68% since 1970 (WWF, 2020c). In China, the concept of 'Ecological Civilization' has emerged, and this chapter explores such an ideal mechanism in a Chinese context, by investigating the insights from relevant stakeholders and studying a Chinese private company's financial product that significantly engages people in environment-friendly behaviour: Alipay's 'Ant Forest'.

The Emergence and Development of Ecological Civilization

The construction of ecological civilization was firstly proposed in 2007 as one of the new requirements for building a moderately prosperous society in all respects by 2020. It mainly focused on pollution control and emission reduction, and the establishment of the concept of ecological civilization in the society (People.cn, 2007). In 2017, the principal contradiction of Chinese society has been confirmed

DOI: 10.4324/9781003045557-22

as the contradiction between the people's ever-growing needs for a better life and the unbalanced and inadequate development. A better environment constitutes one of peoples' needs (Xinhua, 2017a). Correspondingly, the construction of ecological civilization has been further emphasized and defined as a long-term strategy related to the people's wellbeing and the future of the nation and integrated into all aspects and the whole process of the economic construction, political construction, cultural construction and social construction, so called 'Five in One' overall plan (Xinhua, 2017b). With increasing efforts made by the Chinese government, the ecological civilization has been promoted as mainstream value of the society, and everyone is encouraged to be the constructor of the ecological civilization. It prioritizes resource saving, environmental protection and natural recovery, and integrates indicators like resources consumption, environmental damage and ecological benefits into the evaluation system of socio-economic development (Gov.cn, 2015b). For example, ecological civilization education is taken as an important content of quality-oriented education, and it is integrated into national education system and cadre education and training system (Gov.cn, 2015a). These developments have significantly promoted the legislative process of environment related legislations, such as the amendments of 'Environmental Protection Law', 'Atmospheric Pollution Prevention Law', and 'Wildlife Conservation Law' which have been made in recent years (People.cn, 2018). Furthermore, the construction of ecological civilization has also been written into the national constitution since 2018 to further promote the formulation of ecological regulations (Xinhua, 2018).

Alipay's Ant Forest – a Financial Product with Emancipatory Potential

In supporting COP15 and biodiversity conservation, the China Environmental Protection Foundation (CEPF) cooperated with Shan Shui Conservation Center and Ant Financial Services Group to initiate the first public activity: 'one square meter per person, collectively safeguard biodiversity', which encourages the public to use their green low-carbon behaviour to 'exchange' for biodiversity protection areas in China through the financial product: Alipay's Ant Forest (Ministry of Ecology and Environment of the People's Republic of China, 2020).

'Ant Forest' is a mobile application platform that engages people in environment-friendly behaviour and in sharing ecological lifestyles. It is provided by Ant Financial Services Group and installed in Alipay, which is a popular Chinese online payment and lifestyle platform. Figure 18.1 shows how Ant Forest works: the Alipay users receive a virtual sapling when they open an Ant Forest account, the users' low-carbon behaviours such as walking, public transportation commuting, online utility payment, and online ticketing will be recorded by Alipay platform and generate green energy to grow the virtual sapling. It features social interactive and game entertainment that allow users' friends to 'steal' their green

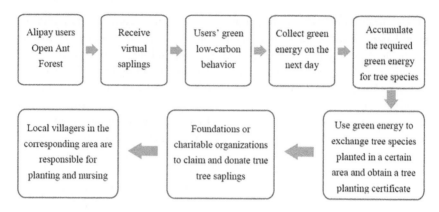

FIGURE 18.1 Ant Forest use process (Yang et al., 2018).

energy or water their saplings. When the virtual tree is measured, the Ant Finan-cial Services Group will cooperate with welfare foundations (e.g. China Green Foundation, Yili Public Welfare Foundation and SEE Foundation) to plant a real tree, or guard an equivalent area of conservation land on earth (Yang et al., 2018). As China's largest private sector tree-planting initiative, Ant Forest re-ceived the 2019 UN Champions of the Earth Award (UN Environment, 2019) and the 2019 UN Climate Action Award (UN Climate Change, 2019). Over 500 million users planted over 100 million real trees in some of China's most arid regions (Ant Financial, 2020), and over 39,000 mu of conservation land are guarded through the platform. Users can monitor their real tree through the Ant Forest page in real time on their phone; through satellite, they can see how their tree can bring changes to the planet (China Daily, 2018).

Ant Forest provides an information technology-based approach to attract peo-ple to engage in green behaviour (Zhang et al., 2020). It positively takes users' fragmented time to cultivate ecological awareness and habit; the perceived per-suasiveness and continuance intention result in ultimate behaviour change (Yang et al., 2018). The young generation takes significant proportion of the users: around 60% of users are under 28 years old (Wang, 2019). The sense of achieve-ment and perceiving entertaining have encouraged young people to realize mul-tiple self-worth through their mobile phone: apart from their real-life identity, they also have multiple online identities such as Ant Forest Forester. The users can receive a certificate for each planted tree or safeguarded conservation land (see Figure 18.2 below for example). These online certificates are acknowledged by the National Forestation Committee for users to perform their legal duty on tree planting (Ant Financial, 2020).

Planting trees and safeguarding conservation land are not the only forms that the Ant Forest operates in protecting environment; it also explores inno-vative solutions to alleviate poverty and improve the livelihood of local people

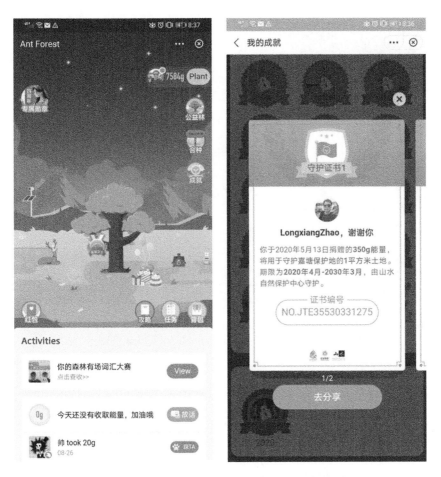

FIGURE 18.2 Sample of Ant Forest virtual tree and safeguard certificate.

through digital technology (UN Environment, 2019). Ant Forest has created over 400,000 job opportunities in relation with tree planting, forest maintenance and conservation land patrol. It provides a sustainable, participatory, and reproducible approach to support local poverty reduction (Xinhua, 2019). To further expand its operations and maintain users' interests, Ant Forest also cooperates with celebrities, businesses, universities and social institutions to utilize their influence to encourage users to 'water' the 'public welfare forest' that they supported. Inspired by Ant Forest's public participation model and supported by Ant Financial's technical support, the Philippines' mobile payments platform GCash has launched 'GCash Forest' in encouraging citizens to participate in environmental conservation and tree planting activities in Philippines (Wang, 2019). The practices of Ant Forest demonstrated that digital technology can effectively increase individuals' intention to protect the environment and offer a means to

FIGURE 18.3 Species living in Jiatang conservation land (Ministry of Ecology and Environment of the People's Republic of China, 2020).

quickly identify the online green users who are most willing to combat global environmental issues, thus, to create a new opportunity to promote greater public participation in the global action in addressing environmental issues (Chen et al., 2020).

Ant Forest also significantly promotes biodiversity conservation activities in China: the conservation lands that listed on Ant Forest are enriching in biodiversity. Specifically, with Ant Forest users' support, the biodiversity conservation NGO Shan Shui is able to continue and expand its research and field practices on habitat conservation for native species in Jiatang grassland (see Figure 18.3 shown below) (Ministry of Ecology and Environment of the People's Republic of China, 2020).

As introduced in the study of panda accounting and accountability in China (Zhao and Atkins, 2019), Shan Shui Conservation Center aims to achieve co-existence between human and nature. It provides an innovative and effective approach in connecting public, government, and private sectors into biodiversity conservation practices. Its 'Value Chain' projects such as Panda Honey and China Nature Watch have significantly influenced the public's involvements in biodiversity conservation and the mainstreaming process of biodiversity conservation. For example, its China Nature Watch Database, which is mainly updated by the public, can now be used to monitor the development and construction projects' potential impact on local biodiversity, thus, to provide early warnings and promote relevant policies and legislations. By actively working with private sectors like Ant Financial, 48.3% of Shan Shui's funds are raised from companies (Shan Shui Conservation Center, 2020).

The Need to Investigate different Stakeholders' Perceptions on 'Business and Biodiversity' in China

The practices of Ant Forest and Shan Shui provide us some ideas in drafting the ideal mechanism for 'Business and Biodiversity' in China, while as emphasized by Walters (1977): 'social responsibility is not telling society what is good for society but responding to what society tells the firm the society wants and expects from it' (p. 44); it is essential to investigate the society's perceptions regarding to the proposed ideal mechanism. It is in line with the notion of General System Theory (GST), which believes that everything (e.g. climate, human body, society) could be considered as a system; the systems are not just as an independent unit but also as a compilation of a multitude of parts and processes (Coetzee and Van Niekerk, 2012), and ignoring the interactions between the system and other systems might lead to misunderstanding (Gray et al., 2014). Various researchers (Von Bertalanffy, 1964, Laszlo, 1972, Hofkirchner, 2005, Pouvreau, 2014, Rousseau, 2015, Atkins and Atkins, 2016) believe that GST could be used as a strategy and action plan to avert the emerging social and environmental crisis for our civilization, opening up a pathway towards a better world. Biodiversity conservation is a complex process that involves multi-disciplines and requires efforts from different 'individuals'. 'Individuals' here are broadly construed by Rousseau (2015) as not only referring to individuals, but also representing other levels of society such as family, community, organization and country. Tackling the trend of mass extinction not only leads to a better world but also saves our world by saving our planet. As humans, we need to at least satisfy our needs of survival in the future. Therefore, biodiversity loss should be a concern for every 'individual'. The disciplines which created by humans would take part of the solution, based on their specialties to respond to this challenge.

Moreover, based on the construction of the new pragmatist emancipatory accounting which is defined as a more cautious and pragmatic approach to deal with the complexities and uncertainties posed by the significance of difference in the real-world context, a plurality of interests, identities and projects should be acknowledged, understood and aligned, to form a collective force for emancipatory praxis (Gallhofer et al., 2015). This constructed differentiated universalism combines the strengths of both universalism and difference and provides a critical perspective to involve a pragmatic and discursive appeal to common values (Gallhofer and Haslam, 2017). As this study is aiming to make progressive improvement of 'Business and Biodiversity' practices, the multiple progressive objectives from diverse legitimate interests, identities and projects should be addressed and sought to align these in a progressive movement (Gallhofer and Haslam, 2017), thus, leading to a potential emancipatory outcome: the extinction prevention (Atkins and Maroun, 2018).

To ensure the proposed mechanism for 'Business and Biodiversity' in China is systemic, progressive, and most importantly, pragmatic, the perspectives from different social actors that are significantly relevant with biodiversity conservation should be interpreted and respected. Their diverse interests, identities and projects should be aligned to form a differentiated universalism to develop the desired mechanism for 'Business and Biodiversity' that is especially fitted within China context to bring about attitude and behaviour change for Chinese companies, as well as the society.

In addressing this need, qualitative interviews are used to investigate relevant stakeholders' perceptions towards 'Business and Biodiversity' in China as it can help to explore people's understanding, experiences and imaginings through their ways of expressing (Edwards and Holland, 2013). Totally, 19 face-to-face semi-structured in-depth interviews (including two pilot interviews) have been carried out with respondents from a broad range of institutions or organizations representing different stakeholders, including companies, NGOs, CSR consulting companies, academies and government department. These respondents are directly or indirectly involved in the projects that are relevant to 'Business and Biodiversity'. They are approached based on the snowball basis (Gilbert, 2008) and the insights of the theoretical sampling approach which roots in grounded theory (Corbin and Strauss, 2012). Rather than develop concepts to form theory, the theoretical sampling approach is partly employed in this study in seeking to discover the ideas and issues that emerged in the interviews in depth, thus, to refine the ideas or improve understanding of issues by contacting the person equipped with adequate experiences or/and knowledge. Grounded theory is also partly employed in this study in analysing the interviews to generate themes and categories. Over 200 themes were generated and classified into four categories: (1) current status of 'Business and Biodiversity' in China, (2) challenges to promoting 'Business and Biodiversity' in China, (3) current attempts to improve 'Business and Biodiversity' in China and (4) recommendations for future improvement of 'Business and Biodiversity' in China. The insights of the interview analysis are identified and discussed in the following part.

Exploring an Ideal Mechanism for 'Business and Biodiversity' in China: The Stakeholders' Insights

From the interview analysis, the stakeholder's insights can be summarized as: (1) biodiversity conservation is currently a marginalized or unrepresented topic in most of companies; (2) stakeholders should also be accountable for 'Business and Biodiversity'; (3) the need to align and integrate forces and resources in promoting 'Business and Biodiversity'; (4) the need to take a pragmatic consideration of non-anthropocentric approach of biodiversity conservation; and (5) the need to address the employment of impression management on biodiversity reporting.

Biodiversity Conservation Is Currently a Marginalized or Unrepresented Topic in Most of Companies

Interview analysis revealed the fact that currently biodiversity conservation is a marginalized or unpresented topic in most of the Chinese companies' CSR practices. Inadequate awareness and understanding, and most importantly, inadequate resources and external pressures are identified as the key reasons.

Compared with biodiversity loss, issues like pollution have higher visibility, more easily understandable concept and more direct impact on people's life. Therefore, these issues are generally perceived as more urgent problems prioritized by the society and are strictly addressed by the regulators. In contrast, biodiversity is perceived in more scientific terms that requires specific knowledge and professionals to deal with, thus, most of responsibilities are assigned to government, research institutions and concerned NGOs. Without specific and robust legislative requirements, companies rarely conduct biodiversity practices or merely perform in basic levels such as tree planting and greening activities. Without sufficient external pressures, the resources for corporate biodiversity conservation are also inadequate, both internally and externally. The internal resources include financial resources and human resources. The concern of cost is significantly addressed in the interview analysis; under the context of the slowing of economic growth and economic transition in China, the market competition is significantly intensified, and Chinese companies are struggling to survive by minimizing the costs. In this context, companies are unwilling to perform biodiversity conservation unless they can financially benefit from it. Moreover, the concern on Small- and Medium-sized Enterprises (SMEs) has been raised in terms of their reckless pursuit of cost minimization and less pressure from supervision, which leads to devastating harm on environment and further intensifies the competition pressures of listed companies. For human resources, most of corporate staffs in the environmental department have an inadequate understanding and knowledge on biodiversity; the relevant training is rarely provided unless there are specific projects in overseas operations, which have strict requirements on biodiversity conservation. There are limited corporate departments and staffs involved in the CSR reporting; some companies even outsource CSR reporting to external CSR consulting companies, resulting in inadequate human resources for biodiversity issues and further increase in the intents for impression management. The concern with the inadequate external resources is discussed in detail in the later section alongside the concern of the unquestioned accountability of stakeholders for companies.

Stakeholders Should Also Be Accountable for 'Business and Biodiversity'

The interview analysis reveals that the conservation stakeholders (e.g. regulators, conservation NGOs and research institutions) should be accountable for companies in biodiversity conservation and reporting; further, other stakeholders (media, developed economy and general public) also play a significant role in promoting 'Business and Biodiversity'.

The external resources for corporate biodiversity conservation refer to: favourable policies from regulators, available information and researches and support from conservation actors like NGOs. These resources are emerging in China, while still inadequate, and most of the companies are unaware of the initiatives provided by the government and NGOs. Companies are expecting more 'attractive' policies such as tax relief on biodiversity conservation projects. As pointed out by one interviewee from the CSR consulting sector, the regulators should focus more on the approaches in providing a 'way out' for companies, rather than stricter regulations and supervisions. The relevant biodiversity consulting service and training are limited. Moreover, as demonstrated in companies' performance in overseas practices and the cases of 'Ant Forest' and panda conservation (Zhao and Atkins, 2019), the close partnerships or engagement with conservation stakeholders such as NGOs, research institutions, local communities and local government are essential for emancipatory transformation. However, most of the companies do not have contact with these stakeholders, and some NGOs are refusing to work or contact with companies in certain industries. This leads to the concern about stakeholders' accountability for companies. These conservation stakeholders are equipped with adequate awareness, knowledge and projects in relation to biodiversity conservation; they should utilize these resources to guide and support 'Business and Biodiversity'. Therefore, they should be accountable for companies, focus more on the approaches to provide a 'way out' and to 'clear the path' for companies, rather than merely monitor and accuse corporate practices. Although companies might not be interested in these initiatives at present, the available and prepared 'way out' is necessary for them to take a first step and could significantly accelerate that process. In result, more communication and engagements between companies and conservation stakeholders are encouraged to effectively identify the companies' needs for external resources. However, the responsibilities and boundaries of conservation stakeholders need to be outlined and supervised to avoid situations such as taking too much work from companies by providing outsourced services.

Apart from the main conservation stakeholders, the accountability of other stakeholders like media, developed economics, general public and company staffs in promoting 'Business and Biodiversity' also have been emphasized in the interviews. Firstly, as revealed by interviewees from corporate sector, most of their awareness and knowledge of biodiversity issues are acquired through the mainstream media channels in terms of the absence of relevant training in companies. Moreover, the companies' improving disclosures and transparency are significantly influenced by the development of new media. On the one hand, new media provides more channels and approaches for companies to discharge accountability; on the other, which is more significant, new media brings more supervision and exposure pressures for companies to comply. The media community is expected to play roles as disseminator, promoter and supervisor of 'Business and Biodiversity'. However, currently the media community in China is concerned with their independence, inadequate knowledge on biodiversity issues and sense of social responsibility. Suggestions are proposed in improving the accountability of media for 'Business and Biodiversity', such as active engagement with conservation bodies, providing educative information and knowledge and providing constructive suggestions for companies alongside the release of corporate native practices. Secondly, as pointed out by interviewees from the CSR consulting sector, the development of 'Business and Biodiversity' in China should also incorporate the considerations of global industry chain, which has a significant impact on the environment and biodiversity in China. It is believed that the globalization and global trade have encouraged the transfer of environmental destructive productions and operations from developed economics to developing economics, thus, intensify the pressures and difficulties for corporate biodiversity conservation in developing economics like China. As a result, developed economics should sharing more burdens for the biodiversity conservation in China. This view is in line with the principles of CBD, that the developed countries should provide resources or support in different forms to compensate the developing countries' growing expenses and inadequate technologies on conservation actions (Wang, 2015). The developed economics' accountability for 'Business and Biodiversity' in China would significantly depends on the Chinese government's negotiation with international forces. Thirdly, as demonstrated by 'Ant Forest', the external pressures and resources for 'Business and Biodiversity' are sourced from the society, which is composed by individuals. The relevant education should be provided for the general public.

The Need to Align and Integrate Forces and Resources in Promoting 'Business and Biodiversity'

The interviews reveal that there are some communication gaps existing among different stakeholder groups, which indicate the need to align the resources from a wide range of stakeholders and to promote active engagement and interactions among them.

The case of 'Ant Forest' and conservation on giant panda (Zhao and Atkins, 2019) demonstrate how the social forces can be aligned to contribute to the extinction prevention of species. Companies are widely supervised and motivated; the resources and support for companies' participation are also widely provided by conservation actors like NGOs. These cases are lying in the demonstration about how the social awareness and understanding could foster the genuine concern of the species, thus, leading to the conservation commitment and actions. The interview analysis also addresses the need to improve the awareness and abilities of government officials in terms of their significant influence and authority in China. The concern about the governance of local government have been addressed, especially those located in the places with backward economic and abundant nature resources. Without sufficient awareness and external supervision, they tend to sacrifice the environment in exchange of economic development. This involves complex factors such as local's livelihood, corruption and loosened supervision. Apart from the suggestions about providing adequate training for governmental officials, integrating environmental and biodiversity conservation into the performance appraisal proposed by interviewees, the social engagement and supervision could also be considered to further improve the governance of local government. In terms of the engagement with government, as one interviewee from NGOs emphasized, there is a need to establish an effective even dialogue platform between government and other conservation stakeholders to better supervise and improve the local government's governance on environmental and biodiversity issues. With Chinese central government's increasing attention and emphasis on the construction of ecological civilization in recent years, the local government's awareness and governance on biodiversity issues are gradually improving (e.g. Luo, 2018), providing significant opportunities for further engagement and supervision among conservation stakeholders. As one of the significant parts of both companies and society, the corporate staffs' awareness and behaviours on biodiversity issues are also influential. The interview revealed that there were some good biodiversity conservation examples from international companies' practices in China, and Chinese companies' practices in overseas operations. However, companies' good practices in overseas operations are rarely reflected in domestic operations. The main reasons are relevant with the voluntary nature of CSR reporting, lower awareness and external pressures, and the intensified competition in China. One of the most efficient and promising approaches in promoting 'Business and Biodiversity' in China is to incorporate overseas experiences and practices.

The Need to Take a Pragmatic Consideration of Non-anthropocentric Approach of Biodiversity Conservation

The interview reveals that the current practices on 'Business and Biodiversity' are mainly anthropocentric, while it is certain that the increasing involvement and understanding of biodiversity conservation would lead to more non-anthropocentric behaviors.

The interviewed corporate employees, especially those who have experiences in overseas operations do have awareness and concern about the biodiversity loss in China. As a person living in society, they are yearning for a higher quality of living environment and nature with abundant species, while as corporate employees, they are concerning more about the competition pressures and other difficulties that keep companies away from participation in biodiversity conservations at present. Moreover, as mentioned earlier, compared with biodiversity issues, they are concern more about the issues like pollution which have more direct impact on them. Their perceptions could be perceived as anthropocentric. However, they also expressed their pragmatic considerations. For example, they acknowledge the necessity to address the biodiversity issues, while they believe should only be based on the good performance of basic environmental issues (e.g. pollution), which has higher priority and would provide foundation for biodiversity conservations. Furthermore, other interviewees also expressed their considerations for more possibilities to promote biodiversity conservation, such as the potential of people's collective demand and the problems of current regulatory power relations. These perceptions suggest their pragmatic considerations for promoting 'Business and Biodiversity' in China, which could be perceived as the compromise between the ideal dreams and the reality. It indicates the non-anthropocentric potential of people's values. As demonstrated in the case of 'Ant Forest', the users are tending to have separate online identities such as 'Ant Forest Forester' apart from their real-life identity, which express the values that would address their self-worth. There is a process to develop non-anthropocentric behaviours. The increasing concerns and involvement are necessary to foster this process.

The interview's analysis revealed the need for more non-anthropocentric concerns. For example, one interviewee from CSR consulting sector indicates that the setting of current environmental standards and indicators is mainly based on the 'harm level' for humans rather than other species. Moreover, most of the conservation projects are designed and implemented without genuine considerations of the actual impact on species. The conservation actions should be species or biodiversity centred.

The Need to Address the Employment of Impression Management on Biodiversity Reporting

To address the impression management that is commonly employed by companies on biodiversity reporting, the companies are suggested to carry out continuous/-long-term conservation projects in cooperation with conservation stakeholders and demonstrate their continuous improvement by putting more emphasis on the actual impact on species. Moreover, companies are encouraged to perceive biodiversity conservation as opportunities rather than risks.

As indicated in the study of Chinese companies' biodiversity reporting (Zhao and Atkins, Forthcoming), the continuous projects usually result in improving engagement and partnerships with conservation stakeholders, thus, allowing for in-depth integration of conservation practices into corporate operations.

Moreover, with consistent engagement and practices, corporate employees' awareness, understanding and abilities for biodiversity conservation would be significantly improved, thus, leading to more genuine commitment. Furthermore, the continuous concern of biodiversity issues and engagement with leading conservation organizations allow the companies to flexibly adapt to the demand of the external context. What is more, by concentrating on a specific project, the accumulated resources and progresses easily result in scientific or practical breakthrough, thus, to further promote the conservation researches or practices. Finally, the continuous project would hold companies accountable as their performance could be compared and monitored along the time. In terms of the disclosed performance, companies' disclosures should be based more on the long-term positive impact on species, rather than the conservation action itself or short-term achievements. Therefore, the demand for continuous/long-term projects and the demonstration of meaningful performance (e.g. the survival rate of specific species, the improvement of ecological balance or generic balance and the maintained or improved ecological services) would significantly prevent practices of impression management.

Another significant factor that could keep companies away from the employment of impression management is their perceptions about the biodiversity conservation. Companies have less interests in biodiversity conservation when they perceive it as risks. They tend to associate it with additional costs and labour. Therefore, they are more likely to employ impression management to merely meet the relevant legislative requirements. In contrast, companies could seek opportunities from biodiversity conservation such as taking advantages of ecological services to save costs or provide benefits (e.g. living environment) for employees (Zhao and Atkins, Forthcoming). However, these practices are significantly driven by anthropocentric view; without genuine consideration of native species and guidance from professional conservation stakeholders, there is a danger that companies' practices cannot improve but create harm on native species or ecosystems. To avoid such practice, as mentioned earlier, companies need to actively engage with conservation stakeholders, seeking guidance and supportive resources, thus, to improve their understanding and abilities in biodiversity conservation. In other words, it is not only about the opportunities for companies but also for other stakeholders including regional environment and species to benefit from 'Business and Biodiversity'. Interviewees generally agreed that there is a need for a mechanism to align the diverse interests from different stakeholders to collectively promote biodiversity conservation. Only perceiving 'Business and Biodiversity' as an opportunity could lead to effective participation. No matter whether the pursued opportunity is anthropocentric or non-anthropocentric, the key is to get it started; the continuous development would progressively shape the mechanism for a better world. The government is considered to play an important role in this mechanism in terms of its significance in policy and funding support.

Proposed 'Business and Biodiversity' Mechanism to Ensure the Open and Effective Engagement among Stakeholders

Based on the 'Ant Forest' case and discussions above, the key to construct the ideal mechanism for 'Business and Biodiversity' in China is to address the following issues: (1) Ensure open and effective engagement among stakeholders, (2) Ensure that the biodiversity conservation and reporting are species/biodiversity centred, (3) Ensure the accountability of stakeholders for companies on biodiversity conservation, (4) To address not only risks but also opportunities and (5) To form a social force in participating and supervising biodiversity conservations.

Figure 18.4 shown below is the proposed mechanism in further promoting 'Business and Biodiversity' in China. It is species/biodiversity-centred, composed by three major function components namely management, practice and research which are based in China and six significant international forces namely

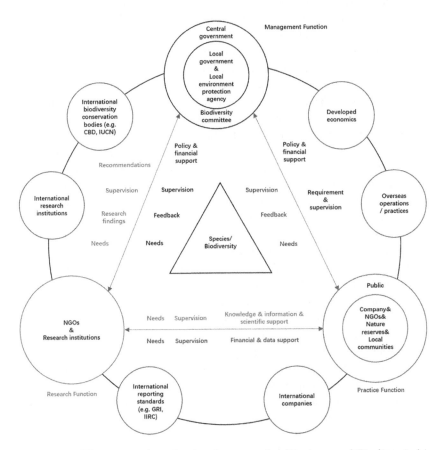

FIGURE 18.4 The proposed mechanism in promoting 'Business and Biodiversity' in China.

international biodiversity conservation bodies, international research institutions, international reporting standards, international companies, overseas operations/practices and developed economics. The lines and circles that connect these components, forces, and diverse stakeholders represent the engagement and interactions between them through the communication approaches in various forms including accounting. The main engagement and interactions among the three major function components are labelled.

The management function is performed by the Chinese government in terms of their significant influence, resources and authority in China. It contains two general levels. The central government and China National Committee for Biodiversity Conservation are the central management that is mainly responsible for the significant decision-makings (e.g., national policies and projects), the organisation and coordination of conservation projects and actions, the negotiation and cooperation with international forces and the supervision of local management and other functions. The local government and local environment protection agency are the local management that is mainly responsible for the implementation of central management's decisions, the organization and coordination of specific conservation projects and actions, the engagement with local stakeholders and relevant supervision and forwarding the feedback of performance and any issues to central management. In relation to the management component's engagement with others, the government in general is expected to provide policy and financial support to both practice and research components and supervise their actions and performance. It also provides relevant requirements for the practice component (especially companies) to comply and provides feedback and further needs for the research component to carry out further researches. Moreover, in the international context, the Chinese government's engagement with international biodiversity conservation bodies and developed economics are essential to obtain international support and resources. At the same time, the Chinese government should also under the supervision of other stakeholders, especially the local government, prevent any corruptions or wrongdoings.

The practice function is ideally to be performed by each individual in the society, while in most of the cases they are mainly performed by the practice part of conservation NGOs, nature reserves, local communities and, what we are trying to address in this study, companies. These forces are expected to be supported, as well as supervised by the public, to carry out biodiversity conservation practices. As discussed earlier, without adequate conservation professionals and resources, companies should actively engage with other stakeholders within the practice component, as well as research component, management component and international forces to seek for support and resources. As part of the practice component, companies should communicate their needs with the management and research components. Moreover, as conservation stakeholders should also be accountable for companies, both management and research components should also be under the supervision of companies, as well as other practice forces and the society. Apart from that, companies and other practice forces should provide feedback to the government in terms of relevant policies, requirements and support, for further improvement. Furthermore, companies and other practice forces should provide financial or/and data support for research component to carry out relevant researches in improving biodiversity conservation practices. In the international context, companies should incorporate their good biodiversity practices in overseas operations and good practices of international companies into their practices in China. Moreover, companies could also incorporate the global leading reporting standards in their reporting practices to further improve their accountability. As for other practice forces, they could also cooperate with international companies in promoting further conservation opportunities.

The research function is mainly performed by research institutions in different areas and the research part of the conservation NGOs. Their major responsibility in this mechanism is to carry out researches based on the needs of government and practice forces for conservation practices, thus, to provide findings and recommendations to the management component and to provide knowledge, information and scientific support to the practice component. At the same time, the research component should also effectively communicate its needs to the management and practice components to gain adequate support and resources for continuous researches. Moreover, its strength in scientific knowledge and researches could also be used to supervise the practices of government and practice forces for further improvement. In the international context, the research component has significant role in engaging with international research communities and conservation bodies to communicate the latest status and challenges of biodiversity loss, and the relevant plans and approaches in addressing those challenges, thus, to fulfil its function to provide adequate support and information for the management component to make decisions and for the practice component to carry out field conservation actions. Moreover, in this mechanism, the research component is also expected to engage with international reporting standards and international companies to further develop and shape corporate reporting practices in China.

Summary and Conclusion

This study was inspired by an innovative financial product for social welfare: Alipay's 'Ant Forest', which significantly influences the society's attitudes and behaviors on biodiversity conservation. It reminds us that we should not solely focus on the requirements for companies in developing 'Business and Biodiversity'; a broader context needs to be considered. In responding to the increasing appeals for actions to bend the curve of biodiversity loss (WWF, 2020c) and to provide alternative insights through China's practices and experiences (Zhao and Atkins, 2019), this study is intent to explore an ideal mechanism with emancipatory potential for 'Business and Biodiversity' in China. In order to construct the mechanism with systemic and critical considerations from different perspectives, interviews are being carried out with people from diverse stakeholders' groups. Their perceptions have been elaborated in detail in identifying the key issues that need to be addressed in the proposed mechanism. In result, an ideal mechanism with an emancipatory potential for developing 'Business and Biodiversity' in the Chinese context has been proposed. Further research is needed to explore the opportunities and challenges in implementing such mechanism. Moreover, a relevant reporting framework could be explored in guiding companies, as well as other stakeholders for biodiversity reporting.

In terms of practical contributions, this study has elaborated how financial instruments could contribute in addressing biodiversity crisis. Moreover, this study also addresses the current status, difficulties and potentials of 'Business and Biodiversity' in China, provide progressive and pragmatic recommendations with consideration of both anthropocentric and non-anthropocentric perceptions. The proposed mechanism is expected to specifically guide further development of 'Business and Biodiversity' in China. The recommendations are not only for the improvement of companies' accountability but also other stakeholders', including every individual's accountability for biodiversity. Therefore, the recommendations of this study have wider applications in not only the corporate sectors but also other sectors to further improve their practices in addressing biodiversity loss. Furthermore, the insights of this study could contribute to the development of ecological civilization, which is to be shared in the forthcoming 2020 UN Biodiversity Conference to provide insights in addressing biodiversity crisis. Finally, as this study is also grounded in critical perspectives, the recommendations including proposed mechanism could be adapted to address other global challenges or sustainability topics. All these practical contributions indicated above would help lead our world to be a 'better place', enhancing societal welfare.

Apart from suggestions for further studies indicated above, there are more possibilities, such as follow up studies to capture the process of the possible change in mind-set or social change alongside the continuous development of 'Business and Biodiversity' and the influential factors and challenges. Moreover, studies could be carried out to investigate the non-anthropocentric considerations of sustainability development, such as the classification of pollution harm on humans and other species.

References

Ant Financial 2020. Moving towards a better society for the future - Alipay 2017/2018 Sustainablity Report.

Atkins, J. & Atkins, B. 2016. Bee decline: An integrated approach. *In:* ATKINS, J. & ATKINS, B. (eds.) *The Business of Bees: An Integrated Approach to Bee Decline and Corporate Responsibility.* Greenleaf Publishing, 2–18.

Atkins, J. & Maroun, W. 2018. Integrated extinction accounting and accountability: building an ark. *Accounting, Auditing & Accountability Journal,* 31, 750–786.

Chen, B., Feng, Y., Sun, J. & Yan, J. 2020. Motivation analysis of online green users: Evidence from Chinese "Ant Forest". *Frontiers in Psychology,* 11, 1335.

China Daily. 2018. *The Ministry of Ecological Environment Is Working with Ant Forest to Call Hundreds of Millions of Users to Construct a Beautiful China* [Online]. China Daily. Available: http://cnews.chinadaily.com.cn/2018-06/05/content_36331389.htm [Accessed 20th February 2019].

Coetzee, C. & Van Niekerk, D. 2012. Tracking the evolution of the disaster management cycle: A general system theory approach. *Jàmbá: Journal of Disaster Risk Studies*, 4, 1–9.

Corbin, J. & Strauss, A. 2012. *Basics of Qualitative Research: Techniques and Procedures for Developing Grounded Theory*, Thousand Oaks, AGE Publications.

Edwards, R. & Holland, J. 2013. *What Is Qualitative Interviewing?*, A&C Black.

Gallhofer, S. & Haslam, J. 2017. Some reflections on the construct of emancipatory accounting: Shifting meaning and the possibilities of a new pragmatism. Critical Perspectives on Accounting.

Gallhofer, S., Haslam, J. & Yonekura, A. 2015. Accounting as differentiated universal for emancipatory praxis: accounting delineation and mobilisation for emancipation (s) recognising democracy and difference. *Accounting, Auditing & Accountability Journal*, 28, 846–874.

Gilbert, N. 2008. *Researching Social Life*, Sage.

Gov.cn. 2015a. *The Central Committee and the State Council's Opinions of Accelerating the Construction of Ecological Civilization* [Online]. The Central People's Government of the People's Republic of China. Available: http://www.gov.cn/xinwen/2015-05/05/content_2857363.htm [Accessed 3rd December 2018].

Gov.cn. 2015b. *The Understanding of 'Opinions of Accelerating the Construction of Ecological Civilization' from the Director of the Development and Reform Commission* [Online]. The Central People's Government of the People's Republic of China. Available: http://www.gov.cn/xinwen/2015-05/06/content_2857592.htm [Accessed 4th December 2018].

Gray, R., Adams, C. & Owen, D. 2014. *Accountability, Social Responsibility and Sustainability: Accounting for Society and the Environment*, Pearson Higher Ed.

Hofkirchner, W. Ludwig von Bertalanffy. Forerunner of evolutionary systems theory. The new role of systems sciences for a knowledge-based society, Proceedings of the First World Congress of the International Federation for Systems Research, Kobe, Japan, CD-ROM (ISBN 4-903092-02-X), 2005.

Laszlo, E. 1972. *The Relevance of General Systems Theory*. New York: George Braziller.

Luo, S. 2018. *Our County Is Constructing Biodiversity Conservation Network to Strengthen the Protection of Ecological Systems* [Online]. People's Government of Nanhua County. Available: http://www.ynnh.gov.cn/file_read.aspx?id=17811 [Accessed 20th February 2019].

Maroun, W. & Atkins, J. 2018. The emancipatory potential of extinction accounting: Exploring current practice in integrated reports. *Accounting Forum*. Elsevier, 102–118.

Ministry of Ecology and Environment of the People's Republic of China. 2020. *One Square Meter per Person, Collectively Safeguard Biodiversity* [Online]. Available: https://www.mee.gov.cn/ywgz/zrstbh/swdyxbh/202004/t20200420_775276.shtml [Accessed 30th August 2020].

People.cn. 2007. *Speech by Hu Jintao at the 17th National Congress of the CPC* [Online]. News of the Communist Party of China. Available: http://cpc.people.com.cn/GB/64093/67507/6429846.html [Accessed 3rd December 2018].

People.cn. 2018. *The Suggestion from the Central Committee of the CPC on Amending Part of the Constitution: Writing Ecological Civilization into the Constitution* [Online]. Ecological Civilization of China. Available: http://www.cecrpa.org.cn/sxyw/yw/201803/t20180301_636315.shtml [Accessed 9th December 2018].

Pouvreau, D. 2014. On the history of Ludwig von Bertalanffy's "general systemology", and on its relationship to cybernetics-Part II: Contexts and developments of the systemological hermeneutics instigated by von Bertalanffy. *International Journal of General Systems*, 43, 172–245.

Rousseau, D. 2015. General systems theory: Its present and potential. *Systems Research and Behavioral Science*, 32, 522–533.

Shanshui Conservation Center 2020. 2018 Annual Report Shanshui Conservation Center.

UN Climate Change. 2019. *Winners of the 2019 UN Climate Action Awards Announced* [Online]. United Nations Climate Change. Available: https://unfccc.int/news/-winners-of-the-2019-un-climate-action-awards-announced [Accessed 29th August 2020].

UN Environment. 2019. *Chinese Initiative Ant Forest Wins UN Champions of the Earth Award* [Online]. UN Environment Programme. Available: https://www.unenvironment.org/-news-and-stories/press-release/chinese-initiative-ant-forest-wins-un-champions-earth-award#:~:text=19%20September%202019%20%2D%2D%20Ant,of%20China's%20%20most%20arid%20regions. [Accessed 29th August 2020].

UNDB. n.d. *Taking Action for Biodiversity* [Online]. United Nations Decade on Biodiversity. Available: https://www.cbd.int/2011-2020/about/undb [Accessed 1st January 2019].

von Bertalanffy, L. 1964. The world of science and the world of value. *Teachers College Record*, 65, 496–507.

Walters, K. D. 1977. Corporate social responsibility and political ideology. *California Management Review*, 19, 40–51.

Wang, C. 2019. *Can Mobile Payment Apps Spur Green Living?* [Online]. China Dialogue. Available: https://chinadialogue.net/en/business/11672-can-mobile-payment-apps-spur-green-living/ [Accessed 30th August 2020].

Wang, Z. 2015. *'Convention on Biological Diversity' Come into Force at 29th December 1993* [Online]. China Science Communication. Available: http://www.xinhuanet.com/science/2015-12/29/c_134957037.htm [Accessed 12th December 2018].

WWF 2018. Living Planet Report 2018.

WWF 2020a. Covid 19: Urgent Call to Protect People and Nature.

WWF 2020c. Living Planet Report 2020: Bending the Curve of Biodiversity Loss.

Xinhua. 2017a. *Infographic: Highlights of Xi's Report to 19th CPC National Congress* [Online]. Available: http://www.xinhuanet.com/english/2017-10/18/c_136689568.htm [Accessed 1st December 2018].

Xinhua. 2017b. *Infographic: The Thought on Socialism with Chinese Characteristics for a New Era* [Online]. Available: http://www.xinhuanet.com/english/2017-10/22/c_136696339.htm [Accessed 1st December 2018].

Xinhua. 2018. *Ecological Civilization Has Been Written into the Constitution* [Online]. Ecological Civilization of China. Available: http://www.cecrpa.org.cn/stjj/stfy/201803/t20180313_636760.shtml [Accessed 9th December 2018].

Xinhua. 2019. *From 'Millions' Project' to 'Ant Forest', China's 'Green Governance' Is Acknowledged by the World* [Online]. Xinhua Net. Available: http://www.xinhuanet.com/fortune/2019-09/29/c_1125054293.htm [Accessed 31st August 2020].

Yang, Z., Kong, X., Sun, J. & Zhang, Y. 2018. Switching to green lifestyles: Behavior change of ant forest users. *International Journal of Environmental Research and Public Health*, 15, 1819.

Zhang, Y., Xiao, S. & Zhou, G. 2020. User continuance of a green behavior mobile application in China: An empirical study of Ant Forest. *Journal of Cleaner Production*, 242, 118497.

Zhao, L. & Atkins, J. 2019. Panda accounting and accountability: Preventing giant panda extinction in China. *Around the World in 80 Species: Exploring the Business of Extinction*. Routledge, UK.

Zhao, L. and Atkins, J. (2021) "Assessing the Emancipatory Nature of Chinese Corporate Reporting on Conservation and Biodiversity", *Social and Environmental Accountability Journal*, Vol.41(1-2), pp.8-36.

19

THE INVESTORS' POLICY DIALOGUE ON DEFORESTATION (IPDD) CASE STUDY

A Collaborative Engagement Initiative with Governments to Mitigate Investment Impacts Resulting from Deforestation

My-Linh Ngo, Magdalena Kettis, Emine Isciel and Danielle Carreira

Introduction

Until recent times, investor engagement on biodiversity related matters has largely been limited to dialogue with companies and driven by concerns about ecosystem and societal health and well-being. With the focus on biodiversity hotspots, many of which are in developing countries, equity investors have tended to lead the charge. With other asset classes such as fixed income beginning to take a more strategic approach to incorporating ESG/sustainability factors into account, and as issues such as climate change show themselves to present systematic risks to financial markets, so we have also seen a shift in engagement beyond corporates to encompass sovereigns and broadening of emphasis to highlight the business case for tackling such matters. By complementing company-level engagement with sovereign-level engagement, investors can increase the likelihood of success in addressing such matters which being systematic in nature require a more holistic and multi-pronged approach.

The Investors Policy Dialogue on Deforestation (IPDD) Initiative

The Investment Case for Addressing Deforestation

Most countries do have some measures in place to combat deforestation, while at the same time providing favourable conditions for business and investments. However, escalating deforestation in recent years in countries rich in natural resources such as those in Latin America and South East Asia, combined with concerns about weakening environmental and human rights policies as well as lack of effective enforcement, is creating widespread uncertainty about the conditions for investing in or providing capital funding to these countries.

DOI: 10.4324/9781003045557-23

Investors are concerned about the financial impact that deforestation (and the subsequent impact on biodiversity and ecosystems services) and the violation of the rights of indigenous peoples and local communities may have on their clients and investee entities (which span corporate and sovereign issues), by potentially increasing reputational, operational and regulatory risks (see Figure 19.1). For instance, investors are concerned that companies exposed to potential deforestation in their direct operations and supply chains in these countries will face increasing difficulty accessing international markets. On the other hand, there may also be risks for the governments of those countries themselves in terms of impact on their ability to access capital (particularly from international investors) and/or the cost of accessing capital should they be deemed high credit risk if deforestation trends continues. Ultimately, investors want to continue to invest in many of the countries where deforestation is a concern and help show that economic development and protection of the environment need not be mutually exclusive. Financial institutions have a fiduciary duty to act in the best long-term interests of their beneficiaries. Investors, therefore, recognise that ESG or sustainability matters increasingly represent long-term market risks which need to be managed and accounted for more systematically. There is strong evidence to show that deforestation and land conversion are key drivers of biodiversity loss, climate change and water stress. Engaging with companies is important to halt deforestation, but there are limits to what individual firms can achieve. Given

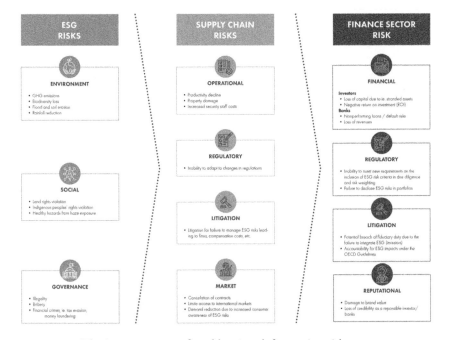

FIGURE 19.1   The investment case for addressing deforestation risks.
Source: IPDD, March 2021.

that responsibility for oversight of forests and nature lies with governments, it is not surprising that investors have shifted to engaging more directly with policy makers.

The Need for a Fresh Approach to Investor Engagement

The Investors Policy Dialogue on Deforestation (IPDD) initiative was established in July 2020 in direct response to the increasing rates of deforestation being observed in Brazil and other countries. The creation of this longer-term global collaborative investor engagement effort was not a planned development, but this step was taken due to the positive traction investors received following their initial engagement efforts.

From an organisational and governance perspective (see Figure 19.2), there is an IPDD Advisory Committee which sets the strategy and direction of the work of the IPDD initiative, with input and support from the wider supporting investor members and the various formal country workstreams. Secretariat support is provided by the Tropical Forest Alliance (TFA), an initiative hosted by the World Economic Forum, with the Principles for Responsible Investment involved in a Support role.

The IPDD initiative does not prescribe a set of action for investor members to follow, resulting from its engagement activities. Investors are free to incorporate

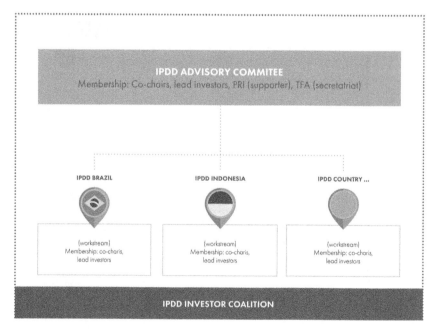

FIGURE 19.2 Governance of IPDD.
Source: IPDD, March 2021.

the insights from its activities as it sees fit. All investors' decisions that relate to the countries that participate in the engagement initiative shall be part of each institution's own decision-making process.

Engagement in Action: IPDD Brazil Workstream

Evidence of escalating rates of deforestation in recent years are creating widespread uncertainty about the conditions for investing in or providing capital to Brazil. Biodiversity and climate change represent potential systemic risks that can impact a country's creditworthiness. High and increasing deforestation rates are not only making Brazil less appealing as a sovereign investment on ESG grounds given the critical role they play in providing ecosystems and regulating the climate, but they are also impacting its ability to harness its forestry assets in the future for positive sustainability and finance initiatives, such as carbon financing, as well as in meeting its climate change obligations set out in the Paris Agreement. Increased deforestation is becoming both an environmental issue and a credit concern for sovereign bond investors for those countries where this is a material issue. Ultimately, forest fires degrade Brazil's creditworthiness and will likely cause deterioration in the price of its assets. Investors want to continue to invest in the country and contribute to its economic development and protection of the environment.

Initially, investors in June 2020 wrote an open letter to the Brazilian embassies in their home countries, signalling growing concerns about the forest fires. Having initially only sought to seek an audience with Brazilian embassy representatives, the investor group was contacted by and met with the Governor of the Central Bank of Brazil, who in turn facilitated a meeting with the Vice President of Brazil in his capacity as chair of the Amazon Council which is charged with addressing deforestation in the Amazon (see Figure 19.3). There was also widespread media coverage of the campaign. Given the engagement investors had witnessed and the recognition that sustained ongoing dialogue with the Brazilian government and other related stakeholders would be needed, it became evident that there would be value in formalising investor efforts. So, the IPDD was created, with an initiate term of two years agreed.

IPDD Brazil is the first formal country workstream of the IPDD. Its goal is to coordinate a public policy dialogue with Brazilian government related authorities and associations, as well as other stakeholders, on halting deforestation. It will do this by encouraging adoption and implementation of regulatory frameworks that ensure protection of forests, native vegetation and human rights.

Whilst much of the IPDD's efforts have highlighted the risks associated with deforestation, it has also been clear about the financial opportunities for countries which manage natural resources such as forests more sustainably.

To inform on activities and enable evaluation of progress, five specific outcomes were set out in relation to the engagement with the Brazilian government:

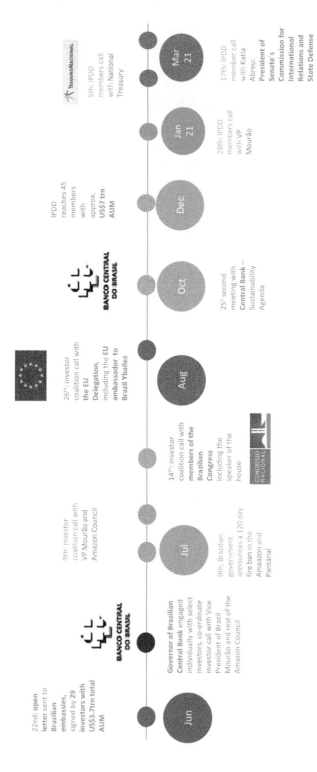

FIGURE 19.3 IPDD Brazil activities to date: June 2020–March 2021.

Source: IPDD, March 2021.

1. Significant reduction in deforestation rates, i.e. showing credible efforts to comply with the commitment set down in Brazil's Climate Law, article 19
2. Enforcement of Brazil's Forest Code.
3. The ability of Brazil's agencies tasked with enforcing environmental and human rights legislation to carry out their mandates effectively and any legislative developments that may impact forest protection.
4. Prevention of fires in or near forest areas, in order to avoid a repetition of fires like in 2019.
5. Public access to data on deforestation, forest cover, tenure and traceability of commodity supply chains.

Against these outcomes, investors have identified an initial set of stakeholders and specific objectives to be addressed. A formal stakeholder mapping exercise was conducted to further inform on the IPDD's engagement activities for the Brazil workstream. A more detailed work programme was also developed for regular intervals (quarterly), as well as appropriate metrics to evaluate progress and impact over the course of the initiative.

Evaluating the Impact of the IPDD Initiative

The IPDD was set up to run for an initial two-year term and will evaluate progress over this period. Given it was only formalised in July 2020, it remains too early to see any actual progress against the five outcomes of the Brazil workstream. This is particularly true when it comes to such a complex issue as deforestation, and engaging at the government and policy level, given the many different stakeholders and dynamics involved.

However, that is not to say it has not already had an impact in other ways which are just as important in terms of increased awareness and greater engagement from key stakeholders, all of which provides a foundation for increasing the likelihood of success in achieving the stated outcomes.

Direct engagement at the government level can add value.

In the case of Brazil, the IPDD has established an open dialogue and met with various government-related entities and associations, since the IPDD was established in July 2020 (see Figure 19.3). The dialogue also includes other stakeholders who themselves are interacting with the Brazilian government. The Government demonstrates its responsiveness to the investor concerns. While the messaging from the top is not always conducive to our efforts on matters of the environment and deforestation, the IPDD has been encouraged that this does not run through the entire government. Indeed, there are many strands of opinion within it – some departments clearly appreciate the severity of the issue and are working hard to address it. For example, in September 2020, the Central Bank launched a new sustainability agenda; at a meeting in early 2021, Vice President Mourão, Chair of the Amazon Council, presented a strategic plan on how to fight illegal deforestation and confirmed that the Council shares the objectives of the IPDD; and at a recent March 2021 meeting, the National Treasury of Brazil informed that they are currently working on an ESG framework and also working on giving investment funds and rating agencies more data and clarification on ESG topics. Whilst investors and the different governmental functions or individuals might differ over the best approaches and solutions to do this, the underlying impetus to preserve the rainforest is there. As such, the IPDD believes it is a case of identifying the right pressure points and working with the right people to move policy in a positive direction – as the political will exists – IPDD believes there is scope to succeed here.

Conveyed to governments that financial market participants consider issues like deforestation to be investment relevant material. Countries risk losing access to capital markets – or face higher borrowing costs – if they do not ensure effective management.

The IPDD's intervention and positioning on deforestation in Brazil does not seek to infringe on sovereignty and is not intended to be seen as interference. Rather, investors are looking to convey to government and their debt management offices specifically as well as the central bank, that how they manage critically important natural resources such as forests can risk their ability to secure external funding to support their domestic efforts. Furthermore, by coordinating investors together, and aligning messaging and insights, this has helped investors to 'speak' with one voice, and so be more likely to be heard as it adds a level of seriousness and legitimacy to the calls to halt deforestation which has been missing before and which governments will want to be seen to be responding to, for instance as restrictions on access to capital could materially impact their ability to deliver on their government's commitments to the people and so risk their ability to get re-elected.

Raised broader investor awareness of the issue of deforestation risk as an investment issue.

Initially the investor group comprised of 34 investors representing US$3.7 trillion in assets under management (AUM, as of June 2020). As of March 2021, there are now 51 investors representing approximately US$7 trillion in AUM. The investor group itself has furthered their own awareness, knowledge and understanding of deforestation issues and this continues to inform on the IPDD's work program.

Created a space and reference point for other stakeholders also working in this area, who share investor's concerns about deforestation risks, to reinforce their messaging and align their efforts.

The intervention of investors has added weight to their own efforts, and by all parties sharing insights and perspectives, it has been possible to identify shared objectives, barriers and explore potential solutions.

Contributed to the number of investor related ESG / sustainability initiatives which focus on systematic stewardship to tackle systematic issues like deforestation.

Whilst it is important investors continue to engage with specific companies and drive more sustainable natural resource practices, it is clear that the sheer scale and complexity of the various drivers of deforestation mean a more strategic approach is needed. Conducting engagement at the public policy level and with governments directly is critical to solving systematic issues like climate change and deforestation.

Finally, the IPPD has added to broader societal awareness about the issue of deforestation and the role financial markets can play in addressing this.

By highlighting the issue of deforestation risks and its link to climate change, biodiversity and human rights, the IPDD is helping to ensure the public and society at large keep this issue in mind in their own actions as well as in influencing others such as governments to take action.

Summary and Looking Ahead

Sustainability challenges like climate change, and their link with deforestation and biodiversity, are increasingly representing potential systematic market risks. Added to this, investors are considering the financial opportunities from acting on deforestation. The increasing focus of investors on delivering real-world outcomes means they are seeking to ensure their investment activities result in positive outcomes and avoid doing significant harm. Where this is occurring proactively or in response to expectations from the end beneficiaries, investors are looking to evidence that they are playing their part in contributing to the UN Sustainable Development Goals (UN SDGs).

The establishment of the IPDD initiative signals a shift and widening in the level and nature of investor stewardship efforts. Whilst it remains too early to assess fully the effectiveness of the Brazil IPDD workstream, it is clear its intervention is contributing constructively to the discussion and helping to keep the issue of deforestation on the government's agenda.

Ultimately, the measure of success remains in achieving real change on the ground in terms of deforestation rates in Brazil, and on that, we have yet to see progress. But the learning the investor group is gaining from this strategic engagement will add to the knowledge and toolkit available to investors when seeking to engage on systematic ESG/sustainability issues and which can be applied to other efforts. IPPD has now formalised a country workstream for Indonesia, recognising the need to ensure the authorities there also hear investor concerns, and the message that investors are ready and willing to work with governments to protect our planet's natural resources.

20

ENDING EXTINCTION

Taking Action to Transform the Financial System

Nick Robins

The Need for Systems' Transformation

There is little disagreement that ending extinction and restoring biodiversity will require transformational change, not least in the financial system. The Dasgupta Review on the Economics of Biodiversity, for example, argues that

> enabling the changes that we need will also require collective and sustained action to transform the systems that underpin our engagements with Nature, above all our financial and education systems. (Dasgupta, 2021). Similarly, the theory of change underlying the draft post-2020 global biodiversity framework is based on the recognition that urgent action is required "to transform economic, social and financial models so that trends that have exacerbated biodiversity loss will stabilise in the next 10 years (by 2030) and allow for the recovery of natural ecosystems in the following 20 years, with net improvements by 2050 to achieve the Convention's vision of living in harmony with Nature.
>
> *(CBD, 2020)*

Many steps will need to be taken as part of this transformational process. At present, most financial initiatives to end extinction and restore biodiversity focus on changing specific practices rather than the system as a whole. Amongst the many areas for systemic intervention, two stand out: sovereign bonds and central banks. The rest of this chapter will explore what transformation could look like for these and concludes with some recommendations for action through to 2030 and beyond.

DOI: 10.4324/9781003045557-24

Sovereign Bonds: The Systemic Asset Class

Sovereign bonds are one of the largest asset classes in the financial system, with an outstanding global value of over $60 trillion. Sovereign bonds connect the macro-economy and public finances with capital markets and set the risk-free rate which provides the benchmark for asset pricing across the system. They are also core holdings for institutional investors, commercial banks as well as central banks: they are in effect the 'universal asset classes'. And in terms of biodiversity, sovereign bonds both contribute to the destruction of natural capital and are also impacted by the consequences of ecosystem decline.

To understand these dynamics better, the LSE's Grantham Research Institute and Planet Tracker have developed a sovereign health model, by which we mean a framework which ensures that sovereign bonds are supporting the full implementation of the Sustainable Development Goals (Pinzon and Robins, 2020). This builds on the conventional frameworks used by credit rating agencies to assess the risks facing sovereign debt – and extends this to incorporate the interrelationships with natural capital. This model is set out in Figure 20.1, below.

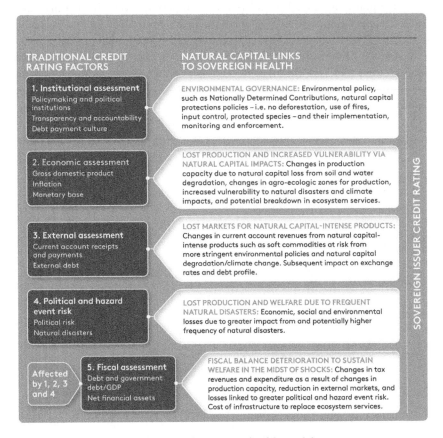

FIGURE 20.1 The natural capital and sovereign health model.

In the case of Brazil, for example, this framework involves addressing the following questions:

- **Institutional:** how is the failure to enforce and implement forest and climate policies creating systemic risks for sovereign debt?
- **Economic:** how will agricultural production be impacted by continuing degradation of nature (notably deforestation)?
- **External:** how could the country's trade balance be impacted by shifts in regulation and market preferences that restrict imports linked to deforestation?
- **Event risk:** how will agricultural production be affected by intensifying physical impacts of climate change (notably drought)?
- **Fiscal:** how will the fiscal balance be influenced by the compounded impact of these factors?

Importantly, there is strong visibility over the future maturity profile of sovereign debt, which provides key moments when environmental conditionalities could be added to the purchase of sovereign bonds by investors. The Inevitable Policy Response initiative has underscored two periods over which climate and land-use expectations will be tightened: the first is up to 2030 and the second is up to 2050. The IPR approach is applied to Brazil's debt profile in Figure 20.2.

In the face of the accelerating nature crisis, sovereign bond issuers have two choices: either they take the High Road, where they actively restore ecosystems and ensure that funds raised by sovereign bonds are aligned with biodiversity conservation as part of the delivery of the SDGs, or they continue down the

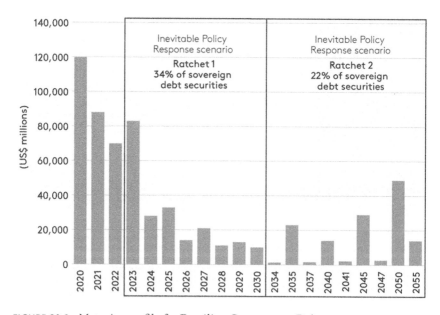

FIGURE 20.2   Maturity profile for Brazilian Government Debt.

Low Road, where the extraction of natural capital progressively undermines the ability both to raise funds for government spending and build a resilient economy over the long-term.

For sovereign bond investors, the task is three-fold. The first task is to understand how nature- and biodiversity-related risks impinge on risk-related returns from sovereign bonds. Here, the introduction of a consistent disclosure regime for sovereign issuers could greatly assist financial analysis and investment stewardship. The second task is to assess how the proceeds of sovereign bonds are being used either to enhance or to degrade natural capital. This is a crucial point of leverage in order to redirect the estimated $500bn in public subsidies that are harmful to biodiversity. By holding sovereign bonds that channel public spending to these destructive activities, sovereign bond investors are contributing to the degradation of ecosystems on which long-term returns rely. And the third task is to use their position as stewards of capital to engage with government issuers to bring the alignment of sovereign bonds with national and global biodiversity goals.

In the case of Brazil, the early signs of a transformation towards sovereign health emerged in 2020 with the launch of the Investor Policy Dialogue on Deforestation (IPDD). The IPDD's goal was to bring to the Brazilian government's attention the fact that failure to tackle deforestation represents 'a systemic risk for investors', adding that 'beyond the serious environmental costs, if the government doesn't address this issue, Brazilian sovereign & corporate financing costs could go up' (Stock, 2021). A detailed examination of IPDD is provided in Chapter X. Looking ahead, the IPDD is a foretaste of the transformations that will be needed in sovereign bond markets during the 2020s and beyond to end extinction and restore nature. Growing issuance of green sovereign bonds also points to a moment in the future when all sovereign debt becomes consistent with the conservation of biodiversity by 2030.

Central Banks: The Systemic Institution

Central banks and financial supervisors are the guardians of financial stability and are by definition the archetypal systemic institutions. These public authorities are already taking action to drive better management of climate-related financial risks. Over 80 central banks and supervisors are now members of the Network for Greening the Financial System (NGFS), undertaking work to incorporate climate factors into micro- and macro-prudential oversight as well as monetary policy and efforts to scale up sustainable financial solutions.

A growing number of central banks recognise the need to extend their focus from climate change to the wider nature and biodiversity agenda. This has been accelerated by the COVID pandemic and the recognition that zoonotic diseases driven by biodiversity loss and climate change can be regarded as 'Green Swan' events (Bolton et al, 2020). De Nederlandsche Bank has been in the vanguard, with its report, Indebted to nature, which was the first from a central bank to evaluate some of the challenges facing the financial sector. This concluded that 'biodiversity loss is a driver of financial risks' and recommended that 'financial institutions identify the physical, transition and reputational risks resulting from the loss of biodiversity' (DNB, 2020).

Unlike conventional financial risks, nature-related financial risks (NRFR) are characterised by deep uncertainty. According to the Dasgupta Review, this means that risks are subject to tipping points and regime shifts, complex transmission channels, and potentially far-reaching impacts on all agents in the economy, along with significant uncertainty over the exact timing of some nature-related risks. As a result, NRFR cannot be sufficiently managed through traditional 'market-fixing' approaches such as improved information disclosure and quantitative risk estimates. Instead, financial authorities will need to apply the long-standing precautionary principle to support a controlled regime shift towards more sustainable capital allocation (Kedward et al., 2020). A starting point for such a precautionary policy would be the identification and exclusion of clearly unsustainable activities, the financing of which should be discouraged via micro- and macro-prudential policy tools. Monetary policy tools, such as asset purchase programmes, should also exclude assets linked to nature-depleting activities (Kedward et al., 2020).

The risk lens is a necessary starting point for central banks given their mandate to ensure financial and monetary stability. To do this effectively, however, they will also need to understand how the financial system is imposing positive or negative impacts on Nature and thereby creating aggregate threats to macro-economic and financial stability. A prerequisite for this to happen would be the introduction of national and international policy programmes which clearly state the imperative of ending extinction and biodiversity loss and translate these into financial system measures.

The comparison between biodiversity and the climate change agenda is instructive. The 2015 Paris Agreement includes the goal of 'making financial flows consistent with a pathway towards low greenhouse gas emissions and climate-resilient development' (Article 2.i.c). An equivalent goal needs to be included in the Convention on Biodiversity's Post-2020 Framework to trigger transformational action across the financial system during the 2020s. In addition, over 120 countries accounting for more than 60% of greenhouse gas emissions have adopted or are considering net-zero targets. Once such targets are set at the national level, central banks are able to align their activities to ensure policy coherence, whether for climate change or the wider Nature agenda.

Here, inspiration can be taken from the steps that central banks could take to introduce 'net-zero central banking', including the requirement for all regulated financial firms to submit net-zero transition plans (Robins et al., 2021). This can be facilitated by clarification of the mandate of central banks. In March 2021, for example, the UK Chancellor sent an updated remit letter to the Bank of England, making clear that its financial and monetary policy operations now needed to have regard to an updated statement of government policy 'to transition to

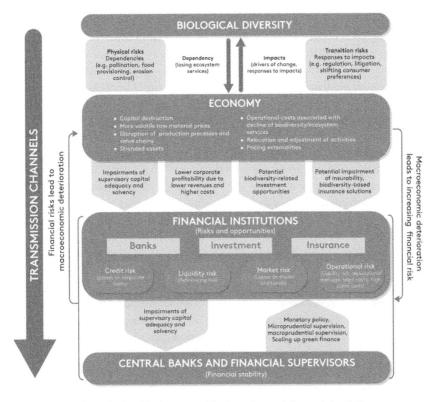

FIGURE 20.3 The relationship between biodiversity and financial stability.

an environmentally sustainable and resilient net zero economy' (Bank of England, 2021).

To identify how central banks and supervisors can best respond to these challenges, a joint study group on biodiversity and financial stability was launched in April 2021. Convened by the NGFS and one of its research stakeholders, the International Network for Sustainable Finance Policy Insights Research and Exchange (INSPIRE), the study group aims to establish an evidence-based approach to how central banks and supervisory authorities can fulfil their mandates in the context of biodiversity loss (NGFS & INSPIRE, 2021a). Its initial Vision Paper sets out the powerful transmission mechanisms that connect biodiversity and financial stability, as illustrated in Figure 20.3 (NGFS & INSPIRE, 2021b).

Towards a Nature-based Financial System

Well before 2050, the financial system will need to have changed completely in terms of its goals, its dynamics and its impacts on Nature, becoming a restorative rather than an extractive force. As part of this, one of the critical themes that will need addressing is the limits of the natural capital approach. The metaphor of natural capital is clearly a powerful tool for financial reform, focusing attention on the 'stocks' of Nature that provide essential flows of ecosystem services that underpin financial returns and system stability. It has enabled banks and investors to mainstream biodiversity into their decision-making as never before. However, natural capital still places biodiversity as subservient to the economy and retains a broader but still instrumental approach to Nature.

To be truly transformational, financial strategies need to start from the core conclusion of the Dasgupta Review that 'we are part of Nature, not separate from it'. Rather than seeking to integrate Nature into financial decision-making, the systemic challenge is to integrate the functioning of the financial system into Nature. Here systemic assets such as sovereign bonds and systemic institutions such as central banks will be critical levers in developing a truly holistic perspective addresses both the dependence of the financial system on Nature as well as the impacts of the financial system on Nature.

At the heart of such a Nature-based financial system would be the exploration of the strategies and tools that ensures that the financial system ceases to facilitate species extinction. This could involve the introduction of micro-prudential expectations on regulated firms such as banks, insurers and pension funds, to set out how they will stop contributing to extinction (perhaps in a manner similar to the way in which firms are dealing with modern slavery in the UK). The shared challenge for the years ahead is to keep a strategic eye on ending the financing of extinction and a tactical focus on how systemic assets and institutions such as sovereign bonds and central banks can support the transformation that is needed to achieve this.

References

Bank of England (2021) *Remit Letter for the Monetary Policy Committee*, March 2021. Link: https://www.bankofengland.co.uk/news/2021/march/mpc-remit-statement-and-letter-and-fpc-remit-letter

Bolton, Patrick, Despres, Morgan, Pereira Da Silva, Luiz Awazu, Samama, Frédéric & Svartzman, Romain (2020) *The Green Swan: Central Banking and Financial Stability in the Age of Climate Change.* Bank for International Settlements. Link: https://www.bis.org/publ/othp31.pdf

CBD (2020) *Update of the Zero Draft of the Post-2020 Global Biodiversity Framework, Convention on Biodiversity.* Link: https://www.cbd.int/article/zero-draft-update-august-2020

Dasgupta Review (2021) *The Economics of Biodiversity: Final Report.* Link: https://www.gov.uk/government/publications/final-report-the-economics-of-biodiversity-the-dasgupta-review

DNB (2020) Indebted to Nature. Link: https://www.dnb.nl/media/4c3fqawd/indebted-to-nature.pdf

Kedward, Katie, Ryan-Collins, Josh & Chenet, Hugues (2020) *Managing Nature-Related Financial Risks: A Precautionary Policy Approach for Central Banks and Financial Supervisors.* UCL, London. Link: https://www.ucl.ac.uk/bartlett/public-purpose/publications/2020/aug/managing-nature-related-financial-risks

NGFS & INSPIRE (2021a) *Press Release: Launch of Joint Study Group on Biodiversity and Financial Stability*. Link: https://www.ngfs.net/en/communique-de-presse/ngfs-and-inspire-launch-joint-research-project-biodiversity-and-financial-stability

NGFS & INSPIRE (2021b) *Biodiversity and Financial Stability: Exploring the Case for Action*, NGFS Occasional Paper Link: https://www.ngfs.net/sites/default/files/medias/documents/biodiversity_and_financial_stability_exploring_the_case_for_action.pdf

Pinzon, Alexandra and Robins, Nick (2020) *The Sovereign Transition to Sustainability: Understanding the Dependence of Sovereign Debt on Nature*, London School of Economics and Planet Tracker. Link: https://www.lse.ac.uk/granthaminstitute/wp-content/uploads/2020/02/The-sovereign-transition-to-sustainability_Understanding-the-dependence-of-sovereign-debt-on-nature.pdf

Robins, Nick, Dikau, Simon & Volz, Ulrich (2021) *Net-Zero Central Banking: A New Phase in Greening the Financial System*, LSE & SOAS. Link: https://www.lse.ac.uk/granthaminstitute/publication/net-zero-central-banking-a-new-phase-in-greening-the-financial-system/

Stock, Graham (2021) *Brazilian Deforestation: Investor Stewardship Update*. Blue Bay, London. Link: https://www.bluebay.com/globalassets/documents/bluebay-brazilian-deforestation-feb21-v2a.pdf

21

EXTINCTION ACCOUNTING AND FINANCE IN ITALY

The Case of Fineco Bank

Federica Doni, Silvio Bianchi Martini and Antonio Corvino

Introduction

A sixth period of mass extinction of flora and fauna, i.e. Anthropocene extinction, is currently affecting the world.[1] This event is caused by multiple factors including industrial activity, growing human populations, global warming, climate change, habitat loss, air and land pollution. Industrial and business activities are affecting natural capital and species extinctions either directly or indirectly. Scientists are warning of "biological annihilation of life" via the ongoing sixth mass extinction,[2] an extinction event caused by humans. The healthy functioning of the ecosystem is the basis of the corporate world as well as society. All species exist on our planet through their interrelationships and every extinction weakens these relationships. Biodiversity loss and ecosystem collapse are material issues for the private sector.[3] This chapter explores biodiversity loss and species extinction from a financial perspective to understand better risk management practices and accounting frameworks for natural capital preservation by collecting suitable data on sustainable business and finance and investment products.

Biodiversity and Pandemic Crisis: A "Driver" for Accelerating Business and Finance Action

Regulators are showing a clear commitment to intensive and systematic action for preventing biodiversity loss. Recently, the European Union (EU) Biodiversity Strategy for 2030[4] has incorporated biodiversity into the EU Green Deal as a core part of the EU's Recovery Plan.[5] The possibility of reemergence of SARS and other novel viruses from animals or laboratories should not be ignored,[6] and currently, coronavirus disease 2019 (COVID-19) confirms this risk, given that

DOI: 10.4324/9781003045557-25

pandemic crisis can be viewed as a boost to push all businesses towards a more sustainable approach on biodiversity topics.

Biodiversity and the Link with COVID-19

Recently, the World Wildlife Fund (WWF) Italy published an interesting document on the relationship between pandemics and the "boomerang" effects of ecosystem destruction.[7] Protecting human health by preserving biodiversity is becoming a mantra. Some shreds of evidence demonstrate that most of the emerging diseases such as Ebola, acquired immunodeficiency syndrome (AIDS), bird flu, severe acute respiratory syndrome coronavirus (SARS), swine flu and, today, the new coronavirus are not random catastrophes but the consequence of our impact on natural ecosystems. In-depth research has recently linked the important role of altering ecosystems on the birth and spread of infectious diseases such as zoonosis.[8] Human activities have significantly altered three quarters of lands and two-thirds of oceans, changing the planet to determine the birth of a new era, the "Anthropocene". Habitat loss, the creation of artificial environments, the manipulation and trade of wild animals and more generally the destruction of biodiversity are affecting the dynamic balance of the biosphere. This was confirmed by the Millennium Ecosystem Assessment (2021).[9] Destructive action of man on nature is unprecedented, as Intergovernmental Science-Policy Platform on Biodiversity and Ecosystem Services (IPBES) emphasized, in 2019.[10] Changes in the use of land and the destruction of natural habitats, such as tropical forests, may be the main origin of more than half of emergent zoonoses.[11]

Nevertheless, the environment can provide natural solutions. Wealth and abundance of species (i.e. two important components of biodiversity) can counteract the spread of disease in several ways. Among these, the *dilution effect* and the *coevolution effect* should be analyzed and discussed.[12] The former, i.e. the *dilution effect*, describes how in an ecosystem with a rich community of potential guests (animals in which a virus or other organism can reproduce), a pathogen has a lesser chance of finding a host where it can easily multiply (highly-competent host) and from which it can spread using another vector animal. In a scenario, rich in different animals, it is easier for the pathogenic body to enter in an unsuitable species that will function as an "ecological trap" for the pathogenic organism or for its vector. Scientists call these animals "dead-end hosts". Recent studies suggest how the dilution effect may explain the reduction of malaria transmission in different regions of the Brazilian Amazon.

In conditions of low biodiversity, few abundant species tend to prevail, which therefore become more exposed to contracting and spreading infections.[13] The *coevolution effect* provides ever-stronger evidence. Some researchers have tried to discover the origins of several new pathogenic organisms that today put our health at risk. Their studies show that in the destruction of habitats, the remaining forest fragments act like islands, where the microbes and the animals hosting them undergo rapid diversification, thereby increasing the likelihood that one or more of these microbes will be able to infect humans, spreading and creating epidemics.[14]

A significant contribution to the spread of serious epidemics also comes from the consumption of contaminated bushmeat. Such kind of consumption moreover is dramatically growing, in many parts of the world. Particularly, wild animals are increasingly an important food and financial vital source in countries where scarcity of food resources (i.e. protein) and economic inequalities are used to be. Wildlife, however, in addition to being a protein resource, can also be transformed into an easy source of earnings and commercial exchange. It is worthwhile to note an inverse relationship between household income and bushmeat consumption: the lower the income, the higher the consumption. Contrarily, in the urban areas, wild meat is preferred for its flavour, its price is higher than domestic meat, and therefore, higher income families make it higher consumption. Measures and actions for stopping or discouraging bushmeat consumption are needed, as they may reduce risks of extinction species to preserve the balance of biosphere.[15]

Trade in wildlife or parts of animal and plant species is not only a primary cause of loss of biodiversity (i.e. the illegal trade in rhino horn or pangolin scales) but can be an important mechanism of spread of zoonosis. The current health crisis is bringing the world's attention to the risks related to illegal wildlife trade. Governments, policy makers and regulators are expected to take into account this problem by requiring worldwide measures to fight this phenomenon, as it is the fourth most important and widespread criminal market in the world, which involves the loss of biodiversity and increases the risk of pandemics.[16]

International Union for Conservation of Nature

The International Union for Conservation of Nature (IUCN) remains committed to preserve the nature for a healthy planet and people. Many IUCN programmes, members and commissions are working to provide a better understanding of this health crisis. Particularly, the IUCN Species Survival and Ecosystem Management Commissions are trying to understand how those transfers of pathogens take place by human activities, such as illegal wildlife trade and land-use change.

One of the key drivers of emerging zoonotic diseases is land use. The interfaces between humans and other animals are potentially growing the possibilities of zoonoses emerging and spreading. They can be stimulated by deforestation, habitat fragmentation and an expanding agricultural frontier. In such a situation, enhancing protected areas and environmental law represents the IUCN's global strategy to reduce or prevent future disease episodes. Its current aim was to assess in-depth the consequences of human activities leading to the spread of zoonotic diseases and to support actors ranging from policymakers to local communities by clearly identifying and disclosing effective long-term remedies.[17]

United Nations Sustainable Development Goals Related to Biodiversity and Land

The COVID-19 virus and the economic crisis need to calibrate a global response to the Sustainable Development Goals (SDGs). In so doing, the UN-led Inter-Agency Task Force on Financing for Development in its new Financing for Development Report emphasized the need for a global and multilateral response that attacks the virus and puts the global economy back on a path to achieve the SDGs and the Paris climate agreement. That effort should start involving an effective action by the International Monetary Fund (IMF) and the World Bank to organize a radical emergency response "to stem the crisis in the developing world in order to steer their economies toward the SDGs". Developing countries are faced with a significant devaluation of their exchange rates and ballooning of debt. Such a situation "is wreaking immediate havoc and derailing efforts to meet the SDGs[18]". Notably, we should take into account SDGs 14 and 15, as they are strictly related to biodiversity issues. Conservation efforts to fight illicit poaching and trafficking of wildlife, to protect animal breeds and to preserve rural areas in developing countries, should be enhanced and taken in place.[19]

Biodiversity and Extinction Issues: Non-Financial Industry in Action

Environmental issues are part of business actions and policies in an increasing number of companies. In more detail, large corporations controlling much of the supply chain in some industries can be considered "the keystone actors of the Anthropocene". Manufacturing industry is gradually oriented to the biodiversity matters and, in particular, animal welfare is sparking the interest of boards of directors, due to pressure from consumers and investment funds. Consumers are paying more attention, in their consumer choices, to the impact on human health, on climate change, the development of sustainable models up to ethical issues on how animals should live on farms. Companies are showing themselves increasingly receptive to this consumer trend. The welfare of farm animals (animal welfare) is seen as an opportunity, in terms of new product offerings and market access and also in terms of brand differentiation and reputation improvement. According to a survey of the Business Benchmark on Farm Animal Welfare (BBFAW),[20] customers and consumers are the subjects that weigh most on the choice of companies to direct their efforts on the animal welfare side. Seventy-eight percent of those who participated in the survey confirmed that the growing interest of consumers can be considered the rationale for which they have started working on these issues. The attention devoted by the media to the phenomenon has been indicated as one of the motivations by 49% of the interviewees, but another interesting fact concerns the role of investors and nongovernmental organizations (NGOs) highlighted by 46% of the respondents. The Italian manufacturing listed companies show an increasing interest in the topics of animal welfare and cruelty free. More precisely, it is worthwhile to evaluate the initiative of the BBFAW benchmark created in collaboration with two leading animal welfare organizations, Compassion in World Farming (CIWF) and World Animal Protection with the investment company Coller Capital. This research explores corporate practices and reporting on animal welfare and assesses animal welfare strategies especially in the food (i.e. Barilla, Ferrero and Camst) and fashion industries (i.e. Moncler). For instance, the Barilla Group is one of the most important Italian cases for its policy on animal welfare.[21] Consistently with its purpose "Good for You, Good for the Planet", the company is turning great attention to animal welfare, which is essential for responsible and sustainable supply chains.

For years, Barilla has committed to ensuring that all suppliers of raw materials of animal origin comply not only with legal requirements, but also with the highest animal welfare standards and criteria. Barilla issued the Barilla Guidelines on Animal Welfare, drafted in collaboration with CIWF. In these guidelines, the group recognizes the importance of respecting the physical and mental well-being of animals and their ability to express species-specific behaviours by promoting the compliance with the Five Animal Freedoms: (1) freedom from hunger and thirst; (2) freedom from discomfort; (3) freedom from pain, injury and disease; (4) freedom to express the species-specific behaviour; and (5) freedom from fear and distress.

In Italy, Barilla has been the leading company in the global benchmark of farmed animal welfare BBFAW, for three years in a row. Moncler, one of the most famous fashion companies in Italy, is also paying attention to animal welfare. Indeed, Moncler[22] demands and verifies that all its down suppliers comply with the strict requirements of Moncler's technical Down Integrity System and Traceability (DIST) Protocol. Starting from the first implementation in 2015, it regulates farming standards, respect for animal welfare, and down traceability technical quality. Moncler only purchases down that is DIST-certified.

The DIST Protocol assesses animal welfare using an innovative approach, because it also provides for the careful observation of the animal itself (as per recent European Commission guidelines), through the so-called Animal-Based Measures (ABMs). The ABMs enable the direct assessment of the animals' conditions by observing how the geese respond to various factors within their environment (i.e. the outcome approach). Given that, the contribution of nonfinancial industries is not enough to preserve our planet.

Biodiversity and Extinction Issues: Financial Industry in Action

An increasing awareness on the contribution of the financial sector to the pathway towards the preservation of nature and ecosystems is perceived at the global level as confirmed by this statement "The finance sector must go beyond business as usual to solve the biodiversity loss crisis".[23] At the end of June 2020, the new report published by the United Nations Environment Programme (UNEP) and the Natural Capital Finance Alliance (NCFA) highlighted an urgent need for all actors of the financial sector (banks, investors and insurers) to set firm targets for reducing biodiversity loss.[24] Nine critical sectors are selected by setting out a step-by-step approach in order to support financial institutions in managing their loans, investments and underwriting activities to halt biodiversity decline.

Among various financial institutions, banks should urgently set targets for financing the protection of nature in the critical next decade in the same way that many organizations have set climate targets, as said by the UN Environmental UN Finance Initiative and the UN Environment Programme World Conservation Monitoring Centre. It is essential to tackle the climate change crisis and biodiversity loss together.

Banking Sector and Biodiversity

All actors in our political economy (i.e. banks, regulators, other financial institutions, the judiciary, governments and communities) must commit themselves to find and apply concrete actions to reverse biodiversity decline. Recently, a growing awareness is extending from the business to the financial context. Governments and companies are increasingly involved in actions to prevent biodiversity risks; instead, the finance sector seems to be inactive by funding the destruction of nature in a very impressive way. Particularly, the banking sector has been scrutinized to investigate how banks are financing biodiversity and ecosystems' destruction. Some empirical evidence seems to demonstrate the alleged "destructive" role of banks in financing biodiversity loss. In 2019, the world's largest banks have financed more than USD 2.6 trillion in sectors that effectively contributed to the ecosystem destruction.

Three important factors can be identified: (1) the lack of rules or regulators that can apply penalties to banks that do not protect biodiversity; (2) the absence of sufficient systems for measuring or controlling the impact of their loans on biodiversity; (3) the absence of effective policies to largely adopt best practices on the protection of biodiversity. There is an urgent claim to radically change rules, systems and responsibilities to halt and reverse the ecosystems decline. Very few signals are coming from some initiatives, such as the Finance for Biodiversity Banking Pledge[25] or in very limited cases banks and financial institutions have started to respond by measuring their impact on the planet through new approaches on biodiversity disclosure. Overall, there were some previous attempts, such as the World Summit on Sustainable Development and the United Nations General Assembly endorsement of the Global Biodiversity targets and the issuing of the Convention on Biological Diversity. Unfortunately, the United Nations realized that no one of the Alchi 20 biodiversity targets[26] set have been met, in 2010. A loss of ecosystems services (between USD 4 and 20 trillion), every year from land-use change alone, is caused by unsustainable business practices.

Recently, pandemic crisis is moreover increasing the general awareness of biodiversity and the risk of a radical decrease in banking sector's reputation is high. To control this risk, it is worthwhile measuring and quantifying the loans and underwriting provided by banks to companies that are largely affecting biodiversity. An interesting analysis carried out by Earth Portfolio used data from Refinitiv database (formerly known as Thomson Reuters Eikon).[27] This study selected 50 active worldwide banks that are included in the S&P Global 100 list or operate in countries or regions that are particularly sensitive to biodiversity and activities' impacts. By identifying five levels of sectors (i.e. economic sector, business sector, industry group, industry and activity), a specific focus is on industries that largely impact biodiversity, such as metals and mining, construction, and engineering. Twenty banks included in the sample are European, other banks are from the Asia-Pacific region and few ones are from South America and Africa. Forty-four of the banks are the largest 100 banks in the world by total assets and it can be considered a representative sample of the banking sector at the global level. The most financed sectors from the top ten banks are infrastructure followed by the metal and mineral mining industry and fossil fuels. On the contrary, industries such as forestry and tourism registered the smallest percentage of financed figures. The sample of banks includes different kinds of finance, such as financial institutions providing credit to a company (i.e. loans and underwriting of share and bond issuances) or investing in the equity and debt of a company by holding shares and bonds. The largest impact on biodiversity is due to some sectors, such as infrastructure (32% of all loans and underwriting) metal and mineral mining (25%) and fossil fuel (20%), while food production is linked to only a small part of investments (10%) despite its negative reputation, in terms of biodiversity impact.

From a geographical perspective, European banks within the top ten focused their funds on the food sector in comparison with USA banks that invested more finance in companies belonging to the transportation and logistics sector. By analyzing the type of biodiversity impact, this research shows a large involvement of the banks in Africa and Asia-Pacific regions (i.e. China) that show a high level of financing with risk of direct impact on biodiversity loss. Main results demonstrated that 66% of the funding analyzed is used for activities having a direct negative impact on biodiversity (i.e. fishing, mining and the extraction of fossil fuels, infrastructure and tourism) and 34% was invested in companies indirectly affecting biodiversity and ecosystems (e.g. by demanding along the supply chain from retail or processing and trading of commodities). On average, it emerges an impressive figure of USD 52 billion of finance that is linked to biodiversity risk.

Although not all finance is causing a negative biodiversity impact, an urgent claim pertains to an appropriate measurement and monitoring system to limit banks' contribution to the biodiversity decline. The research by Earth Portfolio attributed a different score by selecting two kinds of policies, i.e. *commitments* (48/100 points) and *exclusions* (54/100 points). In more detail, commitments include specific actions for implementing sustainability in corporate governance practices, by adopting a specific policy for biodiversity and an adequate reporting system for measuring biodiversity risks of the bank financing activities. Exclusions represent corporate activities that can cause a large impact on biodiversity and are not funded by banks for this reason (e.g. deforestation activities that may alter high conservation value areas). Results are very remarkable, given that all banks accounted less than 40 points out of a total of 100. A quite positive result is that the nine banks that registered the highest score are headquartered in Europe but, at the same time, their scores were still far too low to guarantee that their funding activities are completely not involved in the destruction of our planet.

Findings show that banks are not prepared, reluctant or not so interested in dealing with biodiversity problems by adopting systems and policies for measuring the environmental effects of their finance activities. Biodiversity and extinction accounting issues are not part of the banks' current priorities.

Albeit nearly all banks demonstrated to implement sustainability issues at the highest level of governance, sustainability directors were not able to add veto rights over specific controversial financing activities. For instance, the remuneration and bonus packages of executive compensation system issue incentives linked to environmental, social and corporate governance (ESG) factors, in a broad perspective, but there are no specific connections with biodiversity outcomes. Despite the bulk of banks analyzed adopts the Equator Principles,[28] as a risk management framework, none of them achieved the Alchi Biodiversity Targets of the Convention on Biological Diversity.[29] Other weaknesses regard the lack of adequate reporting on biodiversity risks, especially if compared with climate-related issues disclosures. An essential point refers to the absolute dearth of indicators that are considered crucial for respecting environmental issues, in financing activities. For instance, none of the banks gives to savers adequate information on how their money is being invested, the reporting of biodiversity risks with specific disclosure on loans with a high risk and the stress testing of balance sheets for biodiversity consequences. Banks do not sufficiently control the effects of their lending activities on biodiversity and extinction issues. The highest score in exclusions has been achieved in the fossil fuel industry, followed by the agriculture sector (which includes agricultural commodities, such as palm oil). Fisheries industry registered very low scores in exclusions that reveal a poor interest by banks in a crucial sector for the global biodiversity decline. The other impressive result is that nearly half of all banks of the sample has no exclusion activities that confirm their no awareness about the link of their activities with biodiversity issues.

An overall consideration is that banks do not consider themselves responsible or liable for affecting biodiversity preservation, because of their lending activities. There are few attempts to stabilize biodiversity and to limit funds of the activities with the worst impact or to refuse loans for the coal, oil and gas companies in fragile ecosystems. To make banks liable in case of strong negative consequences on biodiversity, one solution may be represented by the issuing of quite strict legal rules and frameworks. In this perspective, it is becoming essential to rewrite legal rules for financial institutions. Given the large consolidation of the banking sector at the global level and the similar concentration of large companies, an ever-smaller number of banks are offering funds to an ever-smaller number of corporate supply chain actors. Despite the significant impact of these businesses on large geographical areas, banks do not report any liability for their damage to nature and do not have any policy or due diligence mechanisms able to control their impact on ecosystems. Voluntary commitments by banks and companies are not enough to improve this situation and cannot be replaced by a legal and regulatory reform.

All global initiatives and international agreements have failed to achieve effective improvement. Banks now need to implement a new business model with the aim to include appropriate procedures to quantify their impact on nature and to disclose transparency on reporting of risks and impacts. All banks need to be accountable for the impact of their lending activities on nature. For instance, although forests contain around 80% of terrestrial biodiversity, a large percentage of banks did not have any commitments in preventing deforestation risk, in 2019. This result confirms that only voluntary actions will be not enough.

Recently, we have witnessed new initiatives aimed at overhauling the financial industry's impact on biodiversity through corporate investment (Table 21.1). Such recent initiatives confirm increasing scrutiny on the financial sector footprint on biodiversity loss.

Research Method

The empirical research for this chapter consists of a qualitative case study analysis. We chose this approach as we believe it provides more food for thought than quantitative techniques. In accordance with some distinguished scholars,[30] the selection of the Fineco Group takes root in the fact that, in the Italian context, it represents uniqueness, in terms of ownership structure, in the banking industry. Unlike the key players, Fineco Group's major shareholder is the market and its ownership structure is truly dispersed. The latter might be deemed another distinctive feature, given that in Italy there is often a strong ownership concentration "in few hands". The data collection deals with both secondary and primary sources. This activity was carried out from April 2020 to March 2021. The first typology of data was gathered from the following sources:

- – annual reports;
- – sustainability and non-financial disclosure reports;
- – management letters; and
- – Websites' documents.

With the aim of enriching the information database, the research team opted for the preparation of a questionnaire to be administered during the face-to-face interviews with some key people of the Fineco Group's top management.

TABLE 21.1 Biodiversity and financial industry: an overview

Organization	Title	Year	Reference	Aim
UK Government	Dasgupta P., *The Economics of Biodiversity: the Dasgupta Review*	February 2021	https://www.gov.uk/government/publications/final-report-the-economics-of-biodiversity-the-dasgupta-review	Description of the consequence of biodiversity decline, the role of governments and economic actors and solutions
The Bank of the Netherlands (NDB) and the Netherlands Environmental Assessment Agency (PBL)	De Koning, N. *DNB and PBL: loss of biodiversity leads to financial risks*	June 2020	Regulation Tomorrow https://www.regulationtomorrow.com/-the-netherlands/dnb-and-pbl-loss-of-biodiversity-leads-to-financial-risks/	Description of the risks outlined to the financial sector associated with biodiversity loss
The Commonwealth Climate and Law Initiative CCLI	Barker S., Mulholland, E. and Onifade T., *The emergence of foreseeable biodiversity-related liability risks for financial institutions. A gathering storm?*	August 2020	https://ccli.ouce.ox.ac.uk/wp-content/uploads/2020/09/CCLI-Biodiversity-liability-risks-report-vFINAL.pdf	Analysis of the potential biodiversity-related liability risks for financial institution in a legal profession view
Paulson Institute, The Nature Conservancy and Cornell Atkinson Center for Sustainability	Deutz, A., Heal, G. M., Niu, R., Swanson, E., Townshend, T., Zhu, L., Delmar, A., Meghji, A., Sethi, S. A., and Tobin-de la Puente, J *Financing Nature: Closing the Global Biodiversity Financing Gap*	2020	https://www.paulsoninstitute.org/wp-content/uploads/2020/10/FINANCING-NATURE_Full-Report_Final-with-endorsements_101420.pdf	Comprehensive worldwide effort to protect and value nature as an insurance policy Policy for reorienting financial flows towards restoration of nature

(Continued)

Organization	Title	Year	Reference	Aim
ShareAction	Springer K., *Point of No Returns Part IV Biodiversity An assessment of asset Managers' approaches to biodiversity*	June 2020	https://shareaction.org/wp-content/uploads/2020/06/ShareAction-Biodiversity-Report-Final.pdf	This analysis found that: (1) none of the world's largest asset managers have a stand-alone, dedicated policy on biodiversity covering all portfolios under management; (2) Asset manager's publicly available responsible investment policies lack specific commitments on biodiversity related issues
Amazon Watch and Friends of the Earth	Birss M. and Conant J., *BlackRock's Silence on Forest Destruction*	22 June 2020	https://amazonwatch.org/news/2020/-0622-blackrocks-silence-on-forest-destruction	This analysis argued that BlackRock remains the world's largest investor in fossil fuels and it continues to rake in huge profits from that other driver of climate catastrophe: agribusiness-fuelled deforestation
Animal Agriculture Sector	Campaigning pressure of a number of civil society organizations against particular banks	2020	(1) Rainforest Action Network, Banking_on_Climate_Change__2020_vF.pdf (ran.org) (2) Stand Earth and Amazon Watch https://amazonwatch.org/assets/files/-2020-08-12-eu-banks-financing-amazon-oil-summary.pdf	(1) Analysis in the forest risk commodities sector and fossil fuel sector; (2) The role of European banks in financing the trade of controversial oil extracted from the Amazon;

Organization	Title	Year	Reference	Aim
			(3) Mighty Earth http://www. mightyearth.org/wp-content/ uploads/Mighty_Earth_ MichelinReport5Oct2020FINAL.pdf (4) Stop the Money Pipeline https:// stopthemoneypipeline.com/	(3) The role of banks (i.e. BNP Paribas and ADM Capital) in Industrial Deforestation for producing rubber (4) Role of some of the biggest financial actors (BlackRock and JP Morgan) are financing resource extraction
Finance for Biodiversity Pledge F4B Initiative	*Finance for Biodiversity Reverse nature loss in this decade*	2020	https://www.financeforbiodiversity.org/ https://www.financeforbiodiversity. org/wp-content/uploads/2.-Finance- for-Biodiversity-Pledge_Guidance_ Dec2020.pdf	This project aims to strength the link between biodiversity and financing decisions. Development of a Finance Accountability Framework that includes six elements: (1) Grants' Citizens Biodiversity Rights; (2) Disclose Impact; (3) Create Liability for Biodiversity; (4) Align Public Finance with Biodiversity; (5) Align Private Finance with Public Policy; (6) Integrate Biodiversity into Financial Governance

Source: Portfolio Earth (2020), pp. 34–35.\

The structure of the questionnaire mirrors the pivotal guidances highlighted by the current and insightful literature studies.[31] In more detail, the first section is devoted to collect data regarding the financial and especially the banking sector (Table 21.2).

The second part is mainly based on the exploration of the Fineco Group's universe with respect to the firm's policies on sustainability and, in particular, on biodiversity (Table 21.3).

Overall, two (i.e. the seniors) out of the three research team members conducted two interviews, respectively, with the CEO, Alessandro Foti, and some key people in the Fineco Group, such the investor relator, the CFO and the CSR management. Each meeting lasted around one hour and a half and took place on information technology (IT) platforms (i.e. Zoom and Teams), as a consequence of the current pandemic. All data collected were categorized in specific work sheets, in order to build a common data endowment and ease the sharing with each researcher of the team. Subsequently, the researchers read the information gathered many times, first individually and then as a group, to compare the single perception and interpretation. Such steps revealed fundamental milestones for safeguarding the reliability of the empirical evidence. In this regard, Table 21.4 shows the type of validity delved into each activity of the qualitative research blueprint.

TABLE 21.2 List of questions included in the first section of the questionnaire

Number	Question
1	What do you think about the commitment by the financial sector and particularly by the banking sector on biodiversity and species extinction?
2	What do you think about the recent report on Portfolio Earth (Bankrolling plastics; Bankrolling extinction: retrieved mostly from: https://portfolio.earth/)
3	What are the main tools by the financial industry to preserve biodiversity?
4	Focused comments on the Italian financial sectors and banking industry?
5	Is there a specific responsibility amenable to banks?

TABLE 21.3 List of questions included in the second section of the questionnaire

Number	Question
1	What is the Fineco's interpretation of the concept of biodiversity?
2	Which initiatives does Fineco Group back in favour of the FAI (Fondo Ambiente Italia)?
3	Which are the main actions on risk management?
4	Which are the main actions on business strategies?
5	Which are the main actions on sustainability reporting?
6	Which are the main actions on corporate governance?

TABLE 21.4 Steps for the reliability of findings

Type of validity	Steps
Internal validity	• Literature review
	• Analysis of relevant theoretical frameworks
External validity	• Selection of the case study more suitable for the qualitative study
	• In-depth details of the case company selected
Reliability	• Case study database
	• Description of the data collection process
	• Definition and implementation of the questionnaire administered during the face-to-face interviews
	• Triangulation of secondary and primary data sources

The Case of FinecoBank

FinecoBank (hereafter Fineco) is one of the most important FinTech banks in Europe. Listed on the FTSE MIB, Fineco offers a unique business model in Europe, combining advanced platforms with a large network of financial advisors. It offers a single account with banking, trading and investment services, through transactional and advisory platforms developed with proprietary technologies. Fineco is a leading bank in brokerage in Europe and one of the most important players in Private Banking in Italy, offering advanced and tailor-made advisory services. Since 2017, FinecoBank is in the UK with an offer focused on brokerage, banking and investment services. Fineco Asset Management was founded in Dublin in 2018, with the mission to develop investment solutions in partnership with top international asset managers.

Twenty-two years ago, in the Italian banking industry, Fineco SIM triggered a radical change, as a consequence of the launch of the first online retail trading service. One of the most relevant sources of the competitive advantage resides in the development in-house of consulting services and IT platforms that are more and more revolutionary and user-friendly. Along this line of reasoning, the business strategy rests on a sizeable network of financial advisories and mortgage agents. In this sense, a relevant competitive performance regards the attainment of the European leadership in online trading, in 2001.

At a closer look, in only two years 250,000 customers chose Fineco. The existing business model stems from the merger with UniCredit Xelion Bank which took place in 2008. Six years later, Fineco was listed in the FTSE MIB. In 2017, this bank is included in the index of large-cap European companies, namely in the Stoxx Europe 600. A key lever for the growing presence in the European context concerns a crucial cooperation with the best international asset managers so as to setting up an Irish company, named Fineco Asset Management.

The last prominent milestone in the Group's life cycle pertains to the exit strategy from the UniCredit Group, in 2019. Therefore, Fineco evolved into an independent public company, namely into an unusual ownership structure, in the Italian context.

Empirical Evidence and Discussion

Fineco's View on the Commitment of the Financial Industry to Sustainability

By considering the questions included in the first part of our questionnaire, we explored a general view on the main trends of sustainable finance and the investors' needs, at a global level. On this point, Dr. Foti provided us with an interesting standpoint on the main challenge that is affecting the finance sector. He said that investors are increasingly focusing on companies that meet certain characteristics consistent with ESG investment criteria. He argued that the transition to sustainable finance is "something that must be done, absolutely". To address this, he highlighted two important aspects within the banking sector. He said:

> The first one is linked to the offer. Recently the whole range of bank's products must come out with this well-known "quality mark", i.e. ESG, representing a revolutionary change for the entire asset management industry. The second aspect is related to what the bank actually does and which sustainable products it can offer. For instance, we can satisfy our retail customers' needs in both lending and investing, if there is increasing attention to ESG criteria. The Financial sector's activities affects the ecosystem in a light way, but they become decisive considering their impact financing a systematic and coherent approach to a sustainable development.

There is now an urgent demand for ESG scores assigned by rating agencies to companies. The CEO said that a higher rating means higher evaluation by financial analysts and financial markets. He stated that

> in this industry everything is seen in the perspective of increasing earnings: if I am a customer of a bank that respects ecosystems, I can increase my earnings. Broadly speaking, if our customers are treated well year after year, they become richer and the bank can take advantage of an increasing amount of capitals, and consequently become richer too.

He pointed out that *"The most important driver to sustainable development is bottom-up, as it comes from customers. Therefore the pandemic crisis has stimulated human consciousness on environmental issues"*.

We asked the CEO for comments on the responsibility of the banking sector in preserving our planet. He said that there is a very low contribution of banks to global biodiversity. Despite the fact that the banking sector appears to be less directly involved it is actually "the key mechanism of the economic system". He said that *"without the banking system everything stops in our economy"*. Now, customers' investment decisions are very attentive to ESG: for instance, they consider if a financial institution or a trader favours those companies with a sustainable strategy. Then, CEO argued that there is another side where the banks operate directly as lenders and here a very delicate matter opens:

> We are talking about sectors with a crucial weight on world GDP: think for example about the oil or the automotive sector. Banks are in a difficult situation, as an environmental sustainable path also needs to balance with the income statement. Fineco, thanks to its business model, is not involved in this problem, as it manages customer investments and doesn't lend money to companies, thus our task is certainly facilitated. On the opposite side, big traditional banks have this problem: deciding not to finance anymore oil companies, for example, has an immediate impact on revenues. I would like to point out the initiative taken by BlackRock, which sent a letter to all the CEOs of some companies in which they are invested, including Fineco, urging them to move in this direction.

As the CFO confirmed, the evaluation on the commitment of the Italian banking sector on environmental and biodiversity issues is very low. CFO stated that:

> In Italy the banking sector is not engaging so strongly in environmental management systems. For example, only one Italian bank obtained the official certification of its environmental management system in line with the European Commission EMAS (Eco-Management and Audit Scheme) Regulation n. 1221/2009. Thus, Fineco Group would be the first network bank in Italy to obtain the same certification which represents a very strict norm. We think that few Italian banks can obtain it.

As the Italian government can encourage the finance sector to preserve our ecosystem, the CEO believes that:

> The most effective movement comes bottom-up. I used to say that crisis usually stimulates people to do their best, and as a result, negative experiences are followed by big changes. When we refer to sustainability, sanctions are much less useful than stimulating people to act. For example, in Italy we have a serious problem connected to the very low quality of our real estate assets, especially in terms of energy efficiency. The Italian government has launched an environmental incentive, namely eco-bonus, that will have significant impacts on the environment and also on biodiversity. Fineco decided to support this incentive offering to its clients the best offer on the market to take in advance the tax earned with a sustainable renovation. For sure Fineco is not able to influence the production of coal reducing the flow of financing towards that industry, since we are not

committed on corporate loans, but it creates extremely advantageous conditions for our customers to reach the same goal. That's how we actively contribute to the virtuous circle.

Fineco and Its Sustainability Approach: A Focus on Biodiversity

Firstly to assess the Fineco's pathway towards sustainability (see Table 21.2), it is crucial to consider the firm's purpose and vision on sustainability topics as it is confirmed by some statements argued by CEO, CFO and CSR teams. The recent increasing interest in sustainable portfolio investments has been supported by the significant figures of new flows on sustainable funds (about $30.7 trillion at the start of 2018[32]) and records green bond issues. The asset management industry has been able to grasp and interpret this interest by providing investment funds that are more focused on ESG factors and in general on sustainability issues. More and more investors are starting to consider these issues and to align their investment decisions, along with this perspective. In this regard, an additional and interesting point derives from Fineco Group and particularly by Fineco Asset Management (FAM) that is an Irish asset management company wholly owned by Fineco Bank. Its aim was to develop the concept of sustainability within the increasing sensibility of investors to ESG issues by questioning if the sustainability of an asset manager is limited only to the products he builds or he must also deem a more transparent approach towards the customer. By considering these aspects, it is possible to extend the concept of sustainability by adding a new "gusset".

A new "label" named "No performance fees" has been launched by FAM to raise awareness of the entire asset management industry on the impact of performance fees on business sustainability and on the relationship with the final customer. As asset managers, there is an overall recognition of their great responsibility towards the planet and the sustainable investment strategies make it possible to fulfil this responsibility. To do this Fineco's sustainability concept includes a "fair price" for the benefits of all stakeholders, i.e. clients, financial advisors and shareholders. This approach is able to promote an extended interpretation of an "evolved sustainability" by applying a fair remuneration for the service provided to customers.

A "No Performance Fees" sticker allows all stakeholders to distinguish those investment funds and those asset managers who do not apply performance fees, an additional component of costs to the detriment of community savings. In short, Fineco Group's Personal Financial Advisors want to identify ourselves as fully sustainable operators.

This perspective is strongly linked to the Fineco's business model that since 1999 changed its customers' banking experience by promoting three key values: innovation, transparency and simplicity. Such a unique approach is based on the combination of the efficiency of digital channels and the expertise of the largest network of Fineco's financial advisors by suggesting a new concept of sustainability. Despite the importance to develop and offer sustainable investments, the attention on the respect of customers is particularly relevant for FinecoBank. Its mission focuses on offering high-quality services for customers using two key values: simplicity and continuous innovation that are part of the Fineco's strategy and affect the pathway to sustainability. In the same viewpoint, Fineco's CEO and General Manager Dr. Alessandro Foti confirmed this approach and provided a comprehensive insight on the most important features of the firm's sustainable-oriented practices. In this context, the main driver of Fineco's business model is represented by the firm's customers. All activities are focused on the satisfaction of the customers' needs that can be seen as a relevant factor for enhancing the Fineco's sustainable approach.

Along this line of reasoning, Dr. Foti affirmed that

> A very important aspect is how we relate to customers: Fineco has been built on great efficiency, but above all on great transparency and respect for the customer. Being a transparent company, respectful towards its customers, has a gigantic direct impact in the world of finance. For example, if we look at the financial wealth of Italians immediately available to be invested, we could estimate it in about 2.6 trillion euros, almost the same amount of our public debt. Just imagine if these 2.6 trillion would be invested more efficiently and with a more transparent relationship by intermediaries, yielding just 1% more: there would be a positive effect of 26 billion euros per year. Capitalization over 10 years would get to Italians something close to 300 billion euros, namely the UE Recovery fund. If we become a richer and more prosperous society, our respect for the environment can be enhanced. Some emerging countries cannot afford it, while a rich, prosperous country is more attentive to these issues. If people are wealthy, the environment around them is better.

This interesting standpoint goes beyond a traditional approach to sustainability by emphasizing the efficiency of the financial system which by producing wealth in the economic system can, albeit indirectly, make actions in favour of the protection of our planet more accessible.

Given that, Fineco is committed on two sides: on the one hand, it must guarantee its clients to invest in the correct direction and, on the other hand, Fineco itself is the object of investment being a listed company. Being a public company, it in turn can be included in investment funds. The financial company's impact on sustainability is less direct than a manufacturing firm but banks also have a significant influence on society. Therefore, Fineco reveals an increasing attention on sustainability issues, as it is confirmed by some initiatives. For instance, in December 2020, Fineco has officially adhered to the Principles for Responsible

Banking (PRB) of the UN Environment Programme, Finance Initiative. PRB represents a "unique framework for ensuring that signatory banks' strategy and practice align with the vision society has set out for its future in the SDGs and the Paris Climate Agreement".[33] Currently, around 220 banks, i.e. a third of the global banking industry, joined this initiative in collaboration with UN Environment Finance Initiative to pursue an enhancement of sustainable practices in the banking sector. These principles provide banks an effective support to embed sustainability at the strategic, portfolio and transactional levels, and across all business areas. In more detail, signatories' banks have to take three key steps: (1) analyze their current impact; (2) based on this analysis, they set targets where they have the most significant impact, and implement them; (3) publicly report on progress. Eighteen months after signing, banks must report on their impact, how they are implementing the principles, their targets and the progress they have made. Over four years, banks must have met all requirements.

In this perspective, Fineco signals its commitment to systematically implementing the three pillars of sustainability, i.e. economic, environmental and social, into the long-term business strategy. In more general terms, Fineco considers sustainability broadly from an environmental point of view while the specific topic of biodiversity is not explicitly stated, as it does not have an identity of its own in Fineco's strategy. Fineco's business does not consider biodiversity as a crucial issue or a strategic priority.

In line with the recent reports on the impact of the banking sector on the planet (Portfolio Earth, 2020), the main consequences on biodiversity may be related to the financing of particular sectors that may exert significant effects on ecosystems. In this sense, Fineco's CFO argued that:

> Biodiversity is not considered a central theme in Fineco's business model as it does not include corporate financing, therefore by simply giving financing to retail customers. The aspects related to corporate loans and the impact of non financial sectors linked to the loan portfolio are not part of Fineco's impact and therefore in our specific case it disappears, even if we recognize which represents a very relevant financial issue for the entire sector.

A clear linkage between Fineco's activity and biodiversity can be represented by two issues: the former is along the supply chain, since despite the fact that Fineco is a service company and it does not need for the supply of particular raw materials. However, Fineco has a supply component that concerns the use of paper, so consumption of paper derives from the management of woods and forests that affect biodiversity. Currently, Fineco is supplying 100% of the paper at the group level with FSC (Forest Stewardship Council) certification.[34] Therefore, this certification certifies a responsible forest management, which is also related to the protection of ecosystems in forest management for the production of paper used by Fineco. This year the pandemic crisis led 100% of employees to work from home and therefore not to use the company offices. Fineco had registered an increase and a push towards digitization (as stated by the CFO: "Fineco is a digital bank") and all paper consumption has therefore decreased considerably at the group level (20 tons less), in addition to the FSC certification.

As argued by the Fineco's CFO, the other fundamental aspect that can bind Fineco to biodiversity is represented by climate change. By considering that biodiversity is highly impacted (as confirmed by the European Green Deal) by the effects of climate change, this aspect concerns Fineco more directly and therefore an impact, albeit indirect, can also be detected on biodiversity. In this context, the Fineco's impact (direct impact on climate change and vice versa) is in any case quite limited because Fineco does not grant financing to corporate companies. Therefore in view of the loan portfolio, the impact is rather limited and therefore being dedicated to retail customers. Moreover, it is important to consider an additional point, as CFO said:

> The impact on climate change, however, is not limited to the business but also to the operativity of our offices. In this respect in this last year we started to implement an environmental management system to improve our environmental performance. This includes the whole aspect of greenhouse gas emissions and a more responsible use of resources as well as the use of the paper mentioned above. The norm of the reference environmental standard to which we are adapting, which is the European Commission EMAS (Eco-Management and Audit Scheme) Regulation n. 1221/2009, also provides for the assessment of any impacts on biodiversity.

In this context, given the lack of production sites that have a direct significant impact on biodiversity and above all, almost all of Fineco's operating sites are located in cities (such as Milan) that are already urbanized and therefore not close to protected areas. The management of green areas is not under Fineco's control and they cannot be considered a relevant or impacting issue. Apart from these considerations, Fineco is committed to collaborating with the Italian Environment Fund (FAI) to try to guarantee and support the protection of the Italian natural heritage and therefore both through sponsorship and donations to the FAI. Fineco is a Corporate Golden Donor of FAI by supporting several initiatives to preserve biodiversity in specific protected areas as well as historical and artistic heritage in Italy.[35] Additionally, Fineco is bringing forward some redevelopment works of the green areas of the city of Milan in collaboration with the Municipality of Milan and naturally also considered some particular needs regarding biodiversity in the redevelopment of green areas.

Moreover, the CEO emphasized the collaboration with FAI claiming that

All initiatives enhancing biodiversity in Italy are very important. Fineco is particularly sensitive to the enhancement of cultural heritage combined with environmental protection. The main objective of the collaboration with FAI goes in this direction. Enhancing cultural heritage aims to create a better ecosystem in supporting certain protected area. Another important aspect concerns our cities, where Fineco is engaged in the recovery of green areas while developing neighborhoods. For instance, we were pioneers in the creation of rent bike stations. This is very much in continuity with our philosophy: 1) how we structure the range of services for our customers; 2) how we manage the bank in the relationship with our customers. A company that is much more «virtual» than a manufacturing company can play a very significant contribution to protect the ecosystem.

By considering the external disclosure of the sustainability and environmental issues, accountability can enhance transparency and represent a useful tool to control and monitor the progress on the effective embeddedness on these topics, in the finance context. We asked CFO: *"Have you already structured them well or will they represent a milestone in the next financial or non financial communication?"* She replied that the Non Financial Statement 2020 is forthcoming. "These *topics will be published in the 2020 Non Financial Statement (published on 6th April 2021). Additionally, as an environmental certification requirement, Fineco should publish an additional specific environmental analysis document that will be published in July 2021"*.

We asked the CFO for additional topics: "How much complexity did this disclosure generate?". CFO replied that

> It is certainly still in the finalization phase of the environmental management system. It is a considerable effort; it is not a process limited to the sustainability or the real estate function. For instance, this effort deals with all aspects related to firm's buildings. This process analyses all aspects pertinent to the relations with our stakeholders. It should be examined what are the expectations of our stakeholders with respect to the management of environmental and climate risks which is also linked to the recent guidance of the European Central Bank (ECB).

This activity addresses and involves the human resources' function with regard to the training of employees and financial advisors over the environmental field, because they are part of the company resources and they have direct contact with the customers and the community at large. Still, CFO contended that

> We must do an activity to raise their awareness in such a way that they become Fineco's «ambassadors» in the environmental field. Moreover, the business function which is managing the legislative aspects in the

environmental field (i.e. legislation on waste and emissions and all environmental aspects in property management) is involved. The real challenge is being able to manage the entanglement of all these business functions including all business activities, or to develop all the products that consider the ESG criteria with respect of lending and investing activities. This aspect represents a very high effort. Other relevant topic is the formalization of all processes and information flows that lead to ensuring adequate control and management of all environmental aspects and an improvement in our performance (i.e. the flows governing the definition of our environmental objectives and the collection and publication of data regarding the environmental dimension).

Other important points concern the impact of biodiversity issues on the risk management function of the bank. We asked the CFO: *"How much this investment has impacted on risk policy and has required new company know-how: what room for improvement is there?"* and the CFO said that in 2019, a risk analysis was carried out by considering risk indicators and therefore the operational risks that could be related to ESG issues. In 2020, other activities were precisely carried out to implement the ECB's expectations regarding climate and environmental risks. In this sense, the operational risk dashboard was deepened and the Risk Appetite Framework (RAF) was integrated. Specific environmental key performance indicators (KPIs) were integrated into the RAF by managing environmental risks in an integrated way into the business risk management. It certainly did not have an impact on the risk management team, but it certainly did stimulate the risk management team to increase their skills to cope with this type of risk as well.

To integrate these considerations, we wanted to investigate the impact of environmental and biodiversity issues on Fineco's corporate governance. CFO explained that from 2019, an internal board committee dedicated to sustainability issues was established that was identified in the Governance, Appointments and Sustainability Committee. Then, starting from 2020, the Appointment and the Sustainability Committee has been changed and the latter committee has taken the name of Corporate Governance and Environmental and Social Sustainability Committee. Additionally, in Fineco there is an *ad hoc* management committee for sustainability led by the group's top management. There is also a dedicated sustainability office composed of the Head of the CSR Team and a Sustainability specialist.

In addition, we wanted to investigate the impact of COVID-19 on the Fineco's approach to environmental and biodiversity issues. CFO replied that in their group, the pandemic did not have a significant influence over the business strategy. She argued that

> We were already equipped to carry out activities remotely, at the business level in the relationship with customers. We had already digitised part of all business processes, so there was no need to physically meet to carry on the

activities. In the ESG field, all the choices and initiatives mentioned above had already been defined before the pandemic and therefore they were not particularly affected by this event. The pandemic raised awareness on these aspects but did not have a significant decision-making weight.

Finally, we wanted to explore to what extent ESG issues have changed Fineco's business model viewed from a strategic point of view and not conditioned by COVID-19. CFO said:

> I would see it as an upstream reasoning. As a Fineco group we "were born as sustainable", that is our corporate purpose and the mission is «to simplify the customer's life» by trying to provide excellent services at low cost. We were born with this idea of sustainability not immediately declined in ESG criteria but in a broader concept of social responsibility. Over the last few years, this essence of sustainability was declined in the ESG factors. Sustainability issues are growing even if we believe that demand from customers for ESG products and services will increase more and more in the future.

CEO confirmed that Fineco's governance path, risk management policy and business strategy implement a broader concept of sustainability, including all ESG concepts (Table 21.5). He stated:

TABLE 21.5 Responsible products and investment: an overview

Product/Service	Assets	ESG factors
Funds (55% out of 6,200 funds)	11.3 billion euros	ESG rating
Funds (40% out of 6,200 funds)	8.7 billion euros	MorningStar rating equal to "High" "Above average" and "Average"
ESG Private Value Lines	91.4 million euros	Best in Class approach
Core Pension Fund	182 million euros	Integration of ESG criteria
Green mortgage line	16 million euros (15% of the total number of mortgage loans)	Purchase of energy class A or B properties (max 1,000,000 euros or up to 80% of the value of the property)
Sustainable portfolio	135.6 million euros (0.9% Fineco portfolio)	Green and social bonds
FAM (Fineco Asset Management) Sustainable	not disclosed	Investment themes in line with the relevant socio-economic, environmental and technological factors
FAM (Fineco Asset Management) MegaTrends	25% of FAM Megatrends assets refer to sustainability megatrends	

We are structurally «forced» to go in that direction, as Fineco is one of the few real public companies listed on the Italian Stock Exchange. What does this mean? Fineco's owner is the market. More specifically, our main shareholders are BlackRock (9%) and Capital Management (5%), representing the elite of large institutional investors. Why do I say that we are «forced» to be sustainable? I would define the market ferocious and ruthless, because its goal is to earn important returns, which increase over time but which are sustainable and long-lasting. Today's earnings are not enough: calculating the present value involves not only current cash flows, but for how much time a company generates them. If a sustainable growth isn't respected, the market immediately punishes the company selling its stocks. Therefore, a public company would be immediately reported if the management would decide to ignore the sustainability, while a company with a controlling shareholder should answer to his goals, that may not necessarily coincide with those of the market: the history of finance is full of events where the controlling shareholder followed personal interests. Also, a significant part of my shareholder-approved compensation is linked to sustainability. If I wouldn't respect several parameters, my compensation would be less, as the whole top management.

Conclusion

Our analysis suggests that the biodiversity is too vague and abstract for most players in the finance industry to embed it into their processes and harness opportunities arising from it. In Italy, for instance, some industries (i.e. food and fashion) are committing to adopt effective actions and policies on animal welfare and other issues related to biodiversity and extinction risks. Financial institutions can be affected by natural capital and biodiversity risks, as they influence the businesses recipients of their landing or investing activities.[36]

The finance sector and mostly the banking industry has to define and improve its contribution to preserve our planet and ecosystems. In spite of an increasing development of guidelines and reports to support banks in implementing and reporting actions for climate change,[37] reporting of biodiversity issues has not been defined in an appropriate way. Investment funds and ESG ratings are including biodiversity issues, in their methodologies.[38] In addition, the topic of biodiversity finance is becoming well known in the finance context. As climate change has been recognized as the most important driver of the biodiversity loss, the association between these two issues leads to an enhancement of the biodiversity issues.

To make biodiversity bankable, it is important that final borrowers must meet at least one of the following conditions: (1) certified producers; (2) green list activities; and (3) nonstandardized measures. Banks must be equipped to control their involvement in financing companies that may have a direct or indirect effect on biodiversity. In this perspective, Fintech may play a relevant role in enabling banks to develop biodiversity preservation actions. Hence, banks can contribute to directly impact our planet by carrying out their business activities.

In this perspective, few banks are committing to improve their practices for instance by developing environmental policies to obtain specific environmental certifications (i.e. EMAS). In the Italian context, we selected one of the most important banks, i.e. Fineco, to illustrate best practices in managing environmental actions and policies. Fineco puts forth a very broad concept of sustainability by linking ESG issues to one of the most important key values, namely the respect of customers. As a network bank, the Fineco plays an active and proactive role in disclosing its commitment to environmental issues and in raising awareness into its network of financial advisors.

Despite the poor impact on biodiversity loss, Fineco acknowledges the relevance of these topics for the financial industry and it strongly supports several initiatives to preserve directly and indirectly biodiversity crisis, in Italy.

Acknowledgment

We would like to thank CEO, CFO and CSR teams for their availability and for supporting the development of the Fineco's case study.

Notes

1 IPBES (2019); Atkins and Atkins (2019); Atkins and Macpherson (2019).
2 Ceballos et al. (2017).
3 World Economic Forum (2020).
4 https://ec.europa.eu/info/sites/info/files/communication-annex-eu-biodiversity-strategy-2030_en.pdf.
5 https://ec.europa.eu/info/strategy/priorities-2019-2024/european-green-deal_en.
6 Cheng et al. (2007).
7 WWF Italy (2020).
8 Chan et al. (2013); Xu (2020).
9 http://www.millenniumassessment.org/en/index.html.
10 IPBES, 2019. Global Assessment Report on Biodiversity and Ecosystem Services. https://ipbes.net/global-assessment.
11 Keesing et al. (2010).
12 WWF Italy (2020).
13 Lugassy et al. (2019).
14 Zohdy et al. (2019).
15 WWF Italy (2020).
16 https://www.traffic.org/about-us/illegal-wildlife-trade/.
17 https://www.iucn.org/news/secretariat/202004/iucn-statement-covid-19-pandemic.
18 https://www.un.org/en/un-coronavirus-communications-team/calibrating-covid-19-crisis-response-sdgs.
19 https://www.un.org/sustainabledevelopment/biodiversity/.
20 BBFAW, 2018 https://www.bbfaw.com/about-us/.

21 https://www.barillagroup.com/en/groups-position/barillas-position-animal-welfare.
22 https://www.monclergroup.com/en/sustainability/partner/animal-welfare-and-traceability.
23 https://www.reutersevents.com/sustainability/finance-sector-must-go-beyond-business-usual-solve-biodiversity-loss-crisis.
24 https://naturalcapital.finance/blog/beyond-business-as-usual/.
25 https://www.financeforbiodiversity.org/.
26 https://www.cbd.int/sp/targets/.
27 Earth Portfolio (2020).
28 https://equator-principles.com/.
29 https://www.cbd.int/sp/targets/.
30 Eisenhardt (1989); Yin (2008).
31 Jones and Solomon (2013); Atkins and Atkins (2017); Atkins and Maroun (2018); Atkins et al. (2018); Corvino et al. (2021).
32 http://www.gsi-alliance.org/wp-content/uploads/2019/03/GSIR_Review2018.3.28.pdf.
33 https://www.unepfi.org/banking/bankingprinciples/.
34 Bianchi Martini et al. (2019).
35 https://finecobank.com/en/online/fai/.
36 ENCORE (2021).
37 UNEP FI (2021).
38 VigeoEiris (2019); Sustainalytics (2020).

References

Atkins J., Atkins B. (2017). *The Business of Bees. An Integrated Approach to Bee Decline and Corporate Responsibility*, Routledge, New York.

Atkins J., Atkins B. (2019). *Around the World in 80 Species: Exploring the Business of Extinction*, Routledge, UK.

Atkins J., Barone E., Maroun W., Atkins, B. (2018). From the big five to the big four? Exploring extinction accounting for the rhinoceros. *Accounting, Auditing & Accountability Journal*, Vol. 31, Issue 2, pp. 674–702.

Atkins J., Macpherson M. (2019). Developing a Species Protection Action Plan – An Integrated Approach for Taxonomies, Reporting and Engagement for the Financial Services Sector, Concept Paper circulated and presented at Investec Bank's Natural Capital, Species Extinction & Sustainable Financial Markets Event, 30th May.

Atkins J., Maroun W. (2018). Integrated extinction accounting and accountability: Building an ark. *Accounting, Auditing & Accountability Journal*, Vol. 31, Issue 3, pp. 750–786.

Bianchi Martini S., Corvino A., Doni F. (2019). Deforestation risk and the tissue industry in Italy. In Atkins J., Atkins B. *Around the World in 80 Species. Exploring the Business of Extinction* (pp. 273–285). Padstow Cornwall: Greenleaf Publishing Book Routledge Taylor and Francis Group, pp. 273–285.

Ceballos G., Ehrlich P.R., Dirzo R. (2017). Biological annihilation via the ongoing sixth mass extinction signaled by vertebrate population losses and declines, PNAS July 25 114 (30), https://doi.org/10.1073/pnas.1704949114

Chan J. F-W, Kai-Wang To K., Tse H., Jin D.-Y., Yuen K-Y. (2013). Interspecies transmission and emergence of novel viruses: Lessons from bats and birds. *Trends in Microbiology*, Vol. 21, Issue 10, pp. 544–555.

Cheng V.C.C., Lau S.K.P., Woo P.C.Y., Yuen K.W. (2007). Severe acute respiratory syndrome coronavirus as an agent of emerging and reemerging infection. *Clinical Microbiological Reviews*, Vol. 20, pp. 660–690.

Corvino A., Bianchi Martini S., Doni F. (2021). Extinction accounting and accountability: Empirical evidence from the west European tissue industry. *Business Strategy and the Environment*, pp. 1–15, doi: 10.1002/bse.2763

Dasgupta P., (2021). The Economics of Biodiversity: The Dasgupta Review available at https://assets.publishing.service.gov.uk/government/uploads/system/uploads/attachment_data/file/962785/The_Economics_of_Biodiversity_The_Dasgupta_Review_Full_Report.pdf, Last Accessed 31th March 2021.

ENCORE (2021). Embedding Natural Capital into Financial Decision-making Processes available at https://www.mfw4a.org/sites/default/files/resources/webinar_banks_as_agents_for_biodiversity_consolidated_compressed.pdf, Last Accessed 31th March 2021.

Eisenhardt K.M. (1989). Building theories from case study research. *Academy of Management*, Vol. 14, Issue 4, pp. 532–550.

IPBES Report (2019), Summary for policymakers of the global assessment report on biodiversity and ecosystem services of the Intergovernmental Science-Policy Platform on Biodiversity and Ecosystem Services, May, IPBES secretariat, Bonn, Germany https://doi.org/10.5281/zenodo.3553579.

Jones M.J., Solomon J.F. (2013). Problematising accounting for biodiversity. *Accounting, Auditing & Accountability Journal*, Vol. 26, Issue 5, pp. 668–687.

Keesing F., Belden L.K., Daszak P., Dobson A., Harvell C.D., Holt R.D., Hudson P., Jolles A., Jones K.E., Mitchell C.E., Myers S.S., Bogich T., Ostfeld R.S. (2010). Impacts of biodiversity on the emergence and transmission of infectious diseases. *Nature*, 468, pp. 647–665.

Lugassy L., Amdouni-Boursier L., Alout H., Berrebi R., Boëte F., Boulanger N., Cosson J.F., Durand T., de Garine-Wichatitsky, Larrat S., Moinet M., Moulia C., Pagès N., Plantard O., Robert V., Livoreil B. (2019). What is the evidence that ecosystem components or functions have an impact on infectious diseases? A systematic review protocol. *Environmental Evidence*, Vol. 8, Issue 4, https://doi.org/10.1186/s13750-019-0147-5.

Portforlio Earth (2020). Bankrolling Extinction, The banking sector's role in the global biodiversity crisis, available at https://portfolio.earth/, Last Accessed 31th March 2021.

Sustainalytics (2020). Company ESG Risk ratings, available at https://www.sustainalytics.com, Last Accessed 31th March 2021.

UN Environmental Programme Finance Initiative (2021), Collective Commitment to Climate Action, available at https://www.unepfi.org/wordpress/wp-content/uploads/2019/12/PRB-Collective-Commitment-to-Climate-Action.pdf

VigeoEiris (2019). Protection of biodiversity: Companies need to take action as scores remain quite limited, available at https://vigeo-eiris.com/wp-content/uploads/2019/05/VigeoEiris-UN-Biodiv-day-22-05-19.pdf, Last accessed on 31th March 2021.

World Economic Forum (2020). The Global Risks Report, available at https://www.weforum.org/reports/the-global-risks-report-2020, Last Accessed on 31th March 2021

WWF Italy (2020). Pandemie, l'effetto boomerang della distruzione degli ecosistemi. Tutelare la salute umana conservando la biodiversità (Pandemics, the boomerang effect of the destruction of ecosystems. Protecting human health by preserving biodiversity) https://d24qi7hsckwe9l.cloudfront.net/downloads/pandemie_e_distruzione_degli_ ecosistemi.pdf

Xu Y. (2020). Unveiling the Origin and Transmission of 2019-nCoV. *Trends in Microbiology*, Vol. 28, Issue 4, pp. 239–240, https://doi.org/10.1016/j.tim.2020.02.001

Yin R.K., (2008). *Case Study Research. Design and Methods*, Sage Publishing, New York, fourth edition.

PART IV

Extinction Engagement

How Investors Can Save Species

22

THE GLOBAL ASSET MANAGEMENT INDUSTRY'S RESPONSE TO THE BIODIVERSITY CRISIS

Krystyna Springer

This chapter provides an overview of the findings of an assessment of 75 global asset management firms and their approaches to biodiversity loss. It is based on a survey of the asset management industry carried out by the responsible investment organisation ShareAction, and it reflects the state of play with regard to investment and stewardship practices of the world's largest asset managers at the turn of a critical decade for biodiversity.[1]

This research was carried out with the aim of building momentum and pressure on the financial sector to accelerate its efforts to tackle the loss of biodiversity. While reversing the global species and ecosystem decline presents a complex challenge which calls for coordinated multi-stakeholder effort, the financial sector has a pivotal role to play in this mobilisation. The influence that it wields through the ownership and financing of businesses around the world cannot be overstated, and the resulting potential for change can and must be harnessed for the achievement of global biodiversity goals.

Methodology

The 2020 assessment of asset managers' approaches to responsible investment conducted by ShareAction draws predominantly on company responses to a comprehensive survey covering four themes: responsible investment governance, climate change, human and labour rights, and biodiversity.

The survey was developed in collaboration with a range of stakeholders, including civil society organisations, leading institutional investors and technical and industry experts. The questionnaire was structured in line with the Task Force on Climate-related Financial Disclosures (TCFD) reporting framework, following the four core recommendations on governance, strategy, risk management, metrics and targets[2] for all three thematic sections, and consisted of both multiple choice and open-ended questions.

DOI: 10.4324/9781003045557-27

Seventy-five of the largest asset management firms globally were invited to participate in the survey. Companies were shortlisted based on the size of their assets under management, according to the IPE Top 400 Asset Managers list,[3] and on their country of domicile, in order to ensure global coverage. The number of asset managers from the US was set at 20, and the number of European managers at 40, to allow for the inclusion of financial institutions from other regions. For the full list of asset managers including Assets under Management (AUM) and country of domicile, see Appendix 1.

The survey was sent to 75 shortlisted asset management firms, of which 92% agreed to participate. The remaining 8% had their questionnaire populated based on publicly available information and were given the opportunity to review their responses.

Following survey data audit and analysis, ShareAction published a series of research reports titled *Point of No Returns*,[4] which analysed aggregate performance on survey themes and contained recommendations for asset managers, asset owners and regulators. It also included a ranking of asset managers, which showed a breakdown of performance across the four main themes of the survey, thus representing the first global benchmarking of investors on biodiversity-related issues.

Survey responses were collected between July and October 2019. For the purpose of this analysis, these data were complemented with relevant information available in the public domain as of March 2020.

Biodiversity Section of the Survey – Questions

Asset managers participating in the survey were asked to provide responses to the following set of questions relating to biodiversity:

STRATEGY 1.1

Have you identified material biodiversity-related risks to your investments? Please outline these risks

Have you identified material biodiversity-related opportunities to your investments? Please outline these opportunities

STRATEGY 1.2

Have you identified positive biodiversity-related impacts of your investments? Please outline these impacts

Have you identified negative biodiversity-related impacts of your investments? Please outline these impacts

STRATEGY 2.1

Has biodiversity been integrated into your investment policy? Please select all that apply

- We have a policy on specific biodiversity risks and impacts covering all portfolios under management
- We integrate biodiversity into policies for high-risk sectors
- We broadly cover biodiversity in our responsible investment policy

Biodiversity is exclusively an investment consideration for funds and mandates labelled Environmental, Social and Governance (ESG), RI or similar

We do not have a policy relating to biodiversity

STRATEGY 2.2

What specific commitments does your biodiversity policy include? Please specify whether this consideration covers all portfolios under management or relates to specific ESG funds and mandates

RISK MANAGEMENT 1.1

When engaging with investee companies what are your main biodiversity priorities? Please select all that apply and specify whether this consideration covers all portfolios under management or relates to specific ESG funds and mandates

Ensuring a conservation or mitigation hierarchy approach is used where business operations directly or indirectly impact critical habitats, and threatened or endangered species

Certification to appropriate sustainability standards for investee companies' direct operations and/or suppliers (please elaborate)

Ensuring robust third-party Environmental Impact Assessments are conducted

Engagement on corporate strategy on biodiversity

Improved disclosure of the impact of business operations on biodiversity

Improved disclosure of the impact of suppliers on biodiversity

Other (please specify)

We do not have biodiversity engagement priorities

Please provide detail on your selected answer options, or any further comments

RISK MANAGEMENT 2.1

How do you integrate biodiversity risks and impacts into investment decisions?

Positive screening

Negative screening

Use of benchmarks/indices

Best-in-class approach

Use of ESG scores

Other (please specify)

We are developing an approach to integrating biodiversity into investment decisions

We do not assess and integrate biodiversity-related risks and impacts

Please describe how biodiversity risks and impacts are assessed. Please provide any further comments on how biodiversity-related risks and impacts are integrated

METRICS 1

Have you developed, or are you developing, metrics to assess and/or integrate biodiversity into investment decisions?

Biodiversity-related Risks and Impacts –
Investor Awareness

Biodiversity underpins all economic activity and the stability and resilience of our society. The World Economic Forum estimates that US$44 trillion of economic value generation – more than half of the world's total GDP – is moderately or highly dependent on nature and its services.[5] Yet the results of the asset manager survey suggest that investors are failing to recognise the urgency of the biodiversity crisis and the systemic nature of the risks that it poses to their portfolios.

When asked to identify biodiversity-related risks to their investments, survey respondents most commonly identified risks that could be classified as legal or regulatory. Thirty-two per cent of companies that responded to the survey provided detail on these types of risk, mostly in reference to liabilities associated with poor environmental management, difficulty in obtaining licences, and environmental regulation on pesticides and other chemical products. Reputational considerations were almost equally important in this context, with 29% of survey respondents describing reputational risks associated with the impacts of their investments on biodiversity. A quarter of those cited rising public awareness of nature loss as an important factor.

Noticeably, fewer responding companies showed concern with biodiversity loss as a source of other operational and market-wide risks. Fourteen per cent of survey respondents cited the disruption of supply chains among important biodiversity-related risks, linking it to the destabilisation of ecosystems, natural resource scarcity and the decline in natural protection function offered by, e.g. mangroves or coral reefs against extreme natural events. Nine per cent of respondents identified price volatility and rising raw material costs as a source of risk, which may be amplified by natural decline and ecosystem collapse.

When describing biodiversity-related risks to their portfolios, survey respondents typically focused on high-impact sectors, such as agriculture-, oil- and gas-related business activities, mining and infrastructure. Over a quarter of asset managers referred to each of these sectors in their responses. In contrast, very few respondents discussed investments in sectors highly dependent on nature, such as utilities (16% of respondents), pharmaceuticals (8%), beverages (1%) or apparel (1%).

The overriding focus on legal and reputational risks, and minimal consideration given to sectors highly dependent on nature, suggests that investor organisations generally have a poor appreciation for the existential threat that biodiversity loss poses to businesses. It is vital that investors deepen their understanding of risks stemming from the fundamental dependency of all economic activities on nature, to ensure that the loss of biodiversity is given adequate attention, and not simply regarded as another ESG topic.

In addition, only a handful of investors gave a nuanced account of biodiversity-related risks that conveyed a more sophisticated understanding of the interlinkages between the climate crisis and the loss of biodiversity. On the whole, relatively few respondents offered a description of biodiversity-related risks to their investments (61%), relative to the proportion of respondents who provided a description of risks associated with climate change (84%).

Still, fewer survey respondents offered evidence of having considered the impacts of their investments on biodiversity. Positive biodiversity-related impacts were described by 33% of respondents, who almost exclusively identified them in relation to thematic, green investment products, rather than mainstream investments. Negative impacts on biodiversity, identified by 32% of respondents, were mainly restricted to high-level, generalised observations (e.g. "deforestation") or individual case studies. In the case of the latter, examples given by survey respondents largely related to high-profile cases of environmental mismanagement, such as the BP Deepwater Horizon oil spill, or the Brumadinho dam disaster involving Vale, which indicates that the consideration of impacts by the majority of asset managers is often limited to controversy monitoring, rather than being part of a systematic approach.

As in the case of climate change, it is critical that investors consider the impacts of their investments on biodiversity loss, alongside the short- and medium-term risks that it presents to their portfolios. In line with the double-materiality approach proposed in the EU Non-Financial Reporting Directive,[6] asset managers have a better chance of fulfilling their fiduciary duty if the impacts of their investments on nature are adequately managed and accounted for. The financial materiality perspective alone is insufficient in the light of the urgent action needed to tackle the biodiversity crisis.

Engagement with Portfolio Companies on Biodiversity-related Issues

Stewardship is widely recognised as one of the most powerful tools that investors have at their disposal for achieving positive outcomes for people and the planet. Through engaging with companies, governments and regulators, asset managers can most effectively safeguard long-term outcomes for beneficiaries – ordinary citizens whose pensions and savings are being invested – and deliver real change.

Yet despite the potential that active ownership has for influencing markets and achieving real-world outcomes, few of the biggest investors globally have been using it as a means of addressing the systemic risks posed to their portfolios by biodiversity loss.

Survey responses show clearly that most of the biodiversity-related engagement carried out by the world's largest asset managers favours disclosure over action. Fifty-six per cent of the surveyed companies indicated that they had engaged with companies to request improved disclosure of the biodiversity-related impacts of companies' direct business operations and 45% suggested that they had engaged for more transparency on supply chain impacts.

In comparison, only 24% of investors surveyed indicated that they had engaged with companies to ensure that robust third-party Environmental Impact Assessments (EIAs) are conducted, and only 31% stated that they had engaged on certification for investee companies' direct operations and/or suppliers.

Furthermore, only 12% of managers indicated that they had engaged with investee companies on the use of a conservation or mitigation hierarchy approach. The Principles of Responsible Investment (PRI) has since come out in support of the mitigation hierarchy approach, suggesting that investors encourage their portfolio companies to use the framework as means of reducing negative impacts on biodiversity and driving positive biodiversity outcomes.[7] The framework has also been promoted as a potential delivery mechanism that could underpin the achievement of the goals of the Convention on Biological Diversity post-2020 agenda.[8] However, the results of the survey show that the mitigation or conservation hierarchy approach is not yet commonly used by the investor community.

Overall, only 49% of asset managers surveyed indicated that they had engaged with companies on corporate strategy on biodiversity. This finding in particular highlights the lack of investor awareness of the existential threat that unmanaged biodiversity-related dependencies and impacts may pose to portfolio companies' business models.

The focus on disclosure-oriented engagement is unsurprising in the light of the lacking corporate and asset-level data, which is widely cited by investors as a major barrier to assessing exposure to biodiversity-related risks.[9] Given the widespread concerns around the usefulness and comparability of the available data and value chain traceability, levels of engagement on transparency and improved disclosure are still insufficient. The results of the survey indicate that although investors frequently point to the existing data gaps as a major hurdle that prohibits further integration of biodiversity into the investment process, few are pushing portfolio companies to disclose better data.

Nevertheless, given the urgency of the biodiversity crisis, a continued focus on disclosure at the expense of demanding immediate action carries significant risks. It is worth noting that some of the world's most polluting companies stand out in their compliance with disclosure best practice. For example, the reporting produced by all of FTSE 100 electricity, oil and gas companies is fully aligned with the recommendations of the TCFD.[10] This suggests that by prioritising stewardship focused solely on disclosure, investors risk sidestepping more significant challenges and avoid tackling the real-world impacts of portfolio companies.

It is also worth noting that, when asked to specify which areas of engagement are prioritised in the context of biodiversity-related risks, 22% of survey respondents stated that they do not have biodiversity-related engagement priorities. This is in stark contrast with asset managers' approach to climate-related engagement:

only two among the disclosing companies indicated that they did not have any climate-related engagement priorities. While this is likely in part due to the fact that the relevance of climate-related impacts is less context-specific than in the case of biodiversity, this finding does confirm that, on the whole, asset managers are much less advanced in their approach to biodiversity-related engagement.

Proxy Voting – Policy Guidelines on Biodiversity-related Issues

Proxy voting is one of the most cost-effective and impactful engagement tools at asset managers' disposal. Often, it is also the only direct evidence that beneficiaries and asset owners have of their asset managers acting on their behalf on environmental and social issues.

The data collected through the survey did not allow for an assessment of whether investors have been leveraging this tool to support or file biodiversity-focused shareholder resolutions. However, an analysis of asset managers' publicly available proxy voting guidelines showed that very few of the reviewed policy documents contained explicit guidance for proposals relating to the disclosure and management of company impacts on biodiversity.

Only 7% of voting policies included a general commitment to vote in favour of increased transparency with regard to the wider environmental impact of company operations, typically including toxic emissions, resource use and waste management. Among these policies, only one contained an explicit commitment to support proposals asking companies to abstain from operating in environmentally sensitive areas or using products produced from materials extracted from such areas. This finding further highlights investor preference for disclosure-over action-focused engagement.

Themes of Biodiversity-related Engagement

A qualitative analysis of survey responses showed that deforestation in soft commodity value chains had been the most frequent topic of biodiversity-related engagement undertaken by asset managers. While the sustainable sourcing of palm oil featured most prominently, a small number of respondents also cited instances of engagement on other commodities that are known to be the main drivers of tropical deforestation, such as soy, cattle, rubber, timber and pulp.

Notably, engagement on these topics appears to have taken place in large part through collaborative investor initiatives. Initiatives mentioned most frequently by survey respondents included the PRI Investor Working Group on Sustainable Palm Oil, the PRI-Ceres Investor Initiative for Sustainable Forests covering cattle and soybean supply chains, and engagement on issues linked to intensive animal production facilitated by FAIRR.

Other themes of biodiversity-related engagement received significantly fewer mentions across the survey. Only 5% of investors indicated that they had engaged on overfishing and other ocean health issues, 4% mentioned instances of engagement on company impacts on pollinator populations and 3% stated that they had engaged on the protection of the World Heritage Sites.

The predominance of deforestation-related engagement can likely be attributed to the fact that, although investors have been engaging on certain biodiversity-related issues for a number of years, the outcomes of engagement appear to have been linked more often to climate- rather than biodiversity-specific objectives.

On the whole, asset managers' responses provided very little evidence of investors having a stewardship approach built on a nuanced understanding of biodiversity loss as a systemic and portfolio-level risk. Some survey respondents suggested that their organisations' engagement on biodiversity issues was limited because of the prioritisation of governance, climate change or human rights engagement, and none of the responding companies provided evidence of having an overarching engagement programme on biodiversity covering their whole portfolio.

Investor Transparency on Engagement Activities

As investors build up their engagement programmes on biodiversity, it is important that they ensure sufficient transparency around these efforts. Comprehensive reporting on engagement is crucial to ensuring accountability; it enables clients and other stakeholders to determine whether engagement strategies result in sufficient progress. In recognition of this, clauses referring to the disclosure of active ownership activities have been included in the stewardship codes of several countries,[11] as well as in the EU's Shareholder Rights Directive II.[12]

While the survey did not include indicators on the disclosure of biodiversity-related engagement specifically, the results of the analysis showed that, on average, the quality of reporting on engagement on environmental issues remained low.

Notably, 36% of the assessed asset managers had not disclosed any information about their engagement activities publicly at the time of the survey. A further 24% of asset managers, while providing a certain level of transparency around the type and methods of engagement, had not published any information on the degree to which stated engagement objectives had been achieved.

In addition, at the time of the survey, 45% of the assessed asset managers provided no systematic disclosure on how they voted on individual resolutions at companies' annual general meetings. Of the asset managers that regularly disclosed their proxy voting records, only 28% included rationales for their voting decisions.

The lack of transparency around outcomes of stewardship activities prevents stakeholders from building an understanding of what happens when company dialogue is not constructive and calls into question the efficacy of engagement. For an overwhelming majority of the assessed asset managers, publicly available reporting did not allow to determine whether a clear escalation strategy had been put in place and consistently applied. Only a small minority of leading investors offered evidence of having time-bound objectives and procedures for when these objectives had not been met, with the latter including co-filing or voting for shareholder resolutions, withholding support from the board or, ultimately, divesting.

Without significant improvements in the quality of public disclosure around engagement on environmental issues, it will remain difficult to scrutinise the efforts made by individual financial institutions to combat biodiversity loss and evaluate the progress being made on the issue by the industry as a whole.

Biodiversity Risk Assessment and Integration Approaches

Overall, the results of the survey indicate that biodiversity remains a marginal consideration in ESG integration and analysis within the asset management industry. Survey responses suggest a high degree of reliance on third-party ESG rating providers, with 65% of asset managers indicating that they integrate biodiversity risks and impacts into the investment process through the use of ESG scores. Only a small proportion of these asset managers gave evidence of having a proprietary scoring system, which integrated third-party data, as well in-house analysis, and included biodiversity-specific criteria. A small number of investors indicated that they carry out additional analysis using non-governmental organisation (NGO) research, tools and datasets, such as ENCORE, SPOTT or TRASE.

Considering asset managers' reliance on third-party data, it is clear that ESG research and rating agencies have a critical role to play in the mainstreaming of biodiversity risks and impacts in the investment decision-making process. The concerns aired more widely around ESG data, providers' diverging methodologies, ratings discrepancy and lack of transparency[13] are no less relevant in the case of biodiversity. There is also a great deal of variation in the degree to which different ESG agencies include and weigh biodiversity indicators in company questionnaires and the wider research process. Investors should therefore be aware of the limited insight that third-party data offer into the impacts of companies on the ground.

The next most popular approach to biodiversity risk integration among survey respondents, after the use of ESG scores, was the use of negative screening. Forty-four per cent of the companies surveyed suggested that they use filters excluding companies with negative impacts on biodiversity, or particularly high exposure to biodiversity-related risks. However, the description of screening activities provided by these asset managers revealed a great deal of variation with regard to the nature of the screening criteria and levels of transparency across the industry. It is also important to note that almost none of the mainstream asset management companies within the scope of the survey appeared to apply biodiversity-specific screening criteria to all portfolios. The vast majority of asset managers using negative screening appeared to be doing so exclusively in relation to ESG thematic funds.

Organisational Strategy on Biodiversity

In order to enable informed decision-making, it is crucial that clients and other stakeholders have access to information that allows them to determine whether asset managers' long-term strategies sufficiently incorporate biodiversity risk considerations and are aligned with global biodiversity goals.

However, an analysis of the publicly available investment policies of the 75 asset managers surveyed showed that investors were still a long way from having coherent organisation-wide strategies on biodiversity. None of the asset managers included in the analysis had published a dedicated policy on biodiversity covering all portfolios under management, which is particularly striking in the light of the fact that a fifth of the institutions within the sample had standalone climate change policies or position statements on the issue. This finding supports the overall conclusion that investors are much less advanced in their thinking about the risks associated with the loss of nature than those linked to climate change, despite these crises being deeply interlinked.

Only 32% of the assessed asset managers mentioned biodiversity, natural capital or ecosystem protection in their investment policies. For the majority of these, the policy did not outline a clear approach that the organisation was taking to the protection of biodiversity, and none of these asset managers made any overarching commitments. About 13% of managers had sectoral or commodity-specific policies which considered biodiversity and which included more detail on investors' approaches to specific biodiversity-related issues. A small number of these included issue-specific commitments, typically with regard to palm oil certification by portfolio companies, or deforestation.

Recommendations for Asset Managers

As the analysis presented in this chapter demonstrates, despite the continued dramatic decline in the health of ecosystems and accelerating extinction rates, biodiversity loss has remained an issue largely neglected by the asset management industry. The vast majority of the world's most influential asset managers included in this analysis have yet to grasp the underpinning role that biodiversity plays in sustaining the stability and resilience of society and the economy as a whole.

The lack of investor awareness of portfolio companies' impacts and dependencies on biodiversity puts at risk both the interests of beneficiaries and the continued stability of the financial system. It is now key that the asset management industry swiftly adopts and implements ambitious strategies that ensure that biodiversity risks and impacts become an integral part of all decision making, and which guarantee both the resilience of the global financial system and a healthy planet.

In the context of this analysis, it is strongly recommended that asset managers and other financial institutions:

- Ensure accountability for biodiversity-related responsible investment issues at the senior executive and board level.
- Ensure adequate resourcing with capacity and expertise internally to assess and manage the complexity of biodiversity-related risks to portfolios. Ensure that staff training on biodiversity-related risks is systematic, incorporates external expertise and covers key decision-makers.
- Develop dedicated policies on biodiversity that cover all portfolios under management, with a particular focus on high-priority sectors.[14]
- Ensure that the policy framework is complete with biodiversity-specific voting and engagement guidelines, with an emphasis on a clear escalation strategy that includes time-bound objectives.
- Improve the quality of corporate engagement by placing greater emphasis on direct action on negative impacts of business operations on biodiversity, in parallel to improved disclosure. Engage with companies on mapping their value chains as a critical first step to understanding their biodiversity footprint.
- Engage with third-party service providers to encourage improved transparency and ensure that biodiversity impacts and dependencies are adequately captured in company assessments.
- Collaborate and share knowledge on measurement approaches to improve understanding of portfolio impacts and dependencies on biodiversity.
- Conduct and publicly disclose the results of biodiversity impact and dependency analysis of portfolios.
- Set science-based targets to reduce negative and increase positive impacts on biodiversity; monitor and publicly report on progress towards achieving them.
- Proactively educate clients on the systemic risks presented by biodiversity loss.

Concluding Thoughts

It should be noted that the analysis presented in this chapter provides a backwards-looking snapshot of the global asset management industry's approach to biodiversity loss and does not capture all currently emerging developments or the changing perceptions around nature loss within the investor community in the wake of coronavirus disease 2019.[15]

A number of efforts are currently underway, both within the industry and across the regulatory landscape, offering hope for rapid improvement on the alarming levels of investor inaction emerging from this analysis.

Several policy developments, particularly in Europe, should help drive better disclosure and practices by both corporate and financial actors. They include, notably, the EU Taxonomy Regulation, the Non-financial Reporting Directive and the Sustainable Finance Disclosure Regulation, all of which could play a positive role in moving the industry forwards on accounting for nature-related impacts of investments. With respect to country-level disclosure regulation, the French regulator has continued to set the pace, most recently replacing the pioneering Article 173, which has required investors to disclose their climate-related risks since 2016, with a new article 29, which integrates biodiversity into reporting requirements. The new decree will require all French financial institutions, including banks and insurers, to disclose nature-related risks, as well as strategies for reducing biodiversity impacts.[16]

In parallel, the launch of the Finance for Biodiversity Pledge[17] in September 2020 shone a light on the rising level of ambition from a number of industry players. As of March 2021, 37 financial institutions have signed the pledge, thereby making a public commitment to assessing the impacts of their investments on biodiversity, setting and disclosing science-based nature-related targets and reporting publicly on their contribution to biodiversity goals by 2024.

In February 2021, ShareAction finalised the *Point of No Returns* research report series by releasing the fifth, concluding report, which outlined leading industry practice on all main themes of the 2019 asset manager survey, bringing together examples of ambitious biodiversity commitments and engagement strategies from a small vanguard of asset managers.[18] While ShareAction observed a degree of progress on the topic made by a number of the surveyed asset managers, some of the leading examples came from smaller investor organisations, not included in the initial assessment, with the noteworthy example of ACTIAM's zero net biodiversity loss commitment across its portfolios by 2030.[19]

Perhaps one of the most telling signs of the rapid increase in investor interest in biodiversity has been the publication of a natural capital engagement strategy by BlackRock, the world's largest asset manager, in March 2021. BlackRock, alongside the other "Big Three" companies, has overwhelmingly dominated inflows into the asset management industry over the past decade and currently holds positions of 5% or more of the shares of almost all of the companies in the S&P 500,[20] which gives it an outsized amount of influence over corporate performance on ESG issues. BlackRock's new natural capital engagement strategy outlines expectations for portfolio companies in relation to the disclosure and management of nature-related impacts and dependencies and, notably, states that the investor may vote against the re-election of board directors at companies which have not effectively managed, overseen or disclosed natural capital-related risks. The release of this strategy is a reason for cautious hope that the world's most influential asset manager, having come under increased scrutiny for its environmental record in the past,[21] will finally step up to the challenge.

There are also multiple collaborative efforts underway to address some of the technical constraints associated with the limited availability of decision-useful biodiversity data. The launch of the Informal Working Group (IWG) for the Task Force on Nature-related Financial Disclosures (TNFD)[22] comprising of 73 financial and private firms has been an important milestone in the development of a unified reporting framework for nature-related risks. In an important departure from the TCFD, the TNFD's counterpart framework for climate, the IWG has agreed to adopt a double-materiality approach for biodiversity-related disclosures. This means reporting companies will be required to disclose the impacts of their operations and investments on nature, as well as biodiversity-related risks to their business. The framework will be tested early in 2022 before being made available worldwide the following year.

In addition, a number of investors and technical expert organisations have been involved in the development of impact measurement approaches, such as the Global Biodiversity Score, the Biodiversity Footprint for Financial Institutions, the Biodiversity Impact Metric or the STAR (Species Threat Abatement and Recovery) metric.

While these efforts are positively encouraging, they remain some way from being finalised and mainstreamed. Given the complexity of biodiversity, it is unlikely that any single metric or methodology becomes the "silver bullet" and that the investment community will coalesce around a single approach immediately. It is therefore paramount that financial institutions do not delay action while they wait for methodologies to be formalised and, instead, use the already available knowledge and data tools to target the most destructive business activities and sectors.[23]

In the last two decades, the international community has twice set ambitious ten-year biodiversity targets without succeeding in delivering on its commitments.[24,25] To avoid the catastrophic consequences of another lost decade for nature, the financial industry must now step up to the challenge and show a sense of urgency and ambition that matches the magnitude of the biodiversity crisis.

Appendix

TABLE A1 Listof companies selected for ShareAction's 2019 asset manager survey

Asset manager	AUM ($ billion)[26]	Country	Disclosed
Aberdeen Standard Investments	778.13	UK	Yes
Aegon Asset Management	381.65	Netherlands	Yes
Alliance Bernstein	554.06	USA	Yes
Allianz Global Investors	597.53	Germany	Yes
Amundi Asset Management	1,711.13	France	Yes
APG Asset Management	568.32	Netherlands	Yes
Asset Management One	503.94	Japan	Yes
Aviva Investors	477.45	UK	Yes
AXA Investment Managers	894.99	France	Yes
Baillie Gifford	242.77	UK	Yes
Bank J. Safra Sarasin	174.41	Switzerland	Yes
BlackRock	6,377.75	USA	Yes
BMO Global Asset Management	260.18	Canada	Yes
BNP Paribas Asset Management	683.12	France	Yes
Bradesco Asset Management (BRAM)	185.46	Brazil	No
Caisse de dépot et placement du Québec (CDPQ)	238.14	Canada	Yes

(Continued)

Asset manager	AUM ($ billion)[26]	Country	Disclosed
Capital Group	1,805.02	USA	Yes
China Asset Management Company	153.76	China	Yes
Columbia Threadneedle Investments	494.34	UK	Yes
Credit Suisse Asset Management	396.18	Switzerland	Yes
Deka Investment	318.37	Germany	Yes
Dimensional Fund Advisors	576.64	USA	Yes
DWS Group	841.99	Germany	Yes
E Fund Management	190.76	China	No
Eastspring Investments	187.85	Singapore	Yes
Eurizon Capital	371.97	Italy	Yes
Fidelity International	323.08	UK	Yes
Fidelity Investments (FMR)	2,403.65	USA	No
Franklin Templeton Investments	753.80	USA	Yes
GAM Investments	162.75	Switzerland	Yes
Generali Investments	555.58	Italy	Yes
Goldman Sachs Asset Management	1,288.37	USA	Yes
HSBC Global Asset Management	468.66	UK	Yes
Insight	790.59	UK	Yes
Invesco	936.75	USA	Yes
Investec Asset Management	140.44	UK	Yes
J.P. Morgan Asset Management	1,765.27	USA	No
Janus Henderson Investors	370.49	UK	Yes
La Banque Postale Asset Management	259.17	France	Yes
Legal & General Investment Management	1,329.05	UK	Yes
Lyxor Asset Management	158.62	France	Yes
M&G Investments	474.43	UK	Yes
Macquarie Asset Management	368.15	Australia	Yes
Manulife Investment Management	391.77	Canada	Yes
MEAG	302.94	Germany	Yes
Mellon Investments Corporation	569.27	USA	Yes
MetLife Investment Management	586.93	USA	Yes
MFS Investment Management	490.68	USA	Yes
Mitsubishi UFJ Trust and Banking Corporation	643.48	Japan	Yes
Nikko Asset Management	211.43	Japan	Yes
NN Investment Partners	236.21	Netherlands	Yes
Nomura Asset Management	433.11	Japan	Yes
Nordea Investment Management	266.80	Denmark	Yes
Northern Trust Asset Management	960.66	USA	Yes
Nuveen	971.94	USA	Yes
Ostrum Asset Management	415.87	France	Yes
PGGM	261.57	Netherlands	No
PGIM Fixed Income	1,392.54	USA	Yes
Pictet Asset Management	197.25	Switzerland	Yes
PIMCO	1,754.73	USA	Yes
RBC Global Asset Management	335.68	Canada	Yes
Robeco	193.25	Netherlands	Yes
Royal London Asset Management	154.96	UK	Yes

Asset manager	AUM (\$ billion)[26]	Country	Disclosed
Santander Asset Management	213.75	Spain	Yes
Schroder Investment Management	571.39	UK	Yes
SEB	223.09	Sweden	No
State Street Global Advisors	2,779.52	USA	Yes
Sumitomo Mitsui Trust Asset Management	787.65	Japan	Yes
Swiss Life Asset Managers	229.29	Switzerland	Yes
Swisscanto Invest by Zürcher Kantonalbank	163.56	Switzerland	Yes
T. Rowe Price	990.33	USA	Yes
UBS Asset Management	796.18	Switzerland	Yes
Union Investment	388.66	Germany	Yes
Vanguard	4,907.45	USA	Yes
Wellington Management	1,079.45	USA	Yes

Notes

1 Greenfield, P. (13 January 2020). UN draft plan sets 2030 target to avert Earth's sixth mass extinction. *The Guardian*. Available online at: https://www.theguardian.com/environment/2020/jan/13/un-draft-plan-sets-2030-target-to-avert-earths-sixth-mass-extinction-aoe [accessed 24 March 2021].

2 TCFD (2017). *Final Report: Recommendations of the Task Force on Climate-related Financial Disclosures*. Available online at: https://www.fsb-tcfd.org/recommendations/ [accessed 13 November 2020].

3 IPE (2018). *The Top 400 Asset Managers*. Available online at: https://www.ipe.com/Uploads/k/x/x/Top-400-Ranking.pdf [accessed 13 November 2020].

4 ShareAction (2020). *Point of No Returns: A ranking of 75 of the world's asset managers approaches to responsible investment*. Available online at: https://shareaction.org/research-resources/point-of-no-returns/ [accessed 13 November 2020].

5 World Economic Forum (2020). *Nature Risk Rising: Why the Crisis Engulfing Nature Matters for Business and the Economy*. Available online at: http://www3.weforum.org/docs/WEF_New_Nature_Economy_Report_2020.pdf [accessed 13 November 2020].

6 European Commission (2019). *Guidelines on reporting climate-related information*. Available online at: https:// ec.europa.eu/info/publications/non-financial-reporting-guidelines_en#climate [accessed 18 November 2020].

7 PRI (2020). *Investor action on biodiversity: discussion paper*. Available online at: https://www.unpri.org/download?ac=11357 [accessed 13 November 2020].

8 Sinclair, S. *et al.* (2020). The Conservation Hierarchy: Underpinning the Post-2020 Biodiversity Framework. Available online at: https://www.cbd.int/doc/strategic-plan/Post2020/postsbi/biodiversify1.pdf [accessed 13 November 2020].

9 PRI (2020). Investor action on biodiversity: discussion paper.

10 Innes, A. (2019). Market incentives are stacked against companies that try to care about climate change. *LSE Business Review*. Available online at: https://blogs.lse.ac.uk/businessreview/2019/06/08/market-incentives-arestacked-against-companies-that-try-to-care-about-climate-change/ [accessed 13 November 2020].

11 FLCT Global (2019). Interactive Portal to Global Stewardship Codes. Available online at: https://www.fcltglobal.org/interactive-portal-to-global-stewardship-codes/ [accessed 13 November 2020].

12 Directive (EU) 2017/828 of the European Parliament and of the Council of 17 May 2017. Available online at: http://data.europa.eu/eli/dir/2017/828/oj [accessed 13 November 2020].

13 Poh, J. (11 December 2019). Conflicting ESG Ratings Are Confusing Sustainable Investors. *Bloomberg.* Available online at: https://www.bloomberg.com/news/articles/2019-12-11/conflicting-esg-ratings-are-confusing-sustainableinvestors [accessed 13 November 2020].

14 UN Environment Programme, UNEP Finance Initiative and Global Canopy (2020). *Beyond 'Business as Usual': Biodiversity targets and finance. Managing biodiversity risks across business sectors.* UNEP-WCMC, Cambridge, UK. Available online at: https://www.unepfi.org/wordpress/wp-content/uploads/2020/06/Beyond-Business-As-Usual-Full-Report.pdf [accessed 13 November 2020].

15 Atkins, J., Doni, F., Hassan, A. and Maroun, W. (2020) Revealing Plato's 'Shadow Kingdom': Rendering pandemic risk explicit in integrated extinction accounting and engagement, working paper presented at the *Egyptian Online Seminars in Business, Accounting and Economics* on 22nd May.

16 TNFD (17 March 2021). France's Article 29: biodiversity disclosure requirements sign of what's to come.

17 Finance for Biodiversity Pledge. Available online at: https://www.financeforbiodiversity.org/ [accessed 13 November 2020].

18 ShareAction (2021). Point of No Returns Part V – Leading Practice. A ShareAction leading practice guide for *asset managers on responsible investment.* Available online at: https://shareaction.org/wp-content/uploads/2021/02/ShareAction-Leading-Practice-2021.pdf [accessed 24 March 2021].

19 ACTIAM's Sustainable Investment Policy describes how it aims to reach zero net biodiversity loss and zero net deforestation in its portfolios by 2030. While in investment decision-making and active ownership activities, ACTIAM addresses both goals, measuring progress on biodiversity across portfolios is still challenging. As there are currently no reliable measurement approaches in this area, ACTIAM has been focusing on measuring the major causes of biodiversity loss (climate change, water use, and deforestation) and participating in working groups to develop scientifically grounded methods to measure biodiversity impacts.

20 Bebchuk, L. A. and Hirst, S. (2019). The Specter of the Giant Three. *Boston University Law Review,* 99:721-741. Available online at: https://ecgi.global/sites/default/files/working_papers/documents/finalbebchukhirst2.pdf [accessed 24 March 2021].

21 ShareAction (2020). *Voting Matters 2020. Are asset managers using their proxy votes for action on climate and social issues?* Available online at: https://shareaction.org/wp-content/uploads/2020/11/Voting-Matters-2020.pdf [accessed 24 March 2021].

22 UNEP Finance Initiative (25 September 2020). *Task Force on Nature-Related Financial Disclosures (TNFD) gathers momentum.* Available online at: https://www.unepfi.org/news/themes/ecosystems/tnfd-informal-working-group/ [accessed 13 November 2020].

23 UN Environment Programme, UNEP Finance Initiative and Global Canopy (2020). Beyond 'Business as Usual': Biodiversity targets and finance. Managing biodiversity risks across business sectors.

24 Jowit, J. (29 April 2010). International failure to meet target to reduce biodiversity decline. *The Guardian.* Available online at: https://www.theguardian.com/environment/2010/apr/29/international-failure-biodiversity-decline [accessed 13 November 2020].

25 Greenfield, P. (15 September 2020). World fails to meet a single target to stop destruction of nature – UN report. *The Guardian.* Available online at: https://www.theguardian.com/environment/2020/sep/15/every-global-target-to-stem-destruction-of-nature-by-2020-missed-un-report-aoe [accessed 13 November 2020].

26 AUM values are based on the IPE "The Top 400 Asset Managers" 2018 list and converted from EUR to USD based on historical exchange rates.

23

ENGAGING TO PROTECT AND RESTORE BIODIVERSITY

Sonya Likhtman

Introduction

Engagement, in this context, is a way through which investors and investor representatives influence companies to address environmental, social and governance (ESG) issues. It is one method through which investors can contribute to solving global challenges; engagement on topics ranging from gender equality to bribery and corruption has led to positive outcomes in many sectors and scenarios. Academic studies have also shown that successful engagement is correlated with improved financial returns.[1]

The variation of life on Earth at genetic, species and ecosystem levels is defined as 'biodiversity'. Engagement on biodiversity has, on the whole, been limited in breadth and depth until recent years. While investor focus on climate change has been impressive, with demonstrable progress in encouraging companies to commit to net-zero emissions with time-bound targets, it has somewhat dominated the discourse. A sustained focus on climate change remains vital in order to achieve the goals of the Paris Agreement and, if successful, would help to protect biodiversity. However, to properly protect and restore biodiversity, this investor agenda must be broadened.

As environmental risks are systemic and tightly intertwined, we need more holistic, system-based thinking to solve these complex challenges and create socio-economic systems that operate within planetary boundaries. Addressing climate change is, of course, an important part of halting biodiversity loss. However, a direct biodiversity lens is also needed, and we are pleased to see the topic gain traction in the financial community. This is happening in part because ecosystem collapse and declining biodiversity pose real and substantial risks to companies and their investors. Simultaneously, protecting and restoring biodiversity offer a range of opportunities for innovative companies and investors with a long-term outlook.

DOI: 10.4324/9781003045557-28

This chapter outlines how investor engagement with companies is a key means by which biodiversity loss can be halted and reversed. It highlights the reasons why biodiversity should command more attention from investors, followed by a section that introduces our expectations of companies along the dimensions of governance, measurement, targets, strategy and disclosure. The chapter features case studies of engagements that support biodiversity and ecosystem health: preventing deforestation, improving ocean sustainability and transitioning to regenerative agriculture. It concludes by offering some practical suggestions for engaging on biodiversity.

EOS at Federated Hermes

Equity Ownership Services (EOS) at Federated Hermes (EOS) represents a broad range of institutional investors, who seek to be active stewards and owners of their beneficiaries' assets, including the shares and credit instruments issued by the companies in which they invest. EOS engages with these companies to promote long-term, sustainable returns. As of 30 June 2021, EOS advises on behalf of over $1.75 trillion of assets held by institutional investors.

EOS' philosophy is one of the holistic returns. We have developed long-standing relationships with board directors and senior management representatives at companies around the world over more than 15 years of stewardship. Our conversations, guided by trust and common goals, often offer the external validation that is needed to build an internal case for change; we help to equip companies with the research, evidence and business case for taking transformational action that will lead to better outcomes for the company, the environment and society. Research on EOS' engagement activity has found that engaged companies generate higher annualised returns and that successful engagement leads to reductions in downside risk.[2]

Many of the social and environmental issues we engage on are interconnected. For instance, there are multiple links between climate change mitigation and adaptation, preventing human rights abuses, transitioning to sustainable food systems and reversing biodiversity loss. We seek to align our engagements with the Sustainable Development Goals (SDGs). While two of the SDGs – Life Below Water and Life on Land – are explicitly linked to biodiversity, analysis shows that the decline of biodiversity and ecosystems will undermine progress towards 80% of the assessed SDG targets.[3]

Why Biodiversity Matters to Investors

Without having quantified it, many companies and therefore investors derive significant value from nature. The first valuation attempt was made in 1997, when Robert Costanza and colleagues estimated that $33 trillion per year was generated from ecosystem services and natural capital.[4] The research group reissued their estimate in 2014 at over four times higher (between $125 and $145 trillion per year).[5] Various further attempts have been made over the years, including the recent conclusion that over half of global gross domestic product (GDP) is moderately or highly dependent on nature.[6]

These figures should not be surprising; our economies and societies are deeply embedded in nature, rather than existing alongside it. Nature, and the biodiversity within it, is our life support system through the ecosystem services it enables and sustains. Our life on Earth critically depends on the water cycle, clean air and the provision of food. Healthy soils in which the cycling of organic matter, carbon sequestration, and the regulation of nutrients function smoothly enable food crops and other plants to grow. Ecosystem services also include climate regulation, protection from natural hazards, pollination and many more invaluable functions. Healthy levels of biodiversity, including amongst plants, animals and microorganisms, enable ecosystem services to function effectively and retain resilience to change.

All businesses, to varying degrees, are dependent on the common goods provided by nature. If we are to avoid a continuation of the 'tragedy of the commons', companies and their investors must play a more proactive role in protecting them. As outlined in Table 23.1, the loss of biodiversity poses material business risks to many sectors, while presenting opportunities that can be grasped by transitioning to nature-positive business models. The decline of ecosystems and ecosystem services also presents a systemic risk to the financial system and the global economy.[7] The risks to human health became apparent through the coronavirus disease 2019 (COVID-19) pandemic, which has brought our unsustainable relationship with other species to the forefront. Research shows that human activities – the exploitation of wildlife through trade, hunting and land-use changes that result in habitat destruction – create more opportunities for the transmission of viruses from animals to humans.[8]

Despite the immense value of biodiversity, it has not routinely been considered in the context of either risk management or strategic decisions by the private sector. The lack of attention on the issue has also contributed to the ongoing depletion of species, with the Living Planet Index showing an average 68% decrease in mammal, bird, amphibian, reptile and fish population sizes between 1970 and 2016.[9] The comprehensive study of nature by the Intergovernmental Science-Policy Platform on Biodiversity and Ecosystem Services (IPBES) revealed that up to 1 million species are at risk from extinction, out of a known 8 million species, and that the rate of extinction is accelerating.[10] As ecosystems exist in a delicate balance and feature numerous interdependencies between species, the risk of dangerous tipping points is also increasing.

The challenge of addressing biodiversity risks in the private sector is that it is generally difficult, if not impossible, to trace the extinction of a single species back to individual company actions. We can conclude that if a company's activities are contributing to the destruction of a habitat, such as through indirectly causing deforestation or requiring the expansion of agricultural land in the supply chain, the company is complicit in causing species decline. However, the

TABLE 23.1 Summary of key risks and opportunities for companies

Supply capacity	Some sectors are almost completely dependent on ecosystem services and therefore healthy levels of biodiversity throughout their supply chains. These sectors include agriculture, food and beverage, forestry, household products and cosmetics. Many companies look increasingly likely to face direct challenges in sourcing raw materials due to disruptions to pollination, soil health and other ecosystem services that enable their business model.
Consumer	Consumers are progressively indicating their preference for greater sustainability and transparency through purchasing patterns. As the risk and impact of biodiversity loss gains greater public attention, it will become another lens through which consumers can assess and develop preferences around companies and products. Companies that are found to be responsible for deforestation, oil spills in precious ecosystems and any other form of biodiversity decline are likely to face severe reputational and financial risks.
Market	It is estimated that 'nature-positive' solutions could create approximately $10 trillion in business opportunities and almost 400 million jobs by 2030[11]. Companies should be proactive and innovative in developing nature-positive operations, products and supply chains. Doing so will improve the resilience of their business model, enable them to realise significant business opportunities and genuinely contribute to the SDGs.
Policy and legal	Companies are likely to face increasing regulations relating to biodiversity, including penalties to hold them to account for ongoing environmental damage. Similar to the Paris Agreement for climate change, countries and companies will be expected to deliver global biodiversity goals. The EU biodiversity strategy already targets the protection of at least 30% of land and seas by 2030. It also features ambitions to increase organic agriculture to 25% of total EU agriculture, halve the use of the most hazardous pesticides and reverse the decline of pollinators.

causes and effects are difficult to quantify and express with certainty. Furthermore, company supply chains are generally extensive and complex, meaning that there may be gaps in knowledge about the geographical reach of a company's impact. Even if all this information is established, there are no single metrics – like CO_2e – that would allow us to easily compare between species and ecosystems.

Yet, these excuses – being too far removed from the species themselves or the challenges of measurement – can no longer be used as a reason for inaction. On the contrary, we need to accelerate the rate and scale of action; the mindset of taking nature for granted and assuming its permanence must change. According to the World Economic Forum, three systems are responsible for endangering 80% of threatened or near-threatened species.[11] These systems are food, land and ocean use; infrastructure and the built environment; and energy and extractives.

Companies operating within these systems must urgently make the necessary transformations to their own operations and supply chains. Investor engagement with companies can help to influence the pace and direction of change in order to halt and reverse biodiversity loss.

Engagement Priorities and Expectations

Companies' relationship with nature can be characterised by impacts and dependencies. We have identified the following sectors as having high biodiversity impacts and dependencies: consumer goods and retail, agrochemicals, mining and materials, oil and gas, utilities, construction and real estate, and finance. Our engagement with companies seeks to understand the ways in which biodiversity and ecosystem services are relevant to companies, be this through their sourcing practices and supply chains, in the construction of new sites on land, especially if this is an ecologically important habitat, or through the way their operations interact with surrounding ecosystems.

The first engagement priority is to encourage companies to assess the extent to which their business models are dependent on biodiversity and ecosystem services, and the potential risks and opportunities associated with this dependency. The second engagement priority is for companies to understand, mitigate and reverse the negative impact their operations and supply chains are having on biodiversity and ecosystems. This will include mitigating their contribution to the drivers of biodiversity loss, such as climate change, pollution and land-use change. Companies must acknowledge how central nature is to their long-term success and take responsibility for actively contributing to its preservation and restoration.

Given the extent of biodiversity loss, conserving existing biodiversity will not be enough; it will also be necessary to restore biodiversity and the capacity of ecosystems. As such, we expect companies to work toward implementing measures that will have an overall net-positive impact on biodiversity. While the commitment may be at the organisational level, much of the work required to ensure a net-positive impact on biodiversity will be conducted at a local level.

Governance

We expect companies to establish strong governance and oversight for biodiversity; in our opinion, this is a necessary prerequisite for success. Climate change has become an important board-level issue and the company's relationship with nature can be an organic extension to this conversation. The board should work to understand the company's key risks, dependencies and impacts in relation to biodiversity and ecosystem services; it should take responsibility for ensuring that the company's operations and supply chain make a positive contribution to nature. Through voting and other forms of stewardship, board directors will increasingly be held accountable for ensuring sustainable land use throughout the supply chain, including eliminating links to deforestation. Good governance of this issue includes advocating for the protection of nature through public policy, as well as working with governments and peers to ensure that effective regulatory frameworks are developed and enforced. Biodiversity risks and opportunities should be deeply integrated into all relevant processes, including risk management, business strategy, supply chain management, procurement, research and development, and operations.

Measurement

A priority for many companies will be to improve the understanding of the company's relationship with nature. This may require additional internal or external expertise to be brought in. Measuring a company's dependence and impact on biodiversity is challenging, as the systems are multifaceted, and impacts are situation-specific. However, frameworks and metrics are emerging and will improve as adoption by companies increases. The Cambridge Institute for Sustainability Leadership has compiled a list of tools and data that can support companies in measuring their relationship with nature.[12] Options, depending on what is most relevant for a company, include an environmental profit and loss assessment and the healthy ecosystem metric framework. Building on the widespread adoption of the Task Force for Climate-related Financial Disclosures (TCFD), the Task Force for Nature-related Financial Disclosures (TNFD) is planning to release a reporting framework to help companies measure their nature-based risks. An impact and dependency assessment, even if qualitative at first, will help companies to understand where their most material challenges are, which may be sourcing from a particular region, reliance on a commodity, or a key stage of the production process. In many cases, companies' contributions to the decline of biodiversity will be through high greenhouse gas emissions, significant land use, unsafe levels of pollution and other such pressures, some of which may already be measured. Companies will benefit from understanding their relationship with nature; the outcomes of this work will enable them to build nature-positive operations, supply chains and products.

Targets

We strongly encourage companies to aspire to have a net-positive impact on biodiversity at the organisational level, including throughout the value chain. The net-positive principle follows the four stages of the mitigation hierarchy[13]: companies should avoid the impact to the extent possible; minimise the remaining impact; rehabilitate the land and habitat where possible; and, as a last resort, offset the remaining impact at a suitable location. Research on previous corporate commitments to no net-loss or net-positive impact on biodiversity highlights the need for more science-based criteria and more transparent reporting of progress towards the commitments.[14] Initial guidance on setting Science-Based

Targets for Nature has been published, providing a five-step guide to setting science-based targets and introducing the AR^3T Action Framework (avoid, reduce, restore and regenerate and transform).[15] The goal will require companies to have a good grasp of where their most material-negative impacts are, as well as the levers that can be pulled to reverse these impacts. For instance, a food production company sourcing high volumes of corn will be able to influence how the corn is produced, including the extent to which soil health and biodiversity on growing sites are core considerations within the farming process. A mining company that is winding down a site will play an important role in ensuring that the land is rehabilitated to become a thriving habitat for native plant and animal species. Kering, a luxury fashion company, committed in 2020 to have a net-positive impact on biodiversity by 2025 by regenerating and protecting an area about six times its total land footprint.[16] For some companies, aspiring to have a net-positive impact on biodiversity for new and existing sites, projects or products will be a first step to achieving a net-positive impact on biodiversity at the organisational level. BP, for instance, announced in 2020 its goal to achieve a net-positive impact on biodiversity in new projects from 2022.[17] We recognise that having a net-positive impact on biodiversity as an organisation is a challenging goal, but one that is critical to the long-term restoration of biodiversity and the continuity of ecosystem services.

Strategy

Once a company has identified its material dependencies and impacts on biodiversity and ecosystem services, it will be able to design impactful interventions to enable it to have a net-positive impact on biodiversity. The goal should be to integrate nature considerations into risk management and strategic decisions taken throughout the company. The highest dependencies and impacts for many companies are likely to be found in the supply chain, so improving supply chain oversight and engagement will be a key aspect of the biodiversity strategy. The strategy may target particular geographical areas, commodities and processes. It may include nature-based solutions to address the dual challenges of climate change and biodiversity loss, as well as nature-focused innovation and new product development. This includes technology and artificial intelligence products for monitoring changes in land use and deploying alternatives to chemical fertilisers that do not damage soil and aquatic biodiversity. As explored further in the case studies, preventing deforestation, improving ocean sustainability and transitioning to regenerative agriculture may be relevant pillars of biodiversity strategies for some companies. Certain interventions are likely to overlap with existing initiatives on climate change and water, as they are closely linked to biodiversity and sustainable land use. For instance, existing work on reducing greenhouse gas emissions, eliminating links to deforestation or promoting sustainable agriculture can be strengthened through a biodiversity lens and more systems-based thinking. Much of the work to protect and restore biodiversity will need to be done through coalitions and partnerships due to the scale, urgency and complexity of the challenge.

Disclosure

Companies should regularly report on their approach, including the process for assessing biodiversity dependencies and impacts, the long-term goals, the assumptions used in developing a strategy to achieve these goals, and the progress made towards them. It should follow emerging best-practice disclosure frameworks, such as the TNFD. Investors, consumers and other stakeholders will increasingly be interested in how companies think about nature-related risks and opportunities and how the approach is governed.

Case Studies

Preventing Deforestation

Halting and reversing tropical deforestation in particular is essential for avoiding the consequences of severe climate change and biodiversity loss. However, in spite of continued public and investor attention, deforestation and forest degradation continue. Alarmingly, the rate of deforestation has increased in Asia, Africa and Latin America during the COVID-19 pandemic.[18]

We have been engaging with a range of companies on deforestation for many years. One example is a Malaysian company that produces and processes palm products and natural rubber. It has plantations in Indonesia, Malaysia and Liberia. EOS has been engaging with the company since 2012, following allegations of deforestation and poor labour standards. Our engagement objectives have focused on sustainable palm oil production (SDG 12 and 13) and supply chain labour standards (SDG 8).

Since our initial engagement, the company has achieved Roundtable on Sustainable Palm Oil (RSPO) certification for its operation in Malaysia, in an effort to curb deforestation. The company has also adopted a group-wide sustainability policy, including establishing consequences for suppliers who are in breach, and a programme to support smallholder suppliers to attain RSPO certification. It has demonstrated a proactive approach to addressing supply chain labour issues and strengthened its labour standards and disclosure. We continue to engage on the company's overall sustainability action plan, including its no-deforestation commitments.

Companies that source palm oil, soy, beef and leather, pulp and paper, amongst other relevant commodities, must urgently commit to clear timelines for eliminating deforestation from their supply chains. The commitment should cover all commodities, regions and suppliers, including indirect suppliers.[19] We expect companies to communicate a clear strategy for how a deforestation-free supply chain will be achieved through implementation measures, monitoring, independent verification and collaboration. Companies that can achieve traceability of commodities back to the source will be best placed to achieve a deforestation-free supply chain.

Improving Ocean Sustainability

Oceans provide livelihoods for millions of people around the world, enable climate regulation and are vastly biodiverse. However, warming and acidification, loss of oxygen and changes in nutrient supplies have placed ocean ecosystems under severe stress.[20] Engaging on sustainable fish sourcing, pollution and waste, climate change adaptation and mitigation, and the circular economy can help to support ocean sustainability.

We engage with a global leader in recreational marine products that produce marine engines, parts and accessories and recreational boats. Studies have found that lakes with high boat traffic experience a higher growth of algae and kick-up of sediment, affecting water quality and clarity.[21] Every year in the USA an increasing number of recreational fibreglass boats reach their end of life without a sustainable option for disposal – many are abandoned on land or in coastal areas, harming the natural ecosystem.

One of our engagement objectives for the company relates to end-of-life recycling of fibreglass vessels (SDG 12 and 14): we would like the company to establish an approach, in collaboration with value chain partners, to enable collection and recycling of fibreglass boats. Since 2018, the company has been supporting the Rhode Island Fibreglass Vessel Recycling Pilot Project initiated by the Rhode Island Marine Trades Association. The project is exploring solutions for the sustainable disposal of fibreglass boats by dismantling and reprocessing fibreglass hulls into alternative materials, as well as other opportunities to preserve value.

We have also engaged with the company on product development (SDG 7 and 14) and carbon reduction (SDG 7 and 13), which will support ocean ecosystem health. Through engagement, we are encouraging the company to develop a more explicit green product suite of engine and boat offerings. We would also like to see the company commit to a long-term plan for carbon-neutral production.

Transitioning to Regenerative Agriculture

Approximately half of the world's habitable land is now used for agriculture, with 77% of that proportion being used for animal grazing or growing crops for animal feed.[22] As agricultural land increases, less land is left for forests, grasslands and other natural ecosystems that provide habitats for wild species.

The need to transition to more sustainable forms of agriculture is evident. Industrialised farming requires high chemical inputs, promotes monocropping and destroys the soil's natural ability for carbon sequestration. This contributes to climate change and the loss of biodiversity. With 690 million people still undernourished[23] and the global population expected to reach 9.7 billion by 2050, the challenge is how to feed a growing number of people sustainably. While the exact definition varies, regenerative agriculture is based on principles and practices that protect soil quality, improve water flow and increase levels of biodiversity.[24] It seeks to restore the soil's natural ability to absorb and retain carbon, minimises chemical inputs and integrates crops with animals and forestry.

We are engaging with global food and beverage companies on their approach to regenerative agriculture (SDG 2, 12, 13 and 15). We have probed the level of ambition in the regenerative agriculture strategy of one US-headquartered staple food manufacturer, building on a previous engagement on watershed sustainability. We explored the scale and speed of transformation it is seeking to achieve for a range of ingredients and sourcing regions. With a UK-headquartered beverage company, we have explored how regenerative agriculture will fit into its 2030 sustainability strategy. We also questioned how the inputs and outcomes of its work, in terms of biodiversity, carbon and other indicators, will be measured and disclosed. We have started a conversation with a Swiss-headquartered food and beverage company about how regenerative agriculture will help it to achieve its net-zero by 2050 goal.

Companies with agricultural supply chains should actively encourage and support farmers in transitioning to regenerative agriculture. By setting targets to source ingredients from regenerative agriculture and working with farmers to implement the change, companies can contribute to a system-wide change in how food is produced. The transition will play a critical role in mitigating climate change and restoring biodiversity. Innovation and technological disruption, such as precision agriculture, vertical farming and laboratory-grown proteins will play an important role alongside regenerative agriculture.

The Practicalities of Engaging on Biodiversity

As with all engagements, it is necessary to work out the levers through which one can drive change. Who are the key stakeholders to speak to within a company? Are any board members particularly open to the biodiversity agenda and therefore likely to be key agents in extinction governance? Can previous discussions on climate change, the circular economy or sustainable food systems be naturally extended to include biodiversity and encourage systems-based thinking? Site visits to key locations or operations that may interfere with local habitats may also be important tools. For instance, an insightful aspect of our engagement with a pulp and paper company was a visit to its managed forest plantations. In instances where engagement is not proceeding well, it may be necessary to escalate the engagement; methods include using voting power to signal disappointment at the lack of action (as we already do by recommending votes against directors at companies where we think climate change risks and opportunities are being inadequately managed) or through filing shareholder resolutions.

We can learn valuable lessons from investor engagement on climate change, including the need for clear goals, consistent messages and common frameworks. The value of collaboration is also apparent; to date, over 500 investors with more than US $47 trillion in assets under management have signed up to the Climate Action 100+ initiative,[25] sending a message to companies on climate change that is loud and clear.

To support engagement efforts, it can be useful to involve NGOs and other expert organisations. This is especially true for a complex and multifaceted challenge like protecting and restoring global biodiversity levels and transitioning to socio-economic systems that operate within planetary boundaries. Stronger regulatory frameworks and improved enforcement around the world are necessary parts of the picture, so the role of investors in public policy engagement is equally important.

Conclusion

While biodiversity and ecosystem services form the basis of our economies and societies, they remain overlooked as key value drivers and risks by companies and their investors. The value of nature needs to urgently be acknowledged and internalised by key economic actors. Investor engagement with companies can contribute to the goal of halting and reversing biodiversity loss. Given the significant decline of biodiversity, conserving valuable ecosystems and species must be complemented with effective measures to restore biodiversity around the world. We therefore encourage companies to implement measures that will have an overall net-positive impact on biodiversity throughout their operations and supply chains. The goal should be accompanied by strong governance, effective measurement, an impactful strategy and regular disclosure.

Notes

1 Dimson, Elroy, Oğuzhan Karakaş, and Xi Li. "Active ownership." *The Review of Financial Studies* 28.12 (2015): 3225–3268.
2 Hoepner, A.G.F., Oikonomou, I., Sautner, Z., Starks, L.T., and X.Y. Zhou. (2020). ESG Shareholder Engagement and Downside Risk. ECGI Finance Working Paper 671/2020.
3 UN sustainable development blog
4 Costanza, Robert, et al. "The value of the world's ecosystem services and natural capital." nature 387.6630 (1997): 253–260.
5 Costanza, Robert, et al. "Changes in the global value of ecosystem services." *Global environmental change* 26 (2014): 152–158.
6 World Economic Forum and PWC, Nature Risk Rising (2020).
7 Finance Watch, Making Finance Serve Nature (2019).
8 Johnson Christine K. et al. (2020) Global shifts in mammalian population trends reveal key predictors of virus spillover risk. *Proc. R. Soc. B.*28720192736
9 WWF and ZSL, Living Planet Report (2020).
10 Intergovernmental Science-Policy Platform on Biodiversity and Ecosystem Services (IPBES), Global Assessment Report on Biodiversity and Ecosystem Services (2019).

11 World Economic Forum and AlphaBeta, The Future of Nature and Business (2020).
12 University of Cambridge Institute for Sustainability Leadership (CISL 2020). Biodiversity Loss and Land Degradation: An Overview of the Financial Materiality.
13 IUCN, Net Positive Impact on biodiversity (2016).
14 de Silva, et al. "The evolution of corporate no net loss and net positive impact biodiversity commitments: Understanding appetite and addressing challenges." Business Strategy and the Environment 28.7 (2019): 1481–1495.
15 Science-Based Targets for Nature: Initial Guidance for Business (2020).
16 Kering, biodiversity strategy (2020).
17 BP, biodiversity position (2020).
18 FT, Global deforestation accelerates during the pandemic.
19 Ceres, The Investor Guide to Deforestation and Climate Change (2020).
20 Mingle, Jonathan. "IPCC Special Report on the Ocean and Cryosphere in a Changing Climate." (2020): 49–51.
21 Asplund, Timothy R. *The effects of motorized watercraft on aquatic ecosystems.* Wisconsin: Wisconsin Department of Natural Resources, 2000.
22 Our World in Data, Half of the world's habitable land is used for agriculture.
23 FAO, The State of Food Security and Nutrition in the World (2020).
24 regenerativeagriculutredefinition.com
25 climateaction100.org

24

BIODIVERSITY LOSS AND ITS IMPACT

A Practical Implementation in Portfolio Construction

Clarisse Simonek and Carmine de Franco

Introduction

Biodiversity refers to all the variety of life that can be found on Earth (plants, animals, fungi, and microorganisms) as well as to the communities that they form and the habitats in which they live. The impact of businesses on nature such as pollution, climate, and deforestation are harming biodiversity and threatening species. Approximately 1 million of the world's 8 million species are at risk of extinction within a few decades unless powerful measures are put in place to stop the negative development. The targets set to halt biodiversity loss by 2020 were not met (IPEBS, 2018). Countries have been unable to identify the main drivers behind biodiversity loss, to implement adequate legislation, or to gather the necessary financial resources to stop the exploitation of species, the report concludes. As a result, we are experiencing an extinction rate estimated as being 1,000 times higher than the background (pre-human) rate, thereby threatening to induce our planet's sixth mass extinction (Díaz et al., 2019).

Loss of biodiversity is not only a tragedy for nature but also a major problem for humanity and the economy. The knock-on effects will harm people – and businesses – that depend on biodiversity for their survival. On a planet totally deprived of biodiversity, there is no life. As an example, 75% of the global food crop types, with an economic value of up to USD 577 billion, rely on animals for their pollination). The disappearance of natural capital is the second major risk factor the world faces in the next ten years, according to the Davos Forum Annual Global Risks Report of 2019. To put the urgency in perspective, the long-run economic damages of greenhouse gas emissions are estimated at

DOI: 10.4324/9781003045557-29

around USD 1.7 trillion per year. Those from biodiversity loss are estimated to range between USD 2.0–4.5 trillion per year (Evison & Knight, 2010).

Investors and Biodiversity

This level of damage, however, does not have to materialize. The financial sector can play an important role to halt the global loss of biodiversity. Investors can take a lead in two key ways. First, they can support the development of a robust methodology for measuring biodiversity loss and use it in investment decision-making. It would enable investors to allocate assets towards companies that operate in environmentally sustainable ways and produce biodiversity-positive technologies. Second, fund managers and asset owners can embed biodiversity protection at the heart of their approach to responsible investment by engaging with issuers to disclosure, monitor, and manage their impact on biodiversity. Constructive engagement with government and collaboration with reporting initiatives would be particularly relevant given the complexity of the subject and the need for different industrial processes and consumer behavior to address it.

While we focus on impact, at times indicators and action on impact on biodiversity and risks from biodiversity loss overlap. Where that is the case, incorporation of these issues by companies and investors could contribute to greater resilience for companies, investment portfolios, and the economy as a whole.

Quantitative Indicator

If investors are to contribute to the reversion of this trend, robust indicators on the impact on biodiversity are needed. A physical, quantitative indicator is a measurement of the real impacts a company has on the environment. The measurement is usually expressed in a tangible unit (e.g., tons of greenhouse gas (GHG)), conducted ex post based on data published by the companies or estimated when such data are unavailable. Quantitative indicators that measure the physical impact of biodiversity make it possible to demonstrate the impact of an investment portfolio and display progress as capital is steered to activities that are less harmful. Eventually, science-based targets for biodiversity could even be implemented. Such type of indicator also allows investors to more effectively prioritize engagement to increase awareness on those companies that have the highest negative impact on biodiversity.

We acknowledge that physical, quantitative indicators are challenging to develop and pose considerable methodological hurdles. Given the complexity of biodiversity itself, a quantitative indicator is even more challenging than most of those put forward to date. At this stage, many responsible investors prefer to stick with qualitative Environmental, Social, Governance (ESG) reports or multicriteria indicators, which is understandable. Nonetheless, the ambition to go beyond, even with hurdles and setbacks on the way, remains.

Physical, Quantitative Indicators

The Stockholm Resilience Centre's concept of 'planetary boundaries' (Steffen et al. 2015) is an effective model to illustrate what society's impact is on biodiversity loss. The framework is based on nine critical environmental processes that influence the healthy functioning of the biosphere and portrays Earth's natural tipping points (i.e., points with a high risk of no recovery). Two of the planetary boundaries are considered as 'core', because of their fundamental importance for the biosphere: climate change and biosphere integrity (e.g., biodiversity loss and extinctions). One of the biosphere integrity's components, genetic diversity, is estimated to already be beyond the zone of uncertainty; that could mean that, left unaddressed, the planet could be at high risk.

The same academics who developed the concept of planetary boundaries also developed the indicator for mean species abundance (MSA). The MSA compares the abundance of species in a pristine ecosystem to the abundance of species in an ecosystem under human-induced pressure. The indicator ranges from 0 to 1: 1 means that the abundance of species is intact and 0 means that all original species are (locally) extinct. This indicator models the impact of human activity pressures (Schipper et al., 2019) and can be used from project-level assessment through to a portfolio biodiversity footprint (Lammerant et al., 2019). The academics involved in the development of the planetary boundaries and the MSA calculate a 'safety boundary' of Earth at an MSA of 0.72. Perhaps unsurprisingly, our society has crossed this boundary and is now close to 0.65. While much needs to be done to revert this trend, the indicator provides stakeholders a science-based target to strive for.

There are other indicators developed by or in partnership with academia: (1) the Biodiversity Intactness Index (BII), (2) the Potential Disappearance Fraction (PDF), and (3) the Species Threat of Abatement and Recovery (STAR). The BII is an indicator that focuses on species abundance of an intact environment compared to a human-impacted environment. The main difference between MSA and BII is that every hectare is given equal weight in MSA, whereas BII gives more weight to species-rich areas, and the MSA compares changes in populations to a 1970 baseline, rather than to primary vegetation (Brink, 2006). The PDF is an ecosystem-level indicator that measures the rate of species loss in a specific area or volume of water over a year. The limitations on the PDF are that it excludes invasive species and overexploitation which are two key human-induced drivers and is biased to species living in moderate climates (Slay, 2011) (Lammerant, 2018). The STAR is a species-level indicator that links the risk of extinction of endangered species with human activities. It calculates the sum of risks of extinction of species weighted by their threat status and thus enables the identification of regions high in threatened species. STAR has two main limitations. First, it focuses strictly on the International Union for Conservation of Nature (IUCN) species and not species more broadly. Second, because it is one-dimensional (i.e., considering only species and not ecosystem), it could inadvertently lead to 'allowing' activities in pristine environments where there are no threatened species (Lammerant et al., 2019).

ESG Data Providers

Even though physical, quantitative biodiversity indicators exist, they remain largely underused in the investment industry. One of the main reasons is the lack of data, both in terms of reporting by companies as well as compiling or modeling by ESG data providers. A brief review of the three main ESG data providers indicate that biodiversity is considered within their impact frameworks, however remains largely a qualitative score. Two ESG data providers consider companies' impact on biodiversity within their Sustainability Development Goals (SDGs) framework as part of SDG 14, life below water, and SDG 15, life on Earth. The scores are a qualitative assessment that incorporates companies negative and positive impact via products, services and operations (using policies as proxies), and controversies related to biodiversity loss. The third ESG data provider calculates the percentage of companies' revenue that is deemed to contribute to biodiversity, such as sales of organic food or of sustainable water technology. While this is an initial proxy for a company's positive impact on biodiversity, it would need to be complemented with negative impacts in order to provide a full picture of a company's impact. The current offers by these providers are a first step in helping investors consider biodiversity within their investment decision-making, yet do not calculate or consider a company's effective biodiversity footprint.

Case Study: Biodiversity in the Food Industry

We integrated biodiversity in the portfolio construction of an investment strategy focused on the food industry value chain, including producers, distributors, retailers, supermarkets, and restaurants. The food sector is particularly relevant for biodiversity, as its impact on sustainability and on biodiversity is significant. Kok et al. (2018) attribute almost 60% of the terrestrial biodiversity loss regarding mean species abundance to the agriculture and forestry sectors.

We incorporated biodiversity by utilizing an innovative dataset, developed by the environmental data provider Iceberg Data Lab, which measures a company's MSA footprint that allows us to compare it with those of peers. The choice of the MSA was due mostly to availability, as at the time it was the only physical, quantitative indicator dataset, we identified with significant coverage of listed companies worldwide (though restricted to the food industry at the time). While all indicators have strengths and shortcomings, we were comfortable with the choice of MSA as it is widely used by the United Nations' Intergovernmental Science-Policy Platform on Biodiversity and Ecosystem Services (IPBES) and Intergovernmental Panel on Climate Change (IPCC), as well as the Organisation for Economic Co-operation and Development (OECD). We believe that convergence of indicators and methodologies across key stakeholders such as governments, companies, and investors is critical, if not a requirement for efficiency of efforts to address sustainability issues.

The MSA is calculated as an aggregation of four impacts: land use, GHG emissions, nitrogen oxide (NOx) emissions, and freshwater use. The MSA data are adjusted for the size of the company to consider size-adjusted biodiversity impact (i.e., biodiversity efficiency). It's important to note that the MSA calculation is based on input–output models that consider the typical characteristics of companies at a sector level. More granular, company-level data are integrated into the model when that company does report details regarding their business model, production input, etc. Unfortunately, that is still a minority of the companies. In this first version of the dataset, companies' policies regarding biodiversity are not taken into consideration.

The portfolio construction is based on an investment universe consisting of over 185 companies listed in developed markets in the food sectors as described above. A two-step process is implemented:

1. Filtering
   Selecting companies that meet minimum requirements in terms of sustainability. This is achieved through a best-in-class selection across all the subsectors in the food industry using both standard ESG data and GHG emissions (total emissions and intensity).
2. Biodiversity integration
   The portfolio is built in order to maximize the aggregate biodiversity efficiency constrained by minimum requirements around liquidity and diversification. The portfolio is also optimized to deliver a reduction in the carbon footprint of at least 30% in comparison with the food industry (i.e., investment universe).

The fundamental driver of the portfolio construction is the biodiversity impact of companies. The more a company's processes are efficient with regard to its impact on biodiversity, the higher the weight it would have in the strategy, within the liquidity and diversification constrains required for a robust portfolio construction.

Results

The portfolio that optimizes for biodiversity (denominated Biodiversity Strategy) achieves a substantial 75% reduction in its biodiversity impact ratio (MSA/size) when compared to a cap-weighted portfolio of all stocks in the food industry (denominated Food Industry). For further details on the biodiversity reduction, refer to Exhibit 1. While achieving zero impact on biodiversity is not possible today due to the current status of the food industry and the lack of consideration of positive biodiversity impact by the current methodology, we are hopeful that a net-zero strategy might indeed be possible in the coming years (Figure 24.1).

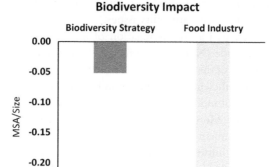

FIGURE 24.1 Simulated biodiversity impact for the Biodiversity Strategy and its benchmark, the Food Industry. Data from April 2018 to July 2020, from Datastream, Sustainalytics, Trucost, and Iceberg Data Lab. The impacts are averaged over that period.

The ESG and GHG characteristics of the Biodiversity Strategy were also better than that of the Food Industry, as shown in Exhibit 2. While the portfolio was managed to deliver a 30% reduction in GHG emissions and intensity, the reduction in GHG emission was significantly higher, at 82%. While that scale of reduction may be surprising, it is – at least partially – explained by the fact that carbon emission is also a factor in the MSA calculation. As a result, the optimization to reduce the MSA naturally leads to a reduction in carbon emissions as well. The ESG score of the Biodiversity Strategy observed an 11% improvement in comparison with the Food Industry. Since the ESG score of the portfolio was not optimized, the improved rating is explained by the best-in-class filter applied in the first step of the portfolio construction (Figure 24.2).

A backtesting of the Biodiversity Strategy and the Food Industry as defined between the period of April 2018 and July 2020 suggests that the integration of biodiversity does not necessarily lead to weaker risk-adjusted return profile. (Note: the backtesting period is short and constrained by the availability of historical data regarding biodiversity impact.) The Biodiversity Strategy would have delivered a slightly higher performance (10.61% per year versus 9.12% for the Food Industry), with similar levels of risk (both in volatility and maximum drawdown). The two portfolios have a Capital Asset Pricing Model (CAPM) beta of about 0.67, which is typical in the food sector that usually has a low beta. Exhibit 3 presents the cumulative returns, and Exhibit 4 presents key performance indicators of the Biodiversity Strategy and the Food Industry benchmark.

Despite the limitations imposed by a very short period of data, it is encouraging to see that integrating biodiversity in the portfolio can indeed create value. More importantly, as biodiversity is the most important driver in the portfolio construction, the results can be attributed to that factor. In fact, liquidity and

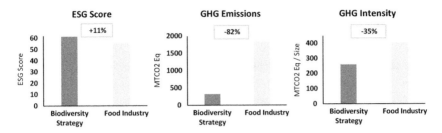

FIGURE 24.2 Simulated ESG and carbon footprint for the Biodiversity Strategy and its benchmark, the Food Industry. Data from April 2018 to July 2020, from Datastream, Sustainalytics, Trucost, and Iceberg Data Lab. GHG emissions and intensity are calculated assuming 1mln USD investment in both portfolios. Scores are averaged over that period.

TABLE 24.1 Simulated historical portfolio levels for the Biodiversity Strategy and its benchmark, the Food Industry. Data from April 2018 to July 2020 in USD, from Datastream, Sustainalytics, Trucost and Iceberg Data Lab. Net dividends are reinvested in the index

Key Performance Indicators	Biodiversity Strategy	Food Industry
Annual Performance	10.61%	9.12%
Annual Volatility	15.30%	14.98%
Max. Drawdown	−26.84%	−25.09%
Sharpe Ratio	0.58	0.49
CAPM Beta	0.67	0.67
CAPM Alpha	5.91%	4.45%

financial capacity constraints were the only financial factors included in the process (Table 24.1; Figure 24.3).

Opportunities for Improvement

We believe that our strategy provides one of the first pieces of evidence that investors can steer capital to activities that are considerably less harmful to biodiversity without a negative impact on return. While much research is still needed in this area, the findings allow us to be hopeful that the investment industry can contribute to an economy that has reduced impact on biodiversity. We identify three key actions that could accelerate this contribution.

Data Needed on Physical, Quantitative Biodiversity Impact Indicators

A review of three of the largest ESG data providers highlighted that data on physical, quantitative indicators on biodiversity remain underdeveloped. Unlike the

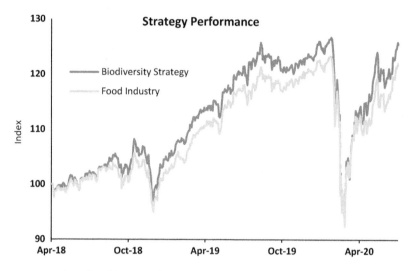

FIGURE 24.3   Simulated historical portfolio levels for the Biodiversity Strategy and its benchmark, the Food Industry. Data from April 2018 to July 2020 in USD, from Datastream, Sustainalytics, Trucost and Iceberg Data Lab. Net dividends are reinvested in the index.

level of understanding and commitment by government, business, and finance on climate change, biodiversity is only starting to show up on the agenda of these actors. While intragovernmental initiatives can fast-track the level playing field amongst businesses to report on such data, investors can also engage with companies on the importance of managing and reporting on biodiversity impact.

Methodology Needs to Continue to Evolve

The methodology on biodiversity impact needs to evolve in a way similar to that of climate change. Methodologies on climate change impact began by strictly calculating carbon footprint. They later incorporate the notion of the positive contribution a company can make to low-carbon economy via its products and services (i.e., solutions). Finally, today methodologies have evolved to consider science-based targets. Methodologies on biodiversity impact will need to go through similar evolutions if they are to enable investors and other stakeholders to contextualize a company's reduction of impact on biodiversity and assess to what extent it is 'sufficient'. The science around the MSA has already defined 0.72 as the safe planetary boundary, yet further details are needed to understand each sectors and regions' contribution to that threshold.

Convergence Will Be Needed

We anticipate that, once the industry and sector become fully aware of the need to manage biodiversity, a multitude of methodologies may arise. This is a challenge that methodologies regarding climate change indicators still suffer from. The comparison of funds is hampered; significant divergence in results conceals important differences in scope and methodology. If there is no standardization of the data taken into account (source, scope, etc.), it will be difficult to compare the biodiversity impact of funds as well. A methodological consensus will be needed to make the funds comparable with each other and to improve measurement of the absolute performance of investments in ESG terms. The criteria used could become real indicators for managing funds, making it possible to demonstrate the ESG added value they offer, in addition to the financial performance investors expect.

In conclusion, investors can steer capital to companies and activities that have reduced impact on biodiversity without financial loss. As our case study demonstrates, that is true in a sector such as food which has a significant impact on biodiversity and especially on mean species abundance. While much research is still needed to enable the industry to develop investment products that are aligned with a science-based target for biodiversity across all sectors in the economy, we hope this piece of work is an encouraging case study that demonstrates that it can be done.

References

Brink, B. 2006. "A Long-Term Biodiversity, Ecosystem and Awareness Research Network". ALTER-Net, pp. 22–31. https://unstats.un.org/unsd/envaccounting/seeaLES/egm/ALTERNet_bk.pdf

Díaz, S., Settele, J., Brondízio, E.S., Ngo, H.T., Agard, J., Arneth, A., Balvanera, P. et al. 2019. "Pervasive Human-Driven Decline of Life on Earth Points to the Need for Transformative Change". Science 366 (6471): eaax3100. doi:10.1126/science.aax3100.

Evison, W. and Knight, C. 2010. "Biodiversity and Business Risk: A Global Risks Network Briefing". World Economic Forum (WEF), Geneva. http://www.weforum.org/pdf/globalrisk/Biodiversityandbusinessrisk.pdf

IPBES. 2018. "Summary for Policymakers of the Regional Assessment Report on Biodiversity and Ecosystem Services for Europe and Central Asia of the Intergovernmental Science-Policy Platform on Biodiversity and Ecosystem Services". M. Fischer, M. Rounsevell, A. Torre-Marin Rando, A. Mader, A. Church, M. Elbakidze, V. Elias, T. Hahn, P.A. Harrison, J. Hauck, B. Martín-López, I. Ring, C. Sandström, I. Sousa Pinto, P. Visconti, N.E. Zimmermann and M. Christie (eds.). IPBES secretariat, Bonn, Germany. 48 pages.

Kok, M.T.J., Alkemade, R., Bakkenes, M., van Eerdt, M., Janse, J., Mandryk, M., Kram, T., et al. 2018. "Pathways for Agriculture and Forestry to Contribute to Terrestrial Biodiversity Conservation: A Global Scenario-Study". Biological Conservation 221: 137–150. doi:10.1016/j.biocon.2018.03.003.

Lammerant, J. 2018. "Critical Assessment of Biodiversity Accounting Approaches for Businesses. Discussion paper for EU Business @Biodiversity Platform". https://ec.europa.eu/environment/biodiversity/business/assets/pdf/B@B_Assessment_biodiversity_accounting_approaches_Update_Report_1_19Nov2018.pdf

Lammerant, J., Grigg, A., Dimitrijevic, J., Leach, K., Brooks, S., Burns, A., Berger, J., Houdet, J., Oorschot, M., and Goedkoop, M. 2019. "Assessment of Biodiversity

Measurement Approaches for Businesses and Financial Institutions". https://ec.europa.eu/environment/biodiversity/business/assets/pdf/European_B@B_platform_report_biodiversity_assessment_2019_FINAL_5Dec2019.pdf

Schipper, A.M., Hilbers, J.P., Meijer, J.R., Antão, L.H., Benítez-López, A, de Jonge, M.M.J., Leemans, and L.H., et al. 2019. "Projecting Terrestrial Biodiversity Intactness with GLOBIO 4". *Global Change Biology* 26 (2): 760–771. doi:10.1111/gcb.14848.

Slay, C. M. 2011. "A Review of Biodiversity and Land-Use Metrics, Indices, and Methodologies as Related to Agricultural Products". A Business Report for the Food, Beverage, and Agriculture Sector of the Sustainability Consortium. Fayetteville, University of Arkansas, 1, 25. https://saiplatform.org/uploads/Library/Biodiversity%20and%20Land%20Use%20Business%20Report.pdf

Steffen, W., Richardson, K., Rockstrom, J., Cornell, S.E., Fetzer, I., Bennett, E.M., Biggs, R., Carpenter, S., Vries, W., de Wit, C., Folke, C., Gerten, D., Heinke, J., Persoon, L., Ramanathan, V., Reyers, B., and Sörlin, S. 2015. "Planetary Boundaries: Guiding Human Development on a Changing Planet". *Science* 347 (6223): 1259855–1259855. doi:10.1126/science.1259855.

25

ADDRESSING THE ECOLOGICAL TRANSITION THROUGH ENVIRONMENTAL, SOCIAL AND GOVERNANCE INVESTING POWERED BY ARTIFICIAL INTELLIGENCE AND FINTECH

Nicolas Jacob

Introduction

Biodiversity is declining faster today than at any time in human history: 1 million animal and plant species, or 25% of the total, are threatened with extinction. Intensive agriculture, deforestation, the conversion of wild spaces into agricultural land, and even pollution are among the main causes of this accelerated decline. This observation is inseparable from the acceleration of global warming over the past 50 years and confirms, if necessary, the prevalence of its anthropogenic origins. Failing to reverse the trend quickly, a significant part of the earth's surface will become habitable, accompanied by an explosion of conflicts over the use of resources. Awareness is accelerating on the need to make a global ecological transition leading us towards a sustainable development model renewing our ways of producing, consuming and even moving around. Today, this is the prerequisite for meeting the challenges of climate change, the scarcity of resources and the accelerated loss of biodiversity.

What Are the Key Challenges for Investors Tackling Climate and Ecosystem Services Losses?

Faced with this challenge, the mobilization of public and private actors must make it possible to meet an investment need of 1,500 to 2,000 billion USD per year by 2030. As a responsible asset manager, ODDO BHF Asset Management aims to make a key contribution to tackle this major issue that involves a massive reallocation of capital towards the ecological transition.

Much has already been achieved by the financial world in recent years when and where climate risk and sustainability issues are concerned, but a large part of the initiatives up to now have mainly focused on limiting global warming

DOI: 10.4324/9781003045557-30

by supporting the (green) energy transition, i.e. the transition from an energy system based on energy production from polluting fossil sources, emitting greenhouse gases and exhaustible to an energy mix centred around renewable energies. But many other issues such as biodiversity and ecosystem collapse require urgent and consolidated investor action.

The International Energy Agency (IEA) believes that while energy sector transformation projects are necessary to limit global warming, initiatives solely focused on energy transition will not be sufficient to achieve carbon neutrality and preserve our ecosystems. Biodiversity plays an essential role in mitigating the effects of global warming, thanks in particular to natural carbon sinks (oceans, forests and soils) which make it possible to capture part of the greenhouse gases of anthropogenic origin, and its preservation is therefore of vital importance.

So How Can One Effectively Contribute to the Ecological Transition as an Investor?

Since innovation and Environmental, Social and Governance (ESG) research are at the heart of our DNA as a long-term sustainable investor, we have decided to combine our expertise in environmental and climate topics with the use of artificial intelligence to build a unique investment process.

After having identified and defined the four areas that make up our approach for the ecological transition – clean energy, energy efficiency, sustainable mobility, preservation of natural resources – and carrying out several months of research in collaboration with an external partner specializing in large-scale data processing, we are able to offer a thematic portfolio of 200 companies from a global investment universe that addresses climate, natural capital and biodiversity challenges regardless of the size of the company or its capitalization.

To achieve this result, the first step consists in establishing a semantic map to qualify the themes of the ecological transition. About 700 words or groups of keywords have been identified, including more than 200 on the sole theme of the preservation of natural resources: "protection of watersheds", "recycling", "reforestation", "water management", "sustainable agriculture", "sustainable fishing", "waste recovery", "forestry assets" and so on. It is at the end of this step that our big data partner runs a natural language processing (NLP) algorithm that can process up to 4 million textual data per day. Over 80% of global data today remains unstructured; the use of this technology is therefore decisive, and this constitutes a real competitive advantage in our investment process.

What's the Role Artificial Intelligence and Fintech Can Play to Enhance Environmental, Social and Governance Methodologies?

NLP technology allows us to filter a global universe of listed companies around five parameters:

1. the number of occurrences of a company in the textual data processed on the basis of the semantic map;
2. the sentiment associated with the company, a relevant indicator of future growth if it is positive;
3. the company's expertise through the number of citations related to its core business;
4. the diversity of citations within the semantic map for the same company, confirming the relevance of its positioning on the desired theme; and
5. finally, the trend over time in order to capture weak signals of positive dynamics.

Starting from around 4,000 companies, this artificial intelligence process allows us to result in an investment universe of 200 companies strongly involved in the development, manufacturing, or distribution of products and solutions with environmental benefits.

A "Step-by-step" Investment–Decision-making Process towards the Ecological Transition and the Sustainable Development Goals

By way of illustration on the subject of the preservation of natural resources, we manage to target companies in key areas such as water and waste management, circular economy and recycling, eco-design or sustainable agriculture.

The portfolio construction phase then consists of a multifactorial financial analysis of these 200 companies taking into consideration quality elements of business models (profitability, balance sheet strength and cash flow generation), growth, valuation and stock market momentum. Finally, the management team systematically conducts a fundamental review to eliminate potential biases and special situations.

This innovative investment process therefore allows us to participate effectively in the financing of the global ecological transition, including the protection of biodiversity. In order to ensure the environmental relevance of our investment choices, we analyze the exposure of the companies constituting the final portfolio to 6 of the 17 United Nations Sustainable Development Goals (SDGs): Clean Water and Sanitation (SDG 6), Affordable and Clean Energy (SDG 7), Industry, Innovation and Infrastructure (SDG 9), Sustainable Cities and Communities (SDG 11), Sustainable Consumption and Production (SDG 12) and Climate Action (SDG 13).

The SDGs being above all objectives are intended for countries and are having an important macrodimension, our choice is based on the effective transposition of a certain number of subobjectives to the activity of private companies and their contribution to the targeted targets.

- For example, the American company Evoqua Water Technologies, specializing in water treatment, recycling and desalination services, meets target

6.4 of SDG 6: By 2030, the "rational use of water resources in all sectors to ensure the sustainability of withdrawals and freshwater supply to take into account water scarcity and significantly reduce the number of people who suffer from water scarcity".

- Likewise, the Belgian group Umicore, which specializes in recycling waste and batteries to reuse precious and nonferrous metals, meets target 12.5 of SDG 12: "By 2030, considerably reduce the production of waste by prevention, reduction, recycling and reuse".

Concluding Remarks

The accelerated loss of biodiversity and the risk of a "sixth mass extinction" as scientists now call it goes hand in hand with global warming. We collectively face an existential risk and contributing in the best possible way as an investor to the global ecological transition is now a necessity. By combining our investor know-how with artificial intelligence, we want to take our full place in this transition.

26

REVEALING PLATO'S 'SHADOW KINGDOM'

Rendering Pandemic Risk Explicit in Extinction Engagement

Jill Atkins, Federica Doni, Abeer Hassan and Warren Maroun

Introduction

An existing framework for institutional investor engagement[1] on species extinction and biodiversity[2] implicitly includes risk management and anticipation of high consequence risks such as pandemics and COVID-19.[3] The framework's focus on enhancing biodiversity, protecting species, protecting ecosystems from biodiversity loss and extinction, and protecting habitats implicitly drives business practices to protect humanity from global and local risks arising from the erosion of ecosystems, species and their habitats. The extinction engagement framework was developed on the foundation of financial risk management and the incorporation of material financial risks linked to biodiversity loss and species extinction into investor chains and governance. The framework, with its associated extinction accounting framework, provides a means of integrating species protection and biodiversity enhancement into the heart of finance, accounting and governance. The financial rationale for species protection and extinction prevention, as well as for enhancing biodiversity and protecting habitats, built upon the interconnectedness of all life on earth and, from an anthropocentric perspective, the reliance of humans on 'natural capital', on flora and fauna, for our survival.[4] We only have to consider estimates of ecosystem services loss to appreciate the direct financial impacts of declining biodiversity. For example, the harrowing report produced by IPBES last year stated that $577 billion in annual global crop output are at risk as a result of pollinator loss (IPBES, 2019).[5,6] IPBES estimates that 1 million species are now threatened with extinction. There is also pressure at governmental level with efforts to conserve biodiversity included in a substantial initiative to save endangered animals from extinction in a call for urgent action to tackle the drivers and impacts of climate change.[7] This has been in tandem with a UK Government's review to assess the economic benefits of

DOI: 10.4324/9781003045557-31

biodiversity globally, assess the economic costs and risks of biodiversity loss and identify a range of actions that can simultaneously enhance biodiversity and deliver economic prosperity.[8]

The financial implications of biodiversity loss and habitat degradation are now well-documented, but other side effects of anthropogenic ecological degeneration are emerging. It is increasingly clear that high consequence risks are amassing as a result of anthropogenic loss of species, biodiversity and habitat.[9] Indeed, human destruction of biodiversity creates the conditions for new viruses and diseases such as COVID-19, and activities such as road building, mining, hunting and logging triggered the Ebola epidemics in the 1990s. Humans disrupt ecosystems when cutting the trees, killing animals or caging and sending them to markets: viruses have lost their hosts and are looking for new hosts that ultimately transfer to human beings (Quammen, 2013; 2020a, 2020b). Further, Jones et al. (2008) explained how species in degraded habitats are likely to carry more viruses that can infect humans. Shrinking natural habitats and changing behaviour add to the risk of diseases spilling over from animals to humans (Hassan et al., 2020b). When habitat and biodiversity decline, the buffer between humans and the natural world weakens, pathogens 'spill over' to human populations and can cause pandemics, such as COVID-19. Deforestation increases the likelihood that viruses and other pathogens will jump from wild animals to humans (Bloomfield et al., 2020).

The loss of habitat and exploitation of wildlife through hunting and trade has increased the risk of infections (Johnson et al., 2020). The vast illegal wildlife trade and humanity's excessive intrusion into nature are to blame for the coronavirus pandemic (Weston, 2020). Einhorn (2020) mentioned that one way to decrease the likelihood of recurrent pandemics is to decrease the potential for people to come into contact with wild animals. The 'wet market' in Wuhan, thought by the Chinese government to be the starting point of the current COVID-19 pandemic, was known to sell wild animals including live wolf pups, salamanders, crocodiles, scorpions, rats, squirrels, foxes, civets and turtles. Countries must act to prevent future pandemics by banning 'wet markets' that sell live and dead animals for human consumption (Greenfield 2020). However, communities, particularly from low-income rural areas, are dependent on wild animals to sustain the livelihoods of millions of people: banning could engender illegal trade in wild animals, which currently is already leading species to the brink of extinction, unless alternative food supplies can be found. Shenzhen became the first Chinese city to ban the sale and consumption of dog and cat. Society globally may need to cut down meat consumption (Cohen, 2020). Microsoft's new commitment is to master a plan to create a 'planetary computer' for assessing, monitoring and managing natural ecosystems data in a more timely manner. The initiative builds on their artificial intelligence (AI) for Earth programme, which has supported grants for more than 500 environmental data projects in 81 countries (Clancy, 2020).

In addition to concerns around transmission of coronavirus from land mammals and bats to humans, there is also scientific evidence that marine mammals, such as dolphins and beluga whales, may carry similar diseases (Woo et al., 2013). Further, plastics polluting marine environments, a concern for environmentalists worldwide, may also pose a threat. Researchers are exploring how pathogens bind to plastics in the ocean and how this process helps bacteria spread across the world. There are concerns that potential impacts on humans could arise from the food chain. Ocean zooplankton consume plastics, which are then eaten by fish and, ultimately, humans. Similarly, people ingesting water, swimming in the sea or lying in the sand near marine plastics could provide possible disease transmission.[10] This has implications for fishing, seafood and tourism, to name but a few sectors. The onset of COVID-19 has raised global awareness around wildlife trafficking, the illegal consumption of wild, protected and endangered species and health risks. At European Union (EU) level, a recent consultation document on a renewed sustainable finance strategy highlights the interlinkages between COVID-19, illegal wildlife trades, and ecosystem and habitat degradation.[11]

COVID-19 reminds us that upsetting the balance of nature and interfering directly with wild animal species can threaten the very existence of humans on the planet. Human extinction is a real and terrifying reality.[12] The aims of this chapter are threefold: (i) to explore perceptions of the institutional investor and governance community towards the impact of COVID-19 on extinction engagement; (ii) to render pandemic risk and risk management an *explicit* element of the existing extinction engagement frameworks so that they may be implemented institutional investor practice in order to prevent a re-occurrence of the current crippling global pandemic; and (iii) to theorise the emergence of COVID-19 through a Becksian lens which draws on Plato's *'Allegory of the Cave'* in order to demonstrate the intangible, hidden and surreptitious nature of pandemic threats on human existence.

In the next section, there is a discussion of the theoretical lens through which we view and interpret our interview data, deriving from Beck's Risk Society thesis and in particular his interpretation of Plato's *'Allegory of the Cave'*. Section 'Extinction Engagement and Extinction Accounting' reviews the literature on extinction engagement and related areas. Section 'Research Method' outlines the research method. In Section 'The Views of Practitioners on Links between Covid-19, Biodiversity, Species Extinction, and Extinction Engagement', we present the findings of extensive interviews with senior representatives of the international institutional investment and governance communities. Section 'Rendering Pandemic Risk Explicit in the Extinction Accounting and Engagement Frameworks' presents an updated extinction engagement framework which renders pandemic risk management explicit and visible. The chapter concludes in Section 'Concluding Discussion: Revealing the Shadow Kingdom?' with a discussion of the framework in the light of Beck's writings around a 'Shadow Kingdom'.

Biodiversity Loss, Species Extinction and COVID-19: Unveiling a 'Shadow Kingdom'?

Beck's work drew on Plato's *'Allegory of the Cave'* to highlight the invisible nature of ecological risks arising from scientific and industrial development. This philosophical dialogue is book seven of Plato's *Republic* (Plato: Watt, 1997) and is one of over twenty similar pieces of writing produced by the philosopher.[13] The book begins with a hypothetical situation where several men are in captivity in an 'underground cavernous chamber' and forced to sit facing the cave's back wall. They cannot turn their heads at all and can only witness the shadows cast on the cave's wall from events taking place outside. The entrance to the cave is wide, and there is a low wall running from one end to the other, '... like the screens which conjurors put up in front of their audience, and above which they exhibit their wonders' (Plato: Watt, 1997, p. 225). Behind the wall is a brightly burning fire. People are walking along an elevated road at the other side of the wall from the captives, and although they do not cast their own shadows onto the cave wall, as their heads and bodies do not reach above the wall, the things they carry do, namely, 'statues of men and images of other animals, wrought in wood and stone and all kinds of materials' (ibid, p. 225). The captives can only see the shadows of these strange ornaments, yet they can hear the voices of the people carrying them but given the strange situation they would only be able to attribute the voices to the ornaments rather than to the people, who remained invisible, such that, '... such persons would hold the shadows of those manufactured articles to be the only realities' (ibid, p. 226). The book goes on to describe what happens when one of the captives is released. He is blinded by the bright light and the dialogue considers whether he welcomes the new reality or whether he prefers to see the world as he had always seen it before. The transition to seeing the 'real world' clearly involves first looking at shadows of real objects and people, because of their brightness, and then gradually the things themselves. The allegorical dialogue continues, with discussions between the two imaginary people around the importance of education and philosophical training. The concept of a shadow reality perceived by people effectively shrouded in ignorance inspired Ulrich Beck in his sociological writings around the 'Risk Society' in relation to ecological risks arising from industrialisation, especially invisible anthropogenic ecological threats such as pollution and toxins,

> In Plato's 'Allegory of the Cave', the visible world becomes a mere shadow, a reflection of a reality that by nature escapes our possible knowledge.
>
> *(Beck, 1992, p. 73)*

He interprets the world hidden behind the wall as a 'shadow kingdom', unperceivable by society, that needs to be explored and mapped out, through looking at the world around us twice, in a 'double gaze', or in two different manners,

Threats from civilisation are bringing about a kind of new *'shadow kingdom'*, comparable to the realm of the gods and demons in antiquity, which is hidden behind the visible world and threatens human life on this Earth..... Dangerous, hostile substances lie *concealed behind the harmless façades.* Everything must be viewed with a *double gaze,* and can only be correctly understood and judged through this doubling. The world of the visible must be investigated, relativized and evaluated with respect to a second reality, only existent in thought and yet concealed in the world. The standards for evaluation lie only in the second, not in the visible world.

(Beck, 1992, p. 72, emphasis added)

The implication of these ideas is that humanity is labouring under a false perception of the world around them and that individuals' collective consciousness is not raised high enough to allow them to see beyond the shadows presented to them as 'everyday reality',

What becomes the subject of controversy as to its degree of reality is instead *what everyday consciousness does not see*, and cannot perceive: radioactivity, pollutants and threats in the future.

(Beck, 1992, p. 73, emphasis added)

Although Beck was at the time preoccupied with pollution and its invisible effects on society, we can see from the following quotation that his discussion around 'multifarious effects' on 'health' allowed for risks unforeseen by Beck, as he was clearly aware that by their very nature, ecological high consequence risks arising from industrial activity and their impacts on the environment and nature could not be predicted or foreseen. Perhaps we can also see portents of social distancing and illness/death from COVID-19 encapsulated in Beck's prophetic risk society writings, where he talks of effects on the 'social life of people',

What is astonishing ... is that the industrial pollution of the environment and the *destruction of nature,* with their *multifarious effects on the health and social life of people,* which only arise in highly developed societies, are characterised by a *loss of social thinking.* The loss becomes caricature – this absence seems to strike no one ....

(Beck, 1992, p. 25, emphasis added)

Beck outlined the globalisation of risks of civilisation, and again, his thoughts were prophetic of the current pandemic as a leveller, as although he was referring to pollution, he underlined the potential for risks to escape class and geography as they impact everyone and anyone equally,

> ... poverty is hierarchic, smog is democratic. With the expansion of modernization risks – with the endangering of nature, health, nutrition and so on, - the social differences and limits are relativized.
>
> *(Beck, 1992)*

The impact of globalisation and the non-discriminatory nature of risks may manifest in a type of apathy, as,

> Where there is no escape, people ultimately *no longer want to think about it.* This eschatological eco-fatalism allows the pendulum of private and political moods to swing in any direction. The risk society shifts from hysteria to *indifference* and vice versa.
>
> *(Beck, 1992, p. 37)*

This concept of indifference within Beck's work in the face of catastrophic ecological risks was also alluded in the work of Anthony Giddens, where he talked of 'engulfment'[14] and paralysis when faced with high consequence risks such as climate change and global warming,

> .... In an external environment full of changes, the person is obsessively preoccupied with apprehension of possible risks to his or her existence, and paralysed in terms of practical action ... People *engulfed* by such anxieties may seek to *'blend with the environment'* so as to escape being the target of the dangers which haunt them.
>
> *(Giddens, 1991, pp. 53–54, emphasis added)*

Blending with the environment is, adopting Plato's allegorical image, staying in the cave, preferring to watch the puppets and the false images on display before them. This state of mind and mental paralysis render people unable, or unwilling, to look beyond the shadows. Fear of hazards (in the current context, fear of the consequences arising from biodiversity loss and mass extinctions) creates engulfment such that society prefers to see the façade presented to them, where the world seems safe. Again, using Beck's language quoted above, such engulfment results in a 'lack of social thinking'. This lack of social thinking, lack of consciousness, is the vexry state of mind alluded to in Plato's *Republic*. It seems that COVID-19 has shifted societal perceptions and human consciousness to a new level. COVID-19 has broken people's ontological security (Giddens, 1991). COVID-19 is a 'keying', in Goffman's (1974) *'Frame Analysis'*, causing us to 'break frame', to find ourselves in a new frame, where destruction of nature and ecological damage are creating threats to our health and conjuring images of human extinction. As the scales fell from Saul's eyes, society is now seeing the world hitherto invisible to so many.[15]

We suggest that the threat of a global pandemic, discussed in recent years, has been perceived as something intangible and unmanageable and also therefore given inadequate attention by businesses, financial markets and the accounting function. Further, the links between biodiversity loss and destruction of habitat and endangered species with pandemics have been largely ignored. We suggest that this effectively invisible threat must be made explicit and rendered visible within current accounting and finance frameworks.

In the next section, we demonstrate how extinction engagement can assist in revealing the reality of these risks by making the second reality visible through investor engagement and dialogue and consequently through extinction accounting. It is now time to enhance human consciousness of high consequence risks such as pandemics and make them visible and explicit throughout society and the economic and financial systems around the world. As Plato explained, we need to learn to see and understand the world around us in a different manner,

> .... There is a faculty residing in the soul of each person, and an instrument enabling each of us to learn; and that just as we might suppose it to be impossible to turn the eye round from darkness to light without turning the whole body, so much this faculty, or this instrument, be wheeled round, in company with the entire soul, from the perishing world, until it be enabled to endure the contemplation of the real world and the brightest part thereof.
>
> *(Plato: Watt, 1997, pp. 229–230)*

As stated by Beck, perceiving a second reality allows society to develop a more effective consciousness and awareness around high consequence risks,

> ... the step to cultural risk consciousness is everyday thought and imagination removed from its moorings in the world of the visible.
>
> *(Beck, 1992, p. 73)*

Extinction Engagement and Extinction Accounting

Institutional investors have, in recent years, escalated their engagement with investee companies on environmental, social and governance (ESG) issues. By ESG engagement, we refer to the process of one-on-one meetings between institutional investors and their investee companies that aim to gather private disclosures from companies on ESG risks as well as to call companies to account for their ESG impacts. Responsible investors, since the turn of the century, have developed increasingly formalised structures of engagement and dialogue around social and environmental issues, with a two-way relationship evolving (Solomon and Solomon, 2006). Although engagement in this area has been interpreted as imbued with impression management and myth creation (Solomon and Darby, 2005, Solomon et al., 2013), there has been some evidence that responsible investor engagement on climate change and other environmental factors are an important element in risk management for investors (Solomon et al., 2011) and that it can change investor and investee behaviour, as well as impact investment decisions (Solomon et al., 2013). Of particular relevance is the finding that there is a two-way relationship between public social and environmental reporting and private social and environmental reporting (i.e. one-on-one investor/investee meetings, known also as engagement and dialogue) whereby the public reporting feeds into investor/investee meetings, informing investor questions, and consequently, the engagement/private reporting process feeds back into the public reporting through investees taking investor questions from the meetings and incorporating their responses into their reports (Solomon and Solomon, 2006). In the specific area of engagement and dialogue on biodiversity and natural capital, there is very little research, which is a reflection of the newness of this area of practice within the investment industry. However, practitioners have identified the development of engagement practice in this area on bees and pollinators (Herron, 2016; Thamotheram and Stewart, 2016) and on marine stewardship and fish/seafood species (Herron, 2019).

The past year has witnessed a wide range of initiatives launched by the financial community to explore embedding biodiversity and natural capital into the financial system more deeply. Investec Bank hosted an event, 'Natural Capital, Species Extinction & Sustainable Financial Markets' on 29 May 2019 at which the Species Protection Action Plan for the Financial Markets was officially launched (Atkins and Macpherson, 2019).[16] This event involved speakers and panels from the investment industry, banking, accounting and conservation and led to other initiatives, as outlined here. In September 2019, an investor briefing entitled, 'The State of the Apes', was published by ShareAction[17] outlining steps investors should be taking to assist in conservation and biodiversity protection.[18] Further, ShareAction conducted a ranking of 75 of the world's leading asset managers' approaches to responsible investment, which included a ranking on biodiversity activism (ShareAction, 2020). They highlight biodiversity as one of the most important and relevant environmental, social and governance (ESG) factors that needs addressing in the face of climate and nature-related risks and conclude that responsible investors are 'sub-standard' in their efforts to address risks in this area. The report stated that only two asset managers surveyed offered a product that can be characterised as biodiversity-specific, confirming that biodiversity remains on the periphery of investor attention. A further ShareAction report (Springer, 2020) found that although biodiversity-related risks were starting to appear on the radar of some asset managers, none has developed a comprehensive, dedicated biodiversity policy. In the academic accounting literature, however, a framework for engagement on biodiversity and species extinction has been presented in the form of a series of questions that institutional investors can pose at private meetings with investees (Atkins and Maroun, 2018; Atkins and Atkins, 2019).

If the international institutional investment community begins to focus more attention on biodiversity issues among investees, there is likely to be a growing demand from investors for increased corporate reporting on biodiversity, habitat, species extinction and other factors relating to potential pandemics, given the strong links between public and private reporting on social and environmental factors. Indeed, prior research has demonstrated that investors perceive environmental (and social) reporting to be decision-useful, at least to some degree, even 40 years ago (Buzby and Falk, 1978; Belkaoui, 1980; Benjamin and Stanga, 1977), and an investor demand for environmental information was identified some 20 years ago (Deegan and Rankin, 1997). Some studies found evidence of a positive stock price reaction to social disclosures (Ingram, 1978; Anderson and Frankle, 1980). There was also early evidence of a demand for social disclosure among ethical investors (Rockness and Williams, 1988). Research has also shown that investors have consistently bemoaned the state of environmental, social and (more recently) climate change reporting (Buzby and Falk, 1978; 1979; Harte et al., 1991; Solomon et al., 2011). Further, research has shown that investor engagement (through private reporting mechanisms) on climate change and related environmental factors is driven in part by this inadequacy of publicly available disclosures (Solomon and Solomon, 2006; Solomon et al., 2011; Atkins et al., 2015). Investor engagement has also been found to increase in intensity where investees have misrepresented environmental externalities (Solomon et al., 2013).

Given this chapter's focus on extinction engagement, a comprehensive review of the accounting for biodiversity literature is beyond the scope of the chapter. Briefly, there has been a recent proliferation of practitioner-focused initiatives and frameworks in the biodiversity accounting area (GRI, 2007; 2016; United Nations, 2019). In December 2019, the Climate Disclosure Standards Board (CDSB) initiated an open public consultation and call for evidence on advancing nature-related financial disclosures and use of CDSB Framework. They hosted a webinar at the end of April 2020 to discuss the results of the consultation and the future of natural capital accounting.[19] The CDSB states that its existing reporting frameworks for climate-related disclosures can be adapted to provide a tried and tested framework for natural capital reporting.[20] A Biological Diversity Protocol (the BD Protocol) for corporate reporting on biodiversity and natural capital will soon be published which provides detailed stages and a framework for reporting in this area. The Natural Capital Coalition has also been working extensively to integrate biodiversity into their reporting framework, the Natural Capital Protocol. Similarly, the academic literature has explored the evolution of accounting for biodiversity and motivations for reporting in this area (Jones, 1996; 2003; Jones and Solomon, 2013) and critiques of existing accounting for biodiversity based on approaches, techniques and motivations (Milne, 1996; Gray, 2010; Milne and Gray, 2013; Cuckston, 2013; Freeman and Groom, 2013; Tregidga, 2013; Cuckston, 2017; Russell et al., 2017) with some focusing on deep ecological conceptualisations of value (Feger and Mermet, 2017; Sullivan and Hannis, 2017). Accounting for biodiversity has been assessed in various countries, for example Sweden (Rimmel and Jonäll, 2013) and Denmark (van Liempd and Busch, 2013) and in developing economy contexts (Siddiqui, 2013; Zhao and Atkins, 2019). Acknowledging the infeasibility of a complete reorganisation of the capital market and supporting accounting systems, a body of work has sought to provide a framework for reporting on biodiversity and species extinction that is consistent with integrated reporting (IIRC, 2013) and existing accounting frameworks (King with Atkins and Atkins, 2016; Atkins and Maroun, 2018; Maroun and Atkins, 2018; Atkins and Atkins, 2019), inspired by the emancipatory accounting movement (Gallhofer et al., 2013; 2015; Gallhofer and Haslam, 2019). Despite the evident interest among practitioners and academics, low levels of reporting have been found (Mansoor and Maroun, 2016; Adler et al., 2018) with impression management motivations for biodiversity and extinction accounting being identified (Gray, 2010; Tregidga et al., 2014; Boiral, 2016; Maroun et al., 2018; Hassan et al., 2020a).

If extinction engagement intensifies as a result of COVID-19, then this could stimulate an increase in quantity and (hopefully) quality of disclosure on biodiversity and related areas.

Research Method

The research method involved two stages. Firstly, we conducted a series of interviews with institutional investors and governance experts, to garner their thoughts on the links between COVID-19, accounting for biodiversity/species extinction, and the role of investor engagement. Our method was forced to adapt to the confines of the ongoing pandemic context. Although we would normally have chosen to conduct face-to-face interviews,[21] social distancing measures and the lockdown meant this was not possible. We therefore conducted the interviews via whichever media platform was most readily available to the interviewees, given restrictions and limitations including time zone, working hours and multifarious commitments on the part of interviewers and interviewees. Therefore, our interview data were collected via Skype, Zoom and telephone in addition to email dialogue in order to gather the most up-to-date views and reactions from senior-level actors in international financial markets. All participants are senior practitioners in leading roles within their organisations, and we contacted them directly and individually with an invitation to participate. We also attempted to invite interviewees to take part in our research by sharing an invitation through our LinkedIn networks, although this produced little response (two participants in total). Recruiting interviewees involved a snowball process as we gained additional interviewees from those we contacted initially. Interviewees were asked to talk broadly in response to three general research questions around COVID-19, biodiversity/extinction accounting and investor engagement on biodiversity, species extinction and habitat loss. They were all invited to discuss at length (and in some cases write at length, broadly around the subject in email dialogue and exchanges) about any related issues they felt were important. The three overarching, general research questions were:

How do you think investor engagement on ecosystem services, biodiversity and species extinction could assist in preventing another pandemic in the future?

Do you think that Covid-19 has affected investor demand for corporate disclosures on biodiversity, species extinction and related areas?

Will biodiversity reporting and extinction accounting be given more attention in the wake of Covid-19?

A total of 28 senior representatives from the international institutional investment and governance communities took part in our research, and the details of the participants' roles within their organisations are displayed in Table 26.1. All participants were assured confidentiality so that their responses could not be attributed to them or to their organisations. The codes attributed to each participant are included in Table 26.1.

TABLE 26.1 Interviewees' details

Code	Respondents' roles
R1	Corporate governance and integrated reporting specialist
R2	Senior ESG investor in a leading investment institution
R3	Senior climate and disaster resilience advisor
R4	Consultant on biodiversity reporting
R5	ESG consultant and rating specialist
R6	Director and owner of a certified chartered accountant's office
R7	Corporate governance consultant
R8	Institutional investor lobby group
R9	Institutional investor lobby group
R10	Institutional investor lobby group
R11	Corporate governance consultant
R12	Investment banker
R13	Investment analyst
R14	Fund manager
R15	Fund manager
R16	Fund analyst
R17	Risk analyst
R18	Attorney
R19	Senior Member of AIAF's Sustainability and ESG Observatory
R20	Member of AIAF's Sustainability and ESG Observatory
R21	Corporate governance consultant
R22	SDGs product manager, investment consultancy
R23	Senior Partner, ESG Investment Institution
R24	Academic in ESG? Or practitioner as well
R25	Risk analyst
R26	Risk analyst
R27	Fund manager
R28	Director of a sustainability rating agency (Italy)

The interviewees' utterances were collated and analysed interpretively, with the researchers drawing out themes from the data. In some cases, follow-up conversations were held to clarify further some of the points made by interviewees, and also, given the dynamic, fast-moving situation around COVID-19, many interviewees contacted us after they provided their initial response to the research questions with further thoughts and reflections.

The second stage of the research involved integrating the findings from our interview research and our literature survey, into the existing extinction engagement frameworks, in order to render pandemic risk explicit and visible. We sought to identify intervention points where ESG investor engagement could increase resilience and strengthen systems against the risk of future pandemics. We interpreted our resulting frameworks and survey findings through a theoretical lens derived primarily from the work of Beck and his Plato's *Allegory of the Cave*, as outlined earlier.

The Views of Practitioners on Links between COVID-19, Biodiversity, Species Extinction and Extinction Engagement[22]

The interviewees emphasised the interdependence of investor engagement and reporting on biodiversity and species extinction and the ways in which investor demand for biodiversity information and engagement processes represent a primary driver of reporting in these areas, which adds to external drivers of increased accounting for biodiversity such as the United Nations or national initiatives, and other motivations discussed above (impression management, deep ecology and ethics) in addition to heightened societal awareness and pressure for greater accountability. The analysis of the interviewees' utterances revealed several themes as discussed below.

COVID-19 Has Accelerated a Shift in Societal Awareness of Links between Biodiversity, Species Extinction, Habitat Loss, Business Risk and Pandemics

The interviewees identified the treatment of 'nature' by humanity as a causal factor underlying the outbreak of COVID-19,

> There can be no question whatsoever that the manner in which we have treated ecosystem services, biodiversity and species extinction has played a major role in the pandemic through which we are living and which, sadly, will continue to live in for a relatively long period of time.
>
> *(R18)*

Interconnectedness was considered to be exaggerated by COVID-19. Such interconnectedness was identified as core to the extinction accounting and engagement frameworks (Atkins and Maroun, 2018),

The speed and impact of this Covid-19 crisis has highlighted the interconnectedness of (systemic) ESG issues, which has likely been accelerated by the onset of global warming and the destruction of biodiversity, species and natural habitat.

(R5)

One African risk analyst connected humanity's treatment of nature not only with the roots of the current pandemic but also with business activities, in terms of mining and other points where people come into direct contact with wildlife,[23]

There is a lot of talk about how this [the pandemic] started because of people trafficking and eating things they should not be. So you say [one may say] that this has nothing to do with companies and in a lot of cases that is true but the lesson to take away is that how we engage with the environment can have an impact on how we live and do business. It's unlikely that our companies are going to start serving bats and pangolins to the staff for lunch but the bigger picture is being brought into focus. How you extract natural resources and your contact with the environment has consequences, some of which are not foreseen. In my view, Covid-19 has brought environmental risks into focus and this will include biodiversity and how companies manage their impact and exposure.

(R17)

Indeed, interviewees emphasised that COVID-19 has raised societal awareness around human impacts on nature, to a higher level than was previously the case,

I believe people are now realising that they are not in control of nature. This is raising biodiversity issues.

(R1)

Similarly, the implications of such a shift in societal attitudes around nature and biodiversity for business were identified by a corporate governance consultant,

…public understanding can pressure investors and boards into having a more 'ecological/systems' mindset once the virus is under way. Thus prevents rapid spreading and saves lives.

(R11)

This is suggestive of a raised societal consciousness and consequently a raised corporate and investor consciousness around the need to protect biodiversity which resonates with the concept of people coming out of Plato's cavern and seeing another reality for business and society.

Investor Engagement on Biodiversity Can Reduce Pandemic Risk

There was an unambiguous view among many interviewees that engagement on biodiversity, extinction and related issues could potentially prevent another pandemic, if not at least reduce the likelihood,

> I absolutely believe that investor engagement could assist [in preventing another pandemic].
>
> *(R18)*

One interviewee, who described herself as an 'authentic investor', commented that,

> I am convinced that engagement on biodiversity depletion and preserving biodiversity ecosystems is really relevant to prevent eventual future pandemics. The destruction of the wild habitat as a result of increasing deforestation and urbanization, particularly in South East Asia, the Amazon region and Africa is at the core of the outburst of recent epidemics - SARS, Ebola, etc.
>
> *(R23)*

Others felt that if a link were to be clearly established, then engagement would follow,

> I suppose from an awareness point of view. I mean, if these [biodiversity and extinction] environmental issues are central to the business, there is engagement on them. We are engaging on issues like climate change already so I suppose we will see how Covid-19 affects businesses and how that translates into risk exposure. If the link between biodiversity and risk is clear, it will get tracked.
>
> *(R14)*

A senior ESG engagement specialist highlighted external initiatives that were already driving enhanced engagement on biodiversity and related issues, also identifying COVID-19 as an additional catalyst,

> My thinking on this isn't mature yet but so far I am very pleased to see biodiversity has a much more prominent role in the ESG world than .... in late 2018. Perhaps this is because of UN's 15th COP on the Convention for Biological Diversity in October of 2020 and HM Treasury's Dasgupta Review on the Economics of Biodiversity. Hopefully we will see a clear link drawn between habitat loss and the spread of novel viruses as a lasting effect of Covid-19.
>
> *(R2)*

In a European context, the financial analysts' perspective was,

> We think Covid-19 is embedding the strategic importance of sustainable investments particularly focused on healthcare, education and financial inclusion. We highlight how the EU developments in defining a framework with taxonomy, reporting and incentives indicated in the European green deal, but also from the European Renewed Sustainable Finance Strategy, take into account Covid-19, minimum safeguard standard and certainly environmental standards also in the field of biodiversity. As indicated in the framework of the Stockholm Resilience Centre[24] two limits have been exceeded; one is precisely the loss of biodiversity that has now entered a point of no return.
>
> *(R19–20)*

One interviewee, a specialist in ESG investment, said that,

> I think that the participation of investors within the framework of international or a national plan that includes environmental diversity will be positive and make a difference in reducing the size of the impact or preventing future pandemics.
>
> *(R6)*

A risk analyst in the investment industry asserted the importance of engagement in raising corporate awareness around issues of concern to investors and the emancipatory nature of engagement,

> [Covid-19] Will play an important role – if companies are not engaged, they assume that the investors don't worry about it. You know that we say, if it's not measured it doesn't get done. It's the same when it comes to the analysis. If we don't ask the questions, companies assume that the information is not important so then they stop reporting it. It is as simple as that.
>
> *(R17)*

COVID-19 Is a Catalyst Highlighting the Importance of Engagement on Biodiversity

Interviewees indicated that COVID-19 seems to be a catalyst shifting attitudes around biodiversity to a higher level,

> To date it's fair to say that engagement on ecosystem services, biodiversity and species extinction has been contained to a small enlightened group of investors … However, the pandemic highlights the need to scale up engagement on these issues to focus on the risks of tipping points both in relation to ecosystem collapse and to human health. *Engagement in this area*

has the potential to move from being a niche engagement stream to a fundamental philosophical principle that underpins investment strategies, where investors understand that the stability and resilience of ecological systems are linked to the resilience and stability of societies, businesses and ultimately their portfolios and the capital markets.

(R8–10, emphasis added)

Furthermore, interviewees asserted that biodiversity had been eclipsed by climate change but that this shadowing will change in the wake of COVID-19, as biodiversity loss and species extinction are at least equal threats to humanity and from a Becksian perspective, at least equivalent as high consequence risks,

> Climate change seems to be the focus of trade-offs at present – but species extinction etc. is inter related but is much lower in visibility by media etc. I think this year may be seen as a turning point to move to the E in ESG.
>
> *(R7)*

One interviewee suggested possible intervention points for responsible investor engagement, which can be directly integrated into the extinction engagement framework,

> It [investors] could ask questions about the location and scale of impacts of supply chains as well as the mitigation measures put in place. Depending on the specifics, it [investor engagement] could request further information on red flag areas or species traded; which may lead to difficult discussions about business strategy going forward.
>
> *(R4)*

From the perspective of our theoretical framework, COVID-19 seems to be a catalyst revealing a second reality and from that raised consciousness, accelerating action among the investor community on biodiversity and species extinction.

Need for ESG Investor Training

A salient recommendation was for more specialised training in ESG for investors,

> In my opinion the way that investor engagement can be improved is by both training investors to have high and due regard for ESG issues and also, sadly I may say, having the obligations on investors part of a statute with draconian punishment for not complying.
>
> *(R18)*

With reference to our theoretical framework, in Plato's 'Allegory of the Cave', the philosopher discussed the need for education and philosophy in order to bring enlightenment and raised consciousness. Training, education and reflection are critical to raising awareness among financial institutions and businesses in relation to biodiversity.

Increased Engagement on Biodiversity Will Drive Increased Biodiversity Reporting

The interviewees believed that COVID-19 has increased consciousness in the international investment community around the need for biodiversity reporting. When asked if she thought COVID-19 may affect investor demand for corporate disclosures on biodiversity and related area, one senior member of the investment community stated emphatically,

> Yes, I think that more and more investors will engage with companies to improve their disclosure on biodiversity and related areas such as deforestation, intensive farming, plastic pollutions of the oceans, ice melting, etc. A few dialogues on these topics started already in recent years, however investors are going to focus their attention more.
>
> (R23)

This confirms a strong relationship between private and public reporting on biodiversity and species extinction, which has been found in earlier studies for social and environmental reporting more broadly, but not specifically for biodiversity issues (Solomon and Solomon, 2006). The interviewees also confirmed that COVID-19 is acting as a catalyst, accelerating an increased investor focus on biodiversity and consequently an increased demand for corporate reporting,

> I believe that biodiversity reports will receive extraordinary attention, which has made the Covid-19 pandemic a positive opportunity to disclose biodiversity.
>
> (R6)

Indeed, the interviewees highlighted the powerful influence of the pandemic in these areas,

> Given the better understanding among investors of the interconnectedness of these ESG issues, a stronger focus on extra-financial risks and an increasing corporate effort around defining disclosure, metrics and frameworks, there is and will be a stronger focus on biodiversity reporting. Especially now, in the context and in the aftermath of Covid-19.
>
> (R5)

Interviewees suggested that there had recently been a heightened interest in biodiversity reporting, driven by external factors such as EU-wide initiatives, as discussed earlier, but that COVID-19 had accelerated this change.

We're already seeing the European Commission re-emphasising the importance of disclosure on biodiversity and climate in the context of Covid-19. That said, the EC *was already paying attention to this area before the pandemic...* It's also possible that the new international targets to be set at CBD COP will be framed in the context of the pandemic. Since there's a push for these to be 'smarter' and more easily translated for private sector actors, there may be more attention on reporting and disclosure as a result.

(R8–10)

Senior financial analysts working within the institutional investment industry pointed out that enhanced biodiversity reporting in the wake of COVID-19 could assist in preventing future pandemics; in other words, they seem to perceive biodiversity reporting as emancipatory in this respect,

So future policies, reporting and monitoring will have to help maintain optimal biodiversity in order to hope to survive and avoid catastrophic events that are now very intense and frequent all over the world as described by WWF.

(R19–20)[25]

One fund manager emphasised the importance of integrated reporting as a vehicle for accounting for biodiversity and species extinction, as suggested by King with Atkins and Atkins (2016),

I think people will report on pandemics and biodiversity will come in as part of that. It will be part of explaining the risks and how the risks are managed and it will form part of the integrated report. So I don't think we'll see a special report on biodiversity. I would not think that this is very useful. It [accounting on biodiversity] *must be part of the integrated report* and the link to the numbers must be clear.

(R14, emphasis added)

Not only was the materiality of biodiversity and species extinction recognised and highlighted by our interviewees but also the concept of double materiality for biodiversity was viewed as an important issue to be explored in the current context,

Finally should be considered, for the materiality of non-financial information related to biodiversity, the concept of *double materiality*, previously absent, as defined for climate change information by the EU group of Technical Experts on Sustainable Finance (TEG): Information on biodiversity communicated, if necessary, to understand the internal impacts on company's performance and outcome; Biodiversity information must even be disclosed, if necessary, to understand the external impacts of the company's activities.

(R19–20, emphasis added)

There was a strong endorsement that COVID-19 will drive investor interest in biodiversity and that investors will in turn demand more biodiversity information from companies,

> ...- there's no doubt that investor interest in biodiversity and related areas will have surged as a result of the pandemic and that this will have sparked a demand from investors for greater corporate disclosure on biodiversity-related impacts and dependencies.

(R8–10)

Mandatory Approaches to Reporting and Engagement on Biodiversity as a Result of COVID-19

The interviewees felt that the voluntary environment for extinction accounting and extinction engagement had failed to encourage adequate practice in these areas and that legislation, a mandatory approach, was now necessary in the wake of the current pandemic. An attorney involved in governance commented that a mandatory approach to engagement in the biodiversity area was necessary,

> The problem of course is that most investors are passive and the only interest is the dividends received. In my opinion the way that investor engagement can be improved is by ... sadly I may say, having the obligations on investors part of a statute with draconian punishment for not complying.

(R18)

Similarly, an interviewee[26] suggested a shift to mandatory reporting in the biodiversity space,

> Likely that other drivers of corporate disclosure, such as mandatory regulation - as well as developments in the corporate liability space - at the national/regional level will force both corporates and investors to pay closer attention to disclosure and transparency.

(R8–10)

There has been debate in the academic accounting literature for many years around whether environmental reporting should be mandatory. Although there has been a shift towards mandatory environmental disclosures, especially in relation to climate change and greenhouse gas emissions, perhaps COVID-19 is the catalyst required to force mandatory extinction and biodiversity accounting.

There were also suggestions that governments needed to take a lead to engender greater attention to accounting in these areas,

> Finally, I do not see how individual companies reporting on their biodiversity policies and action will have any impact on the cause or containment of this or future pandemics without government policy changes to provide the climate and environment with adequate protection.
>
> *(R12)*

Need for Stakeholder as Well as ESG Engagement on Biodiversity and Pandemic Risk

One corporate governance expert raised stakeholder engagement in addition to investor engagement as an important mechanism for protecting biodiversity and species,

> I think it's stakeholder engagement rather than only investor. Further, engagement will not prevent another pandemic but will make the world better prepared to deal with it. A stakeholder engagement approach will better support human well-beings. It will also result in a more protective approach to plant & animal life... stakeholder engagement will slow down human conduct which is unnaturally accelerating extinction.
>
> *(R1)*

Indeed, another interviewee saw stakeholder engagement, as well as investor engagement, key to driving an increase in corporate reporting on biodiversity and extinction of species,

> Probably – in our experience, companies react to stakeholder engagement. If stakeholders start asking questions, they will start reporting.
>
> *(R17)*

Obstacles to Increasing Extinction Accounting and Engagement in the Wake of COVID-19

Despite an endorsement of the need to increase focus on extinction accounting and engagement as a result of COVID-19, some interviewees suggested obstacles, at least in the short term, to this shift in attitudes and practice. These included the proliferation of competing frameworks in the biodiversity area, and impression management in biodiversity reporting and extinction accounting.

Competing Frameworks: An important obstacle to progress in the area of biodiversity reporting and extinction accounting identified by our participants was the increasing competition in the reporting space, with so many organisations producing 'their' frameworks,

The ESG framework providers are dealing with matters of public interest & should merge. Social outrage to regard each other as competitors. There is movement now on convergence of providers in the ESG cluster ...... I have argued that they should not see themselves as competitors because they are dealing with public interest issues. There should be collaboration and convergence, for example of the SASB and the GRI. This plethora of framework providers in the ESG cluster leads to confusion for preparers and a dilution of comparability. The end result is "non disclosure"out of uncertainty and confusion on materiality.

(R1)

Some of the interviews indicated that the immediate concern for investors and businesses is (obviously) to deal with health and medical issues and economic impact, but as this subsides, the focus will shift to biodiversity and will be related as causal factors of the pandemic. While acknowledging the importance of bio-diversity and extinction engagement, there was a feeling that in the short term, other issues would have to take priority,

> ... at the moment, people are looking at how Covid-19 is impacting their business. The focus is very much on the economic fundamentals. We want to know if companies will get through this. After we have gotten past that, there will be a lot of reflection. People will start to think long and hard about how this started and how we need to fix the fundamentals.
>
> *(R14)*

Impression Management: Another obstacle, identified by the interviewees, to improved and enhanced reporting in the area of biodiversity and extinction was the potential for impression management,

> ... the directors, officers and committee members will have no choice but to report widely and deeply on biodiversity because, as I have stated, the law will require them to do so. Sadly research has shown that *there is not always a correlation between what companies say in their reporting and what they actually do.*
>
> *(R18, emphasis added)*

This quotation indicates possible impression management in biodiversity report-ing as an obstacle to genuine accountability in this area in line with. Interestingly, biodiversity reporting is referred to as 'platitudes' in the following quotation from an investment banker, as this is suggestive of impression management rather than genuine accountability for biodiversity impacts,

> Platitudes in annual reports are a long way down the list of information that is moving markets today. The pandemic itself may have made a posi-tive contribution to improving biodiversity, but at a significant cost.
>
> *(R12)*

Obstacles may be interpreted through our theoretical framework as the shackles preventing the prisoners from turning to see the light, or their desire having seen a second reality to return to the darkness of the cave.

Raised Consciousness of a Second Reality: The Emergence of a Shadow Kingdom?

The interviewees believed that in response to COVID-19, we are now witnessing a raising of consciousness and awareness of the importance of enhancing biodiversity habitats and preventing species extinctions, at a societal level and throughout businesses and investment institutions. Interviewees described COVID-19 as a crisis point, 'tsunami', a catalyst, a stepping stone, a 'piece of alchemy', even a reincarnation. This perception was also associated with a feeling of hope that, despite the ongoing global human tragedy, positive change in attitude and behaviour would ensue from the crisis,

> Covid-19 has caused me to have a very real and very realistic view of the world. But I remain hopeful that *the new world coming will be positively different to the world that we leave behind* and that all of our hopes and dreams for proper attention to be given to ecosystem services, biodiversity and species extinction will become a reality and an absolute must for us all.
>
> *(R18, emphasis added)*

Indeed, there have been suggestions that it is increasingly clear that further pandemics will arise unless human behaviour changes and societies seek to nurse the planet back to health (Hassan et al., 2020a; Roberts et al., 2020). Indeed, one corporate governance consultant considered that urgent change in behaviours and attitudes was critical in the wake of COVID-19,

> Covid-19 is a *very major message to Humanity to change its behaviour immediately* ... If Humanity thinks it can simply sweep Covid-19 under the carpet *without any real change* then this will not be possible; *not without a major shift in our behaviour* .... we haven't been as conscious of it as now ... How we change Humanity and organisations in their behaviours ... is utterly critical but it needs to happen at a *deep personal level not just as a tick on a corporate and social environmental checklist!!* ... but tough to get people to shift quick enough.
>
> *(R21)*

From the perspective of our theoretical framework, COVID-19 may be seen as a catalyst, or a Goffmanesque key, that is forcing an increased societal awareness around the impact of human and business behaviour on nature and consequently on ourselves. This raised awareness is shifting people's perceptions outside Plato's

'Cave', so they view the second reality, or the Shadow Kingdom, as Beck discussed, the reality behind the façade of safe, everyday reality. One interviewee emphasised that COVID-19 may be with us permanently and that, therefore, changes in attitude and behaviours may be forced to persist.

There were, however, interviewees who did not see a need for change and did not anticipate a shift towards increased accounting and engagement on biodiversity and extinction (R15, 16). We could interpret them as continuing to sit in the 'Cave' due to a lack of awareness, although the societal shift in awareness may alter their perceptions. For example, one commented,

> …. not sure what biodiversity reporting is.
>
> *(R15)*

Perhaps there is a separation of society into those whose awareness and consciousness are raised by COVID-19 and those for whom this shift does not happen, as suggested by one interviewee,

> There is a bifurcation taking place. Humanity will split. There are individuals who have their consciousness raised but only some will move on. For others the planet continues to be just a resource for us to abuse.
>
> *(R21)*

Given the endorsement by the majority of our interviewees that there is an urgent need to integrate pandemic risk into engagement and disclosure, we now turn to rendering it explicit within the existing extinction accounting and engagement frameworks.

Rendering Pandemic Risk Explicit in the Extinction Accounting and Engagement Frameworks

The latest version of the extinction accounting framework (Atkins and Maroun, forthcoming) and the extinction engagement framework (Atkins and Maroun, 2018) may be adapted to incorporate pandemic risk management. Our interviewees indicated that biodiversity, species extinction and related issues will receive heightened attention in accounting and investor engagement. Consequently, we established a series of intervention points for investor engagement on pandemic risk reduction, based around the linkages between COVID-19, biodiversity decline, species extinction, habitat loss and related areas. These interventions are expressed as questions that investors may pose to investee organisations and similarly questions organisations can respond to in their reporting. The questions were derived from the findings of our interviews as well as from the scientific and interdisciplinary literature summarised in this chapter. For each investor engagement question, relevant industries are suggested where these interventions could be effective.

BOX 26.1 INCORPORATING PANDEMIC RISK INTO EXTINC-TION ENGAGEMENT

Focused Questions on Pandemic Risk Management

How do you protect against wildlife trafficking/poaching throughout your value/supply chain?

(airline industry, shipping industry, agricultural/farming industry, tourism/hotel industry)

How do ensure that every part of your value/supply chain takes precautions to avoid cross-species contamination from animals to employees, customers and other stakeholders?

(food industry (production/retail), agriculture/farming industry, timber/paper industry, mining and extractives industry, fishing/seafood industry, tourisms/hotel industry)

How do you ensure that your value/supply chain has no connection with 'wet markets' or the human consumption of endangered wildlife, such as pangolin and bats?

(food industry (production/retail), tourism/hotel industry, fishing/seafood industry)

What efforts are you making to reduce meat content of your products, or explore and find meat alternatives in your products?

(food industry (production/retail), agriculture/farming industry, tourism/hotel industry)

How are you seeking to reduce deforestation in your supply/value chain?

(agriculture/farming industry, timber/paper industry, mining/extractive industry)

How do you engage with your stakeholders to reduce pandemic risk (with reference to all of the above questions)?

(all industries)

How do you protect customers, employees and other stakeholders from potential contamination (animal to human transmission) passed through plastic waste?

(all industries)

Can you explain how your business continuity strategies incorporate effective measures to deal with global pandemics?

(all industries)

Can you identify where you may have weaknesses in your systems of internal control and risk management that relate to disease transmission, such as coronavirus?

(all industries)

Broad Questions on Biodiversity and Extinction (all industries)

How do you inform yourselves about species decline and extinction threats in relation to your business activities?

In what ways is your supply chain, both upstream and downstream, likely to be affected by species loss?

Have you commissioned any studies to determine which species threatened with extinction on the IUCN Red List are directly or indirectly affected by your operations, or those of organisations within your supply chain?

If you have commissioned studies, what were the outcomes? Have you identified which species are most at risk and what the financial (and other: reputational, social responsibility, ethical, moral) consequences of decline and extinction of these species are for your organisation?

Are you engaging, or partnering, with any wildlife organisation regarding species threatened with extinction, for example the WWF? If so what are the outcomes of these engagements/partnerships?

Are you engaging, or partnering, with any NGOs regarding the reduction of wildlife trafficking and the trade in endangered animals in order to reduce risks of disease transmission from animals to humans?

What contingency measures, risk scenarios and mitigation strategies have you considered regarding species decline and extinction?

What measures are you taking to reduce and limit the impact of your operations on ecosystems?

What measures are you taking to protect and enhance habitats which you own or have an impact on in order to protect wildlife and keep them away from human activity?

What initiatives, policies and strategies have you implemented in order to prevent species extinction?

Have you assessed the impact of these initiatives, policies and strategies on species populations?

Have your assessments led to alterations and improvements in your initiatives, policies and strategies?

If they have, in what ways has your extinction prevention strategy altered?

Are you employing/developing AI to assist in habitat and species protection through your value/supply chain?

Concluding Discussion: Revealing the Shadow Kingdom?

Interviews with 28 members of the international institutional investment community and governance experts revealed that as a result of COVID-19 they believed: investor engagement on biodiversity and extinction will grow; investor demand for corporate reporting on biodiversity will increase; and there will be a corresponding increased focus on biodiversity in corporate reporting. Further, we sought to integrate pandemic risk management into the existing extinction engagement frameworks. In addition to the financial rationale for preventing extinctions and protecting species, habitats and ecosystems that has been explored in earlier papers, the onslaught of COVID-19 and its causality lying in animal to human species transmission (and associated links with habitat loss and biodiversity issues), there is now another pertinent rationale for preventing poaching, illegal wildlife trafficking and the human consumption of endangered species. By rendering explicit various elements within the frameworks, their implementation can assist in reducing the risk of a re-occurrence of the current crippling COVID-19 outbreak. If business and financial institutions incorporate these elements into their reporting and governance frameworks, then there should be greater protection from potential future crises. A more respectful and holistic approach to human's relationship with nature and wildlife around the world is needed if we are to prevent extinction of the human race.

The findings are interpreted through a Becksian theoretical framework drawing from Plato's 'Allegory of the Cave' to show that COVID-19 has acted as a catalyst, heightening consciousness in society, and among investors and companies, around the importance of enhancing biodiversity and habitats and reducing species extinctions. Part of this raising of consciousness is increasing transparency and accountability. Rendering pandemic risk and risk management explicit within the extinction accounting and engagement frameworks assists in this process of raising societal and business awareness around biodiversity and extinction risk and their links with the risk of pandemics. This chapter seeks to contribute to the established academic accounting literature, by resonating with earlier seminal work on construction and communication of realities through financial accounting, especially the need to, '...*breach* a way of seeing or a worldview, in order to create a new way of seeing .... "Stopping the world", or dissolving our taken-for-granted conception of reality...' (Hines, 1988, p. 258).[27] The second reality discussed in this chapter, the 'Shadow Kingdom', revealed by COVID-19, is certainly 'stopping the world' and has shattered global societies' taken-for-granted conception of reality, especially in terms of the critical interdependencies and linkages between extinction engagement, extinction accounting and pandemic risk. This chapter seeks to 'stop the world' of institutional investment and accounting practice and research in a similar way that Ruth Hines sought to, '... momentarily breach or "stop the world" of mainstream financial accounting research' (1988, p. 258). We only hope that this awakening of the investment and accounting industries may be permanent and not momentary.

We can see from the discussion above that enhancing biodiversity, protecting species from extinction, preventing deforestation, protecting habitat and ecosystems no longer rely solely on ethical arguments or cases of financial risk management but have an imperative around human health and survival, as a result of COVID-19. Dolphin-friendly tuna is no longer an ethical issue but one grounded in protecting stakeholders from potential disease transmission. COVID-19 as a catalyst has shifted biodiversity from occupying solely the 'E' (environmental) category of ESG, to the 'S' (social) category due to connections with human health and survival, and also 'G' (governance) as biodiversity and ecological considerations are becoming core elements of a holistic approach to governance and accountability (King et al., forthcoming). There may also be legal liabilities and issues of human rights for organisations that do not take precautions to protect stakeholders from contamination in the ways outlined in the framework above.

Challenges abound in the wake of COVID-19. One significant challenge for the financial and accounting communities is the ongoing proliferation of competing disclosure frameworks, leading to confusion and lack of comparability among preparers and users. The intention of the extinction framework is, and has always been, to provide a structure around which organisations can report on biodiversity, species, habitat and ecosystems within the existing integrated reporting framework, as endorsed by King with Atkins and Atkins (2016). Further, the interview findings provide an imperative for mandatory reporting on biodiversity and species extinction.

In conclusion, there are growing hopes in societies around the world that we do not return to the way the world was viewed before – we need to stay in this raised state of consciousness and not return, dazzled and blinded into Plato's cavern. The cataclysmic impact of one isolated instance of coronavirus transmission from a wild animal (probably a bat/pangolin) to one human on global trade, global economies and the global financial system is only just beginning to be revealed. Such risks have to be made explicit within our accounting frameworks and our investor engagement processes in order to ensure that another strand of coronavirus is never transmitted to humans again. Protection of businesses, the financial markets and people from pandemics needs to be made explicit within accounting, finance and governance frameworks as critical elements of all systems of internal control and risk management. COVID-19 has catapulted responsible investor engagement on biodiversity and species protection, as well as accounting for biodiversity and extinction accounting, onto centre stage. The challenge now is to keep these crucial financial market mechanisms at the forefront of practice and policy in order to enhance resilience and protect the world from a re-occurrence of the current pandemic.

Acknowledgements

We are grateful to the 29 members of the international investment and governance community who participated in this study, providing rich interview data by Zoom, Skype, email dialogue and other media during these unprecedented and challenging times. Thanks also to delegates who attended a presentation of this paper for the Egyptian Online Seminars in Business, Accounting and Economics on 22 May 2020, for their valuable comments and questions. We are also grateful to the British Academy for supporting this research. We are also grateful to Barry Atkins and Zoe Clare Solomon for their helpful insights on drafts of this paper.

Notes

1 Investor engagement involves direct engagement and dialogue between institutional investors and their investee companies around a variety of issues, often in the form of one-on-one meetings. In the academic literature, this process is often referred to as private reporting.
2 See Atkins and Maroun (2018).
3 The extinction engagement framework has been developed in a number of papers and books, specifically: Atkins and Maroun (2018) and Atkins and Atkins (2019).
4 Many examples have been cited to demonstrate the material financial implications of losing various species including bees (Atkins and Atkins, 2016), rhinoceros (Atkins et al., 2018), fruit bats (flying foxes) (Atkins and Macpherson, 2019).
5 IPBES Report, Summary for policymakers of the global assessment report on biodiversity and ecosystem services of the Intergovernmental Science-Policy Platform on Biodiversity and Ecosystem Services, May 2019.
6 See also Atkins and Atkins (2016) which builds a case for businesses to protect bees and other pollinators grounded in financial risk as well as deep ecology and intrinsic value.
7 https://www.gov.uk/government/news/pm-launches-new-action-plan-to-save-the-natural-world.
8 The Review will report ahead of the 15th meeting of the Conference of the Parties to the Convention on Biological Diversity – an international biodiversity summit taking place in Kunming, China, in October 2020; see more details at https://www.gov.uk/government/collections/the-economics-of-biodiversity-the-dasgupta-review.
9 A recent media report stated that, 'Large-scale deforestation, habitat degradation and fragmentation, agriculture intensification, our food system, trade in species and plants, anthropogenic climate change – all these are drivers of biodiversity loss and also drivers of new diseases. Two thirds of emerging infections and diseases now come from wildlife.' (BBC, 2020).
10 See further details of this research at https://www.bangor.ac.uk/research/news/-1-85m-study-to-investigate-microbes-hitch-hiking-on-marine-plastics-39114.
11 Consultation document: Renewed sustainable finance strategy, https://ec.europa.eu/info/consultations/finance-2020-sustainable-finance-strategy_en.
12 See Gray and Milne (2018).
13 Plato was born in Athens around 429BC and died in 347BC. He wrote over 20 philosophical dialogues, a form of philosophical writing through argument and conversation, as dialogues between imaginary characters were used as a means of presenting opposing arguments in an approachable form (Watt, 1997).
14 Giddens defines this state, or rather process, of engulfment as occurring where, '… an individual feels overwhelmed by a sense of powerlessness in the major domains of his phenomenal world, we may speak of a process of engulfment. The individual feels dominated by encroaching forces from the outside, which he is unable to resist or transcend' (1991, p. 193).
15 The conversion of St Paul on the road to Damascus is documented in the Bible, in Acts 9:1-19, Acts 22:6-21 and Acts 26:12-18. Originally, Saul of Tarsus, made every effort to wipe out the new Christian church but following his conversion which blinded him, regained his sight and saw the Truth, saw the world around him in a completely different way.
16 See the write-up of the event at https://www.investec.com/en_gb/focus/investing/-to-bee-or-not-to-bee-species-extinction.html.
17 ShareAction is a non-profit aimed at building a global investment sector which is responsible for its impacts on people and planet.
18 https://shareaction.org/wp-content/uploads/2019/09/State-of-the-Apes-investor-briefing-compressed.pdf.

19 Details at https://www.cdsb.net/events/1028/consultation-results-advancing-nature-related-financial-disclosures-and-use-cdsb.

20 It is notable that CDSB attended and spoke at the Investec event in May 2019 and at that time, in response to the discussions on extinction accounting and engagement, and the newly launched Species Protection Action Plan for the Financial Markets, raised the idea of using the existing CDSB climate framework for natural capital.

21 As this research forms part of a fully funded research project researching the implementation of extinction accounting and extinction engagement, we have funds available for interviewing, travel, transcription but at present cannot use these, given the restrictions. We therefore decided to continue with our research online – research ethics approval has been given in advance for this research for interviews without specifying method.

22 Note that although we use the term extinction accounting and engagement throughout the paper, in this section we also use the terms accounting for biodiversity, biodiversity reporting and engagement on biodiversity interchangeably, to reflect the questions posed to practitioners in the interviews, as a variety of terms are currently used in practice for issues relating to biodiversity, species extinction, habitat. This lack of consensus on terminology among practitioners, and in the academic literature, is, we feel, symptomatic of the newness of this area.

23 Mining which forced close contact between employees and wildlife, especially bats, was at the root of the Ebola outbreak.

24 Stockholm Resilience Center, 'The nine planetary boundaries', https://www.stockholmresilience.org/research/planetary-boundaries/planetaryboundaries/about-the-research/the-nine-planetary-boundaries.html.

25 The interviewee was referring here to the WWF, 'Living Planet Report 2016. Risk and resilience in the new era' and subsequent updates.

26 This institutional response was sent by email, following up from an online informal discussion with three members of a shareholder lobby organisation working with and influencing the international institutional investment community.

27 Hines (1988) built on the social construction framework of Berger and Luckmann (1966) and Giddens (1984).

References

Adler, R., Mansi, M. and Pandey, R. (2018), "Biodiversity and threatened species reporting by the top Fortune Global companies", *Accounting, Auditing & Accountability Journal*, Vol. 31 No. 3, pp. 787–825.

Anderson, J.C. and Frankle, A.W. (1980), "Voluntary social reporting: An iso-beta portfolio analysis", *The Accounting Review*, Vol. 55 No. 3, pp. 467–479.

Atkins, J. and Atkins, B. (eds.) (2016), *The Business of Bees: An Integrated Approach to Bee Decline and Corporate Responsibility*, Routledge, UK.

Atkins, J. and Atkins, B. (2019), *Around the World in 80 Species: Exploring the Business of Extinction,* Routledge, UK.

Atkins, J., Atkins, B., Thomson, I. and Maroun, W. (2015), 'Good' news from nowhere: Imagining utopian sustainable accounting. *Accounting, Auditing & Accountability Journal*, Vol. 28 No. 5, pp. 651–670.

Atkins, J. and Macpherson, M. (2019), "Developing a species protection action plan – An integrated approach for taxonomies, reporting and engagement for the financial services sector", Concept Paper circulated and presented at Investec Bank's Natural Capital, Species Extinction & Sustainable Financial Markets Event, 30th May.

Atkins, J. and Maroun, W. (2018), "Integrated extinction accounting and accountability: Building an ark", *Accounting, Auditing & Accountability Journal*, Vol. 31 No. 3, pp. 750–786.

Atkins, J. and Maroun, W. (forthcoming), "The *Naturalist's Journals* of Gilbert White: Exploring the roots of accounting for biodiversity and extinction accounting", *Accounting, Auditing & Accountability Journal* 33(8), 1835-1870. doi:10.1108/aaaj-03-2016-2450.

Atkins, J., Maroun, W., Atkins, B., Barone. E. (2018), "From the big five to the big four? Exploring extinction accounting for the rhinoceros?" *Accounting, Auditing & Accountability Journal*, Vol. 31 No. 2, pp. 1–31.

Atkins, J. F. Solomon, A., Norton, S. D. and Joseph, J.L. (2015), "The emergence of integrated private reporting", *Meditari Accountancy Research*, Vol. 23, No. 1, pp. 28–61.

BBC. (2020). Shenzhen becomes first Chinese city to ban eating cats and dogs. 2nd April. https://www.bbc.co.uk/news/world-asia-china52131940?at_medium=custom7&at_custom1=%5Bpost+type%5D&at_campaign=64&at_custom3=BBC+News&at_custom4=4BF95526-74C0-11EA-A6C0-97C296E8478F&at_custom2=facebook_page&fbclid=IwAR3bb9IothZgxG5NPaGD7CbQVfJYlhTM_h0s6XaCcArdQR0n-cwf-EnFIKI.

Beck, U. (1992). *Risk Society: Towards a New Modernity*, SAGE Publications Ltd, London.

Belkaoui, A. (1980), "The impact of socio-economic accounting statements on the investment decision: An empirical study", *Accounting, Organizations and Society*, Vol. 5 No. 3, pp. 263–283.

Benjamin, J.J. and Stanga, K.G. (1977), "Difference in disclosure needs of major users of financial statements", *Accounting and Business Research*, Vol. 7 Summer, pp. 187–192. doi: 10.1080/00014788.1977.9728702.

Berger, P. and Luckmann, T. (1966), *The Social Construction of Reality: A Treatise in the Sociology of Knowledge,* Penguin Books, London.

Bloomfield, L., McIntosh, T. and Lambin, E. (2020), "Habitat fragmentation, livelihood behaviors, and contact between people and nonhuman primates in Africa", *Landscape Ecol* Vol. 35, pp. 985–1000. https://doi.org/10.1007/s10980-020-00995-.

Boiral, O. (2016), "Accounting for the unaccountable: Biodiversity reporting and impression management", *Journal of Business Ethics*, Vol. 135 No. 4, pp. 751–768.

Buzby, S.L. and Falk, H. (1978), "A survey of the interest in social responsibility information by mutual funds", *Accounting, Organizations and Society*, Vol. 3 Nos 3/4, pp. 191–201.

Buzby, S.L. and Falk, H. (1979), "Demand for social responsibility information by university investors", *The Accounting Review*, Vol. 54 No. 1, January, pp. 23–37.

Clancy, H. (2020), "Microsoft is building a 'Planetary Computer' to protect biodiversity". *Green Biz*, 16 April 2020, available at: https://www.greenbiz.com/article/microsoft-building-planetary-computer-protect-biodiversity (accessed on 18.04.2020).

Cohen, N. (2020), "Surely the link between abusing animals and the world's health is now clear. *The Guardian*, 11 April 2020 available at: https://www.theguardian.com/commentisfree/2020/apr/11/surely-the-link-between-abusing-animals-and-the-worlds-health-is-now-clear?CMP=fb_gu&utm_medium=Social&utm_source=Facebook&fbclid=IwAR2EILUsl6NCyRdtPmdSpWbkx4Wu03LpG-jsoZ0Gn_utbjcxt0WSUpBao2sU#Echobox=1586682476 (accessed on 20.04.2020).

Cuckston, T. (2013), "Bringing tropical forest biodiversity conservation into financial accounting calculation". *Accounting, Auditing & Accountability Journal*, Vol. 26 No. 5, pp. 688–714.

Cuckston, T. (2017), "Ecology-centred accounting for biodiversity in the production of a blanket bog". *Accounting, Auditing & Accountability Journal*, Vol. 30 No. 7, pp. 1537–1567.

Deegan, C. and Rankin, M. (1997), "The materiality of environmental information to users of environmental reports", *Accounting, Auditing & Accountability Journal*, Vol. 10 No. 4, pp. 562–583.

Einhorn, C. (2020), *"Animal Viruses Are Jumping to Humans. Forest Loss Makes It Easier".* *The New York Times*, 9 April 2020, available at: https://www.nytimes.com/2020/04/09/climate/animals-humans-virus-covid.html?smid=fb-share&fbclid=IwAR3xsq_zfaO7V93m4JyVk7L0FeDvhyQyJa8Pcr0iJA_s9zxDb2e6yPkQ. (accessed on 10.04.2020).

Feger, C. and Mermet, L. (2017), "A blueprint towards accounting for the management of ecosystems". *Accounting, Auditing & Accountability Journal*, Vol. 30 No. 7, pp. 1511–1536.

Freeman, M. and Groom, B. (2013), "Biodiversity valuation and the discount rate problem". *Accounting, Auditing & Accountability Journal*, Vol. 26 No. 5, pp. 715–745.

Gaia, S. and Jones, M. (2017), "UK local councils reporting of biodiversity values: A stakeholder perspective", *Accounting, Auditing & Accountability Journal*, Vol. 30 No. 7, pp. 1614--1638.

Gallhofer, S. and Haslam, J. (1996), "Accounting/art and the emancipatory project: Some reflections". *Accounting, Auditing & Accountability Journal*, Vol. 9 No. 5, pp. 23--44.

Gallhofer, S. and Haslam, J. (2019), "Some reflections on the construct of emancipatory accounting: Shifting meaning and the possibilities of a new pragmatism". *Critical Perspectives on Accounting*, Vol. 63 No. 5, pp. 1124--1140.

Gallhofer, S., Haslam, J. and Yonekura, A. (2013), "Further critical reflections on a contribution to the methodological issues debate in accounting". *Critical Perspectives on Accounting*, Vol. 24 No. 3, pp. 191–206.

Gallhofer, S., Haslam, J. and Yonekura, A. (2015), "Accounting as differentiated universal for emancipatory praxis: Accounting delineation and mobilisation for emancipation(s) recognising democracy and difference". *Accounting, Auditing & Accountability Journal*, Vol. 28 No. 5, pp. 846–874.

Giddens, A. (1984), *The Constitution of Society: Outline of the Theory of Structuration*, Polity Press, Cambridge, UK.

Giddens, A. (1991), *Modern and Self-Identity: Self and Society in the Late Modern Age.* Blackwell Publishing, Cambridge.

Goffman, E. (1974), *Frame Analysis: An Essay on the Organization of Experience.* Northeastern University Press, New England.

Gray, R. (2010), "Is accounting for sustainability actually accounting for sustainability...and how would we know? An exploration of narratives of organisations and the plane", *Accounting, Organizations and Society*, Vol. 35 No. 1, pp. 47–62.

Gray, R. and Milne, M. (2018), "Perhaps the Dodo should have accounted for human beings? Accounts of humanity and (its) extinction", *Accounting, Auditing & Accountability Journal*, Vol. 31 No. 3, pp. 826–848.

Greenfield, P. (2020), "Ban wildlife markets to avert pandemics, says UN biodiversity chief", *The Guardian*, 6 April 2020, available at: https://www.theguardian.com/world/2020/apr/06/ban-live-animal-markets-pandemics-un-biodiversity-chief-age-of-extinction?CMP=fb_gu&utm_medium=Social&utm_source=Facebook&fbclid=IwAR1eLBzbvIBYysr35Ybicfbx1BCVnwRYuInrmDqYcylPg8u2eajmFj18kQU#Echobox=1586154099 (accessed on 10.04.20).

GRI. (2007), "Biodiversity: A GRI reportingresource". Available: http:/www.globalreporting.org/resourcelibrary/Biodiversity-A-GRI-Resource-Document.pdf [Accessed 1 August 2014].

GRI. (2016), "Consolidated set of GRI sustainability reporting standards". Available: https://www.globalreporting.org/standards/gri-standards-download-center/?g=

ae2e23b8-4958-455c-a9df-ac372d6ed9a8 https://www.globalreporting.org/reporting/g4/Pages/default.aspx [Accessed 10 February 2017].

Harte, G., Lewis, L. and Owen, D. (1991), "Ethical investment and the corporate reporting function", *Critical Perspectives on Accounting*, Vol. 2, pp. 228–253.

Hassan, A., Nandy, M. and Roberts, L. (2020b), "Does loss of Biodiversity by businesses cause Covid 19? Available at: https://www.eauc.org.uk/does_loss_of_biodiversity_by_businesses_cause_c

Hassan, A., Roberts, L. and Atkins, J. (2020a) "Exploring factors relating to extinction disclosures: What motivates companies to report on biodiversity and species protection?". *Business Strategy and the Environment Journal*. Vol. 29 No. 3, pp. 1419–1436.

Herron, A. (2016), "Pollinators as a portfolio risk: Making the case for investor action", chapter 7 in Atkins, J. and Atkins, B. (eds.) (2016), *"The Business of Bees: An Integrated Approach to Bee Decline and Corporate Responsibility,"* Routledge, UK, pp. 131–150.

Herron, A. (2019), "Extraction and extinction: The role of investors in ensuring the marine health of the planet", chapter 7 in Atkins, J. and Atkins, B. (2019), *"Around the World in 80 Species: Exploring the Business of Extinction"*, Routledge, UK, pp. 146–150.

Hines, R. (1988), "Financial accounting: In communicating reality, we construct reality", *Accounting, Organizations and Society*, Vol. 13 No. 3, pp. 251–261.

Ingram, R.W. (1978), "An investigation of the information content of (certain) social responsibility disclosure", *Journal of Accounting Research*, Vol. 16 No. 2, Autumn, pp. 270–285.

IPBES. (2019), "Global Assessment Report on Biodiversity and Ecosystem Services for the Americas". Available: https://ipbes.net/assessment-reports/americas

IIRC. (2013), "The International Framework: Integrated Reporting". Available: http://www.theiirc.org/wp-content/uploads/2013/12/13-12-08-THE-INTERNATIONAL-IR-FRAMEWORK-2-1.pdf [Accessed 1 October 2013].

Johnson, C., Hitchens, P., Pandit, P., Rushmore J., Evans, T., Young, C., Doyle, M. (2020), "Global shifts in mammalian population trends reveal key predictors of virus spillover risk", *Proceedings of the Royal Society*, April, pp. 1–10. http://dx.doi.org/10.1098/rspb.2019.2736. https://royalsocietypublishing.org/doi/10.1098/rspb.2019.2736.

Jones, K., Patel, N., Levy, M, Storeygard, A, Balk, D., Gittleman, J. and Daszak, P. (2008), "Global trends in emerging infectious diseases", *Nature*, Vol. 451, pp. 990–993.

Jones, M. (1996). "Accounting for biodiversity: A pilot study". *The British Accounting Review*, Vol. 28 No.4, pp. 281–303.

Jones, M. J. (2003). "Accounting for biodiversity: operationalising environmental accounting", *Accounting, Auditing & Accountability Journal*, Vol. 16(5), 762–789.

Jones, M. and Solomon, J. (2013). "Problematising accounting for biodiversity", *Accounting, Auditing & Accountability Journal*, Vol. 26 No. 5, pp. 668–687.

King, M., Atkins, J. and Maroun, W. (forthcoming) "A framework for extinction governance", chapter three in Atkins, J. and Macpherson, M. (eds.) (forthcoming) *Extinction Governance: Implementing a Special Protection Action Plan for the Financial Markets*, Routledge, UK.

Mansoor, H. and Maroun, W. (2016), "An initial review of biodiversity reporting by South African corporates - The case of the food and mining sectors". *South African Journal of Economic and Management Sciences*, Vol. 19 No.4, pp. 592–614.

Maroun, W. and Atkins, J. (2018), "The emancipatory potential of extinction accounting: Exploring current practice in integrated reports". *Accounting Forum*, Vol. 42 No. 1, pp. 102–118.

Maroun, W., Usher, K. and Mansoor, H. (2018), "Biodiversity reporting and organised hypocrisy: The case of the South African food and retail industry". *Qualitative Research in Accounting & Management*, Vol. 15 No. 4, pp. 437–464.

Milne, M. (1996), "On sustainability; the environment and management accounting". *Management Accounting Research*, Vol. 7 No. 1, pp. 135–161.

Milne, M. J. and Gray, R. (2013). "W (h) ither ecology? The triple bottom line, the global reporting initiative, and corporate sustainability reporting", *Journal of Business Ethics*, Vol. 118 No. 1, pp. 13–29.

Quammen, D. (2013), *Spill Over: Animal Infections and the Next Human Pandemic*, W.W. Norton & Company, Inc., New York.

Quammen, D. (2020a), "We Made the Coronavirus Epidemic", *The New York Times*, 28 January 2020, available at: https://www.nytimes.com/2020/01/28/opinion/-coronavirus-china.html?smtyp=cur&smid=tw-nytopinion.

Quammen, D. (2020b), "We Made the Coronavirus Epidemic" https://www.nytimes.com/2020/01/28/opinion/coronavirus china.html?smtyp=cur&smid=tw-nytopinion.

Rimmel, G. and Jonäll, K. (2013), "Biodiversity reporting in Sweden: Corporate disclosure and preparers' views". *Accounting, Auditing & Accountability Journal*, Vol. 26 No. 5, pp. 746–778.

Roberts, L., Hassan, A., Nandy, M. and Elamer, A. (2020), "Nursing both the Covid-19 and Biodiversity Crisis Together, available at: https://www.eauc.org.uk/nursing_both_the_covid_19_and_biodiversity_crisis https://www.eauc.org.uk/7008 (accessed on 10.04.2020).

Rockness, J. and Williams, P.F. (1988), "A descriptive study of social accounting responsibility mutual funds", *Accounting, Organizations and Society*, Vol. 13 No. 4, pp. 397–411.

Russell, S., Milne, M. and Dey, C. (2017), "Accounts of nature and the nature of accounts: Critical reflections on environmental accounting and propositions for ecologically informed accounting". *Accounting, Auditing & Accountability Journal*, Vol. 30 No. 7, pp. 1426–1458.

ShareAction (2020), *Point of No Returns: A Ranking of 75 of the World's Largest Asset Managers' Approaches to Responsible Investment*, Report, ShareAction, London, UK, March.

Siddiqui, J. (2013), "Mainstreaming biodiversity accounting: potential implications for a developing economy". *Accounting, Auditing & Accountability Journal*, Vol. 26 No. 5, pp. 779–805.

Solomon, J. (2020, forthcoming) "*Corporate Governance and Accountability*", 5th edition, final draft submitted to publisher December 2019, John Wiley & Sons Inc.

Solomon, J. F. and Darby, L. (2005), "Is Private Social, Ethical and Environmental Disclosure Mythicizing or Demythologizing Reality?", *Accounting Forum*, Vol. 29, pp. 27–47.

Solomon, J. F., Joseph, N. L., Norton, S. D. and A. Solomon (2013), "Impression management, fabrication and myth creation in private social and environmental reporting: Insights from Erving Goffman", *Accounting, Organizations and Society*, Vol. 38, pp. 195–213.

Solomon, J. F. and Solomon, A. (2006), "Private Social, Ethical and Environmental Disclosure", *Accounting, Auditing & Accountability Journal*, Vol. 19, No. 4, pp. 564–591.

Solomon, J. F., Solomon, A. Joseph, N. L. and Norton, S. D. (2011), "Private Climate Change Reporting: A Discourse of Risk and Opportunity?", *Accounting, Auditing and Accountability Journal*, Vol. 24, No. 8, pp. 1119–1148.

Springer, K. (2020), *Point of No Returns. Part IV Biodiversity: An Assessment of Asset Managers' Approaches to Biodiversity*, Report, ShareAction, London, UK, March.

Sullivan, S. and Hannis, M. (2017), "Mathematics maybe, but not money": On balance sheets, numbers and nature in ecological accounting". *Accounting, Auditing & Accountability Journal*, Vol. 30 No. 7, pp. 1459–1480.

Thamotheram, R. and Stewart, O. (2016), "Bee colony and food supply collapse: Could investors be the cavalry?", chapter 9 in Atkins, J. and Atkins, B. (eds.) (2016), "*The Business of Bees: An Integrated Approach to Bee Decline and Corporate Responsibility*," Routledge, UK, pp. 170–186.

Tregidga, H. (2013), "Biodiversity offsetting: Problematisation of an emerging governance regime". *Accounting, Auditing & Accountability Journal*, Vol. 26 No.5, pp. 806–832.

Tregidga, H., Milne, M. and Kearins, K. (2014), "(Re)presenting 'sustainable organizations'". *Accounting, Organizations and Society*, Vol. 39 No.6, pp. 477–494.

United Nations. (2019), "*SEEA Experimental Ecosystem Accounting Revision* [Online]. United Nations Statistical Commission". Available: https://seea.un.org/content/seea-experimental-ecosystem-accounting-revision [Accessed].

Van Liempd, D. and J. Busch. (2013). Biodiversity Reporting In Denmark. *Accounting Auditing & Accountability Journal*, Vol. 26, No. 5, pp. 833–872.

Watt, S. (1997), Introduction, to Plato (1997) *Republic*, translated by Davies, J. L. and Vaughan, D. J., Wordsworth Classics of World Literature, Wordsworth Editions, UK.

Weston, P. (2020), "'We did it to ourselves': scientist says intrusion into nature led to pandemic", *The Guardian*, 25 April 2020, available at: https://www.theguardian.com/world/2020/apr/25/ourselves-scientist-says-human-intrusion-nature-pandemic-aoe?CMP=fb_gu&utm_medium=Social&utm_source=Facebook&fbclid=IwAR3wyT-5RrcV9eKnaaidjtydEj7XOYlBRCMMrgIRKoQIZupo2SJKVNH1mkw#Echobox=1587807034 (accessed on 25.04.2020).

Woo, P. C. Y, Lau, S. K. P, Lam, C. S. F., Tsang, A. K. L, Hui, S-W., Fan, R. Y. Y., Martelli, P., Yuen, K.-Y. (2013), "Discovery of a Novel Bottlenose Dolphin Coronavirus Reveals a Distinct Species of Marine Mammal Coronavirus in Gammacoronavirus", *Journal of Virology* December, Vol. 88 No. 2, pp. 1318–1331.

Zhao, L. and Atkins, J. (2019), "Panda accounting and accountability: Preventing giant panda extinction in China". In: Atkins, J. & Atkins, B. (eds.) *Around the World in 80 Species. Exploring the Business of Extinction*, Routledge, London, UK, pp. 201–219.

PART V

Extinction Accounting

How Accounting Can Save Species

27

THE IMPACT OF THE NATURAL CAPITAL AND BIODIVERSITY CRISES ON THE CORPORATE AND INVESTMENT VALUE CHAIN

Mark Gough

There is a common saying that 'we only understand the value of something when it is gone'. We have seen this again, and again, and again when losing relationships, our youth, and money. We cannot though allow this to happen with biodiversity. We are part of, and depend on, the diversity of life that biodiversity brings, and if we do allow it to disappear, we will also go with it, and there will be no one left to know what we have lost.

It is obvious therefore that we must understand biodiversity's value to us now and not when it has gone. If we can, we will all be inspired to protect, and even enhance it and we might just avoid extinction.

So first let us start by what we really mean by the term 'value'. To value is to understand the relative importance, worth, or usefulness of something. When we value something, we understand its context. We have better information about how it is going to affect us and how we effect it.

It is this valuation of the world around us that informs the decisions we each make. From which coffee we have in the morning, through to big life choices such as who we have children with or where we live. If we value something, we invest time and energy to look after it. If we do not value it, we let it deteriorate.

There is another saying that 'You can only manage what you measure'. I disagree.

Measurements provide us with quantities but not with the necessary context to inform a decision. Take water for example. A company will often measure and report the amount of water that it uses in its operations each year. This number (let us say it is 1,000 m^3) may be presented to the board, to shareholders, and to stakeholders. But by itself, this number does not actually mean very much. Is 1,000 m^3 a lot in that river basin? And more importantly, is 1,000 m^3 a year sustainable or are there risks for the business and biodiversity from extracting this amount?

DOI: 10.4324/9781003045557-33

In a board room, there are three Cs that will often be used to act upon this sort of measurement information: compliance, competition, and champions.

Compliance defines the boarders around the legal action that a business can take and therefore the first question is often do these metrics have to be acted upon or not. Most of the time it is not. Competition is a significant driver and is often seen between businesses in the same sector. For example, if a competitor extracts 900 m^3, your business may want to do better than that and extract less water to improve its reputation or gain market advantage. The third C is a champion – someone who argues for a better more sustainable way of doing things.

These are all important, but if the value of the water to the business and, or, society was included as well, then there would be context to inform action. For example, knowing the number of people who depend upon the water the business is abstracting allows them to understand whether $1,000 \text{ m}^3$ is a lot or not and whether they are causing an impact upon the community and their business. Valuation is essential to stimulate positive action. Therefore, the saying should be changed to:

You can only manage what you measure <u>and understand the value of.</u>

There are many people around the world who have already recognized that valuation will play a significant and foundation role in the protection of biodiversity. They have come together to collaborate through the Capitals Coalition[1] with a shared ambition that by 2030, the majority of business, finance, and government will include nature and people in their decision-making.

Originally established in 2012 as the TEEB[2] for Business Coalition and hosted by ICAEW in Singapore, the Natural Capital Coalition quickly grew to become the central space for mainstreaming natural capital approaches in the private sector. At that time, there were 40 different approaches including the value provided by nature in business decision-making. The first effort of the coalition, therefore, was to harmonize these. By bringing together all of the authors and experts, they undertook a global consultation, which culminated in the development of an internationally accepted framework.

The Natural Capital Protocol[3] was published in 2016 and has now been applied many thousands of times all around the world, helping organizations to make more informed decisions.

Referring to nature as a capital has opened many doors, particularly in the business world, but it should also be recognized that this is not whole-heartedly supported, especially by some in the conservation community. A capital is a resource that, if invest into, creates returns. Financial capital is the one that most people will be familiar with. This idea though can be used for anything. With natural capital, the same premise stands that if we invest in the stock of natural capital, we get a return in the flow of ecosystem and abiotic services. If we do not invest in natural capital, then these services are threatened and may stop altogether. Whilst this approach helps us to see the benefits that nature provides more clearly, it can also come across as rather perfunctory and heartless and not take into account the intrinsic quality of nature. It is important therefore to think of a capital's approach as another tool in the box to support, legislation and conservation efforts and not something that is in conflict with them.

Part of the challenge is the preconception that some people have that because capital is most commonly associated with finance, we are just putting a price on nature. It would then follow that if we add a price to nature, it can just be bought and sold. What is missing here is the understanding of the difference between price and value. A price is what someone is willing to pay. The value, as I have already said, is the relative importance and worth. Natural capital helps us to understand the value of the benefits that nature provides and does not simply add a price on nature. It is obvious to many that the economic system does not price things correctly based upon their value. Otherwise, we would pay more for services that look after those that we most care about, like childcare. A capital's approach is therefore challenging the present economic system and the way we price and not supporting the existing way of doing things.

It is important here to recognize the difference between nature, natural capital, and biodiversity as the terms are often confused, even by those who are experts. Natural capital is the stock of natural renewable and nonrenewable resources that combine to create a flow of benefits to people. Biodiversity is the diversity of life that underpins and allows the natural capital to flourish.

Whereas the measurement and valuation of air, water, and land in natural capital assessments have developed considerably, biodiversity has often been excluded, due to the complexity and a wide number of different approaches in the conservation and scientific community. Specific supplementary biodiversity guidance[4] has therefore been produced to better incorporate biodiversity into natural capital assessments, and the work is ongoing to ensure that the importance of biodiversity is always included.

One of the things that become very obvious when you start to apply a capital's approach to your thinking is that everything is interconnected. Now, this should be obvious, but so many decisions are taken in isolation without an understanding of the impact and dependency that they have. This is the reason why it is not enough to just focus on protecting biodiversity alone. We have to think about how nature, people, and the economy interconnect. A good example can be found in the ocean. Plastic waste is obviously an environmental problem, but when we ask how the waste ended up there, we quickly understand that low pay and even modern slavery play an important part. We cannot therefore solve the environmental problem unless we understand the role of people, and how it all comes together as a system.

For many hundreds of years, and most definitely since industrialization, we have been becoming more and more specialized in the approach that we take. These deep dives in our understanding have led to significant breakthroughs in science and medicine. Now is the time to see how these all connect. To think more generally and encourage systems thinking. A good analogy here is the human body. Although each part of the body is important by itself, it is when they all come together that the body functions.

In order to address this system's challenge, the Social and Human Capital Coalition was founded by the World Business Council for Sustainable Development in 2018 and brought together those who specialized in measuring the value that people and society create for one another. It released its own internationally accepted framework, the "Social and Human Capital Protocol" in 2019.

Both the Natural Capital Coalition and the Social and Human Capital Coalition developed strong foundations, built broad and diverse communities, and spearheaded global programs to ensure that the value of nature and people sit alongside financial value in the minds of decision-makers at all levels.

As the two coalitions continued to flourish, it became increasingly clear to all involved that the issues must be addressed together and therefore they united as the Capitals Coalition in 2020. See Figure 27.1 for a timeline summary.

So, what has a capital's approach taught us? There are three main shifts as shown in Table 27.1.

The first is that we have to think of the world both in terms of the impact we have upon it and how it impacts us. This double materiality of both impacts and dependencies is extremely important. Up until recently, the majority of work in the sustainability field has all been focused on impact. And yet, it is often through our dependency on the world that we really understand the value of something.

The second is the need to measure and value these impacts and dependencies. And, the third is the need to continually consider the interconnections and relationships through a systems approach.

Going forward, a capital's approach will play a significant part in our struggle to avoid extinction (see Figure 27.2 below). The foundational work that has been

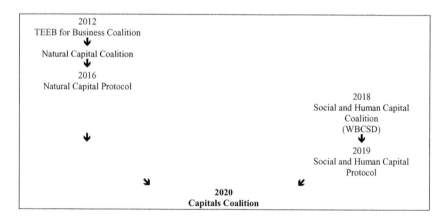

FIGURE 27.1 Capitals Coalition in 2020.

TABLE 27.1 The three shifts of capital's approach

Impact and Dependency

A capital's approach highlights impacts and dependencies on nature and people, making it a critical issue relevant to everyone, and therefore embedded in all decisions.

Measure and Value

A capital's approach values impacts and dependencies so that we understand their relative importance and worth and are driven to transform the way we act.

System

Capital's thinking exposes the shared risks and opportunities, clearly indicating how everything is connected.

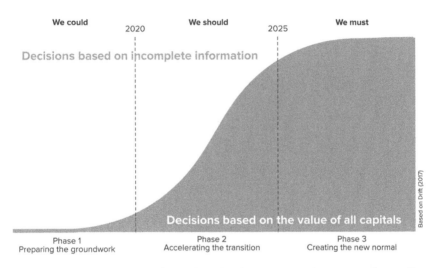

FIGURE 27.2 The Capitals Coalition shared ambition to transform our understanding of value.

carried out now needs to be accelerated. Rather than just the leading organizations thinking about value, we need a critical tipping point where the majority of business, finance, and government do so. We must move from a voluntary approach of 'could' to 'should' and ultimately 'must'.

We will achieve this by changing the way we account for nature (the math), and building stronger communities of practice, listening to those who disagree, and working collaboratively to change the conversation. We must also change the rules of the game, with positive incentive mechanisms, legislation, and social norms. Most importantly, we will have to do this together. Everyone thinks that they have the answer. They are in part all right, but it will take a systematic approach to transform the way that decisions are made and save us from extinction.

Notes

1 http://teebweb.org/.
2 https://naturalcapitalcoalition.org/natural-capital-protocol/.
3 https://naturalcapitalcoalition.org/biodiversity/.
4 https://www.wbcsd.org/

28

THE BIODIVERSITY DISCLOSURE PROJECT

From Business Mainstreaming Guidelines, the Biodiversity Performance Rating of Listed Companies to the Biological Diversity Protocol

Y. Friedman, C. Hoogstad, A. Cherrington,
H.T. Davies-Mostert, M. Murison and J. Houdet

Introduction to the Endangered Wildlife Trust

The Endangered Wildlife Trust (EWT) is dedicated to conserving threatened species and ecosystems to the benefit of all people. The EWT is a non-governmental, non-profit, conservation organisation, founded in 1973, and operating throughout southern and East Africa. The organisation conserves threatened species and ecosystems by initiating research and conservation action programmes, implementing projects that mitigate threats facing species and supporting sustainable natural resource management. The EWT communicates the principles of sustainable living through awareness programmes to the broadest possible constituency for the benefit of the region. It has developed a unique operational structure through which its mission and objectives are achieved – meeting its conservation goals through the work of specialist, thematic programmes, designed to maximise effectiveness in the field and enhance the development of skills and capacity. These programmes form the backbone of the organisation, and they harness the talent and enthusiasm of a dynamic network of individuals who specialise in an area of conservation importance and have developed unique expertise in response to the challenges they face. Programmes work with multiple stakeholders and harness their diverse but relevant expertise to address environmental priorities. Stakeholders include national and provincial government, other NGOs, landowners, local communities, farmworkers, conservancies, academic institutions and industry. For instance, EWT is a Natural Capital Regional Platform of the Natural Capital Coalition, an international collaboration that unites the global natural capital community. The coalition is made up of almost 300 organisations (and engages many thousands more) who together represent all parts of society and span the global economy. The EWT also acts as a public watchdog,

DOI: 10.4324/9781003045557-34

often taking government and industry to task for decision-making that does not meet sustainability criteria.

The National Biodiversity and Business Network

The world of risks and opportunities within which businesses operate is rapidly changing. Companies are facing increasing pressure from consumers who want to know that they are dealing with responsible corporate citizens, and the impact that companies have on biodiversity has become a critical element of this. Companies are also becoming increasingly aware of the important role that biodiversity and ecosystem services play in their value chains. For some companies, there is an urgency to cost-effectively identify and manage the business risks and opportunities that result from their interactions with biodiversity to avoid negative impacts on their bottom line.

The National Biodiversity and Business Network (NBBN) is a member of the Global Partnership for Business and Biodiversity (GPBB) of the Convention on Biological Diversity (CBD). The GPBB currently comprises 21 national and regional business and biodiversity initiatives, all working towards greater business engagement on biodiversity-related issues, including but not limited to sustainable supply chains, biodiversity no-net-loss initiatives and biodiversity reporting/disclosure.

In the early 2010s, EWT recognised the need for a body to assist the private sector in the integration or mainstreaming of biodiversity into its strategies and activities in South Africa. This led to the establishment of the NBBN in 2013, in partnership with the Department of Environmental Affairs, De Beers, Pam Golding Properties, Nedbank Limited, Hatch, Pick n Pay, and Transnet. In 2016, the list of NBBN partners grew to include Woolworths and Eskom. The aim of the NBBN was to facilitate a reduction in the negative impacts of business on biodiversity in South Africa. The NBBN achieves this by assisting businesses with the development and dissemination of guidelines and tools. The NBBN also presents capacity-building events that provide a platform for businesses to proactively engage with each other and discover solutions that lead to pro-biodiversity business growth.

Biodiversity Mainstreaming: From Building the Business Case to the Rating of the Biodiversity Performance of Listed Companies

In response to the growing call for voluntary business contributions to national and global biodiversity targets[1] (e.g. Karlsson-Vinkhuyzen et al., 2017), the NBBN launched the Biodiversity Disclosure Project (BDP) in 2018. Three key gaps were identified by NBBN members:

- The lack of guidance on biodiversity mainstreaming in business in South Africa;

- The lack of regular, public biodiversity performance rating of companies listed on the Johannesburg Stock Exchange (JSE);
- The lack of standardised accounting framework to help consolidate net biodiversity impact data from different sites.

To address the first gap, alongside a biodiversity mainstreaming readiness self-assessment, case studies and other resources,[2] biodiversity mainstreaming guidelines were released in early 2020. These were organised in several steps to help organisations:

- Understand why biodiversity matters to their business;
- Identify the biodiversity dependencies and impacts of their company;
- Measure these biodiversity dependencies and impacts;
- Assess whether these biodiversity dependencies and impacts have material consequences for the business or its stakeholders;
- Develop biodiversity policies, targets, strategies, action plans and key performance indicators (KPIs);
- Effectively manage biodiversity dependencies and impacts so as to avoid or minimise the associated risks and seize the associated opportunities; and
- Disclose meaningful biodiversity information according to the needs and expectations of different stakeholders, from management to external non-governmental organisations.

To address the second gap, the biodiversity performance rating of JSE-listed companies started in 2018 (Houdet & Lizzio, 2018). This assessment was conducted using publicly available information, including company websites and 2017 annual reports (e.g. annual integrated reports, sustainability reports). Each company was contacted electronically to offer them the opportunity to review their individual results and share any additional information if warranted. To assess the biodiversity mainstreaming performance of the target organisations eight key questions were asked, which reflect the key steps that a company needs to follow to effectively mainstream biodiversity into its activities:

- What is the biodiversity policy of the company?
- What are the biodiversity dependencies and impacts of the company?
- Does the company measure its biodiversity dependencies and impacts?
- Does the company value its biodiversity dependencies and impacts? What are the most material ones?
- Does the company have a biodiversity strategy, biodiversity targets and associated KPIs?
- Does the company have a biodiversity action plan? vii. Does the company disclose its biodiversity risks and performance?
- Does the company have a biodiversity monitoring system in place for continuous improvement?

There were five possible answers with corresponding scores (0 to 4) for each question.

Initially, all JSE-listed companies (more than 300 equity-listed) and two state-owned enterprises were assessed. This exercise was repeated in 2019 (Houdet & Cherrington, 2019). The same methodology was used, though the company sample changed slightly due to bankruptcies, delisting and the addition of 26 SOEs to the 2018 sample of 2. The 2019 biodiversity performance rating of SA companies was a very exciting and successful endeavour for the BDP. In 2018, the company response rate was very low. Fifteen companies provided feedbacks on our initial ratings and three meetings were organised. In 2019, the company response rate significantly improved, with 36 company feedbacks received and 16 meetings organised. Building on this success, for the 2020 rating, we entered into a partnership with Ecoacsa Reserva de Biodiversidad to do the same process for companies listed on the IBerian IndEX (IBEX 35) (Spain's principal stock exchange index). This will further increase our international exposure towards a global biodiversity performance rating platform.

Introducing the Biological Diversity Protocol

Accounting for biodiversity from a business perspective has been the focus of recent academic research and practitioner work (e.g. Atkins & Maroun, 2018; Houdet & Germaneau, 2014; Houdet et al., 2016; Lamerant et al., 2019; Maroun & Atkins, 2018), alongside efforts to integrate biodiversity considerations within institutional investor engagement (e.g. Herron 2016, 2019; Thamotheram 2016). Concerns over biodiversity data quality, consistency and comparability in corporate biodiversity impact accounting and reporting have been widely discussed by academia and practitioners (e.g. Addison et al., 2018; Atkins et al., 2018; Boiral 2016; Houdet et al., 2016; Jones & Solomon, 2013; Maroun & Atkins, 2018) as well as the CBD[3] (e.g. see 2018 report presented at the Subsidiary Body on Implementation 2 meeting[4]). As shown by the Aligning Biodiversity Measures for Business (ABMB) collaboration led by UN Environment Programme World Conservation Monitoring Centre (UNEP-WCMC forthcoming) and supported by the EU Business and Biodiversity Platform, while there are a growing number of biodiversity impact measurement approaches, an accounting approach, as proposed by the Biological Diversity Protocol (BD Protocol), is essential to compile consistent, comparable and regularly produced biodiversity impact data at the company level (EU Business @ Biodiversity Platform and UNEP-WCMC, 2019; UNEP-WCMC 2020). These persisting issues are preventing the private sector from cost-effectively managing its biodiversity risks and impacts.

The NBBN has developed the BD Protocol to address some of these key gaps in current biodiversity impact measurement, monitoring, disclosure and accountability (third gap identified by NBBN members and highlighted in the previous section). It provides an accounting framework to record systematically and consolidate net biodiversity impact data, over time, at the company level. It supports (not replaces) existing impact measurement approaches so that biodiversity impact disclosure becomes comparable across industries and companies.[5] Besides, biodiversity impact measurement and accounting are critical steps before any valuation exercise, should they be required. Companies need to know the scale of their impacts (i.e. how much they impact on biodiversity) before starting to value them (i.e. how important, in qualitative, quantitative and/or monetary terms, are these impacts from a business and/or social perspective).

Accordingly, the BD Protocol focuses on measuring and consolidating the biodiversity impacts of a whole company or organisation, according to its chosen organisational and value chain boundaries. This is instrumental to setting-up targets, notably in the context of the post-2020 Global Biodiversity Framework of the CBD. Specifically, it helps provide guidance on how to (a) measure change(s) in the state of impacted ecosystems and species and (b) value these impacts in qualitative and quantitative (not monetary) terms. Furthermore, the BD Protocol provides guidance on how to:

- Select the appropriate organisational and value chain boundary;
- Develop and manage a biodiversity impact inventory;
- Determine material biodiversity impacts;
- Assess impacts on biodiversity, considering the nature of the biodiversity features impacted (i.e. ecosystems and taxa);
- Account for net changes in biodiversity, in accordance with the mitigation hierarchy and the associated equivalency principle;
- Apply the Biodiversity Accounting Framework to build Statements of Biodiversity Position and Performance and account for biodiversity gains and losses over time;
- Validate or verify a biodiversity impact assessment;
- Report on or disclose business impacts on biodiversity in a coherent and meaningful manner.

For any impact accounting framework to present a complete and accurate representation of the net situation of an organisation, it must be able to account for both periodic (e.g. annual) and historical (e.g. since the start of a business) performances. This is the case with financial accounting. The BD Protocol builds from the foundations of financial accounting through two simple equations, adapted from double-entry bookkeeping, which ensures that the total biodiversity impacts of a company are equal to the sum of its accumulated positive and negative impacts (see theoretical foundations in Houdet et al., forthcoming). Accounting for biodiversity impacts thus revolves around the following equations:

- Statement of Biodiversity Position: (A) total impacts on biodiversity features = (B) accumulated positive impacts on biodiversity + (C) accumulated negative impacts on biodiversity (for all periods to date);

- Statement of Biodiversity Performance: (X) net biodiversity impacts on biodiversity features over the accounting period = (Y) periodic positive biodiversity impacts or gains - (Z) periodic biodiversity negative impacts or losses.

Moreover, the BD Protocol was developed in a phased approach. A draft concept document, which covered the proposed aims, scope and structure of the BD Protocol, was produced in mid-2018. The concept document was based on:

- The GHG Protocol Corporate Accounting and Reporting Standard (i.e. the GHG Protocol[6]), as the benchmark standard for the vision and structure of the BD Protocol;
- An alignment with the Natural Capital Protocol (Natural Capital Coalition 2016), which is a standardised framework to identify, measure, and value direct and indirect impacts (positive and negative) and/or dependencies on natural capital.

By mid-March 2019, a first draft BD Protocol (V1.1) was completed, involving around 20 co-authors and contributors. A formal consultation process was then launched. It involved three components: An online international, public consultation process hosted by the Natural Capital Coalition through Collaborase, several events/workshops and many direct engagement processes. All comments, questions and contributions made through the consultation processes, including direct engagements with businesses, academia and NGOs, were collected and analysed by the BD Protocol project team. The key points were summarised in a stakeholder feedback report, which was published in December 2019 (Houdet et al., 2019). The final version of the BD Protocol was completed in April 2020. Copy editing was finalised in July 2020 and design started in July 2020. The EWT–NBBN hopes to formally launch the BD Protocol online in late 2020. Pilot case studies are ongoing or under negotiations with several companies in the forestry, mining and energy sectors, in South Africa, Europe and Australia. Notably, Eskom is applying the BD Protocol to two sites, the Sere Wind Energy Facility and the Ingula Pumped Storage Scheme.

Highlights

- The EWT is a non-governmental, non-profit, conservation organisation, dedicated to conserving threatened species and ecosystems to the benefit of all people.
- This chapter presents EWT's contributions to biodiversity mainstreaming in the private sector, notably the NBBN and the BDP.
- Key outcomes include biodiversity mainstreaming guidelines, the regular, public biodiversity performance rating of companies listed on the JSE and the development of a standardised accounting framework, the BD Protocol,

to record systematically and consolidate net biodiversity impact data, over time, at the company level.

- This accounting framework focuses on measuring and consolidating the biodiversity impacts of a whole company or organisation, according to its chosen organisational and value chain boundaries. This is instrumental to setting-up targets, notably in the context of the post-2020 Global Biodiversity Framework of the CBD. Specifically, it helps provide guidance on how to (a) measure change(s) in the state of impacted ecosystems and species and (b) value these impacts in qualitative and quantitative (not monetary) terms.
- The BD Protocol builds from the foundations of financial accounting through two simple equations, adapted from double-entry bookkeeping, which ensures that the total biodiversity impacts of a company are equal to the sum of its accumulated positive and negative impacts. This allows companies to produce Statements of Biodiversity Position and Performance.

Notes

1 For instance, consult the note by the Executive Secretary of the CBD: Engaging business in the development of a post-2020 Global Biodiversity Framework; URL: https://www.cbd.int/doc/c/9b08/d19e/1fbeec1724642fe73810e71f/cop-14-inf-31-en.pdf.
2 URL: https://www.nbbnbdp.org/.
3 URL: https://www.cbd.int/business/projects/reporting.shtml.
4 Note by the Executive Secretary of the CBD: Guidance for reporting by businesses on their actions related to biodiversity; URL: https://www.cbd.int/doc/c/ff6d/906c/ebebc273f27f8e9416bba00b/sbi-02-04-add2-en.pdf.
5 Lack of comparability and substantial variability in biodiversity reporting has been highlighted by researchers as a significant problem (e.g. Rimmel & Jonäll, 2013; Atkins et al., 2014).
6 The GHG Protocol Corporate Accounting and Reporting Standard provides a step-by-step guide for companies to use in quantifying and reporting their greenhouse gas emissions. URL: https://ghgprotocol.org/corporate-standard, accessed on 7 Feb 2019.

References

Houdet, J., Cherrington, A., Hoogstad, C., Murison, M. (2019). Consultation on the Biological Diversity Protocol (draft 1.1): Stakeholder feedback report. Endangered Wildlife Trust - Biodiversity Disclosure Project.

Karlsson-Vinkhuyzen, S., Kok, M.T.J., Visseren-Hamakers, I.J., Termeer, C.J.A.M., 2017. Mainstreaming biodiversity in economic sectors: An analytical framework. *Biological Conservation* 210 (Part A), 145–156, ISSN 0006-3207, https://doi.org/10.1016/j.biocon.2017.03.029.

Natural Capital Coalition (2016). Natural Capital Protocol. (Online) Available at: www.naturalcapitalcoalition.org/protocol, accessed on Nov. 9, 2019.

UN Environment Programme World Conservation Monitoring Centre 2020. Biodiversity Measures for Business: Corporate Biodiversity Measurement and Disclosure within the Current and Future Global Policy Context. Cambridge, UK, 64 pp.

29

RESEARCH METHODS

The Role of Ecolinguistic Analysis in Species Protection – A Toolkit for Practitioners and Academics

Mira Lieberman

Introduction

The social and ecological issues that humanity currently faces are so severe that they call into question the fundamental stories that societies are based on. Language is instrumental to how we conceive of and interact with the natural environment, at the level of an individual, family, community or society.[1] As Haugen[2] notes, language is socially situated, it '[...] does not breath, it has no life of its own apart from those who use it'. Reality and 'common sense' are not

> something readymade and waiting to be meant – it has to be actively construed; and that language evolved in the process of, and as the agency of, its construal. Language [...] is a product of the conscious and the material impacting each on the other [...].[3]

Ecolinguistics provides tools for revealing the stories we live by, questioning them from an ecological perspective and contributing to the search for new stories to live by. Are the stories that underlie texts encourage us to care about people and the ecosystems that life depends on?

This chapter introduces the concept of the stories we live by. Clearly, the current stories we live by are not working, as the world experiences the sixth mass extinction. The chapter elucidates the way in which ecolinguistics can be used by anyone, whether academic or practitioner to reveal and question the stories we live by and contribute to the search for more beneficial ones. It discussed what the 'eco' of ecolinguistics refers to: the life-sustaining relationships of humans with other humans, other species and the physical environment. It also described the linguistic tools that can be used to analyse language in various texts. The chapter describes how stories are judged as being destructive or beneficial using

DOI: 10.4324/9781003045557-35

an ecological philosophy (ecosophy) and presents a case study analysis of an agro-chemical company's integrated report.

Ecolinguistics: The Stories We Live By

The stories we live by are cognitive structures in the minds of individuals or across society that shapes the way in which we live, behave, think and act.[4] Linguistic structures, through which these stories or discourses are built, shape our relationship with each other, including other species, and with the natural world.

The Development of Ecolinguistics

Ecolinguistics as a field evolved over the last 45 years and its genealogy has been presented in several detailed reviews.[5] Extinction of species and diminishing linguistic diversity are linked. Language loss and species loss has been described in an ecolinguistics branch termed biolinguistic diversity[6] which investigates the extinction of languages, correlating how language diversity in different geographies reflects the complex relationship between the communities, the natural environment and species loss. Hale et al.[7] claim that 'just as the extinction of any animal species diminishes our world, so does the extinction of any language'. In fact, it was Haugen[8] who articulated the connection between language loss and biodiversity loss and extinction, arguably influenced by and drawing on Arne Naess' deep ecology. The current ecolinguistic approach rests on Haugen's identification of the need for an ecological philosophy that underpins current ecolinguistic studies[9] and differentiates it from sociolinguistics.[10]

There is a direct link between linguistic diversity, biodiversity, ecological health and survival, as Stibbe and Alexander[11] note,

> when local languages are displaced by dominant world languages such as English what is lost are the discourses which encode everything people have learned about living sustainably in the local environment. These are replaced by discourses such as those of economic growth, consumerism and neoliberalism that are at the core of an unsustainable society.

Current ecolinguistic scholarship has diverged from the Haugenian metaphorical conceptualisation of the ecology of language and is interested in how linguistic structures could play a role in determining the survival of all life on Earth.

Framework and Ecosophy

The ecolinguistic framework[12] followed in this chapter describes eight ways that language encodes the stories that society is based on: ideologies, framings, metaphors, evaluations, identities, convictions, erasure and salience (Table 29.1).

TABLE 29.1 Ecolinguistic framework[13]

Form of story	Definition	Linguistic features
Ideology	A story about how the world was, is and should be in the minds of members of a group	Discourses i.e. characteristic language features used by members of a group
Framing	The use of a source frame to structure a target domain	Trigger words that bring a particular source frame to mind
Metaphor	A type of framing where the source frame is from an imaginable area of life that is distinctly different from the target domain	Trigger words that bring the source frame to mind
Evaluation	A story in people's minds about whether an area of life is good or bad	Appraisal patterns, i.e. patterns of language, which represent things positively or negatively
Identity (Stibbe, 2013)	A story in people's minds about what it means to a particular kind of person	Forms of language that characterise people*
Conviction	A story in people's minds about whether a particular description if true, certain, uncertain or false	Facticity patterns, i.e. linguistic patterns that represent a description as true, uncertain or false
Erasure	A story in people's mind that something is unimportant or unworthy of consideration	Patterns of language which erase or diminish
Salience	A story that something is important or worthy of consideration	Patterns of language which foreground an area of life

Ideologies are belief systems about how the world was is, will be or should be which are shared by members of particular groups in society. Ideologies have structure and they can be identified through the choices made in language and semiosis.[14] Ideology, created, reinforced and maintained through language over time, becomes a 'common-sense' that shapes a pervasive, accepted worldview replete with values and beliefs. For ecolinguistic analysis, the aim is not to question the facticity of a text or an ideology but whether the ideology encourages the protection or destruction of the ecosystem. For example, the ecosophy followed in this chapter calls for the protection and consideration of all species, so a story that sets some species as more important is a speciesist one and stands in opposition to the ecosophy.

Frames 'are the mental structures that allow human beings to understand reality – and sometimes to create what we take to be reality. [T]hey structure our ideas and concepts, they shape how we reason, and they even impact how we perceive and how we act'.[15]

Conventional metaphors, which are a type of frame, have a strong influence on our everyday thinking and are overwhelmingly negative to animals.[16] Examples include the following: You greedy pig; ugly dog; stupid cow; bitch.

The way in which actors or things are represented, or evaluated, is a linguistic pattern that can be analysed to reveal an ideology, or cultural evaluations. For example, the evaluation that SUNNY WEATHER IS GOOD is an appraisal that creates the story that travelling to a sunny location on a holiday is a positive activity that encourages increased air travel.

Identities are stories about who we are as people, particularly about the groups that we belong to, and the place of those groups in society.[17] If we view annual reports for example as a form of advertising, we could say that the companies exploit identity when they attempt to persuade stakeholders, particularly shareholders, that purchase of their products is necessary to become a particular kind of person. For example, by framing the company as scientifically minded, and ecologically driven, Bayer constructs its identity and the stakeholders as rational and caring about the environment.

In appealing to a rational scientific and objective identity, a company would use particular voices to reinforce that identity. To reinforce their convictions, the company will attempt to present their own account as neutral, and independent of the speaker using presupposition, expert voices, and modality, that is, how likely, unlikely, true or untrue 'reality' is. The 'repertoire of empiricism' is commonly used to represent facts as deriving directly from the evidence without human interpretation.[18]

When investigating erasure, ecolinguistic analysis centres on entities who are suppressed, backgrounded or wholly excluded. Erasure is a natural part of discourse where the representation and the social construction of categories in society highlight or suppress certain actors according to the prevailing dominant ideology. As Stibbe[19] signals, erasure has been used in a multitude of studies across the social sciences, from gender and racism to cultural studies and includes various levels: suppression, backgrounding, exclusion and abstraction. Following Stibbe, 'erasure' is defined as something important that is excluded, marginalised or ignored when it should be accounted for. Stibbe[20] presents three-level abstraction for erasure to analyse which actors are excluded: (1) the void, where a complete exclusion occurs; (2) the mask, where erasure occurs through a distorted version of the entity excluded; and (3) the trace, where someone or something is partially erased, but elements of them are still present. The exclusion could be manifest through linguistic devices such as passives, metonymy, hyponymy and nominalisation.

The final type of story is salience, a concept often used in visual analysis, where Kress and van Leeuwen[21] describe it as 'The degree to which an element draws attention to itself due to its size, its place in the foreground or its overlapping of other elements, its colour, its tonal values, its sharpness of definition and other features'. Through analysing what is in focus, given prominence, centralised, backgrounded we can determine what or whom is given salience, what or whom is erased.

A key element of the ecolinguistics approach[22] refers to the worldview and ecosophy against which texts are judged. The notion of ecological philosophy was first developed by Naess[23] who coined the term deep ecology in his *article The Shallow and the Deep, Long-Range Ecology Movements*[24] as both ethical and scientific frameworks. For Naess, philosophy was a way out of the ecocatastrophe, a way to action. The oppression of nature and speciesism involves multiple human groups interacting and co-creating a complex reality that undermines the systems on which life depends. As a result, to answer the question: 'what makes a discourse positive', for ecolinguistics that will depend on the analyst's ecosophy.

Case study

Background

The industrial method of farming currently incentivises monocultures and cash crops and is one of the main drivers of ongoing biodiversity losses in agricultural landscapes.[25]

Over the last 20 years, the shift in use and application of pesticides shifted from reactive to prophylactic. Now, many fungicides, pesticides and herbicides are applied to the seeds before sowing, with farmers 'stuck' on a pesticide treadmill.[26] Resistance of plants and target species incurs larger and larger doses of applications. Neonicotinoids working systemically through plants reach target and non-target species, negatively affecting them directly and sub-lethally. Insects die en masse, not only acutely but chronically. Sub-lethal effects weaken the immune system of nearly all living beings and have been demonstrated in bees, fish, amphibians, birds and mammals.[27]

The segmentation of responsibility and accountability chain is evident in the process of formulating, registering, discharging and applying pesticides. Starting with the production of adjuvants or co-formulants, these involve the manufacturing of chemical components that are specifically added to increase the efficacy of the active ingredient and are 'inert' only with respect to the pesticide's mode of action targeting a given class of pests. The classification of a compound as 'inert' or 'active' has serious consequences for pesticide manufacturers and users. It determines the set of tests that have to be performed to assess the toxicity of pesticide ingredients.[28] The identity and concentration of the co-formulants in end-use pesticide products are proffered as confidential business information (CBI) by industry and accepted as such by regulators and hence are rarely disclosed on product labels or via any publicly accessible source.

Data

The data for this chapter have been collected from Bayer's 2016 Integrated Report[29] and include both visual and textual modes that deal with animals, sustainability and the environment (sections Magazine pp. 10–23, and 1.1.3, 1.2.3,

1.4.3.1, 1.4.3.3.) Bayer's key role in developing insecticides, particularly neon-icotinoids (neonics) are now some of the most widely used biocide products in agriculture and veterinary medicine.

The rationale behind the choice of Bayer's IRs (Integrated Reporting) is two-fold. Firstly, as Maroun and Atkins[30] indicate, 'large listed companies are [...] more likely to have mature reporting systems, a developed accounting infra-structure and the expertise to prepare high-quality sustainability or integrated reports' that achieve more than impression management.[31] Secondly, the way in which their Animal Health division intersects with their Biocides division repre-sents interesting loci where different animals' lives possess different values. This arena is therefore particularly useful for an analysis of species protection.

Analysis

The first void erasure that can be observed concerns the terms *biodiversity* and *ecosystems* recurring three times and once, respectively, in the annual report. As signalled by Stibbe and Zunino,[32] the high level of abstraction of the terms and diverse meanings cannot be captured by one definition. DeLong[33] investigated the various meanings of *biodiversity* and suggests that the primary danger of using the terms is its vulnerability to the manipulation of interested entities to suit their needs. The challenge of inscribing and channelling something as complex as the interconnectedness of life on Earth through the limited lens of human language is akin to one of the main criticisms directed at conventional accounting. Simi-larly to accounting's technological processes, biodiversity's various meanings can serve various ideologies. Specifically, in Bayer's IR, in T3 *biodiversity* is relegated to the role of circumstance:

> *(1) We take into account influences <u>on biodiversity</u> throughout the entire value chain and have established our principles in our own position.*

The use of collective or mass nouns, such as *biodiversity* runs the risk of massi-fication, of abstracting and erasing the 'direct relationships with individual an-imals: an individual can be seen, heard, and empathised with, but a "species"' (occurring only once in the entire IR),[34] or a 'biodiversity' (occurring three times) cannot. Indeed, the only nonhuman animals mentioned in the entirety of the report are bees, occurring only once as a non-modified plural noun, versus six times as a premodifier noun in phrases such as in T7 *bee health*, *bee care program* (see Appendix 2 and 5).

Concerning the erasure of responsibility, the use of the lexical choice for the object goal, *influences*, in T3 (1) above, allows Bayer to evade responsibility in that the semantic prosody of *influence*★,[35] checked in the BNC (British National Corpus) to find neutral to positive collocations indicating a relationship with power. For example, as both a noun and verb *influence* has a strong connection to decision-making, change and control (Table 29.2):

TABLE 29.2 BNC results for the node *influence*

have had a determining	*influence*	*on art*
impact upon police practice and	influence	change
the committee can	influence	the club like that

In the report, *influence**** appears 18 times with a majority of 11 neutral occurrences not indicating whether Bayer's activity has positive or negative ramifications, e.g. *Production fluctuations and building refurbishment/land remediation work also influence waste volumes and recycling paths.* Positive instances of *influence**** pertain to Bayer's activities and control, e.g. *This enables Bayer to significantly influence its financial and operating policy decisions.* There are only two instances of negative prosody of influence, both used for evading Bayer's responsibility, through the absence of a material actor in a subordinate clause: *Every day, cancer cells are formed in the human body [because of a genetic predisposition [or [as a result of [exposure to [cigarette smoke, UV radiation or other environmental influences].*

The entire section titled 'Our commitment to preserving Biodiversity' (T3) concerns not animals, but what Bayer refers to as *(3) genetic resources* in which a division, Crop Science is held responsible:

> *(4) Crop Science commits itself through an internal policy [to ensure [that Bayer only acquires and uses genetic resources] in harmony with international and national legislation*

The use of metaphor *genetic resources* erases any trace of animals or any other life forms such as crops and vegetation that are used by Bayer for breeding, experimentation and food, in effect reducing life to genetic information that can be traded. The responsibility for adhering to the United Nations Convention on Biological Diversity and the associated Nagoya Protocol mentioned in clause (2) is bandied around through changes in labelling Bayer-related actors which can be illustrated in this lexical chain: T3 *(1) we – (2) we – (4) Crop Science – (4.1) Bayer.* While all labels could be deemed to belong to the same entity, it is noteworthy to point the change and deafening silence on naming individual people as responsible. Additionally, it is important to note the way in which *Bayer (4.1)* is metaphorically used as a human participant throughout the texts analysed (e.g. T3 (4.1); T7 (3)). I classified it as a human participant in my analysis following Stibbe's[36] analysis of the conceptual metaphor CORPORATION IS A PERSON in which he finds that the metaphor is 'employed ideologically in legal discourse by a particularly powerful group in society: corporate lawyers, together with legislators who have been influenced by the corporate world'. Seeing that corporations were allocated personhood (later amended on 1/4/2012 when the New York City Council adopted a resolution supporting an amendment to the constitution 'to provide that corporations are not entitled to the entirety of protections or "rights" of natural persons') while animals are still today denied equal rights is a marked example of the perpetuation of inequality in which the wants and will of oppressors are reinforced while those of the oppressed are denied.

Another erasure of animals occurs through the use of metonymy. Living beings in Bayer's IR are referred to using metonymy, e.g. in T7, *(1) bees and other pollinators* juxtaposed in the same text with *(2) pests, parasites*.

Transitivity patterns within the discourse of agribusiness implicitly erase animals' mental lives and treat them as objects. Transitivity concerns three types of processes or verbs that have been found in the IR: material, mental, and relational. In material processes, two main participants, the actor and goal, reveal who is doing what in the world and to whom. In the report, Bayer is the only human entity that is actor in transitive clauses with goals as objects or products: T1 *(9) our antiparasitics business; (8) the innovative, nonantibiotic immunostimulant Zelnate™*. It is interesting to note that the morphology of *antiparasitics* with prefix *anti-* and suffix *−ics* erases and distorts animals and living beings who are subsequently categorised are as parasites.

The discursive shift from exploitation to animal protection (and back again) is strongly evident when we consider the category of 'pest' animals.[37] For example, badgers in the United Kingdom (UK) and North America are considered occasional pests due to digging[38] and due to their supposed role in the distribution of bovine tuberculosis (The Wildlife Trust, no date). Traditional accounting's power lies in its assignment of social categories, thus playing an important role in creating a social reality in which certain determined categories are then taken into account, while others do not. The categories assigned to various groups and entities 'are indicative of our perceptions of them − and of our stance toward them'. They also determine their worth and future wellbeing. Therefore, the way in which people speak about different animals and the naming systems different languages employ, both 'reflect and facilitate human practice'. In keeping with the Whorfian concept of linguistic relativity theorising that linguistic resources available to speakers constrain to some extent their cognitive ability to understand and experience events, meaning-making is relatively determined and constrained by language. Therefore, the naming resources and categories used in a particular culture and social community reify the public perception of different animals and their use for various industries.

The final step after identifying beneficial discourses is promoting the language and linguistic features such as presuppositions, pronouns, participants and verbs, and on a macrolevel, the discourses that 'tells a useful story' (Stibbe, 2015: 33). Importantly, these beneficial discourses can transcend genre types and become the dominant discourse such as 'to be more not to have more', to which I discuss next.

Positive Discourse Analysis (PDA): Alternative Imaginary Accounts

The potential for accounting to be emancipatory and to drive positive change is always there,[39] as

> ... an appreciation of accounting's emancipatory possibilities implies seeing accounting as at least potentially aiding (and being integral to) or giving further help to an emancipatory project. Critical researchers thus envisage accounting as functioning to help overcome repressive obstacles so that a better state is realised ...A vision of accounting as an emancipatory force is consistent with seeing accounting as a communicative social practice that functions as a system of informing that renders transparent and enlightens with the effect of social betterment.[40]

Ecolinguistics attempts to accomplish two goals: the first, expose the dominant discourses of unsustainable industrial civilisation that promote ecologically destructive behaviour. For example, the agricultural industry tends to employ discourse that reduces the natural world to a machine, a resource to exploit. This has been the main focus for CDA, focusing on problematic power relations, oppression and exploitation in texts, and unveiling how these are resisted.[41] However, this step offers little in the way of promoting beneficial alternative forms of language in order to move forward (Stibbe, 2018). But, as Morris[42] says, 'Realism on its own, in the world as he knew it, could lead only to despair'. This is why imaginary, alternative accounts can pave the way for better stories to live by.

Building on the extinction accounting framework as conceived by Atkins and Maroun,[43] I propose an imagined future disclosures of accounting for hedgehog extinction by agrochemical companies. Following the key performance indicators (KPIs) of the framework, the companies will adopt integrated reporting, with the extinction account integrated into their strategy and includes specific information on the initiatives and actions taken: in this case, company X has decided to start a Hedgehog Care Centre housing a hedgehog and wildlife hospital, a research laboratory and an educational visitors' centre. The company invites schools, educators, non-governmental organisations (NGOs) and hedgehog carers to visit our centre. They have also set up a partnership with Wild Hogs Hedgehog Rescue in to develop a cross-country database for collecting data on hedgehogs admitted into care. This way, the data can be shared so that we can learn how best to help hedgehogs and other small mammals.

Why hedgehogs? Their ability to adapt to urban settings and their benign behaviour makes them Britain's iconic one of the most popular mammals, which may account for the extensive folklore and mythology surrounding these wonderful creatures, and why they receive a good deal of attention for the press.

Increasingly, however, press coverage of hedgehogs tells the devastating story of their rapid decline in the last decade by a third, with local extinctions currently underway. Hedgehogs are a priority, bioindicator species of soil health, as they mainly feed on insects such as beetles, slugs and earthworms.

Poisoning from biocides either directly or indirectly, as well as habitat loss, agricultural practices and climate change, is considered a threat for hedgehogs, and most mammals in the UK. Water quality and decreasing food sources are associated with pesticide use and application.

The indirect effect of pesticides is in the reduction of food availability and shares similar concerns many have alerted to in the lengthy and well-studied discussion of pesticides and pollinators. Therefore, the effect of pesticides presents a material risk not only to pollinators and to beneficial insects, but also to mammals and hedgehogs are one example of threatened species right here at home.

The Hedgehog Care Programme works to support farmers to provide habitats to hedgehogs, bringing back hedgerows and wildlife corridors in fields, checking for hedgehog nests in spring and summertime, minimizing crop protection use and correct application.

The programme monitors known hedgehog populations in various areas, in collaboration with the company's partners NGOs across the UK and worldwide.

The company provides a pictorial representation of what success of hedgehog conservation looks like. Specific examples of rehabilitated hedgehogs, provision of habitat and the iterative process of monitoring the actions taken are central in the disclosure. This exemplifies the efforts the company takes to mitigate extinction on a meaningful level, an endeavour that has the potential to go beyond what companies often confront as the main critique from NGOs: greenwashing.

Conclusion: When Discourse Breaks the Cycle of Domination, Then It Becomes Emancipatory[44]

The ecolinguistic analysis revealed textual erasure on three levels: void, mask and trace. By employing mass and count nouns such as biodiversity and ecosystems, the IR erases animals from its report. Save for bees, mostly occurring in names of company initiatives, no other animal is mentioned. Metonymy further erases bees who are only perceived through the label pollinators. Erasure of responsibility is carried out through linguistic features such as metaphors *genetic resources* and nominalisation *animal studies*.

The erasure of animals runs counter to the ecosophy of this paper on several grounds. Firstly, the technocratic dominant discourse in the report fails to recognise the interconnectedness and importance of all living beings in an ecosystem. By placing technology as the primary solution, it devalues the contribution all life has in the maintenance of the health of the planetary and local ecosystems. Secondly, Bayer's perpetuation and benefit from hegemonic ideology of animals used for food and the heavy contribution of the agribusiness to extinction counters to author's position as an animal liberationist. As an activist and researcher concerned not only with animal protection but also with the health of the plant, particularly in the face of the global coronavirus disease 2019 (COVID-19) epidemic that has been shown to be closely linked to animal husbandry,[45] the analysis demonstrates significant ideological and material disconnects between the realities of biodiversity disclosures and Bayer's orientation towards efficiency which is at times in stark contrast to sustainability. We can see this conflation in the labelling of environmental resources together with resource efficiency, occurring twice in the report. Increasing efficiency (of production, of energy, of food) means that more is available to be used, when the focus should be on changing radical cultural and societal paradigms.

Species extinction is not reserved solely for nonhuman species and their survival is indicative of the health of the planet and its capacity to sustain life, as Gray and Milne[46] state, 'Species extinction is fundamentally inseparable from humanity's existence and humanity's putative extinction'. Importantly, this notion is fundamental to the holistic approach taken in extinction accounting and ecolinguistics that sees the Earth and all its living beings as an intricately interconnected system.

APPENDIX

The Bayer Bee Care Program (GRI)

We are the world's leading company in accounting for bee health and bee care. At Bayer, we have been caring for bees since 2011. Our Bee Care Centre researches the best ways to protect crop while making sure bees are not negatively affected. The program encourages dialogue and partnership between stakeholders who care about bees, and enhances farmers' ability to supply the best crop and food—in a world where food security is a main concern. However, bees are not the only species that biocides may affect.

Hedgehogs are a material issue

Hedgehogs are nocturnal generalist feeders, feeding largely on invertebrates such as slugs, worms, caterpillars and beetles.

They travel over 2 kilometres a night, foraging, and looking for mates. Because of land fragmentation and the way cities are built, this is a challenge for hedgehogs.

Our approach to disclosure: transparency

By producing an Integrated Report, we follow the IIRC's and GRI guidelines. This means we see sustainability and the need to protect the environment as part of our strategy, bringing long-term value creation to our investors and stakeholders.

We take the six capitals approach as central to our operations, placing value on all the resources on which our operations depend. But with the IPBES' (2019) latest report, we recognise we must play a part in making sure our products don't negatively affect the environment, and contribute to species extinction.

We care about all living beings and understand how all life depends on the health of the ecosystem.

Our Bee Care Centre makes sure farmers know how to use crop protection products safely and effectively both to ensure high yields and without harming non-target species, which has been a concern for many of our stakeholders, raised in recent listening session we held.

Why does Bayer cares for Hedgehogs? (1)

At Bayer, transparency and actively taking responsibility is a key ethos. At Bayer, we are not satisfied with philanthropic gestures alone. That's why, together with the Bee Care Centre, we have launched the Hedgehog Care Centre in the UK.

Hedgehogs and indeed most living being on Earth are facing extinction in our modern world. Protecting them is a shared responsibility for us all, and this includes the crop protection industry.

Hedgehogs (1) are a priority species in the UK, and have been decreasing dramatically in the last decade. This decline is attributed to human activity, in particular resulting from car accidents, habitat destruction and land conversion to development and agriculture, and parasites, such as nematodes, flystrike, lungworm and many others. Poisoning from biocides is thought to be a risk for hedgehogs as well, as it is claimed to be killing off their food sources.

FIGURE 29A.1 A mock-up imaginary hedgehog extinction account.

❚ *Foraging and nutrition*
❚ *Insect biodiversity*

❚ *Research to combat hedgehog parasitic diseases*
❚ *Habitat management*

❚ *Responsible pesticide use*
❚ *Hedgehog-farmers relations*
❚ *Hedgehogs as natural pest control services*

The Bayer Hedgehog Care Program (2 and 3) focuses on three key areas: 'Feed a Hedgehog', 'Healthy Habitat' and 'Sustainable Agriculture' in order to mitigate hedgehog decline.

Feed a hedgehog aims to expand hedgehogs' foraging and nesting habitats to meet the nutritional and reproductive needs. This means we continue research into the effect of neonicotinoids insecticides on non-target insects and small mammals. Working with individuals and organisations, farmers and local councils, we aim to increase food and habitat availability to hedgehogs.

Healthy Habitats is geared to research and raise awareness of correct practices of maintaining green spaces and private gardens to combat pesticide incorrect and over-use.

Sustainable Agriculture promotes the responsible use of crop protection products to ensure safety for hedgehogs in agricultural and urban landscapes, working to bring hedgehog rescuers, wildlife rescue centres and farmers , through our Forward Farms, close together to find innovative ways to optimize crop yield while providing hedges and verges for hedgehogs to thrive in.

Our partnerships (3)

Hedgehog Care Centre houses a hedgehog and wildlife hospital, a research lab and an educational visitors' centre. Bayer invites schools, educators, NGOs, and hedgehog carers to visit our centre. We have also set up a partnership with Wild Hogs Hedgehog Rescue in to develop a cross-country database for collecting data on hedgehogs admitted into care. This way, the data can be shared so that we can learn how best to help hedgehogs and other small mammals.

The hedgehog Care Program works to support farmers to provide habitats to hedgehogs, bringing back hedgerows and wildlife corridors in fields, checking for hedgehog nests in spring and summertime, minimizing crop protection use and correct application.

The program monitors known hedgehog populations in various areas, in collaboration with our partner NGOs across the UK and worldwide.

FIGURE 29A.2 A mock-up imaginary hedgehog extinction account.

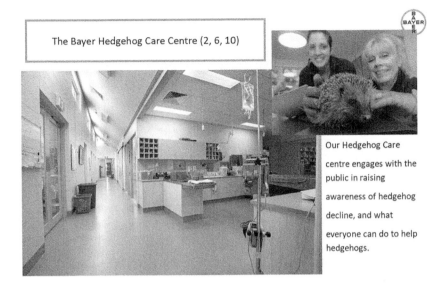

The Bayer Hedgehog Care Centre (2, 6, 10)

Our Hedgehog Care centre engages with the public in raising awareness of hedgehog decline, and what everyone can do to help hedgehogs.

We set up a hedgehog and wildlife hospital, a research lab and an educational visitors' centre. We invite schools, educators, NGOs, hedgehog carers to visit our centre and see what Bayer is doing to help halt hedgehog decline.

We have also set up a partnership with Wild Hogs Hedgehog Rescue in Gloucestershire to develop a cross-country database for collecting data on hedgehogs admitted into care. This way, the data can be shared with academics, conservationists, NGOs so that we can learn how best to help hedgehogs.

Protecting hedgehogs and other endangered species is part of our long-term strategy (7 and 9)

Accounting for hedgehogs and the action we have taken to monitor our products and ensure their safety and correct application is part of our long-term strategy and policy. We would like to assure our investors and stakeholders that we are constantly monitoring our Hedgehog Care program and audit other species that may be affected by our products and activities.

We will continuously be assessing whether our Hedgehog Care Plan is effective in mitigating hedgehog decline. (8 and 9)

(8) The acquisition of Monsanto brought with it a torrent of legal liability and risk. To combat this and regain the trust of our investors and stakeholders we have developed the hedgehog program which we

FIGURE 29A.3   A mock-up imaginary hedgehog extinction account.

Notes

1 Arran Stibbe, "The Stories We Live By: A Free Online Course in Ecolinguistics," 2016, http://storiesweliveby.org.uk/part-1/4593309655.
2 (1972; 2001: 58).
3 "Discourse Analysis in Organization Studies: The Case for Critical Realism," *Organization Studies* 26, no. 6 (2005): 915–939, https://doi.org/10.1177/0170840605054610.
4 Stibbe, "The Stories We Live By: A Free Online Course in Ecolinguistics."
5 Richard Alexander and Arran Stibbe, "From the Analysis of Ecological Discourse to the Ecological Analysis of Discourse," *Language Sciences* 41 (2014): 104–110, https://doi.org/10.1016/j.langsci.2013.08.011; Sune Vork Steffensen and Alwin Fill, "Ecolinguistics: The State of the Art and Future Horizons," *Language Sciences* 41 (2014): 6–25, https://doi.org/10.1016/j.langsci.2013.08.003; Sibo Chen, "Language and Ecology: A Content Analysis of Ecolinguistics as an Emerging Research Field," *Ampersand* 3 (2016): 108–116, https://doi.org/10.1016/j.amper.2016.06.002; F. Fill, Alwin and Hermine Penz, *The Routledge Handbook of Ecolinguistics* (New York: Routledge, 2017).
6 Daniel Nettle and Suzanne Romaine, *Vanishing Voices: The Extinction of the World's Languages* (Oxford: Oxford University Press, 2000), https://ebookcentral.proquest.com/lib/sheffield/detail.action?docID=279654.
7 Ken Hale et al., "Endangered Languages," *Linguistic Society of America* 68, no. 1 (1992): 1–42.
8 Haugen, E. (1972), 'The Ecology of Language', in A. S. Dil (ed.), *The Ecology of Language: Essays by Einar Haigen*, Stanford: Stanford University Press. pp.325-339. Reprinted in A. Fill and P. Muhlhausler (ends 2001, pp. 57-66.
9 Steffensen and Fill, "Ecolinguistics: The State of the Art and Future Horizons."
10 Chen, "Language and Ecology: A Content Analysis of Ecolinguistics as an Emerging Research Field."
11 Alexander and Stibbe, "From the Analysis of Ecological Discourse to the Ecological Analysis of Discourse," 107.
12 Arran Stibbe, *Ecolinguistics, Language, Ecology and the Stories We Live By* (London, New York: Routledge, 2015).
13 Stibbe.
14 Annabelle Mooney and Betsy Evans, *Language, Society and Power: An Introduction*, 4th ed. (London and New York: Routledge, 2015).
15 George Lakoff, *Thinking Points: Communicating Our American Values and Vision: A Progressive's Handbook* (New York: Farrar, Straus and Giroux, 2006).
16 Arran Stibbe, "Language, Power and the Social Construction of Animals," *Society & Animals* 9, no. 2 (2001): 146–161.
17 (Stibbe, 2015) / Stibbe, A., 2015. *Ecolinguistics, Language, Ecology and the Stories We Live By*. Abingdon, New York: Routledge.
18 (Stibbe, 2015) / Stibbe, A., 2015. *Ecolinguistics, Language, Ecology and the Stories We Live By*. Abingdon, New York: Routledge.
19 (2015)
20 Arran Stibbe, *Animals Erased* (Middletown: Wesleyan University Press, 2012).
21 Gunther Kress and Theo Van Leeuwen, *Reading Images: The Grammar of Visual Design* (London: Routledge, 1996).
22 (Naess, 1989) / Naess, A., 1989. *Ecology, community and lifestyle : outline of an ecosophy*. Cambridge: Cambridge University Press.
23 (1990)
24 Arne Naess, "The Shallow and the Deep, Long-Range Ecology Movement: A Summary," *Inquiry (United Kingdom)* 16, no. 1–4 (1973): 95–100, https://doi.org/10.1080/00201747308601682.
25 Richard Heinberg, "There's No App for That: Technology and Morality in the Age of Climate Change, Overpopulation and Biodiversity Loss" (Corvallis, Oregon, 2017), http://noapp4that.org/.

26 Rosemary Mason et al., "Immune Suppression by Neonicotinoid Insecticides at the Root of Global Wildlife Declines," *Journal of Enviromental Immunology and Toxicology* 1, no. 1 (2013): 3–12, https://doi.org/10.7178/jeit.1; Carey Gillam, *Whitewash: The Story of a Weed Killer, Cancer, and the Corruption of Science* (Washington: Island Press, 2017).

27 Tyrone B. Hayes et al., "Pesticide Mixtures, Endocrine Disruption, and Amphibian Declines: Are We Underestimating the Impact?," *Environmental Health Perspectives* 114, no. SUPPL.1 (2006): 40–50, https://doi.org/10.1289/ehp.8051; Mason et al., "Immune Suppression by Neonicotinoid Insecticides at the Root of Global Wildlife Declines."

28 Robin Mesnage, Charles Benbrook, and Michael N. Antoniou, "Insight into the Confusion over Surfactant Co-Formulants in Glyphosate-Based Herbicides," *Food and Chemical Toxicology* 128, no. March (2019): 137–145, https://doi.org/10.1016/j.fct.2019.03.053.

29 Bayer, "Bayer Annual Report," 2016, http://www.annualreport2016.bayer.com/.

30 J. Atkins and W. Maroun, "Integrated Extinction Accounting and Accountability: Building an Ark," *Accounting, Auditing and Accountability Journal* 31, no. 3 (2018), https://doi.org/10.1108/AAAJ-06-2017-2957.

31 (Solomon et al., 2013; Leung, Parker and Courtis, 2015)

32 (DeLong, 1996) / DeLong, D.C.J., 1996. Defining Biodiversity. *Wildlife Society Bulletin,* 24(4), pp.738 -749.

33 (Stibbe, 2012) / Stibbe, A., 2012. Animals Erased. Middletown: Wesleyan University Press.

34 (Stibbe, 2012: 73).

35 (Stibbe, 2013) / Stibbe, A., 2013. The Corporation as Person and Psychopath : Multimodal Metaphor, Rhetoric and Resistance. *Critical Approaches to Discourse Analysis across Disciplines,* [online] 6(2), pp.114 -136.

36 (2013:118).

37 Alison Sealey and Nickie Charles, "'What Do Animals Mean to You?': Naming and Relating to Nonhuman Animals," *Anthrozoos* 26, no. 4 (2013): 485–503, https://doi.org/10.2752/175303713X13795775535652.

38 (Minta and Marsh, 1988).

39 (Gallhofer and Haslam, 2003) / Gallhofer, S. and Haslam, J., 2003. Accounting and emancipation : some critical interventions [e-book]. London: Routledge.

40 Gallhofer and Haslam, 2003, p. 7.

41 Norman Fairclough, "A Dialectical-Relational Approach to Critical Discourse Analysis in Social Research," in *Methods for Critical Discourse Analysis,* 2009.

42 Jill Atkins et al., "'Good' News from Nowhere: Imagining Utopian Sustainable Accounting," *Accounting, Auditing & Accountability Journal* 28, no. 5 (2015): 651–670, https://doi.org/10.1108/MBE-09-2016-0047.

43 Atkins and Maroun, "Integrated Extinction Accounting and Accountability: Building an Ark."

44 Hilary Janks and Roz Ivanic, "CLA and Emancipatory Discourse," in *Critical Language Awareness,* ed. Norman Fairclough, 1st ed. (Harlow: Longman Group UK Ltd, 1992), 306–331.

45 Catherine Paulin, "A Reflection on Human-Animal Relations in Light of COVID-19," Niche Canada, 2020, https://niche-canada.org/2020/04/30/a-reflection-on-human-animal-relations-in-light-of-covid-19/; Nik Taylor and Heather Fraser, "Radically Imagining Human-Animal Relations after the Covid19 Pandemic," Animals in Society, 2020, https://animalsinsocietygroup.wordpress.com/2020/04/06/-radically-imagining-human-animal-relations-after-the-covid19-pandemic/?fbclid=IwAR3qPqtR7rKrgxMW5KE9s7wVCCCUFOZgXGAql1oKHzjQsbaWFqSLXRRigdc; Liz Specht and Jan Dutkiewicz, "Let's Rebuild the Broken Meat Industry—WithoutAnimals:Covid-19HasLaidBareManyFlawsofIndustrializedAnimalAgriculture.Plant-andCell-BasedAlternativesOfferaMoreResilientSolution.,"Wired,2020, https://www.wired.com/story/opinion-lets-rebuild-the-broken-meat-industry-

without-animals/amp?fbclid=IwAR0KqkO4yHYvczNMdxkU8A7CWCLmbC6lw
8EDJKc_IdDXmlPiIhTao4nolAI.

46 (Stibbe, 2015) / Stibbe, A., 2015. *Ecolinguistics, Language, Ecology and the Stories We Live By.* Abingdon, New York: Routledge.

References

Alexander, Richard, and Arran Stibbe. "From the Analysis of Ecological Discourse to the Ecological Analysis of Discourse." *Language Sciences* 41 (2014): 104–110. https://doi.org/10.1016/j.langsci.2013.08.011.

Atkins, J., and W. Maroun. "Integrated Extinction Accounting and Accountability: Building an Ark." *Accounting, Auditing and Accountability Journal* 31, no. 3 (2018). https://doi.org/10.1108/AAAJ-06-2017-2957.

Atkins, Jill, Barry Colin Atkins, Ian Thomson, and Warren Maroun. "'Good' News from Nowhere: Imagining Utopian Sustainable Accounting." *Accounting, Auditing & Accountability Journal* 28, no. 5 (2015): 651–670. https://doi.org/10.1108/MBE-09-2016-0047.

Atkins, Jill, and Martina Macpherson. "Developing a Species Protection Action Plan - An Integrated Approach for Taxonomies, Reporting and Engagement for the Financial Services Sector," A working paper distributed at Investec Bank's "Natural Capital, Species Extinction & Sustainable Financial Markets" Roundtable in London, 2019, pp.1-19.

Bayer. "Bayer Annual Report," 2016. http://www.annualreport2016.bayer.com/.

Chen, Sibo. "Language and Ecology: A Content Analysis of Ecolinguistics as an Emerging Research Field." *Ampersand* 3 (2016): 108–116. https://doi.org/10.1016/j.amper.2016.06.002.

DeLong, Don C. Jr. "Defining Biodiversity." *Wildlife Society Bulletin* 24, no. 4 (1996): 738–749. https://doi.org/10.1007/sl0869-007-9037-x.

Fairclough, N. (2009), A Dialectical-Relational Approach to Critical Discourse Analysis in Social Research. in: Wodak, R. and Meyer, M. (eds.). 2009. *Methods in Critical Discourse Analysis [electronic resource].* London: SAGE.

———. "Discourse Analysis in Organization Studies: The Case for Critical Realism." *Organization Studies* 26, no. 6 (2005): 915–939. https://doi.org/10.1177/0170840605054610.

Fill, Alwin, F., and Hermine Penz. *The Routledge Handbook of Ecolinguistics.* New York: Routledge, 2017.

Gillam, Carey. *Whitewash: The Story of a Weed Killer, Cancer, and the Corruption of Science.* Washington: Island Press, 2017.

Gray, Rob, and Markus J. Milne. "Perhaps the Dodo Should Have Accounted for Human Beings? Accounts of Humanity and (Its) Extinction." *Accounting, Auditing & Accountability Journal* 31, no. 3 (2018): 826–848. https://doi.org/http://dx.doi.org/10.1108/MRR-09-2015-0216.

Hale, Ken, Michael Krauss, Lucille J Watahomigie, Akira Y Yamamoto, C. Craig, L.M Jeanne, and N.C. England. "Endangered Languages." *Linguistic Society of America* 68, no. 1 (1992): 1–42.

Haugen, E. "The Ecology of Language." In *The Ecolinguistics Reader: Language, Ecology and the Environment,* edited by Alwin Fill and P. Mulhausler, 57–66. London and New York: Stanford University Press, 2001. https://doi.org/10.1353/lan.2005.0033.

Hayes, Tyrone B., Paola Case, Sarah Chui, Duc Chung, Cathryn Haeffele, Kelly Haston, Melissa Lee, et al. "Pesticide Mixtures, Endocrine Disruption, and Amphibian

Declines: Are We Underestimating the Impact?" *Environmental Health Perspectives* 114, no. SUPPL.1 (2006): 40–50. https://doi.org/10.1289/ehp.8051.

Heinberg, Richard. "There's No App for That: Technology and Morality in the Age of Climate Change, Overpopulation and Biodiversity Loss." Corvallis, Oregon, 2017. http://noapp4that.org/.

Janks, Hilary, and Roz Ivanic. "CLA and Emancipatory Discourse." In *Critical Language Awareness*, edited by Norman Fairclough, 1st ed., 306–331. Harlow: Longman Group UK Ltd, 1992.

Kress, Gunther, and Theo Van Leeuwen. *Reading Images: The Grammar of Visual Design*. London: Routledge, 1996.

Lakoff, George. *Thinking Points: Communicating Our American Values and Vision: A Progressive's Handbook*. New York: Farrar, Straus and Giroux, 2006.

Leung, Sidney, Lee Parker, and John Courtis. "Impression Management through Minimal Narrative Disclosure in Annual Reports." *British Accounting Review* 47, no. 3 (2015): 275–289. https://doi.org/10.1016/j.bar.2015.04.002.

Mason, Rosemary, Henk Tennekes, Francisco Sánchez-Bayo, and Uhd Palle Jespen. "Immune Suppression by Neonicotinoid Insecticides at the Root of Global Wildlife Declines." *Journal of Environmental Immunology and Toxicology* 1, no. 1 (2013): 3–12. https://doi.org/10.7178/jeit.1.

Mesnage, Robin, Charles Benbrook, and Michael N. Antoniou. "Insight into the Confusion over Surfactant Co-Formulants in Glyphosate-Based Herbicides." *Food and Chemical Toxicology* 128, no. March (2019): 137–145. https://doi.org/10.1016/j.fct.2019.03.053.

Minta, S. C., and Marsh, R. E. "Badgers (Taxidea Taxus) as Occasional Pests in Agriculture." *Proceedings of the Vertebrate Pest Conference* 13, no. March (1988): 199–208.

Mooney, Annabelle, and Betsy Evans. *Language, Society and Power: An Introduction*. 4th ed. London and New York: Routledge, 2015.

Naess, Arne. *Ecology, Community and Lifestyle : Outline of an Ecosophy*. Cambridge: Cambridge University Press, 1989.

———. "The Shallow and the Deep, Long-Range Ecology Movement: A Summary." *Inquiry (United Kingdom)* 16, no. 1–4 (1973): 95–100. https://doi.org/10.1080/00201747308601682.

Nettle, Daniel, and Suzanne Romaine. *Vanishing Voices: The Extinction of the World's Languages*. Oxford: Oxford University Press, 2000. https://ebookcentral.proquest.com/lib/sheffield/detail.action?docID=279654.

Paulin, Catherine. "A Reflection on Human-Animal Relations in Light of COVID-19." Niche Canada, 2020. https://niche-canada.org/2020/04/30/a-reflection-on-human-animal-relations-in-light-of-covid-19/.

Sealey, Alison, and Nickie Charles. "'What Do Animals Mean to You?': Naming and Relating to Nonhuman Animals." *Anthrozoos* 26, no. 4 (2013): 485–503. https://doi.org/10.2752/175303713X13795775535652.

Solomon, Jill F, Aris Solomon, Nathan L Joseph, and Simon D Norton. "Author's Personal Copy Impression Management, Myth Creation and Fabrication in Private Social and Environmental Reporting: Insights from Erving Goffman," n.d. http://www.elsevier.com/authorsrights.

Specht, Liz, and Jan Dutkiewicz. "Let's Rebuild the Broken Meat Industry—Without Animals: Covid-19 Has Laid Bare Many Flaws of Industrialized Animal Agriculture. Plant-and Cell-Based Alternatives Offer a More Resilient Solution." Wired, 2020. https://www.wired.com/story/opinion-lets-rebuild-the-broken-meat-industry-without-

animals/amp?fbclid=IwAR0KqkO4yHYvczNMdxkU8A7CWCLmbC6lw8EDJKc_
IdDXmlPiIhTao4nolAI.

Steffensen, Sune Vork, and Alwin Fill. "Ecolinguistics: The State of the Art and Future Horizons." *Language Sciences* 41 (2014): 6–25. https://doi.org/10.1016/j.langsci.2013.08.003.

Stibbe, Arran. "An Ecolinguistic Approach to Critical Discourse Studies." *Critical Discourse Studies* 11, no. 1 (2014): 117–128.

———. *Animals Erased.* Middletown: Wesleyan University Press, 2012.

———. *Ecolinguistics, Language, Ecology and the Stories We Live By.* Abingdon, New York: Routledge, 2015.

———. "Language, Power and the Social Construction of Animals." *Society & Animals* 9, no. 2 (2001): 146–161.

———. "Positive Discourse Analysis: Rethinking Human Ecological Relationships." In *The Routledge Handbook of Ecolinguistics,* edited by F. Fill, Alwin and Hermine Penz, 165–178. New York and London: Routledge, 2018.

———. "The Corporation as Person and Psychopath : Multimodal Metaphor, Rhetoric and Resistance." *Critical Approaches to Discourse Analysis across Disciplines* 6, no. 2 (2013): 114–136. http://cadaad.net/journal.

———. "The Stories We Live By: A Free Online Course in Ecolinguistics," 2016. http://storiesweliveby.org.uk/part-1/4593309655.

Stibbe, Arran, and Francesca Zunino. "Boyd's Forest Dragon or the Survival of Humanity: Discourse and the Social Construction of Biodiversity." In *Language, Signs and Nature: Ecolinguistic Dimensions of Environmental Discourse,* edited by Martin Doring, Hermine Penz, and Wilhelm Trampe, 165–181. Tubingen: Stauffenburg Verlag, 2008.

Taylor, Nik, and Heather Fraser. "Radically Imagining Human-Animal Relations after the Covid19 Pandemic." Animals in Society, 2020. https://animalsinsocietygroup.wordpress.com/2020/04/06/radically-imagining-human-animal-relations-after-the-covid19-pandemic/?fbclid=IwAR3qPqtR7rKrgxMW5KE9s7wVCCCUFOZgXGAql1oKHzjQsbaWFqSLXRRigdc.

PART VI

Reflections and Conclusion

Establishing a Framework for
Action

30

EXTINCTION, BIODIVERSITY LOSS AND COVID-19

Searching for Meaning[1]

Barry Atkins

It is becoming increasingly evident that people the world over are struggling to come to terms with the biodiversity loss, species extinctions, the destruction of rainforests, the devastating impacts of global warming and generally the ongoing destruction of our natural world. Furthermore, people around the world are in the midst of a previously unimaginable pandemic, which again is leaving them vulnerable, confused, lacking in comprehension and scared. This book focuses on the ways in which the financial markets can make a difference to biodiversity collapse and species extinctions. There are also discussions throughout the book on the impact of the pandemic on financial institutions' attitudes to, and practice around, biodiversity and species protection. However, financial institutions, companies and indeed every human-created organisations consist of people. How are people dealing mentally and emotionally with these overwhelming issues and events? In this chapter, I seek meaning in face of these near-apocalyptic crises, turning to the work of Viktor E. Frankl for inspiration and guidance, as well as drawing from my experience as a mental health counsellor.

Viktor E. Frankl was an Austrian Jew who founded what has come to be known as the Third Viennese School of Psychotherapy – after Freud's Psychoanalysis and Adler's Individual Psychology, the school of logotherapy.[2]

The author Harold S. Kushner succinctly explains the basic, underlying tenet of logotherapy in his preface to Frankl's seminal book *Man's Search for Meaning* (Frankl, 1946):

> Life is not primarily a quest for pleasure, as Freud believed, or a quest for power, as Alfred Adler taught, but a quest for meaning.
>
> *(p. 8)*

DOI: 10.4324/9781003045557-37

Born in 1905, Frankl first published in 1924 in the *International Journal of Psycho-analysis* and had been developing the initial ideas that would eventually evolve fully into logotherapy for a number of years before the defining experience of his life befell him, being captured and cast into the network of Nazi concentration camps, Auschwitz among them.

It was here, in these hells on earth, that his emerging psychotherapeutic beliefs were put to the starkest, most brutal of tests; he could not control the suffering that he would have to endure, but he could control how he *responded* to the suffering – that, despite the fact that he was incarcerated behind electrified barbed-wire fences with machine gun towers covering every inch of compound and that at any moment of any day or night he could be selected for extermination, inside himself he was *free* to choose whether to succumb to the seemingly inevitable (and, given the daily brutalities, degradations and humiliations that were dealt out to prisoners, one can easily imagine why many ultimately chose to take this final course of (in)action, to one day take to one's wooden cot, refuse to get back up, refuse all rations – bread crusts or thin gruel – defy all thrashings and simply wait for death to claim them) or to try to endure, to prevail, to *live*.

But, of course, if a person chooses to endure rather than succumb to suffering, there must be a driving force, a reason to do so; Frankl's experiences teach us that we cannot control fate – the things that happen to us, the things that are inflicted upon us, for example, being randomly directed to the left or the right by an SS officer at Auschwitz railway station (left meant a forced march to the crematorium),[3] or randomly touching a surface tainted by coronavirus disease 2019 (COVID-19) and have limited influence over our individual destinies, but we can, if we accept the responsibility of this freedom to choose, respond *well* to our suffering and thus adopt a posture that can sustain us through our suffering, to give *meaning* to our suffering.

The search for meaning, then, is the key to prevailing though suffering. In his writings, Frankl often paraphrases a famous quote by Nietzsche, "He who has a Why to live for can bear almost any How"[4] (Nietzsche, 1889). In other words, if you can locate meaning in your suffering, a goal that is specific to you, and that only you can achieve, then you can endure almost anything. In Frankl's case, the meaning-making was twofold; on his first day in camp, when he and his fellow prisoners were stripped and robbed of all their possessions, Frankl had tried to take an older prisoner into his confidence, asking him to look after the manuscript that he had smuggled into the camp with him – the early ideas, thoughts and insights that would later evolve into logotherapy – only to be mocked and insulted by the older man. That original manuscript was, inevitably, then confiscated and lost forever. Rather than crushing his spirit, this incident instantly imparted meaning to Frankl's situation; a burning desire to recreate those notes upon his release, and a dream to one day deliver lectures on the lessons to be drawn from his experiences. The second source of meaning derived from the fact that there was no way that he could know of the fate being suffered by his wife, Tilly, living possibly only a couple of hundred metres away in the camp's female quarters. He didn't know whether she was even still alive – she could have been sent to the left by the SS guard, after all – but, still, he mentally evoked her during the forced marches of his work detail through biting winds and rain, summoning forth her image with an uncanny acuteness, each of them asking and answering questions, Frankl seeing "her smile, her frank and encouraging look. Real or not, her look was then more luminous than the sun which was beginning to rise" (p. 48); his rich spiritual life, and the prospect of seeing Tilly again after the war, insulated him from the external horrors.[5]

It is instructive, I believe, to view the ongoing, and accelerating, fight to save the heart and soul and physical self of Planet Earth (from its ongoing, and accelerating humiliation) through the lens of Frankl's work and beliefs. Just like the prisoners who lost all hope, gave up and perished, and the others who chose to suffer well, and took responsibility for their freedom to choose this course of action, I would suggest that the human perspective on, and response to, current events can be (*very*) broadly split into two categories; that which shakes its head, shrugs its shoulders and succumbs to a sense of futility, and that which locates meaning in our global suffering, thus providing an engine, a motivation, to endure and prevail.[6]

The oxygen that nourishes and sustains the first category, that is, the sheer weight of the horrors befalling us – the losses of biodiversity, ecosystems and habitats, the climate crisis, successive pandemics and so on, and the sheer serial ineptitude, arrogance and callous short-termism among national leaderships, multinational corporations and capitalism in its rawest form that underpin them – suggests that it is perhaps understandable, tempting even, to conclude that there is no hope. So why, and how, does the second category exist – thrive, even? Two telling passages from Frankl's work address this dilemma head-on:

> Man's search for meaning is the primary motivation in his life….This meaning is unique and specific in that it must and can be fulfilled by him alone; only then does it achieve a significance which will satisfy his own will to meaning.
>
> *(p. 105)*

And, when discussing how he framed his ethos when attempting to help despairing fellow prisoners locate a will to carry on against all odds:

> It did not really matter what we expected from life, but rather what life expected from us.[7]
>
> *(p. 85)*

In other words, what unique task is life inviting each and every one of us to fulfil? And do we accept that invitation, or do we allow that will to meaning to be crushed beneath the combined forces of dread, terror and hopelessness? Because, to be sure, it is not what happens to us that defines us but, rather, how we *respond* to these challenges.

So how do we locate multiple meanings in this world of dwindling ecosystems and rising temperatures? The key, surely, is within each of us, and personal archaeology may reveal shallow meanings that are easy to cling to, and more likely to disappoint; experience often shows that the richer the meaning, the harder it is to locate and to fulfil.

Let me return, then, to the first category. The *free* choice made here, borne of a sense of futility, nihilism even, is to decide that meaning cannot be located amidst such an accumulation of calamities.

> If politicians can't even agree upon the science, what chance do we have?
>
> I agree with the science, but look at the habitat loss, the accelerating extinctions, the thinning ice sheets. It's probably already too late.
>
> What possible difference can I make, anyway? What does it honestly matter whether or not I eat another snack containing palm oil/book another flight/spray insecticide on my plants/toss a KFC carton into the gutter/buy a bigger car (you get the idea)…..

And so on.

And, of course, such mindsets – in sufficient numbers – create their own self-fulfilling prophesies: Another ice sheet fractures; another thousand square acres of rainforest is logged; another species is declared extinct; another virus goes zoonotic; another unprecedented weather event creates havoc….

> Told you so…told you so…told you so…told you so…told you so…

Which brings us on to the second category:

> Yes, it does exist and, yes, it is definitely thriving.

Evidence of meaning-making, and the responses that spring from it, in these emotionally and spiritually draining times – and certainly the most challenging, in terms of the very survival of our civilisation(s) – is everywhere, if you look for it; like the very best detective novels, it sometimes hides in plain sight and is rarely obvious. Of course, there are some high-profile beacons of hope and inspiration, but for every David Attenborough or Greta Thunberg, or organisations and movements such as Greenpeace, WWF (Worldwide Fund) or Extinction Rebellion, there are a thousand miniature operations and activities, each running and sustaining itself on any one, or combination, of love, enthusiasm and responsibility and each derived from, and embedded in, a will to *meaning* excavated from the substrata of despair: from endangered species conservation compounds to urban apiarists; community litter-pickers (on streets, beaches, canal towpaths etc.) to composters; individual and collective rewilders to recyclers; community bird-ringing groups to butterfly recorders; car-poolers to organic gardeners…. the list is endless.

So what drives someone to, for example, learn apiary skills in a world of hive mites, invasive hornet species, colony collapse disorder, lethal insecticides and rampant monoculture?[8] What possible difference can they make? The philosopher and existential psychotherapist, Emmy van Duerzen, addresses this question neatly and insightfully in a reflection upon Frankl, after observing that because he had been able to face the abyss he didn't fear it any longer:

> Such an example of rising from crisis is hard-earned. We cannot really learn to do this unless we are ourselves exposed to a similar situation.
>
> *(van Duerzen, 2020, p. 27)*

Applying this to the amateur apiarist, then, we can perhaps picture someone, shocked and appalled by the ongoing, and accelerating, unravelling of so many of their everyday taken-for-granteds, and thus finding themselves standing at the fork in the road of their very own existential crisis; do they shake their head and shrug their shoulders, or do they formulate a meaning, and find an answer to life's invitation to fulfil their very own unique, freely chosen task? And, surely, as the first category nihilist might say, what good is one new hive in the battle against pollinator decline? Absolutely no use at all is the answer. But, in 20 years time, one hive may grow to 20,000, with the once amateur apiarist training his five-hundredth student – in the same way, that Frankl's confiscated notes, once reassembled upon his liberation, grew into an influential, global therapeutic modality, with thousands of students, practitioners and healed souls.

Because that's the knowledge that's implicit in human hope – the absence of hope is a dead end; only one outcome is possible. But hope, and the meaning that flows from it, and the responses it engenders, and the tasks it embraces, knows no bounds; it is the exponentiality of hope.

But, of course, generating hopes and meanings is the harder road to take; after all, failure is one of the possible outcomes. How tempting it can be to continue to live in one's (dis)comfort zone.

To find meaning, then, where some will find only meaninglessness is the key to our continued hopes for the well-being of this planet. And it locates just one of its many embodiments in the existence of this book, and the insightful, creative and resourceful contributions of so many practitioners and academics (and one therapist) each of whom have brought their respective talents to bear on the current crises, and found their own, unique will to meaning.

Notes

1 Thanks to Mira Lieberman for reading and commenting on an earlier draft of this chapter.
2 From the Greek *logos*, or 'meaning'.
3 Frankl was one of the approximately 10% who were selected for work and shown to the right. The other 90% did not last the day.

4 The original German translates most closely to, "If we have our own why in life, we shall get along with almost any how".

5 Upon his release in 1945, Frankl learned that all of his immediate family, with the exception of his sister who had emigrated to Australia, had perished in the camps. Tilly died at Bergen-Belsen.

6 One could argue, legitimately, that a third category exists: those that simply do not give a damn, or do not believe the evidence that surrounds them. So I suppose that my proposal pertains to the two categories of human perspective and response that derive from thought and reflection, and reach a conclusion. The blissfulness of ignorance (or protective cloak of denial) can wait for another time.

7 An interesting pre-echo of the famous line from JFK's inaugural speech: "Ask not what your country can do for you – ask what you can do for your country".

8 And, just as crucially, in a world where the *perception* of bees and other pollinators continues to be that of undesirability and deserving of extermination. For proof of this, check the list of target species on the next pest control van you see.

References

Frankl, V.E. (1946). *Man's Search for Meaning*. GB: Rider (2008 reprint).

Nietzsche, F. (1889) *Maxims and Arrows (from Twilight of the Idols)*. Penguin Classics Edition (1990 reprint).

van Duerzen, E. (2020). Surviving and thriving in a global existential crisis. *Therapy Today*, 5(31), pp. 26–29.

31

HOPE FOR THE FUTURE

A CREATIIIVE Approach to Extinction Governance, Accounting and Finance

Jill Atkins and Martina Macpherson

In this chapter, we take the opportunity to highlight the cutting-edge informa-tion on biodiversity, and species extinction governance, accounting and finance discussed by a wide array of academics and industry experts throughout this book. We by no means intend to attempt a summary of each and every initiative, as this would simply result in a repetition of the material contained in the various chapters. However, we have selected some of the pertinent points and summarise the overall thrust of current trends and movements across the financial markets in the biodiversity and species space. Our overall conclusion is twofold: (i) that there is evidence of significant and serious challenges that need to be addressed and (ii) that these challenges are tempered by immense optimism for the future trajectory of the financial markets in contributing to preserving biodiversity and species, based on deep commitment across the finance, accounting and govern-ance sectors to transformational and emancipatory action. We now discuss our overall views and summarise some highlights of the book.

Challenges and Solutions

Throughout this book, we have been led to appreciate the significant challenges posed to business, society and humanity from biodiversity loss and species ex-tinctions. Businesses need to establish commitments and act urgently, as laid out by Zabey and Thissen in Chapter 4. The challenges may be spelt out as follows: a current lack of standardisation around biodiversity impact measurement; the current inadequacy of extinction accounting (as identified particularly by the in-stitutional investment community); and the nascent nature of extinction engage-ment and the need for it to evolve rapidly. All of these hurdles need to be vaulted for the financial markets to achieve any efficacy in addressing species extinction

DOI: 10.4324/9781003045557-38

as well as biodiversity and ecosystem service decline and loss. The contributions in this text provide a multitude of solutions to these challenges including extinction accounting and biodiversity reporting frameworks for organisations and investors, methods for measuring impacts on biodiversity by business and the finance sectors, and investor engagement strategies linked to species protection.

Linked to these challenges, an area that needs to be addressed urgently is data. Box 31.1 explores the ways in which a new data infrastructure can be (and is being) developed to assist the data needs of a more biodiversity and species–aware finance industry.

BOX 31.1 NATURE IN FINANCE NEEDS NEW DATA INFRASTRUCTURE

The financial services industry is in the middle of a data storm. The Taskforce for Nature-Related Financial Disclosures (TNFD) can make it a perfect storm by ensuring that the data flowing into FIs also include actionable nature risk data. The TNFD, alongside new regulation such as SFDR,[1] will drive some of the biggest shifts in nature data markets ever seen. I have one hope to the direction of travel that the TNFD will give to these data markets, which is to require geolocation-specific disclosure as part of the new practice regime. What that means is that companies specify the physical location of their assets and of their suppliers. This is a prerequisite to generate decision-relevant insights which enables financial service institutions to properly manage nature physical and transition risks as well as to formulate nature-related institutional targets. For nature-related target setting to become mainstream practice, such as a net deforestation target or a net zero ocean plastic target, FIs need to be able to link the assets in their portfolio to specific deforestation and plastic leakage behaviours of companies.

Current biodiversity metrics deployed by frontrunner financial service institutions, such the Mass Species Abundance (MSA) or the Potentially Disappeared Fraction of Species (PDF) metrics, will also benefit from availability of geolocation data. With access to such data, these metrics hold great potential to enable FIs to compare material nature risks of different assets as part of an investment decision. It is important that the TNFD offers guidance on a standardised approach to geolocation. Today, it is interpreted in many different ways, which inhibits comparison across assets and jurisdictions. Geolocation disclosed is sometimes at country level, sometimes at regional level and sometimes at specific address level. A geolocation standard needs to be longitude and latitude, so that it becomes easily machine-readable.

Asset geolocation data would also make the zebibytes of satellite images currently available deployable by financial service institutions, such as the Sentinel-2 satellite image repository. The world is inundated with upstream biodiversity data mainly paid for by public money but not deployed by finance in any significant way. Now the question is not how to generate new asset geolocation data sets, rather how to design incentives to make these data sets available to finance and what digital infrastructure is most suited to support these incentives. Without clear regulation, companies are not going to disclose geolocation of all assets in annual reports publicly available anytime soon. A more viable approach is to design new digital infrastructure, where corporations can protect the data from being seen by competitors, whilst showing them to ESG data providers, investors and regulators with a transparency stamp granted for sharing these data as a type of incentive. Such a market infrastructure would be able to offer a stamp of approval that the assets underlying a financial instrument are not nature negative. That is the direction of travel I hope TNFD will give to nature data markets.

Contributed by Marianne Haahr, Executive Director of the Green Digital Finance Alliance and member of the Technical Expert Group on data to the IWG of the TNFD

As well as improving extinction governance and accounting, and biodiversity analysis and reporting, transparency more broadly needs to be enhanced if we are to see genuine improvements in ecosystems and extinction prevention. For example, we see in Chapter 9 that enhanced transparency is recommended as a means of protecting life in water and preventing illegal and excessive fishing, specifically enhancing transparency around vessels, fishing licences and vessel data.[2] Again a focus on developing data and their transparency is crucial in any effort to develop species protection and extinction prevention initiatives.

The book further reveals that it is important to recognise the impact of political and religious conflicts on species extinctions, as well as the pervasive impact of business activity on ecosystem services and biodiversity. These issues are highlighted in relation to camels, as outlined by Lieberman in Chapter 7, and in the creation of safe areas for endangered species caught between conflicts in the Middle East as raised in Chapter 8. It is fair to say that if there is sparse protection for climate refugees, as discussed by Trent in Chapter 9, then what protection is there for animal, non-human species refugees, thrown from their lands by habitat destruction, war and political upheavals? We only have to think of heartbreaking photos of orang-utan clinging desperately to tree branches as they watch their forest being deconstructed and torn down around them. One of the most striking issues raised in Chapter 8 is the development of safe harbours for endangered species in Jordan. The effective granting of 'refugee status' to endangered creatures is explored further in Box 31.2.

As mentioned above, we are not going to attempt a comprehensive summary of all the recommendations for policy and practice mentioned throughout this

---

BOX 31.2 ENDANGERED SPECIES BECOME REFUGEES

There are many animals threatened with extinction because of the unstable situation in the Middle East mainly in Syria, Iraq and Gaza, as highlighted in Chapter 8. As a result of the political tensions and the dangers posed to animals from political unrest, many of these animals are transferred to Jordan (which is a neighbouring country) as 'animal refugees'. Thus, we can see that as well as millions of desperate human refugees entering Jordan, who have fled their home countries due to political instability and war, inter alia, Jordan has also received many animals from counties that have unstable and civil war conditions. In Jordan, both people and animals can live in peace. Indeed, White[3] argues that in the midst of the ongoing refugee crisis, animals need to be taken into consideration as well as human refugees. Planning and execution involving rescue and transferal of endangered and threatened animals from Syria, Iraq and Gaza have been carried out by 'FOUR PAWS International', an NGO.[4] Some of these animals are taken to Jordan and then transferred to South Africa. There is evidence amassing of the extent of the animal refugee crisis.[5] Whilst many may argue that when people are in such terrible situations, having to flee their homes and live in refugee camps, then saving animals is a low priority, we can see the necessity of protecting species that are threatened with extinction as well, where resources allow, in order to prevent the disappearance of unique creatures from these parts of the world. Organising animal refugee transfer and providing them with safe harbour is certainly a form of Extinction Governance by NGOs and those that fund them and assist them in these endeavours.

Contributed by Omar Mowalfi

---

book, as this would be excessive. However, we identify the most salient initiatives in Table 31.1, where we map the cutting-edge initiatives for protecting species and biodiversity, as identified and outlined by the contributors to this book, according to the chapters where they appear.

Emancipatory action and transformative initiatives are at the heart of the Extinction Governance framework presented in Chapter 2. This framework needs to be integrated into governance codes of practice and into organisations' governance the world over if we are to save species and protect biodiversity. Further, integrating the Business for Nature (BfN) model should be a key element of any organisation's extinction governance, as outlined in Chapter 4.

In the area of Extinction Investor Engagement (or 'Private Extinction Accounting' as it is commonly termed in the literature), there are many recommendations, arising from best practice across asset managers and institutional investors. For example, in Chapter 22, Springer provides a list of important steps asset managers can take to ensure biodiversity and species loss are incorporated

TABLE 31.1 Mapping cutting-edge initiatives for protecting species and biodiversity

	Initiative/Mechanism	Chapters
Extinction Governance	Ecological NED (Non-Executive Director)	2
	EVO – Ecological Value Officer	2
	Extinction Accounting Framework – reporting on absence	2
	IUCN's unified classification of threats	3
	Business for Nature High Level Steps for Becoming Nature Positive	4
		5
	Landowning Model for Species Recovery through Rewilding	6
	Sustainability Policy Transparency Toolkit (SPOTT)	9
	Environmental & Ecological Justice	10
	Restorative & Regenerative Approach to Biodiversity & Species	15
	Sendai Framework for Disaster Risk Reduction	20
	Natural Capital & Sovereign Health Model	
Extinction Accounting: Accounting for Biodiversity and Species	Imaginary Emancipatory Account for Camels: Rewilding	7
	Accounting for species extinctions in the Middle East	8
	Transparency in Fisheries	9
	Dual Materiality	1,13,15
	Capitals Coalition – Natural Capital Protocol	27
	BD Protocol – Biological Diversity Protocol	28
	Ecolinguistic Analysis: Method for Analysing Extinction Accounts	29
Extinction Finance: Information Provision & Measurement Tools	The Solactive V.E. Biodiversity Index	12,13
	Sustainability/ESG Ratings	13
	Emerging Biodiversity Measurement Tools	1,13
	Asset Geolocation Data, Sentinel-2 Satellite Image Repository	31
Extinction Finance: Extinction Banking	HSBC Investment in Natural Capital	1
	Fineco Bank	21
Extinction Finance: Extinction Bonds	Extinction Bond Framework	11
	Green Bonds, Biodiversity Loss & Species Extinction	16
	Rhino Impact Bond	17
	Seychelles Blue Bond	19
	Sovereign Bonds & Biodiversity	20
	Nature-Based Financial System	20
Extinction Finance: Extinction Engagement (Private Extinction Accounting)	AXA engagement on biodiversity	1
	IPDD – Investors' Policy Dialogue on Deforestation	19
	ShareAction's *Point of No Returns* Research Reports	22
	ACTIAM's Zero Net Loss Biodiversity Commitment across PFs	1, 22
	BlackRock's Natural Capital Engagement Strategy	22
	Hermes EOS's Engagement on Deforestation, Ocean Sustainability & Regenerative Agriculture	23
		24
	Ossiam's Engagement on Biodiversity in the Food Industry	25
	ODDO BHF Asset Management: Addressing Ecological Transition through ESG Investing powered by AI & Fintech	26
	Rendering Pandemic Risk Explicit in Extinction Engagement	

better into their investment portfolios and decision-making. Regarding investor engagement and the pandemic, Chapter 26 provides a series of questions that may be incorporated into investor engagement in order to reduce pandemic risk in the future by pressurising companies to take greater precautions throughout their supply chains.

As well as wild flora and fauna, habitats, deforestation and life in seas and oceans, an issue of growing relevance to the financial markets is the treatment of animals that are 'used' directly in business activities for a variety of purposes. Animal welfare in areas such as animal testing and animal welfare considerations in farming are becoming increasingly important as a biodiversity-related issue, as discussed in various chapters throughout the book, for example Chapter 21. Many consumers care about animal welfare whilst investors perceive risks in this area, reputationally for instance. Thus, companies are being pressurised by consumers and by investors, as well as by lobby group, to improve their practices in relation to their treatment of animals throughout their value chain.

In addition to the innovations in extinction accounting and extinction engagement, the chapters throughout this book contain critically important concepts and initiatives including the Extinction Bond framework, the Rhino Impact Bond and the reorientation of public finance towards preventing deforestation. All of these demonstrate the way that every part of the financial and economic system around the world can be redesigned and recrafted towards saving species and protecting biodiversity.

Hope for the Future

Pandora's Box has been opened: by the extinction crisis, by climate change and by the global pandemic. It cannot be forced shut. But Hope rises from darkness and despair. We retain immense optimism, in part because of the evident innovative nature of the financial markets. Throughout this book, we get a feel for the brilliant minds involved in searching for solutions, as well as for the moral and ethical character of actors in the financial markets who demonstrate a genuine and deep-rooted desire to address the extinction and biodiversity crises. Building on ideas and concepts in the text such as the extinction bond framework presented in Chapter 14, we suggest extending innovation and imagination. What about the potential for an 'Insect Apocalypse Bond' built on similar principles to the Rhino Impact Bond discussed in Chapter 17? Or could we see the creation of 'songbird bonds' that would reduce songbird extinction threats? Bonds focused around improving soil health or panda bonds could be developed?

Extinction accounting has evolved as a framework in the academic accounting literature. However, extinction accounting is also emerging increasingly in practice, partly due to influence from the literature but also as a natural evolution from accounting for biodiversity practice. Certainly, the Biological Diversity

Protocol, expounded in Chapter 28 by Houdet and the EWT, incorporates elements of the extinction accounting framework from the literature and references these influences directly. 'Accounting for taxa', or as we call it, 'species accounting', is a crucial aspect of any attempt by an organisation to account for, or discharge accountability for, species impacts, as well as to disclose transformational information in reports on how species are being protected by the organisation. As mentioned in Chapter 1, we see species accounting as a necessary and important element of any emancipatory extinction accounting. A crucial development in moves towards an extinction accounting, universal across countries and organisations, is the emergence of dual materiality, as discussed throughout this book. Dual materiality may be interpreted as a stepping stone to reconciling the competing and often inconsistent motivations underlying the various sustainability reporting frameworks, especially in the areas of species and biodiversity. The current discussions around convergence and synthesis of the various sustainability reporting frameworks and principles are not discussed at length in this book, but the ramifications of any outcome in this regard would be significant for biodiversity and species reporting.

Current concerns and critique around harmonisation of existing frameworks arise mainly from their very different underlying principles. It is difficult to see how a merging can take place without domination by one driver over others. Dual and dynamic (or even triple or more) materiality could be a solution to these concerns. The GRI embeds stakeholder accountability, for example, whereas other frameworks focus more on shareholder primacy and financial materiality. The essentially European NFRD approach of dual materiality allows both of these, to some extent inconsistent, rationales to species reporting and extinction accounting to be reconciled. Where a species has a financially material impact on an organisation's value chain, then efforts to preserve the species and prevent its extinction have to be reported. Where a species does not have a definable financial materiality to an organisation's value chain (except by the potential impact of its disappearance due to interdependencies through the ecosystem), then dual materiality dictates the organisation still has to report on how they are conserving and protecting the species where their operations have a direct or indirect negative impact. These dual motivations for extinction accounting, financial materiality and accountability ensure that organisations must commit to extinction accounting.

A relatively minor part of the prior academic accounting literature has suggested that studies of species accounting, where the species studied is not financially material to the reporting entity, are effectively erroneous. This book and the extensive research in this area, as well as developments such as dual materiality, demonstrate that such a narrow perspective of financial materiality and extinction accounting is itself erroneous. For example, the study of extinction accounting for the rhinoceros found that the highest incidence of such accounting practice was by financial organisations such as Investec bank, in South Africa. This may surprise some as at first glance it would appear that there is no financial materiality for the bank arising from rhinoceros' extinction, and therefore, some would suggest that the bank should not need to report on how they are acting to prevent rhinoceros' extinction. Where the bank is reporting in this area, then critiques would argue this was merely an illustration of 'philanthropic accounting' with little or no transformational outcome. We would argue that there is nothing wrong with 'just' philanthropic activity: reporting on conservation arising from philanthropy giving and charitable attitudes is critically important given the extinction crisis. However, there is a more tangible argument for this type of species extinction accounting. The pledges by the banking sector to protect biodiversity and natural capital are based in part upon acknowledgement by the banks that they have indirect (and to some extent even direct) impacts upon species and biodiversity through their lending decisions, through their investments and through their business' own activities, as outlined in Chapter 1 under the section Extinction Banking. Lending to businesses that destroy natural habitat, create pollution or contribute significantly to climate change indirectly contributes to the deterioration of species populations and consequently creates an accountability for the lending organisation. Lastly, where there is no financial materiality, then we would argue that organisations have moral, ethical and religious imperative to reporting how they are preventing species loss and extinctions throughout their operations and activities, given the urgency arising from the mass extinction crisis and its ramifications for nature and society worldwide. These multi-motivational factors for extinction accounting are summarised with illustrative examples in Table 31.2.

One issue that has not been explored to any great degree in this book is the concept of extinction auditing. This is introduced as an important component of any extinction governance in Chapter 2 but not developed in a concrete manner. As extinction accounting evolves in practice as well as in the academic literature, then assurance and auditing of the reporting and disclosures needs to evolve commensurately. Extinction auditing will become increasingly important as shareholders and other stakeholder groups need to have confidence in the information being disclosed in order to bolster their decision-making. Extinction auditing will necessarily involve input from ecologists, conservationists and environmentalists as well as from more traditionally trained auditors. This is an area that needs urgent work to underpin developments such as the Biological Diversity Protocol and those that adopt it in practice. Again, the urgency of the ongoing mass extinction crisis renders extinction auditing a priority for the auditing industry as well as accounting industry. Linked to this is the need for urgent reform to the professional training of accountants and auditors to ensure they have the appropriate and necessary skills to be able to practise extinction accounting and auditing.

TABLE 31.2 Multi-motivational factors for extinction accounting

Motivations for Extinction Accounting	Illustrative Example
Financial materiality: through dual materiality	Threatened bees and other pollinators and the food industry
Accountability for direct impacts: through dual materiality	Threatened parrots and the mining sector operating in pristine rainforest
Accountability for indirect impacts: through dual materiality	Threatened rhinoceros and elephants and the banking sector through lending and investments
Moral and ethical accountability	Preservation and conservation on moral grounds, for example deep ecology perspective
Philanthropic, charitable works and donations	Organisations have a moral and social responsibility to demonstrate how they are contributing to species protection and biodiversity enhancement
Interdependencies and interconnectedness of species	Protection of all insects and creepy crawlies by the agricultural industry due to their interconnectedness and the deleterious impacts of their disappearance on soil health
Religious motivation	Avoiding harm to all flora and fauna and reporting on how an organisation in any sector is contributing to biodiversity preservation and extinction prevention
	See, for example, arguments in Chapter 8

Chapter 26 adopts Plato's (and later Beck's) ideas around a second, shadow reality, to demonstrate the ways in which life continues 'as normal' against a backdrop of ecological destruction. This theoretical framework seems an appropriate way of interpreting human behaviour in the face of apocalyptic changes in the natural world. We hear of mass extinction of species and collapse of biodiversity, of disappearing rainforests, destructive bushfires and ecological disaster, yet the façade, the 'real world' of everyday life continues unperturbed. People go shopping for clothes, buy new cars, decorate their homes and put their children into the best schools, whilst this second, shadow reality continues to grow almost unabated. At what point will that shadow kingdom eclipse and swallow our everyday reality? A second reality, a 'shadow kingdom', surrounds us.[6] When will Plato's cave become our reality? Plato's allegory of the cave suits the way mass extinction is starting to encroach on our everyday reality. The cave of silence with no birds, no mammals and no insects is a cold, dark, damp, empty place that people do not want to dwell in, and one in which they cannot live for long.

.... The visible world becomes a mere shadow, a reflection of a reality that by nature escapes our possible knowledge.

(Beck, 1992, p. 73)

We draw on the work of Beck to interpret and bring understanding to the risks relating to extinction in order to demonstrate the urgent need for businesses, financial institutions, accounting and all levels of organisation in society to address species decline and extinction.

The invisibility of the threats arising from habitat loss, pollution, climate change, deforestation and deterioration of the seas and oceans is made manifest in the mass extinction of species in the world now. Our challenge in this book has been to find ways of rendering the invisible visible. How can we make visible and immanent the potential catastrophic effects of species extinction on our societies, constituted of business, economy and finance, visible to investors, bankers, company directors and accountants? We hope that this handbook can assist in revealing the challenges of biodiversity loss and species extinctions to the finance industry, to accountants and to organisations of every type whilst at the same time providing urgently needed solutions and initiatives that can be implemented at every level.

This book has explored current cutting-edge practices across financial markets, the corporate sector, the public sector and the NGO/conservation space. There are certain characteristics of action that we feel are vital if further progress is to achieve genuine transformation and collaboration between the multiple stakeholders and actors in this field. In summary, new and ongoing initiatives in the areas of extinction governance, extinction finance, extinction accounting and extinction engagement need to have the following characteristics. These characteristics need to form the basis, in our view, of all efforts to implement the Species Protection Action Plan across global financial markets. We define the characteristics and approach of the Species Protection Action Plan and the Extinction Governance Framework as **CREATIIIVE**, as follows (Figure 31.1):

Every part of this text reinforces the undeniable fact that the global financial system is not separate from people, the planet or nature. Financial markets consist of people and are a product of their behaviours, patterns and psychology. Just as the natural world and nature cannot be separated from people, financial institutions, businesses, investors and accountants. Especially since the pandemic, we have realised that we are 'all in this together'. As the perpetrators of the crisis, financial institutions and businesses must be involved in addressing the extinction crisis and improving the ecological health of our planet and our environment. All of us are integrated into the financial system and the business world throughout our lives as customers, employees, clients of pension funds and investment policies, borrowers, mortgage holders and investors. How can we view these institutions and organisations as somehow separate from the flora and fauna upon which we depend for life? Reading the chapters in this book leaves the reader in no doubt of the interconnectivities and interdependencies of our everyday existence as individuals and as societies. The pandemic has shown us that wherever we are in the world, we cannot escape the pervasive effects of a biodiversity-related health crisis.

Collaborative
Radical
Emancipatory
Accountable
Transparent
Interdisciplinary
Imaginative
Innovative
Visionary
Exigent

FIGURE 31.1 The CREATIIIVE approach

The extinction framework at the core of this book brings ecological and extinction governance into the heart of governance for all forms of organisation in an explicit manner. Our ecological and extinction governance framework and the 'Species Protection Action Plan' for the Financial Markets may be viewed by some as a utopian dream, but we present them as realisable objectives that can be progressed towards – and eventually achieved – and translated into concrete financial actions such as 'Extinction Bonds' and 'Extinction Engagement'. These are objectives that must be implemented urgently if society and human beings are to continue to exist and prosper.

Notes

1 The SFDR is the Sustainable Finance Disclosure Regulation that imposes mandatory ESG disclosure obligations for asset managers and other agents in the financial markets, introduced by the European Commission as part of their Sustainable Finance Action Plan.
2 Trent, Chapter 9.
3 White, B.T., (2019). Humans and animals in a refugee camp: Baquba, Iraq, 1918–20. *Journal of Refugee Studies*, *32*(2), 216–236.
4 See, for example, FOUR PAWS (2019). 47 animals from Rafah Zoo in Gaza are freed from their cages [Online]. Available at Save Gaza Animals – Rapid Response for Animals – Topics – Campaigns & Topics – FOUR PAWS International (four-paws.org). FOUR PAWS (2018). WAR LIONS FROM IRAQ AND SYRIA FIND NEW HOME IN SOUTH AFRICA [Online]. Available at War lions from Iraq and Syria find new home in South Africa – Press Releases – Our Stories – FOUR PAWS International (four-paws.org).
5 13 wild animals from war-torn Syria find refuge in Jerash animal shelter | Jordan Times.
   War is hell for animals too: In Jordan, these bears have found a sanctuary | Middle East Eye.
6 Ulrich Beck adopted Plato's Allegory of the Cave in his Risk Society to introduce the concept of a Shadow Kingdom.

INDEX

Note: **Bold** page numbers refer to tables; *italic* page numbers refer to figures and page numbers followed by "n" denote endnotes.

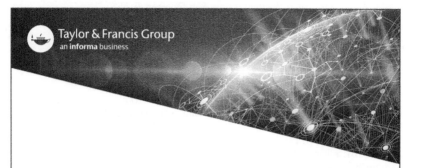